HARVARD UNIVERSITY MONOGRAPHS
IN MEDICINE AND PUBLIC HEALTH

Number 10

PHYSIOLOGY
IN DISEASES OF THE
HEART AND LUNGS

BY

M. D. ALTSCHULE

*Assistant Professor of Medicine, Harvard Medical School; Visiting Physician and
Research Associate, Beth Israel Hospital; Director of Internal Medicine and of
Research in Clinical Physiology, McLean Hospital*

Revised Edition

HARVARD UNIVERSITY PRESS
CAMBRIDGE, MASSACHUSETTS
1954

DISTRIBUTED IN GREAT BRITAIN BY

GEOFFREY CUMBERLEGE

OXFORD UNIVERSITY PRESS

LONDON

LIBRARY OF CONGRESS CATALOG CARD NO. 54–5017

PRINTED IN THE UNITED STATES OF AMERICA

TO MY PARENTS

Members of that vanishing species, the Old-World Idealistic Intellectual

PREFACE

This monograph was written because a number of third- and fourth-year students at the Harvard Medical School requested it. That these men felt a need, or at least a desire, for a work of this sort should be of interest to those who are engaged in the teaching of the various branches of medicine.

The third and fourth years of medical school are often regarded as a period of adolescence, when the painful transition from student in the laboratory and classroom to the well-rounded, though still inexperienced, clinician occurs. According to this concept, a book such as this helps to overcome to some extent the insecurity and bewilderment of this difficult period. While this point of view possibly applies to a small number of the students, it does not appear to be valid for most. It does not, moreover, accurately describe the place of laboratory science in medical education, for, in the words of Bacon, it causes the former to be "degraded most unworthily to the situation of a handmaid, and made to wait upon medicine, . . . and to wash the immature minds of youth and imbue them with a first dye, that they may afterwards be more ready to receive and retain another."

The last two years of the course in medical school resemble for most students a honeymoon period; the men have finally attained their desire, clinical medicine, and never again will it seem so wonderful to them or will they learn so much about it so quickly — and at times, so painfully. The attitude of these students consists in large part of fascinated and amazed delight with the variety, complexity and subtlety of the manifestations of disease, together with a desire for more knowledge concerning them which is not easily appeased. The fact that many of these men wish to refer back to the details of the fundamental sciences of the preclinical years is not a manifestation of insecurity regarding clinical medicine or of lack of satisfaction with it. Rather it is an expression of the desire to enhance their appreciation and understanding of clinical phenomena.

Celsus observed that medicine was the earliest of the sciences to use experiment and most physicans since then have realized that, while it may be possible to practice clinical medicine satisfactorily without a knowledge of fundamental science, it is not possible to do any thinking about medicine without such knowledge. Attempts are made at some medical schools to satisfy the need of the thinking student for continuous contact with laboratory science in one of two ways: by giving a course of lectures or seminars during the third or fourth year designed to correlate the clinical with the preclinical, or by having the student in the fourth year retire for a period from the clinic and return to the laboratory. Both of these devices, while advantageous in some respects, are in many ways defective. A course of lectures or seminars must be given at stated intervals and consequently, coming into conflict with other assigned work, must be limited in regard to time. The content, spirit and tempo of the course are largely determined by the members of the faculty who preside, and active participation by all the students is impossible. The course is arranged to cover many fields and covers none of them well, and since it is designed to fit the needs of many students, suits none completely. On the other hand, requiring that the student spend part of his fourth year in the laboratory is also not desirable. The work done there is often little more than a review of material covered in the first two years, or if investigative work is required, the student is forced to concentrate on one minute field.

An additional approach to the problem is afforded by a work such as the present one. Material is here made available and is at hand at all times, but it is left to the student to obtain as much or as little as he feels he needs, at such times as he chooses. The student may be stimulated to look into this book for the explanation of an unusual or, to him, unexpected clinical phenomenon, or he may merely browse through it when he feels no urge to do anything else.

Many practicing clinicians retain some of the viewpoints and attitude of the student; indeed, it appears to be characteristic of outstanding physicians to do so. Men of this type may also find a work of this sort useful. "Täglich entschwindet die Möglichkeit nicht bloss einer Prufung, sondern selbst eines Verständnisses der neueren Schriften denjenigen mehr und mehr, welche in den oft so mühseligen und erschöpfenden Wegen der Praxis ihre beste Kraft verbrauchen müssen," * Virchow said. The fact that there is little of practical everyday usefulness here is inherent in the nature of this work. Certainly there are available enough excellent clinical texts to supply any need in that direction.

Theoretical considerations have not been emphasized here, for "when facts are numerous, and unquestionable and unequivocal in their significance, theory must follow them as best it may, keeping time only with their step, and not go before them, marching to the sound of its own drum and trumpet." Those who are interested in a physiological discussion of disease will want the data and will be less concerned with the concepts that any author may derive from them. As in other branches of learning, Gresham's law of scholarship applies here; the commentaries have in large measure submerged the original data. Accordingly, an analysis of the conclusions derived by the large number of workers would interest only the historian. Besides, conclusions may sound as authoritative and be as misleading as the striking of hours by a wrong clock. For the most part, in the work reviewed here, there are no important discrepancies between data and conclusions except in the case of an occasional mistaken investigator who, like the squid, beclouds the issue with jets of ink as he proceeds erratically backwards. Therefore the present work has been designed primarily as a review of data included in scientific papers and not of the conclusions derived from them. Some of the research workers whose data are included here may be surprised or even annoyed by the fact that some of these data have been used to support concepts different from or opposite to those derived by the original authors. However, the use of published data in this manner requires no justification. Moreover, the interpretations here employed will undoubtedly undergo revision in the future.

It has been considered important to review all available data in the fields here covered, including the older work. Not infrequently "time, like a river, bears down to us that which is light and inflated, and sinks that which is heavy and solid." Many of the earliest studies, now neglected, contain important contributions not found in more

---

* Frank Chance, translator of Virchow's *Cellularpathologie*, has translated this sentence as follows: "Day by day do those who are obliged to consume their best energies in the frequently so toilsome and so exhausting routine of practice find it becoming less and less possible for them, not only to closely examine, but even to understand the more recent medical works."

recent investigations. Indeed, the increasing simplification of methods has tended at times to encourage hurried and uncritical work. On the other hand, the inclusion of all available papers has resulted in a massive bibliography which "rather inclines us to admire our wealth than to perceive our poverty." Information is incomplete or lacking entirely in many fields discussed in the present work. The filling of these gaps in our knowledge of disease must wait upon the development of new techniques and concepts in the fundamental sciences; "it would be madness and inconsistency to suppose that things which have never yet been performed can be performed without employing some hitherto untried means."

It should also be noted that a large part of the physiologic and chemical research in medicine is of greater value and interest to beginning students in clinical medicine and their teachers than to any other groups. This phenomenon is interesting in itself, for it has no exact counterpart in the other professions. It may suggest an explanation for the fact that many of the best teachers in medicine also do research; indeed, in many instances their work in the laboratory is an expression of their fundamental bent toward teaching. From the administrative point of view, this situation may create difficulties in estimating proportionate time occupied in teaching and in research, and in allocating funds for each, but from the point of view of pedagogy it is a healthy thing, and certainly the validity of this type of research is beyond question. "Our hope of further progress in the sciences will then only be well founded, when numerous experiments shall be received and collected into natural history, which though of no use in themselves, assist materially in the discovery of causes and axioms; which experiments we have termed enlightening, to distinguish them from those which are profitable. They possess this wonderful property and nature, that they never deceive or fail you, for being used only to discover the natural cause of some object, whatever may be the result, they equally satisfy your aim by deciding the question."

M. D. A.

Athens, Vermont

ACKNOWLEDGMENTS

The ideas included in this work have been subjected to discussion, review and criticism by colleagues and students at the Harvard Medical School and Beth Israel Hospital. These individuals are numerous and cannot be singled out; their individual contributions are difficult to delineate and moreover naming a few to the exclusion of the rest would be unfair and not desired by the persons concerned. Nevertheless, each will recognize his own part in the formation of the ideas expressed in the text.

The preparation of this book for publication has been furthered by the aid afforded by a number of other persons who, by good fortune, were drawn into the enterprise. Mrs. Lucy Sagalyn transposed the original notes and typewrote the earliest drafts of the text and bibliography; this enormous task was done expeditiously in spite of other demanding duties and of difficulties consequent to the hurried and otherwise inadequate handwriting of the material presented to her. Miss Edith Morrison typewrote an intermediate draft with fidelity. Mrs. Francis D. Judge prepared the final one with meticulous accuracy after Mr. James F. Ballard and his staff of the Boston Medical Library had corrected many inaccuracies in the bibliography. The Misses Mary Jane McManus and Barbara S. Seamon aided Mrs. Judge in verifying the accuracy of her final copy and then read the galley proof. Miss Evelyn Russ helped with the galley and page proofs and Miss Marylyn M. Rapaquette typewrote the index. Mrs. Katherine R. Drinker proposed a brilliant solution to the problem raised by the large number of bibliographic references in the text; her suggestions in this regard were unique and are responsible for the manner in which this material has been arranged. Mr. Joseph D. Elder, of the Harvard University Press, spent long hours editing the manuscript with extraordinary care and thoroughness; the extent of his efforts is known only to him and to me. The results, which are greatly appreciated by me, are evident.

CONTENTS

I

CHRONIC CARDIAC DECOMPENSATION

1. *Cardiac Output*

Discussion of the pathological physiology of chronic cardiac decompensation properly begins with consideration of the output of the heart in patients with this disorder. The great bulk of the reported data concerns the findings in cardiac patients under basal conditions, or at least at rest. Such data, while of value, give no information as to the cardiac output at a time when patients experience most or all of their symptoms, namely, during exertion; to judge from the scanty data available, values obtained during or after exertion are more strikingly abnormal than those obtained at rest.

Another source of confusion arises from the multiplicity of methods used. The reader is referred to Grollman's book (1932) for a full description of most of the methods which here will be treated only briefly. The methods used fall into two main groups: (i) those which employ the Fick principle and (ii) those which do not.

The Fick principle states that the cardiac output in cubic centimeters per minute is equal to the oxygen consumption of the body in cubic centimeters per minute divided by the arteriovenous oxygen difference per cubic centimeter of blood. In diseases in which oxygen consumption is not markedly altered, data on arteriovenous oxygen difference accordingly have the same significance as measurements of cardiac output itself. Estimation of oxygen consumption can be accomplished by means of direct, simple, and accurate methods. Determination of the arteriovenous oxygen difference, however, is beset with difficulty. While arterial blood can be secured with ease, and so can alveolar air which is in equilibrium with it, mixed venous blood is obtainable only from the right auricle or ventricle by direct puncture or catheterization via an antecubital vein. A variety of methods for the indirect estimation of arteriovenous oxygen difference was developed in the past. For technical reasons certain authors have preferred the use of carbon dioxide or various foreign gases instead of oxygen in measuring cardiac output in man. For oxygen consumption and arteriovenous oxygen difference in Fick's formula may be substituted corresponding figures for any foreign gas, or for carbon dioxide production and arteriovenous difference. The technique of the method depends on the gas employed.

Methods based on the Fick principle.—(a) *Cardiac puncture or catheterization.* Oxygen consumption is measured by the usual procedures and arterial blood obtained from a convenient artery. Mixed venous blood is secured directly from the right auricle or, preferably, the right ventricle. Data obtained by means of these methods in patients with congestive failure are not extensive. Values obtained by these methods in normal man are considerably higher than those obtained by the indirect methods described below (Cournand *et al.*, 1945; Stead *et al.*, 1945; Werkö, Berseus, and Lagerlöf, 1949; Werkö *et al.*, 1949; Chapman *et al.*, 1950).

(b) *Analyses of arterial and peripheral venous blood.* Here again oxygen consumption is estimated by the usual methods. Blood samples taken usually from a femoral or radial artery and the antecubital or femoral vein are analyzed for oxygen or carbon dioxide in order to determine the arteriovenous difference. While the use of blood from an artery is valid, since arterial blood throughout the body is of uniform composition, use of venous blood from a single portion of the body, such as the arm or leg, leads to error, since it differs from mixed venous blood. It should be noted that blood flow through skeletal muscle is small at rest (Holling, 1939), the greater part of the output of the heart being distributed to the viscera. Results obtained from analysis of peripheral venous blood may indicate trends in the cardiac output, but general concepts based on such data must be accepted with reservations. Strictly speaking, studies made by this method measure the blood flow only through some segment of the peripheral circulation, usually that of an extremity. Accordingly, these data will not be analyzed here but rather in Section 3 of this chapter, where peripheral blood flow is discussed.

(c) *Rebreathing methods.* These may be divided into two groups: (i) methods in which rebreathing is used to secure air in equilibrium with mixed venous blood for measurement of oxygen or carbon dioxide content and (ii) methods using a foreign gas. The latter include the nitrous oxide method (Krogh and Lindhard, 1912) and the acetylene method (Grollman, 1932). The last, in a modified form (Grollman et al., 1933), is the method of this type most widely used. These methods employ measurements of rate of absorption of a foreign gas by the blood in the lungs during a period of rebreathing, and are based on the principle that the volume of gas so absorbed in a given time is governed by the volume of pulmonary blood flow. The entire period of rebreathing must be short enough that no appreciable recirculation of blood once exposed to the air in the rebreathing bag can occur; this recirculation may be a source of error in measurements made during periods of rapid circulation, that is, of exercise. Changes in circulation time due to variations in the condition of patients studied at intervals while in failure might also introduce errors. Another source of inaccuracy derives from the fact that it is sometimes difficult to obtain, in a short period, thorough mixing of the gas mixture being rebreathed in patients with changes in the lungs due to congestive failure (page 91). It is therefore necessary to prolong the rebreathing period, thereby increasing the possibility of recirculation of the blood. Still another source of inaccuracy in the acetylene method is the fact that small errors in analysis lead to large errors in results; it may not be possible to obtain duplicate determinations within less than plus or minus 10 per cent. Comparative studies of this method have been published by Werkö, Berseus, and Lagerlöf (1949) and by Chapman et al. (1950).

(d) *Ethyl iodide methods.* In these methods ethyl iodide consumption and arteriovenous difference are substituted for oxygen consumption and arteriovenous difference in Fick's formula. The original ethyl iodide method of Henderson and Haggard (1925) yielded erroneous results because these authors disregarded the presence of ethyl iodide in the venous blood and incorrectly estimated the partition coefficient of that substance between air and blood. These errors were, however, constant, so that many authors believed the method to be useful. Starr and Gamble (1928) revised the method, eliminating many of the errors, but the results obtained in normal subjects are still well below those yielded by the use of catheterization of the heart.

Methods not based on the Fick principle.—The methods for measuring cardiac output that do not use the Fick principle were designed to avoid the criticism that methods based on exchange of gases in the lungs are fundamentally insecure because of the known impairment of pulmonary function in cardiac decompensation (page 76); all of these methods yield data that are of little value unless the oxygen consumption is measured at the same time.

(*a*) *Roentgenokymograph.* The output per cardiac beat is estimated by means of the roentgenokymograph (Keys and Friedell, 1939; LaDue and Fahr, 1943). Errors occur because of the fact that the heart is studied in only one plane and, consequently, changes in volume are estimated by means of formulas that may not be precisely applicable in given cases, especially where the contour of the heart is abnormal. Additional inaccuracies may arise because of the difficulty of defining the cardiac border and because changes in auricular size and shape may be included in the measurements. Moreover, regurgitant valvular lesions cause great errors. Unless many beats are studied, the effects of respiration may also introduce misleading variations.

(*b*) *Dyes.* Dyes may be injected intravenously (Hamilton *et al.*, 1932). In these methods the values obtained are calculated from ideal formulas and errors may be large. In certain cases, however, valid qualitative conclusions may be drawn from repeated measurements (Doyle *et al.*, 1953). Werkö *et al.* (1949) have made a comparative study of this method.

(*c*) *Pulse pressure and pulse-wave velocity.* Methods which use changes in pulse pressure and pulse-wave velocity (Bazett *et al.*, 1935, 1941) have not been widely used in studies on congestive failure. Recent work of Remington *et al.* (1948) shows that such methods give erroneously high values in congestive failure, where values obtained by means of the catheter are low.

(*d*) *Ballistocardiograph.* When the ballistocardiograph is used (Starr, 1941), errors may be introduced by failure to study a large enough number of beats and by the occurrence of marked changes in pulse rate; the method is unreliable in heart disease (Nickerson *et al.*, 1947; Cathcart *et al.*, 1953).

Whatever may be the criticisms that can be leveled at one method or another, valid conclusions as to changes in cardiac output can be drawn if all the diverse methods yield results that are similar qualitatively. Such is fortunately the case in chronic cardiac decompensation.

Observations on cardiac output in congestive failure.—A large number of measurements of cardiac output or arteriovenous difference employing various methods have been recorded. In almost all instances the cardiac output was found to be low or the arteriovenous difference high (Bloomfield *et al.*, 1946, 1948; Howarth *et al.*, 1946; McMichael and Sharpey-Schafer, 1944; Merrill, 1946; Merrill *et al.*, 1946; Sharpey-Schafer, 1946; 1). In addition, studies of peripheral blood gases (page 102) yield comparable results. A certain amount of overlapping occurs, however, when the cardiac outputs of normal subjects and decompensated patients are compared. This is not surprising, for in normal subjects Grollman (1929) found a spread of 30 per cent about the mean obtained by his method, and Donal *et al.* (1934) and Cournand *et al.* (1945), using other methods, found a somewhat greater range of variation. It is apparent that a low normal figure for cardiac output might actually represent a considerable decrease in the case of a patient for whom the normal value before the onset of congestive failure was at the upper limit of the normal range for all individuals. The findings are the same in so-called right- and left-sided failure (Cournand, 1952; Dresdale *et al.*, 1951).

Cardiac decompensation may occur with a normal or even elevated cardiac output in conditions in which the output of the heart is usually increased, namely, febrile diseases, anemia, beri-beri, thyrotoxicosis, pregnancy, acidosis, chronic pulmonary disease, and arteriovenous aneurysm. Data have been obtained in patients in failure with anemia (Sharpey-Schafer, 1944; Stead *et al.*, 1948), with beriberi (Weiss and Wilkins, 1937; Porter and Downs, 1942; Burwell and Dexter, 1947; Fowler, 1953) and with cor pulmonale (McMichael and Sharpey-Schafer, 1944; Sharpey-Schafer, 1945; Howarth *et al.*, 1947; Harvey *et al.*, 1949 and 1951; 2). Studies of the circulation in general in these conditions reveal findings similar to those in patients with ordinary, low-output decompensation except for normal or high cardiac outputs and normal or accelerated circulation times. Although the values for cardiac output are not low in the absolute sense, it is evident that they are diminished relative to the normal in these states; treatment with digitalis results in a rise in cardiac output (Stead *et al.*, 1948; Harvey *et al.*, 1949; Ferrer *et al.*, 1950; Ahmed *et al.*, 1950; Gray *et al.*, 1952; Eichna *et al.*, 1953; van Lingen *et al.*, 1951), in contradistinction to the occurrence of no change or a fall in digitalized normal subjects. In conditions that cause increases in cardiac output, failure when it occurs does so with lesser degrees of organic cardiac damage than in the common, low-output type of failure. In addition, metabolic factors, analyzed by Olson and Schwartz (1951), are of great importance, and if these factors can be ameliorated or overcome, marked and lasting improvement in cardiac failure results. Clinical evaluation of the degree of cardiac failure in conditions that cause high cardiac outputs is difficult since the conditions themselves cause symptoms that, although not cardiac in origin, resemble those of cardiac decompensation. These include dyspnea and water retention in beri-beri and in anemias, and dyspnea and cyanosis in severe pulmonary diseases. Accordingly, analysis of the symptoms of these disorders in relation to cardiovascular dynamics alone may be misleading.

Eppinger and his co-workers (1925, 1927) found a normal or increased cardiac output in ordinary cardiac failure. Their conclusions have been criticized on the basis of faulty technique and are now thoroughly discredited. Schoen and Derra (1930), using cardiac puncture, and Harrison *et al.* (1934) and McGuire *et al.* (1938, 1939*a*, *b*), who employed a modified Grollman acetylene method, found normal or even high cardiac outputs in some patients with cardiac decompensation that were not associated with conditions that cause high-output failure. The data of Schoen and Derra (1930) are scanty and not presented in sufficient detail to permit analysis. The findings of Harrison *et al.* (1934) are seen on closer examination to conform to those of a majority of workers in this field. Many of the patients with more than minimal evidences of myocardial insufficiency who were studied by Harrison and his co-workers had low cardiac outputs and of ten with normal or almost normal values, all but one had basal metabolic rates of from plus 15 to plus 78 per cent. A similar analysis may be made of the data of McGuire *et al.* (1938, 1939*a*,*b*). Obviously, the cardiac output in such cases cannot be compared with that of undecompensated individuals whose basal metabolic rate is within limits of plus or minus 10 per cent of the average normal. The importance of the relationship between cardiac output and oxygen consumption has been stressed by many authors (Davies and Gilchrist, 1927; Grollman, 1929; Krogh and Lindhard, 1912; Lindhard, 1918; Lundsgaard, 1916; Starr et al., 1933). It is probable that, as Means (1924) suggested, a more precise relationship exists between carbon dioxide production by the body and the output of the heart. At any rate, it is apparent that the cardiac output in proportion to the body metabolism is low in patients with cardiac decompensation. When exceptions to this rule are found, they may often be explained on the basis of such complicating factors as anxiety, anemia, arteriovenous aneurysm, elevated metabolic rate consequent to fever or thyroid disease, pregnancy, acidosis, thiamine deficiency or cor pulmonale.

It has been shown (Altschule and Gilligan, 1938) that even a small increase in venous pressure in normal man results in striking increases in cardiac output. Patients with high venous pressure at rest consequent to congestive failure fail to exhibit this response, although McMichael (1938a) concluded that a partial response is present in cardiac patients who are only moderately decompensated. It may be concluded, however, that the output of the heart is always low relative to the venous pressure in chronic cardiac decompensation. In addition, patients with cardiac decompensation do not exhibit the increase in cardiac output caused by anoxia in normal subjects (Doyle, Wilson, and Warren, 1952; Westcott et al., 1951). The cardiac output rises during sleep (Halmágyi et al., 1953), in contradistinction to the fall that occurs normally.

As a rule, diminution in cardiac output per beat is even greater than that in output per minute in cardiac decompensation, since some degree of tachycardia occurs in almost all patients with that syndrome. Even more marked deviations from the normal are found if the cardiac output per minute or per beat is compared to the cardiac size, as was pointed out by Nylin (1933), Lysholm et al. (1934), and by Starr and co-workers (1933, 1934).

The low cardiac output found in congestive failure is largely the consequence of myocardial weakness, but lessened negativity of intrapleural pressure (page 78) and auricular fibrillation or some other arrhythmia may be contributory factors (page 357). The contention of McMichael and Sharpey-Schafer (1944), that overstretching of the heart consequent to greatly elevated venous pressure results in low output, has been criticized (Bloomfield et al., 1947; Lagerlöf and Werkö, 1949) and appears to be unsubstantiated by the data presented.

The rapid filling phase of the heart is shortened, but the duration of isometric contraction, ejection, and relaxation is normal in cardiac decompensation (Heyer et al., 1952).

A decrease in cardiac work occurs in congestive failure, since the work of the heart is directly proportional to its output (Evans and Matsuoka, 1915); in the case of the right ventricle, however, work may be decreased only slightly, or not at all, owing to a considerable rise in right ventricular pressure in cardiac decompensation (page 63). A number of studies of the efficiency — that is, the ratio of work performed to oxygen consumption — of the failing heart have been made on isolated heart or heart-lung preparations, and all show that the efficiency of the heart in failure is much reduced. It is possible that this loss of efficiency has as its clinical counterpart the lengthening of the duration of electrical systole that occurs when the heart fails (Berliner, 1931; Cheer and Dieuaide, 1931, 1932; Geiger et al., 1941; Phang and White, 1943; Sebastiani, 1951); it lengthens even more during exercise in congestive failure, in contrast to the normal, where a decrease is the rule (Sebastiani, 1951). Studies of cardiac efficiency in the intact animal have been reported (Harrison et al., 1936), but are open to criticism on technical grounds. Bing et al. (1949 and 1950) and Lombardo et al. (1952) calculated cardiac oxygen consumption, work, and efficiency in man from data obtained by means of catheterization. The total coronary blood flow is normal or low in cardiac decompensation; relative to the mass of cardiac muscle it is probably low as a rule. The oxygen consumption of the heart is normal, and since the work done is low, it is evident that efficiency must be diminished also. Studies of cardiac metabolism and efficiency in congestive failure are of the greatest importance; at present, much information is available on the role of the heart as a pump, but little is known concerning the heart as a specialized living tissue. It has been suggested (Harrison et al., 1936) that diminished cardiac efficiency rather than low output determines the presence or absence of congestive failure. This is probably not the case, for it is difficult to understand how edema develops in the ankles, merely because the heart, located four feet distant, shows a low ratio of work output to energy input, that is, low efficiency, in patients with cardiac decompensation. Changes in cardiac dynamics can influence the tissues only through the cardiac output and the peripheral and pulmonary venous pressures; it must therefore be concluded that while cardiac inefficiency in failure is theoretically important, it is not directly responsible for the development of signs and symptoms of congestive failure.

On the other hand, consideration of cardiac efficiency is essential for the understanding of some otherwise confusing matters. For instance, it is important to bear in mind the fact that under certain circumstances increases in cardiac output are harmful, whereas in others they are beneficial to patients with cardiac decompensation. Thus, increases in cardiac output brought about by anxiety, fever, effort, anemia, thyrotoxicosis, injection of epinephrine, and probably also the injection of aminophylline, are not associated with increased cardiac efficiency; accordingly, these conditions constitute a burden upon the heart and may precipitate or aggravate its failure. Contrariwise, the increase in the output of the heart that occurs with digitalis (page 267) or during spontaneous recovery from failure is due to increased efficiency and is, therefore, no additional burden upon the heart; the heart can do more work with no increase in energy requirement.

Changes in cardiac output in recovery from congestive failure are variable. Thus, if recovery is associated with increased myocardial strength, either of spontaneous occurrence or as a result of the action of digitalis (page 267), cardiac output rises. If, on the other hand, improvement in signs and symptoms occurs as a consequence of the administration of oxygen or of diuretics, no increase in cardiac output need occur (page 277). Therefore, precise correlation between disappearance of signs and symptoms and changes in cardiac output is fundamentally impossible. An additional source of confusion lies in the fact that a marked fall in basal metabolic rate may occur during recovery from failure, so that the more or less parallel changes in cardiac output give the appearance of a decrease in the latter.

Thus, in the data of Harrison *et al.* (1934) many such instances of decreasing cardiac output in recovery occur, but actually this is more apparent than real, for in nine patients of ten studied by those authors the arteriovenous difference fell or did not change significantly; the cardiac output in these patients was unchanged or increased relative to the metabolic rate. The data of McGuire (1938, 1939a,b) may be analyzed in a similar manner.

The lack of parallelism between fall in cardiac output and severity of signs and symptoms in congestive failure was noted years ago by Lundsgaard (1916) and has been stressed more recently by Harrison (1934, 1935), Starr (1941) and McGuire (1938, 1939a,b). The reasons why this correlation does not, and indeed cannot, exist will be discussed in various portions of this review.

Effects of exercise.—The validity of methods used for measuring the cardiac output at rest has not been satisfactorily established for studies on exercising patients with cardiac decompensation. Accordingly, most data on the effects of exercise have been obtained in experiments on compensated or only mildly decompensated cardiac patients. The amount and type of work used as a test load by various investigators have varied so greatly that precise quantitative analysis of all the available data is difficult. Most authors describe an abnormally small rise in cardiac output in their patients compared to normal subjects performing the same task (McGuire *et al.*, 1939b; Meakins *et al.*, 1923; Moore *et al.*, 1926; **2A**), with normal responses in only a few (Alt *et al.*, 1930; Bansi and Groscurth, 1930a; Means and Newburgh, 1915; Makinson, 1950; Newburgh and Means, 1915; Stevenson *et al.*, 1949). McMichael (1938a) observed a normal response during light exercise and an abnormally small increase in cardiac output in heavier work. McGuire *et al.* (1939b) made a systematic study of patients in various stages of failure and found a smaller than normal increase in cardiac output in compensated patients during exercise and a still smaller rise in those in failure. Hickam and Cargill (1948), Grossman *et al.* (1953), and Lewis *et al.* (1952) have provided excellent data, obtained by means of the catheter, which show that the cardiac output does not increase after exertion in patients with congestive failure.

The significance of an abnormally large arteriovenous oxygen difference after exercise (Bansi and Groscurth, 1930b; Harris and

Lipkin, 1931; Weiss and Ellis, 1935) is the same as that of the aforedescribed data; Weiss and Ellis (1935) found almost complete deoxygenation of venous blood after exercise in some patients. All of these observations explain in part the abnormal rise in venous pressure (page 48), the marked lactic acidosis (page 121) and the large oxygen debt (page 126) of cardiac patients. The rise in cardiac output during exercise, though smaller than normal, apparently lasts longer in cardiac patients, implying a need to discharge the abnormally large oxygen debt that occurs in such individuals. These data are in accord with the increased peripheral "flow debt" observed by Abramson *et al.* (1942) in cardiac patients after exercise.

Bibliography

Chapter I — Section 1

ABRAMSON, D. I., S. M. FIERST, and K. FLACHS, Effect of muscular exercise upon the peripheral circulation in patients with valvular heart disease, *J. Clin. Investigation* **21**, 747 (1942).

AHMED, S., R. I. S. BAYLISS, W. A. BRISCOE, and J. McMICHAEL, The action of G-strophanthin on the circulation in man, and a comparison with digoxin, *Clin. Sc.* **9**, 1 (1950). [1, 2

ALT, H. L., G. L. WALKER, and W. C. SMITH, The cardiac output in heart disease. II. Effect of exercise on the circulation in patients with chronic rheumatic valvular disease, subacute rheumatic fever and complete heart block, *Arch. Int. Med.* **45**, 958 (1930). [2A

ALTSCHULE, M. D., and E. BUDNITZ, Rheumatic disease of the tricuspid valve, *Arch. Path.* **30**, 7 (1940). [1

ALTSCHULE, M. D., and D. R. GILLIGAN, The effects on the cardiovascular system of fluids administered intravenously in man. II. The dynamics of the circulation, *J. Clin. Investigation* **17**, 401 (1938).

ALTSCHULE, M. D., and M. C. VOLK, Therapeutic effect of total ablation of normal thyroid on congestive failure and angina pectoris. XVIII. The cardiac output following total thyroidectomy in patients with and without congestive heart failure, with a comparison of results obtained with the acetylene and ethyl iodide methods, *Arch. Int. Med.* **58**, 32 (1936). [1

ALTSCHULE, M. D., and N. ZAMCHECK, The effects of pleural effusion on respiration and circulation in man, *J. Clin. Investigation* **23**, 325 (1944). [1

ANGELINO, P. F., and A. ACTIS-DATO, La gasometria del sangue venoso renale e le pressioni venose renale studiate mediante cateterismo in soggetti normali, cardiopatici e in altre forme morbose, *Cuore e circolaz.* **35,** 283 (1951).   [1

BALL, J. D., H. KOPELMAN, and A. C. WITHAM, Circulatory changes in mitral stenosis at rest and on exercise, *Brit. Heart J.* **14,** 363 (1952).   [1

BANSI, H. W., and G. GROSCURTH, Die Kreislaufleistung während und nach der Arbeit beim gesunden und kranken Menschen, *Ztschr. f. Kreislaufforsch.* **22,** 657 (1930a).

BANSI, H. W., and G. GROSCURTH, Funktionsprüfung des Kreislaufs durch Messung der Herzarbeit, *Klin. Wchnschr.* **9,** 1902 (1930b).

BANSI, H. W., and G. GROSCURTH, Kreislauffunktionsprüfung bei Herzkranken, *Deutsche med. Wchnschr.* **57,** 1276 (1931).   [2A

BAYLISS, R. I. S., M. J. ETHERIDGE, A. L. HYMAN, H. G. KELLY, J. MCMICHAEL, and E. A. S. REID, The effect of digoxin on the right ventricular pressure in hypertensive and ischaemic heart failure, *Brit. Heart J.* **12,** 317 (1950).   [1

BAZETT, H. C., F. S. COTTON, L. B. LAPLACE, and J. C. SCOTT, The calculation of cardiac output and effective peripheral resistance from blood pressure measurements, with an appendix on the size of the aorta in man, *Am. J. Physiol.* **113,** 312 (1935).

BAZETT, H. C., L. B. LAPLACE, and J. C. SCOTT, The estimation of cardiac output from blood pressure and pulse wave velocity measurements on subjects with cardiovascular disease. I. Cardiovascular disease other than aortic regurgitation, *Am. Heart J.* **22,** 737 (1941).

BERLINER, K., Observations on the duration of the electrical systole of the heart, with special reference to the effect of digitalis, *Am. Heart J.* **7,** 189 (1931–32).

BERSEUS, S., The influence of heart glucosides, theophylline and analeptics on the cardiac output in congestive heart failure; with remarks on the acetylene methods for the determination of arteriovenous oxygen difference, *Acta med. Scandinav., Supp. No. 145* (1945).   [1

BIELSCHOWSKY, P., Ueber das Herz-Minutenvolumen des Menschen, *Med. Welt* **6,** 1301 (1932).   [1

BING, R. J., M. M. HAMMOND, J. C. HANDELSMAN, S. R. POWERS, F. C. SPENCER, J. E. ECKENHOFF, W. T. GOODALE, J. H. HAFKENSCHIEL, and S. S. KETY, The measurement of coronary blood flow, oxygen consumption, and efficiency of the left ventricle in man, *Am. Heart J.* **38,** 1 (1949).   [1

BING, R. J., M. HAMMOND, J. HANDELSMAN, S. R. POWERS, F. SPENCER, J. ECKENHOFF, W. GOODALE, J. HAFKENSCHIEL, and S. S. KETY, Coronary blood flow, cardiac oxygen consumption and efficiency in man, *J. Clin. Investigation* **28,** 771 (1949).

BING, R. J., R. HEIMBECKER, and W. FALHOLT, An estimation of the residual volume of blood in the right ventricle of normal and diseased hearts in vivo, *Am. Heart J.* **42,** 483 (1951).   [1

BING, R. J., F. M. MARAIST, J. F. DAMMAN, JR., A. DRAPER, JR., R. HEIM-BECKER, R. DALEY, R. GERARD, and P. CALAZEL, Effect of strophan-thus on the coronary blood flow and cardiac oxygen consumption of normal and failing human hearts, *Circulation* **2,** 513 (1950).   [1

BLOOMFIELD, R. A., B. RAPOPORT, J. P. MILNOR, W. K. LONG, J. G. MEBANE, and L. B. ELLIS, The effect of ouabain on the dynamics of the circulation in patients with congestive heart failure, *J. Clin. Investigation* **26,** 1174 (1947).   [1

BLOOMFIELD, R. A., B. RAPOPORT, J. P. MILNOR, W. K. LONG, J. G. MEBANE, and L. B. ELLIS, The effects of the cardiac glycosides upon the dynamics of the circulation in congestive heart failure. I. Ouabain, *J. Clin. Investigation* **27,** 588 (1948).   [1

BLOOMFIELD, R. A., H. D. LAUSON, A. COURNAND, E. S. BREED, and D. W. RICHARDS, JR., Recording of right heart pressures in normal subjects and in patients with chronic pulmonary disease and various types of cardiocirculatory disease, *J. Clin. Investigation* **25,** 639 (1946). [1

BORDEN, C. W., R. V. EBERT, R. H. WILSON, and H. S. WELLS, Studies of the pulmonary circulation. II. The circulation time from the pulmo-nary artery to the femoral artery and the quantity of blood in the lungs in patients with mitral stenosis and in patients with left ven-tricular failure, *J. Clin. Investigation* **28,** 1138 (1949).   [1

BORDEN, C. W., R. V. EBERT, R. H. WILSON, and H. S. WELLS, Pulmonary hypertension in heart disease, *New England J. Med.* **242,** 529 (1950).
                                                                         [1

BRIGGS, A. P., D. M. FOWELL, W. F. HAMILTON, J. W. REMINGTON, N. C. WHEELER, and J. A. WINSLOW, Renal and circulatory factors in the edema formation of congestive heart failure, *J. Clin. Investigation* **27,** 810 (1948).   [1

BROD, J., and Z. FEJFAR, The origin of oedema in heart failure, *Quart. J. Med.* **19,** 187 (1950).   [1

BURWELL, C. S., and L. DEXTER, Beri-beri heart disease, *Tr. A. Am. Physicians* **60,** 59 (1947).

CASH, H. R., and H. A. ZIMMERMAN, An evaluation of the effect of Khellin on the pulmonary circulation in man, *Dis. of Chest* **21,** 137 (1952).
                                                                         [2

CATHCART, R. T., W. FIELD, and D. W. RICHARDS, JR., Comparison of cardiac output determined by the ballistocardiograph (Nickerson apparatus) and by the direct Fick method, *J. Clin. Investigation* **32,** 5 (1953).

CHAPMAN, R. V., H. L. TAYLOR, C. BORDEN, R. V. EBERT, and A. KEYS, Simultaneous determinations of the resting arteriovenous oxygen difference by the acetylene and direct Fick methods, *J. Clin. Investigation* **29,** 651 (1950).

CHEER, S. N., and F. R. DIEUAIDE, Studies on the electrical systole (Q-T interval) of the heart. II. Its duration in cardiac failure, *J. Clin. Investigation* **10,** 889 (1931).

CHEER, S. N., and F. R. DIEUAIDE, Studies on the electrical systole (Q-T interval) of the heart. IV. The effect of digitalis on its duration in cardiac failure, *J. Clin. Investigation* **11,** 1241 (1932).

COURNAND, A., A discussion of the concept of cardiac failure in the light of recent physiologic studies in man, *Ann. Int. Med.* **37,** 649 (1952).
[1

COURNAND, A., H. D. LAUSON, R. A. BLOOMFIELD, E. S. BREED, and E. DE F. BALDWIN, Recording of right heart pressures in man, *Proc. Soc. Exper. Biol. & Med.* **55,** 34 (1944).
[1

COURNAND, A., H. A. RANGES, and R. L. RILEY, Comparison of results of the normal ballistocardiogram and a direct Fick method in measuring the cardiac output in man, *J. Clin. Investigation* **21,** 287 (1942).   [1

COURNAND, A., R. L. RILEY, E. S. BREED, E. DE F. BALDWIN, and D. W. RICHARDS, JR., Measurement of cardiac output in man using the technique of catheterization of the right auricle or ventricle, *J. Clin. Investigation* **24,** 106 (1945).
[1

DAUTREBANDE, L., L'équilibre acide-base chez les emphysémateux. Ses variations au cours de la décompensation cardiaque, *Compt. rend. Soc. de biol.* **93,** 1025 (1925).
[2

DAUTREBANDE, L., Contribution à l'étude physiopathologique et thérapeutique des troubles circulatoires dans l'asystolie, *Arch. internat. de méd. expér.* **2,** 413 (1926).
[1

DAUTREBANDE, L., Physiopathologie du ralentissement circulatoire. Ses rapports avec le débit cardiaque, *Arch. d. mal. du cœur* **21,** 296 (1928).
[1

DAVIES, C. E., and J. A. KILPATRICK, Renal circulation in low output and high output heart failure, *Clin. Sc.* **10,** 53 (1951).   [1, 2

DAVIES, C. E., J. MACKINNON, and M. M. PLATTS, Renal circulation and cardiac output in "low-output" heart failure and in myxoedema, *Brit. Med. J.* **2,** 595 (1952).
[1

DAVIES, H. W., and A. R. GILCHRIST, Observations upon the circulation rate in man by the ethyl iodide method, *Quart. J. Med.* **20,** 245 (1927).

DENNIG, H., and S. H. PRODGER, Herzkranke bei Arbeit, *Deutsches Arch. f. klin. Med.* **175,** 170 (1933).
[2A

DENOLIN, H., and J. LEQUIME, Les modifications circulatoires dans le
cœur pulmonaire chronique, *Arch. d. mal. du cœur* **44**, 391 (1951).
[2

DEXTER, L., J. W. DOW, F. W. HAYNES, J. L. WHITTENBERGER, B. G.
FERRIS, W. T. GOODALE, and H. K. HELLEMS, Studies of the pulmonary circulation in man at rest. Normal variations and the interrelations between increased pulmonary blood flow, elevated pulmonary arterial pressure, and high pulmonary "capillary" pressures,
J. Clin. Investigation **29**, 602 (1950). [1

DEXTER, L., B. M. LEWIS, F. W. HAYNES, R. GORLIN, and H. E. J.
HOUSSAY, Chronic cor pulmonale without hypoxia, *Bull. New England M. Center* **14**, 69 (1952). [2

DEXTER, L., J. L. WHITTENBERGER, R. GORLIN, B. M. LEWIS, F. W.
HAYNES, and R. J. SPIEGL. The effect of chronic pulmonary disease
(cor pulmonale and hypoxia) on the dynamics of the circulation in
man, *Tr. A. Am. Physicians* **64**, 226 (1951). [2

DONAL, J. S., JR., C. J. GAMBLE, and R. SHAW, The cardiac output in
man. An adaptation of the katharometer for the rapid determination
of ethyl iodide in estimations of cardiac output by the ethyl iodide
method. A study of the effect of posture upon cardiac output and
other circulatory and respiratory measurements, *Am. J. Physiol.* **109**,
666 (1934).

DOYLE, J. T., J. S. WILSON, C. LÉPINE, and J. V. WARREN, An evaluation
of the measurement of the cardiac output and of the so-called pulmonary blood volume by the dye-dilution method, *J. Lab. & Clin. Med.*
41, 29 (1953). [1

DOYLE, J. T., J. S. WILSON, and J. V. WARREN, The pulmonary vascular
responses to short-term hypoxia in human subjects, *Circulation* **5**,
263 (1952). [1

DRAPER, A., R. HEIMBECKER, R. DALEY, D. CARROLL, G. MUDD, R. WELLS,
W. FALHOLT, E. C. ANDRUS, and R. J. BING, Physiologic studies in
mitral valvular disease, *Circulation* **3**, 531 (1950). [1

DRESDALE, D. T., M. SCHULTZ, and R. J. MICHTOM, Primary pulmonary
hypertension. I. Clinical and hemodynamic study, *Am. J. Med.* **11**,
686 (1951). [1

EICHNA, L., S. J. FARBER, A. R. BERGER, D. P. EARLE, B. RADER, E. PELLE-
GRINO, R. E. ALBERT, J. D. ALEXANDER, H. TAUBE, and S. YOUNG-
WIRTH, The interrelationship of the cardiovascular, renal and electro-
lyte effects of intravenous digoxin in congestive heart failure, *J. Clin.
Investigation* **30**, 1250 (1951). [1

EICHNA, L., S. J. FARBER, A. R. BERGER, D. P. EARLE, B. RADER, E. PELLE-
GRINO, R. E. ALBERT, J. D. ALEXANDER, H. TAUBE, and S. YOUNG-
WIRTH, Cardiovascular dynamics, blood volumes, renal functions and

electrolyte excretions in the same patients during congestive heart failure and after recovery of cardiac decompensation, *Circulation* 7, 674 (1953). [1, 2

EPPINGER, H., F. KISCH, and H. SCHWARZ, Arbeit und Kreislauf, *Klin. Wchnschr.* 4, 1101 (1925).

EPPINGER, H., F. KISCH, and H. SCHWARZ, *Das Versagen des Kreislaufes; dynamische und energetische Ursachen* (Berlin, 1927).

ESPERSEN, T., Studies of the cardiac output and related circulatory functions, especially in patients with congestive heart failure, *Acta med. Scandinav.* 108, 153 (1941). [1

EVANS, C. L., and MATSUOKA, The effect of various mechanical conditions on the gaseous metabolism and efficiency of the mammalian heart, *J. Physiol.* 49, 378 (1915).

EWIG, W., and K. HINSBERG, Kreislaufstudien. II, *Ztschr. f. klin. Med.* 115, 693 (1931). [1

FERRER, M. I., R. M. HARVEY, R. T. CATHCART, A. COURNAND, and D. W. RICHARDS, JR., Hemodynamic studies in rheumatic heart disease, *Circulation* 6, 688 (1952). [1

FERRER, M. I., R. M. HARVEY, R. T. CATHCART, C. A. WEBSTER, D. W. RICHARDS, JR., and A. COURNAND, Some effects of digoxin upon the heart and circulation in man. Digoxin in chronic cor pulmonale, *Circulation* 1, 161 (1950). [1, 2

FISHMAN, A. P., J. McCLEMENT, A. HIMMELSTEIN, and A. COURNAND, Effects of acute anoxia on the circulation and respiration in patients with chronic pulmonary disease studied during the "steady state," *J. Clin. Investigation* 31, 770 (1952). [2

FOWLER, N. O., Cardiac catheterization in the diagnosis of adult heart disease, *Ann. Int. Med.* 38, 478 (1953). [1

FOWLER, N. O., R. N. WESTCOTT, R. C. SCOTT, and E. HESS, The cardiac output in chronic cor pulmonale, *Circulation* 6, 888 (1952). [2

FRIEDMAN, B., G. CLARK, H. RESNIK, JR., and T. R. HARRISON, Effect of digitalis on the cardiac output of persons with congestive heart failure, *Arch. Int. Med.* 56, 710 (1935). [1

FRIEDMAN, B., H. RESNIK, JR., J. A. CALHOUN, and T. R. HARRISON, Effect of diuretics on the cardiac output of patients with congestive heart failure, *Arch. Int. Med.* 56, 341 (1935). [1

FRISK, A. R., L. WERKÖ, and G. WRANGE, A new mercurial diuretic "diurgin" (Disodium salt of N-succinyl-, N^1 (8-carboxymethylmercaptomercuri-B-methoxy) propylcarbamide), *Acta med. Scandinav.* 144, 85 (1952). [1

FRIES, E. D., J. R. STANTON, J. W. CULBERTSON, J. LITTER, M. H. HALPERIN, C. H. BURNETT, and R. W. WILKINS, The hemodynamic effects of hypotensive drugs in man. I. Veratrum Viride, *J. Clin. Investigation* **28**, 353 (1949). [1

GEIGER, A. J., L. F. BLANEY, and W. H. DRUCKEMILLER, A quantitative electrocardiographic study of digitalization, *Am. Heart J.* **22**, 230 (1941).

GELFAND, M. L., Chronic cor pulmonale in long-standing bronchial asthma, *Am. J. Med.* **10**, 27 (1951). [2

GIRAUD, G., C. BÉNÉZECH, A. LEVY, and H. LATOUR, Troubles de l'hydration cellulaire et de la liaison hydroprotéique globulaire chez les cardiaques: déductions physiopathologiques et thérapeutiques, *Arch. d. mal. du cœur* **45**, 1 (1952).

GOLDBLOOM, A. A., Clinical studies in circulatory adjustments. III. Clinical evaluation of cardiac output studies, *Internat. Clin.* **46** [ser. 3], 206 (1936). [1

GRASSMANN, W., and F. HERZOG, Die Wirkung von Digitalis (Strophanthin) auf das Minuten- und Schlagvolumen des Herzkranken, *Arch. f. exp. Path. u. Pharmakol.* **163**, 97 (1932). [1

GRAY, F. D., M. H. WILLIAMS, JR., and F. C. GRAY, The circulatory and ventilatory changes in chronic pulmonary disease as affected by Lanatoside C, *Am. Heart J.* **44**, 517 (1952). [2

GROLLMAN, A., Physiological variations in the cardiac output of man. VI. The value of the cardiac output of the normal individual in the basal resting condition, *Am. J. Physiol.* **90**, 210 (1929).

GROLLMAN, A., *The cardiac output of man in health and disease* (Springfield, Ill., 1932).

GROLLMAN, A., B. FRIEDMAN, G. CLARK, and T. R. HARRISON, Studies in congestive heart failure. XXIII. A critical study of methods for determining the cardiac output in patients with cardiac disease, *J. Clin. Investigation* **12**, 751 (1933).

GROSCURTH, G., and H. W. BANSI, Der Kreislauf bei schwerer körperlicher Arbeit und seine Beeinflussung durch Kreislaufnuttel, *Arch. f. exper. Path. u. Pharmakol.* **169**, 313 (1933). [2A

GROSSMAN, J., R. E. WESTON, and L. LEITER, A method for determining cardiac output by the direct Fick principle without gas analysis, *J. Clin. Investigation* **32**, 161 (1953). [1, 2, 2A

HALMÁGYI, D., B. FELKAI, J. IVÁNYI, T. ZSÓTÉR, M. TÉNYI, and S. SZÜCS, The role of the nervous system in the maintenance of pulmonary arterial hypertension in heart failure, *Brit. Heart J.* **15**, 15 (1953). [1

HAMILTON, W. F., J. W. MOORE, J. M. KINSMAN, and R. G. SPURLING, Studies on the circulation. IV. Further analysis of the injection method and of changes in hemodynamics under physiological and pathological conditions, *Am. J. Physiol.* **99**, 534 (1932).

HAMILTON, W. F., R. L. RILEY, A. M. ATTYAH, A. COURNAND, D. M. FOWELL, A. HIMMELSTEIN, R. P. NOBLE, J. W. REMINGTON, D. W. RICHARDS, JR., N. C. WHEELER, and A. C. WITHAM, Comparison of the Fick and dye injection methods of measuring the cardiac output in man, *Am. J. Physiol.* **153**, 309 (1948).   [1

HARRIS, I., and I. J. LIPKIN, Cardiac output and oxygen utilization in some types of heart disease, *Edinburgh M. J.* **38**, 501 (1931).   [2A

HARRISON, T. R., The pathogenesis of congestive heart failure, *Medicine* **14**, 255 (1935).

HARRISON, T. R., B. FRIEDMAN, G. CLARK, and H. RESNIK, The cardiac output in relation to cardiac failure, *Arch. Int. Med.* **54**, 239 (1934).

HARRISON, T. R., B. FRIEDMAN, and H. RESNIK, Mechanism of acute experimental heart failure, *Arch. Int. Med.* **57**, 927 (1936).

HARVEY, R. M., M. I. FERRER, R. T. CATHCART, D. W. RICHARDS, JR., and A. COURNAND, Some effects of digoxin upon the heart and circulation in man. Digoxin in left ventricular failure, *Am. J. Med.* **7**, 439 (1949).
[1, 2

HARVEY, R. M., M. I. FERRER, D. W. RICHARDS, JR., and A. COURNAND, Influence of chronic pulmonary disease on the heart and circulation, *Am. J. Med.* **10**, 719 (1951).   [2

HENDERSON, Y., and H. W. HAGGARD, The circulation and its measurement, *Am. J. Physiol.* **73**, 193 (1925).

HEYER, H. E., C. H. HOWARD, K. W. WILLIS, and A. C. PICKLE, Alterations of the rapid filling phase in congestive heart failure, *Am. Heart J.* **43**, 206 (1952).

HICKAM, J. B. and W. H. CARGILL, Effect of exercise on cardiac output and pulmonary arterial pressure in normal persons and in patients with cardiovascular disease and pulmonary emphysema, *J. Clin. Investigation* **27**, 10 (1948).   [1, 2A

HICKAM, J. B., W. H. CARGILL, and A. GOLDEN, Cardiovascular reactions to emotional stimuli. Effect on the cardiac output, arteriovenous oxygen difference, arterial pressure, and peripheral resistance, *J. Clin. Investigation* **27**, 291 (1948).   [1

HIMWICH, H. E., and J. E. FAZEKAS, The oxygen content of cerebral blood in patients with acute symptomatic psychoses and acute destructive brain lesions, *Am. J. Psychiat.* **100**, 648 (1944).   [1

HOLLING, H. E., Observations on the oxygen content of venous blood from the arm vein and on the oxygen consumption of resting human muscle, *Clin. Sc.* **4**, 103 (1939).

HOWARTH, S., J. McMICHAEL, and E. P. SHARPEY-SCHAFER, Effects of venesection in low output heart failure, *Clin. Sc.* **6**, 41 (1946).

HOWARTH, S., J. McMICHAEL, and E. P. SHARPEY-SCHAFER, The effects of oxygen, venesection and digitalis in chronic heart failure from disease of the lungs, *Clin. Sc.* **6**, 187 (1947).   [2

IHAYA, H., Studien über die Alveolarluft, Blutgase, Vitalkapazität und Minuten- und Schlagvolumen des Herzens bei Beriberi, Herzklappenfehler und Pleuritis, *Mitt. d. med. Gesellsch. zu Tokyo* **48**, 2167 (1934). [1

KELLY, H. G., and R. I. S. BAYLISS, Influence of heart-rate on cardiac output. Studies with digoxin and atropin, *Lancet* **2**, 1071 (1949). [1

KELLEY, R. T., E. D. FRIES, and T. F. HIGGINS, The effects of hexamethonium on certain manifestations of congestive heart failure, *Circulation* **7**, 169 (1953). [1

KEYS, A., and H. L. FRIEDELL, Measurement of the stroke volume of the human heart from roentgenograms; simultaneous roentgenokymographic and acetylene-rebreathing experiments, *Am. J. Physiol.* **126**, 741 (1939).

KININMONTH, J. G., The circulation rate in some pathological states, with observations on the effect of digitalis, *Quart. J. Med.* **21**, 277 (1928). [1

KINSMAN, J. M., and J. W. MOORE, The hemodynamics of the circulation in hypertension, *Ann. Int. Med.* **9**, 649 (1935). [1

KINSMAN, J. M., J. W. MOORE, and W. F. HAMILTON, Studies on the circulation: an analysis of some problems of the circulation in man in the normal and in the pathological states, by the use of the injection method, *Kentucky State M. J.* **31**, 285 (1933). [1

KOPELMAN, H., The circulation time as a clinical test, *Brit. Heart J.* **13**, 301 (1951). [1

KOPELMAN, H., and G. DE J. LEE, The intrathoracic blood volume in mitral stenosis and left ventricular failure, *Clin. Sc.* **10**, 383 (1951). [1, 2

KROETZ, C., Messung des Kreislaufminutenvolumens mit Acetylen als Fremdgas. Ihre Bishengen Ergebnisse bei arteriellen Hochdruck und bei Dekompensation des Kreislaufs, *Klin. Wchnschr.* **9**, 966 (1930). [1

KROGH, A., and J. LINDHARD, Measurements of the blood flow through the lungs of man, *Skandinav. Arch. f. Physiol.* **27**, 100 (1912).

LA DUE, J. S., and G. FAHR, The effect of the intravenous administration of lanatoside C upon the output, diastolic volume, and mechanical efficiency of the failing human heart, *Am. Heart J.* **25**, 344 (1943).

LAGERLÖF, H., and L. WERKÖ, Studies on the circulation in man. V. The effect of cedilanid (lanatoside C) on cardiac output and blood pressure in the pulmonary circulation in patients with compensated and decompensated heart disease, *Acta cardiol.* **4**, 1 (1949). [1

LAUTER, S., and H. BAUMANN, Zur Theorie der Herzinsufficienz und der Digitaliswirkung, *Klin. Wchnschr.* **8**, 263 (1929).

LENÈGRE, J., I. SCEBAT, H. BESSON, F. BENCHEMOUL, and J. DAMIEN, Étude de la pression capillaire pulmonaire dans différents types de cardiopathies, *Arch. d. mal. du cœur* **46**, 1 (1953). [1, 2

LEQUIME, J., Le débit cardiaque. Études expérimentales et cliniques, *Acta med. Scandinav. Supp. No. 107* (1940).

LEWIS, C. S., M. C. DAINES, A. J. SAMUELS, and H. H. HECHT, Cor pulmonale (pulmono-cardiac syndrome). A case report, *Dis. of Chest* **22**, 261 (1952). [2

LEWIS, C. S., A. J. SAMUELS, M. C. DAINES, and H. H. HECHT, Chronic lung disease, polycythemia and congestive heart failure. Cardiorespiratory, vascular and renal adjustments in cor pulmonale, *Circulation* **6**, 874 (1952). [2, 2A

LINDHARD, J., An attempt of statistical treatment of results from circulation experiments, *Skandinav. Arch. f. Physiol.* **35**, 117 (1918).

LOMBARDO, T. A., L. ROSE, M. TAESCHLER, S. TULUY, and R. J. BING, The effect of exercise on coronary blood flow, myocardial oxygen consumption and cardiac efficiency in man, *Circulation* **7**, 71 (1953).

LUNDSGAARD, C., Untersuchungen über das Minutenvolumen des Herzens bei Menschen. I. Die Methode Krogh und Lindhard's, ihre Anwendung bei Patienten und die Befunde bei Normalen, *Deutsches Arch. f. klin. Med.* **118**, 360 (1916a).

LUNDSGAARD, C., Untersuchungen über das Minutenvolumen des Herzens bei Menschen. II. Patienten mit Herzklappenfehlern. *Deutsches Arch. f. klin. Med.* **118**, 513 (1916b). [1

LYSHOLM, E., G. NYLIN, and K. QUARNA, The relation between the heart volume and stroke volume under physiological and pathological conditions, *Acta radiol.* **15**, 237 (1934). [1

MAKINSON, D. H., Changes in the ballistocardiogram after exercise in normal and abnormal subjects, *Circulation* **2**, 186 (1950). [2A

McGUIRE, J., The role of the cardiac output in congestive heart failure, *Ohio State M. J.* **35**, 1092 (1939). [1

McGUIRE, J., V. HAUENSTEIN, and R. SHORE, Cardiac output in heart disease determined by the direct Fick method, including comparative determinations by the acetylene method, *Arch. Int. Med.* **60**, 1034 (1937). [1

McGUIRE, J., R. SHORE, V. HAUENSTEIN, and F. GOLDMAN, The cardiac output in compensation and decompensation in the same individual, *Am. Heart J.* **16**, 449 (1938). [1

McGUIRE, J., R. SHORE, V. HAUENSTEIN, and F. GOLDMAN, Relation of cardiac output to congestive heart failure, *Arch. Int. Med.* **63**, 290 (1939a). [1

McGuire, J., R. Shore, V. Hauenstein, and F. Goldman, Influence of exercise on cardiac output in congestive heart failure, *Arch. Int. Med.* **63,** 469 (1939*b*). [1

McGuire, J., R. N. Westcott, and N. O. Fowler, Anoxia and human pulmonary vascular resistance, *Tr. A. Am. Physicians* **64,** 404 (1951). [1

McMichael, J., The output of the heart in congestive failure, *Quart. J. Med.* **7,** 331 (1938*a*). [1

McMichael, J., The significance of cardiac venous congestion, *Tr. Med.- Chir. Soc. Edinburgh* **138,** 161 (1938*b*). [1

McMichael J., Hyperpnoea in heart failure, *Clin. Sc.* **4,** 19 (1939). [1

McMichael, J., and E. P. Sharpey-Schafer, The action of intravenous digoxin in man, *Quart. J. Med.* **13,** 123 (1944). [1, 2

Meakins, J., L. Dautrebande, and W. J. Fetter, The influence of circulatory disturbances on the gaseous exchange of the blood. IV. The blood gases and circulation rate in cases of mitral stenosis, *Heart* **10,** 153 (1923). [1

Means, J. H., Dyspnoea, *Medicine* **3,** 309 (1924).

Means, J. H., and L. H. Newburgh, Studies of the blood flow by the method of Krogh and Lindhard, *Tr. A. Am. Physicians* **30,** 51 (1915). [1

Merrill, A. J. Edema and decreased renal blood flow in patients with chronic congestive heart failure. Evidence of "Forward Failure" as the primary cause of edema, *J. Clin. Investigation* **25,** 389 (1946). [1

Merrill, A. J., L. J. Morrison, and E. S. Brannon, Concentration of renin in renal venous blood in patients with chronic heart failure, *Am. J. Med.* **1,** 468 (1946). [1

Mobitz, W., Ergebnisse von 200 Herzschlagvolumbestimmungen beim Menschen, *Verhandl. d. deutsch. Gesellsch. f. inn. Med.* **38,** 314 (1926). [1

Mobitz, W., Die Ermittlung des Herzschlagvolumens des Menschen durch Einatmung von Äthyljodiddampf. IV. Klinische kompensierte Veranderungen des Herzens und der Gefässe und beginnende Kreislaufdekompensation ohne Lungenveränderungen, *Deutsches Arch. f. klin. Med.* **157,** 359 (1927). [1

Moore, J. W., W. F. Hamilton, and J. M. Kinsman, Ethyl iodide method for determining the circulation as a functional test of the heart, *J. A. M. A.* **87,** 817 (1926). [1

Mounsey, J. P. D., L. W. Ritzman, N. J. Selverstone, W. A. Briscoe, and G. A. McLemore, Circulatory changes in severe pulmonary emphysema, *Brit. Heart J.* **14,** 153 (1952). [2, 2A

MYERS, J. D., Observations on the excretion of bromsulphalein, *J. Clin. Investigation* **28**, 800 (1949).   [1

NEWBURGH, L. H., and J. H. MEANS, Blood flow in a patient with double aortic and double mitral disease, *J. Pharmacol. & Exper. Therap.* **7**, 441 (1915).   [2A

NICKERSON, J. L., J. V. WARREN, and E. S. BANNON, The cardiac output in man: Studies with the low frequency critically-damped ballisto-cardiograph, and the method of right atrial catheterization, *J. Clin. Investigation* **26**, 1 (1947).

NIELSEN, H. E., Clinical investigations into the cardiac output of patients with compensated heart disease during rest and during muscular work, *Acta Med. Scandinav.* **91**, 223 (1937).   [2A

NYLIN, G., Clinical tests of the function of the heart, *Acta med. Scandinav., Supp. No. 52*, 1 (1933).   [1

OLSON, R. E., and W. B. SCHWARTZ, Myocardial metabolism in congestive heart failure, *Medicine* **30**, 21 (1951).

PHANG, S. H., and P. D. WHITE, The duration of ventricular systole as measured by the Q-T interval of the electrocardiogram, with especial reference to cardiac enlargement with and without congestive failure. *Am. Heart J.* **26**, 108 (1943).

PRITCHARD, W. H., W. J. MacINTYRE, W. C. SCHMIDT, B. L. BROFMAN, and D. J. MOORE, The determination of cardiac output by a continuous recording system utilizing iodinated (I^{131}) human serum albumin. II. Clinical studies, *Circulation* **6**, 572 (1952).   [1

PORTER, R. B., and R. S. DOWNS, Some physiological observations on the circulation during recovery from vitamin B_1 deficiency, *Ann. Int. Med.* **17**, 645 (1942).

PROGER, S. H., and C. KORTH, Effect of light muscular training on patients with heart disease. Rheumatic heart disease; changes at rest and during exercise, *Arch. Int. Med.* **55**, 204 (1935).   [1

PUGH, L. C. G., and C. L. WYNDHAM, The circulatory effects of mercurial diuretics in congestive heart failure, *Clin. Sc.* **8**, 10 (1949).   [1

REMINGTON, J. W., C. R. NOBACK, W. F. HAMILTON, and J. J. GOLD, Volume elasticity characteristics of the human aorta and the prediction of the stroke volume from the pulse pressure, *Am. J. Physiol.* **153**, 298 (1948).   [1

RESNIK, H., JR., B. FRIEDMAN, and T. R. HARRISON, Effect of certain therapeutic measures on the cardiac output of patients with congestive heart failure, *Arch. Int. Med.* **56**, 891 (1935).   [1

RICHARDS, D. W., JR., Cardiac output by the catheterization technique in various clinical conditions, *Federation Proc.* **4**, 215 (1945).   [1, 2

RIGONI, M., Il ricambio respiratorio, la portata circolatoria e la gittata sistolica nelle cardiopatie compensate e nello scompenso di circolo.

II. Portata circolatoria e gittata sistolica, *Cuore e circolaz.* **21,** 209 (1937). [1

RINGER, M., Studies on the circulation. I. Experiences with the Henderson and Haggard method for measuring the circulation, *Am. Heart J.* **2,** 229 (1927). [1

RINGER, M., and M. D. ALTSCHULE, Studies on the circulation. II. Cardiac output in diseases of the heart, and under the influence of digitalis therapy, *Am. Heart J.* **5,** 305 (1930). [1

SCEBAT, L., J. LENÈGRE, B. RANSON-BITKER, F. BENCHEMOUL, and J. DAMIEN, Étude des gaz du sang et du débit cardiaque dans les différents types de cardiopathies, *Arch. d. mal. du cœur* **46,** 18 (1953). [1, 2

SCHEINBERG, P., Cerebral circulation in heart failure, *Am. J. Med.* **8,** 148 (1950). [1

SCHOEN, R., and E. DERRA, Untersuchungen über die Bedeutung der Zyanose als klinisches Symptom. (I), *Deutsches Arch. f. klin. Med.* **168,** 52 (1930).

SEBASTIANI, A., Sulla durata della sistole elletrica a riposo e dopo sforzo nei normali e nei cardiopazienti, *Cuore e circolaz.* **35,** 229 (1951).

SEYMOUR, W. B., W. H. PRITCHARD, L. P. LONGLEY, and J. M. HAYMAN, JR., Cardiac output, blood and interstitial fluid volumes, total circulating serum protein, and kidney function during cardiac failure and after improvement, *J. Clin. Investigation* **21,** 229 (1942). [1

SHARPEY-SCHAFER, E. P., Cardiac output in severe anaemia, *Clin Sc.* **5,** 125 (1944).

SHARPEY-SCHAFER, E. P., 2-Thiouracil in the treatment of congestive heart failure, *Brit. M. J.* **2,** 888 (1946). [1, 2

SHERLOCK, S., The liver in heart failure. Relation of anatomical, functional, and circulatory changes, *Brit. Heart J.* **13,** 273 (1951). [1

SONNE, C., Über die Bestimmung des Unterschiedes zwischen arterieller und venöser Kohlensäurespannung unter normalen und pathologischen Verhältnissen sowie über die Anwendung dieses Unterschiedes zur Messung von Veränderungen in der Grösse des Minutenvolumens, *Deutsches Arch. f. klin. Med.* **124,** 358 (1918). [1

STARR, I., Clinical studies with the ballistocardiograph; in congestive failure, on digitalis action, on changes in ballistic form, and in certain acute experiments, *Am. J. M. Sc.* **202,** 469 (1941).

STARR, I., JR., L. H. COLLINS. JR., and F. C. WOOD, Studies of the basal work and output of the heart in clinical conditions, *J. Clin. Investigation* **12,** 13 (1933). [1

STARR, I., JR., J. S. DONAL, A. MARGOLIES, R. SHAW, L. H. COLLINS, and C. J. GAMBLE, Studies of the heart and circulation in disease; estimations of basal cardiac output, metabolism, heart size, and blood pressure in 235 subjects, *J. Clin. Investigation* **13**, 561 (1934).   [1

STARR, I., and C. J. GAMBLE, An improved method for the determination of cardiac output in man by means of ethyl iodide, *Am. J. Physiol.* **87**, 450 (1928).   [1

STARR, I., and L. JONAS, The relation between oxygen consumption and cardiac output in the presence and in the absence of cardiac disease, *Am. J. M. Sc.* **204**, 155 (1942).   [1

STEAD, E. A., JR., J. V. WARREN, A. J. MERRILL, and E. S. BRANNON, The cardiac output in male subjects as measured by the technique of right atrial catheterization. Normal values with observations on the effect of anxiety and tilting, *J. Clin. Investigation* **24**, 326 (1945).

STEAD, E. A., J. V. WARREN, and E. S. BRANNON, Cardiac output in congestive heart failure. An analysis of the reasons for the lack of close correlation between the symptoms of heart failure and the resting cardiac output, *Am. Heart J.* **35**, 529 (1948).   [1

STEAD, E. A., JR., J. V. WARREN, and E. S. BRANNON, Effect of lanatoside C on the circulation of patients with congestive failure. A study using catheterization of the right side of the heart, *Arch. Int. Med.* **81**, 282 (1948).   [1

STEVENSON, I. P., C. H. DUNCAN, and H. G. WOLFF, Circulatory dynamics before and after exercise in subjects with and without structural heart disease during anxiety and relaxation, *J. Clin. Investigation* **28**, 1535 (1949).   [2A

STEWART, H. J., and A. E. COHN, Studies on the effect of the action of digitalis on the ouput of blood from the heart. III. Part 2. The effect on the output of hearts in heart failure with congestion in human beings, *J. Clin. Investigation* **11**, 933 (1932).   [1

STEWART, H. J., N. F. CRANE, R. F. WATSON, C. H. WHEELER, and J. E. DEITRICK, The cardiac output in congestive heart failure and in organic heart disease, *Ann. Int. Med.* **13**, 2323 (1940).   [1

SUAREZ, J. R. E., J. C. FASCIOLO, and A. C. TAQUINI, Cardiac output in heart failure, *Am. Heart J.* **32**, 339 (1946).   [1

VAN LINGEN, B., J. H. GEAR, and J. WHIDBOURNE, Ballistocardiographic patterns in congestive cardiac failure before and after the intravenous administration of digitalis, *South African J. Clin. Sc.* **2**, 239 (1951).   [1, 2

WEISS, R., Ueber die klinische Verwendbarkeit der Bestimmung des zirkulatorischen Minutenvolumens mit der Krogh-Lindhard's schen Stickoxydulmethode, *Wien. med. Wchnschr.* **77**, 1367 (1927).   [1

WEISS, S., and L. B. ELLIS, Oxygen utilization and lactic acid production in the extremities during rest and exercise, in subjects with normal and in those with diseased cardiovascular systems, *Arch. Int. Med.* **55,** 665 (1935).

WEISS, S., and R. W. WILKINS, The nature of the cardiovascular disturbances in nutritional deficiency states, *Ann. Int. Med.* **11,** 104 (1937).

WERKÖ, L., The influence of positive pressure breathing on the circulation in man, *Acta med. Scandinav. Supp. No. 193* (1947).   [1

WERKÖ, L., S. BERSEUS, and H. LAGERLÖF, A comparison of the direct Fick and the Grollman methods for determination of the cardiac output in man, *J. Clin. Investigation* **28,** 516 (1949).

WERKÖ, L. and H. LAGERLÖF, Studies on the circulation in man. IV. Cardiac output and blood pressure in the right auricle, right ventricle and pulmonary artery in patients with hypertensive cardiovascular disease, *Acta med. Scandinav.* **133,** 427 (1949).   [1

WERKÖ, L., and H. LAGERLÖF, Studies on the circulation of blood in man. VII. The effect of a single intravenous dose of theophylline diethanolamine on the cardiac output, pulmonary blood volume and systemic and pulmonary blood pressures in hypertensive and cardiovascular disease, *Scandinav. J. Clin. & Lab. Investigation* **1,** 181 (1949).   [1

WERKÖ, L., H. LAGERLÖF, H. BUCHT, B. WEHLE, and A. HOLMGREN, Comparison of the Fick and Hamilton methods for the determination of cardiac output in man, *Scandinav. J. Clin. & Lab. Investigation* **1,** 109 (1949).   [1

WESTCOTT, R. N., N. O. FOWLER, R. C. SCOTT, V. D. HAUENSTEIN, and J. McGUIRE, Anoxia and human pulmonary vascular resistance, *J. Clin. Investigation* **30,** 957 (1951).   [1

WILKINSON, E. L., H. BACKMAN, and H. H. HECHT, Cardiovascular and renal adjustments to a hypotensive agent (l-hydrazinophthalazine: Ciba BA-5968: Apresoline), *J. Clin. Investigation* **31,** 872 (1952).   [1

ZIMMERMAN, H., A study of the pulmonary circulation in man, *Dis. of Chest* **20,** 46 (1951).   [2

2. *Circulation Time*

The significance of the pulmonary circulation time was discussed in 1931 by Blumgart in his review of the subject. Since that time his observations have been corroborated and extended; various segments of the circulation may now be measured through the use of a variety of test substances. The arm-to-tongue, arm-to-face or arm-to-carotid-sinus time measures the circulation time in the antecubital and brachial vein, the superior vena cava, the right heart, the lungs, the left heart, and a short arterial segment. This may be divided into arm-to-lung time by the use of ether or paraldehyde, and lung-to-brain time by the use of inhalation of 15 to 25 per cent carbon dioxide. The arm-to-tongue, -face or -carotid-sinus time is long in almost all patients with cardiac decompensation (3). Blumgart (1931) stressed the relation between this sign of pulmonary congestion and another — diminution of the vital capacity — consequent to an increase in the amount of blood in the lungs. In recovery from congestive failure, both return to or toward normal. A high salt intake results in slowing of the circulation time (Lombardo, 1953).

Blumgart (1931) also pointed out that slowing of the circulation occurs in myxedema, not as a consequence of pulmonary congestion, but as a result of low cardiac output. Altschule and Volk (1936) showed that prolongation of the circulation time parallels reductions in cardiac output in individual patients with hypothyroidism, but that equivalent reductions in cardiac minute volume output in patients with pulmonary congestion are associated with much greater increase in circulation time than in patients without congestion. It may be concluded, therefore, that the slowing of the circulation through the lungs in cardiac decompensation is related to (i) the lowered cardiac output and (ii) the engorgement of the pulmonary vessels which occurs in that condition.

The circulation time is usually normal or rapid in high-output failure (Porter and Downs, 1942; Weiss and Wilkins, 1937; Blankenhorn et al., 1951; Gillanders, 1951; Kopelman, 1951; Stone et al., 1953). There are, however, many exceptions (Blankenhorn et al., 1951; Braun and Fryd, 1951; Gillanders, 1951; Rubin et al., 1952; Stone et al., 1953).

Slowing of the circulation, like diminution of the vital capacity, is frequently associated with dyspnea in patients with congestive failure; measurement of the circulation time is clinically useful in helping to distinguish between dyspnea consequent to cardiac decompensation and dyspnea due to pulmonary disease.

Mild exercise shortens the circulation time by the same number of seconds in normal subjects and in cardiac patients with long circulation times at rest (Cannon et al., 1939), which suggests that an increase in pulmonary congestion does not occur in such patients during exertion. The observations of Gilbert and Goldzieher (1946) that insulin and adrenalin each increase the circulation time in decompensated cardiac patients but not in normal subjects are difficult to accept.

The carbon dioxide time is also increased in patients with congestive failure (Bornstein, 1912; Grubner *et al.*, 1939). It is questionable whether this has any special significance, since it is not ascertainable how much of the elapsed time is occupied by the blood containing the inhaled carbon dioxide in passing through the pulmonary veins on the one hand and the left ventricle, ascending aorta and carotid artery on the other.

The ether time, which measures the venous segment of the circulation time, that is, the portion up to the lungs, is often used to diagnose "right heart failure." The ether time is often long in chronic cardiac decompensation (4; Hitzig, 1935), but is more often normal than is the arm-to-tongue time in patients with congestive failure (Baer and Slipakoff, 1938; Lian and Facquet, 1936; Miller, 1934). Hitzig *et al.* (1935) state that the ether time is normal in "left ventricular failure," but actually it is also not uncommonly normal in patients with edema, hepatomegaly and high venous pressure. Hitzig's (1935) observation that a close parallelism exists between elevated venous pressure and increased ether time is not corroborated by Dresdale *et al.* (1951), Grossman *et al.* (1950), Hussey *et al.* (1942), Epstein and Young (1943), nor Motta (1937). The lack of parallelism between ether time, venous pressure and the presence or absence of edema and hepatomegaly puts any attempts to diagnose "right ventricular failure" on a most insecure basis (see also page 48). The report of Soloff *et al.* (1952) of ether times slower than decholin times is confusing. The ether time is variable in cor pulmonale and beri-beri (Stone *et al.*, 1953; Gillanders, 1951).

Gross (1945) reported estimations of circulation time made by means of inhalation through the nose of amyl nitrite and claimed that this method measured lung-to-face time, much as carbon dioxide does. However, the times so obtained are very variable and in some cases are far too long; moreover, it is unlikely that with his technique enough of the amyl nitrite inhaled through the nose reaches the alveoli in every case. In this connection, it should be remembered that Weiss, Robb and Blumgart (1929) caused their patients to inhale maximally through the mouth and obtained a short circulation time with amyl nitrite; this probably represented the lung-to-face time. It is probable that in some instances, namely, those with long circulation times in the absence of failure, the vapors are absorbed through mucosal capillaries in the nasopharynx in Gross's technique. If this is so, Gross's (1945) method, if standardized, could be one of the most interesting and valuable of all, since it requires no apparatus or injections, and measures the circulation from capillary back to capillary in approximately the same area. Results by this method (Gross, 1945) show slowing in cardiac decompensation.

Nylin (1943, 1945b, 1950; Gernandt and Nylin, 1946) has adopted and developed the idea expressed earlier by David and Bouvrain (1940) that the increased circulation time of cardiac decompensation is a reflection of the accumulation of an increased amount of blood in the heart as a consequence of dilatation of the latter. Nathanson and Elek (1947) have also espoused this concept. Nylin's statistical studies and those of Nathanson and Elek (1947), which show a parallelism between cardiac size and circulation time, do not, however, in themselves, establish a direct relation between the two. Similarly, results of Nylin's above-cited studies, which show delayed mixing of intravenously injected material in patients with cardiac decompensation, are explicable on the basis of the low cardiac output, slow blood flow, and large blood volume of congestive failure. Meneely and Chestnut (1947) have criticized Nylin in a similar vein. It is probable that the increased *cardiac* blood volume, which almost certainly occurs commonly in patients with heart disease, is of little direct importance in causing the manifestations of cardiac decompensation; it is also difficult to see how the stagnation of enough blood in the heart to slow the circulation time can occur with the heart beating 80 to 120 times a minute and expelling liters of blood during this time.

Bibliography

Chapter I — Section 2

ALTSCHULE, M. D., and M. C. VOLK, Therapeutic effect of total ablation of normal thyroid on congestive failure and angina pectoris. XVIII. The cardiac output following total thyroidectomy in patients with and without congestive heart failure, with a comparison of results obtained with the acetylene and ethyl iodide methods, *Arch. Int. Med.* **58**, 32 (1936).   [3

ASCARELLI, E., Rapporti tra velocità di corrente e metabolismo basale nei cardiopazienti, *Cuore e circolaz.* **22**, 44 (1938). [3

BAER, S., The clinical application of the determination of circulation time, *Ann. Int. Med.* **13**, 2246 (1940). [3, 4

BAER, S., and H. J. ISARD, The value of the ether circulation time in the diagnosis of right heart failure, *Am. J. M. Sc.* **200**, 209 (1940). [4

BAER, S., and B. G. SLIPAKOFF, Measurement of circulation times and the agents used in their determination, *Am. Heart J.* **16**, 29 (1938). [3, 4

BAIN, C. W. C., Observations on the speed of the circulation, *Quart. J. Med.* **27**, 237 (1934). [3

BALL, J. D., H. KOPELMAN, and A. C. WITHAM, Circulatory changes in mitral stenosis at rest and on exercise, *Brit. Heart J.* **14**, 363 (1952). [3

BERLINER, K., Use of alpha lobeline for measurement of velocity of blood flow, *Arch. Int. Med.* **65**, 896 (1940). [3

BERNSTEIN, M., and S. SIMKINS, The use of magnesium sulfate in the measurement of circulation time, *Am. Heart. J.* **17**, 218 (1939). [3, 4

BIELSCHOWSKY, P., and K. LANGE, Zur Frage der Blutströmungsgeschwindigkeit, *Deutsche med. Wchnschr.* **59**, 1637 (1933). [3

BLANKENHORN, M. A., C. F. VILTER, I. M. SCHEINKER, and R. S. AUSTIN, Occidental beriberi heart disease, *J. A. M. A.* **131**, 717 (1946).

BLUMBERG, N., and E. M. SCHLOSS, The effect of circulatory factors on the bronsulphalein test in liver disease, *Am. J. M. Sc.* **213**, 470 (1947). [3

BLUMGART, H. L., The velocity of blood flow in health and disease. The velocity of blood flow in man and its relation to other measurements of the circulation, *Medicine* **10**, 1 (1931). [3

BLUMGART, H. L., and S. WEISS, Studies on the velocity of blood flow. III. The velocity of blood flow and its relation to other aspects of the circulation in patients with rheumatic and syphilitic heart disease, *J. Clin. Investigation* **4**, 149 (1927). [3

BLUMGART, H. L. and S. WEISS, Studies on the velocity of blood flow. IV. The velocity of blood flow and its relation to other aspects of the circulation in patients with arteriosclerosis and in patients with arterial hypertension, *J. Clin Investigation* **4**, 173 (1927). [3

BLUMGART, H. L., and S. WEISS, Clinical studies on the velocity of blood flow. IX. The pulmonary circulation time, the velocity of venous blood flow to the heart, and related aspects of the circulation in patients with cardiovascular disease, *J. Clin. Investigation* **5**, 343 (1927–28). [3

BLUMGART, H. L. and S. WEISS, Clinical studies on the velocity of blood flow. X. The relation between the velocity of blood flow, the venous pressure and the vital capacity of the lungs in fifty patients with cardiovascular disease compared with similar measurements in fifty normal persons, *J. Clin. Investigation* **5**, 379 (1927–28).   [3

BLUMGART, H. L., and O. C. YENS, Studies on the velocity of blood flow. I. The method utilized, *J. Clin. Investigation* **4**, 1 (1927).   [3

BORDEN, C. W., R. V. EBERT, R. H. WILSON, and H. S. WELLS, Studies of the pulmonary circulation. II. The circulation time from the pulmonary artery to the femoral artery and the quantity of blood in the lungs in patients with mitral stenosis and in patients with left ventricular failure, *J. Clin. Investigation* **28**, 1138 (1949).   [3

BORNSTEIN, A., Ueber die Messung der Kreislaufzeit in der Klinik, *Verhandl. d. Kong. f. inn. Med.* **29**, 457 (1912).

BRAUN, K., and C. H. FRYD, The effect of priscol on the peripheral venous pressure, *Brit. Heart J.* **13**, 294 (1951).   [3

CANDEL, S., and M. A. RABINOWITZ, Blood velocity rate and venous pressure in the prognosis of heart disease, *Ann. Int. Med.* **10**, 1000 (1937).   [3

CANNON, E. F., S. P. LUCIA, and E. H. BENSON, Circulation time under conditions of work and rest in subjects with normal and abnormal hearts, *Proc. Soc. Exper. Biol. & Med.* **42**, 237 (1939).

COSSIO, P., and I. BERCONSKY, The cyanosis in mitral stenosis, *Am. Heart J.* **17**, 1 (1939).   [3

DAVID, C., and Y. BOURVAIN, Contribution à l'étude physiopathologique de la vitesse de la circulation, *Arch. d. mal. du cœur* **33**, 147 (1940).   [3

DE VRIES, A., C. H. FRYD, and S. GITELSON, Observations on heart failure. The effect of withdrawal and administration of salt on body weight and venous pressure in heart failure, *Cardiologia* **15**, 368 (1950).   [3

DI PALMA, J. R., and P. E. KENDALL, The relationship between blood volume and blood specific gravity in the recovery from cardiac decompensation, *J. Lab. & Clin. Med.* **29**, 390 (1944).   [3

DRENNAN, L. M., JR., The clinical significance of the blood circulation time as determined by the saccharine test, *M. Ann. District of Columbia* **5**, 238 (1936).   [3

DRESDALE, D. T., M. SCHULTZ, and R. J. MICHTOM, Primary pulmonary hypertension. I. Clinical and hemodynamic study, *Am. J. Med.* **11**, 686 (1951).   [3

DOYLE, J. T., J. S. WILSON, C. LÉPINE, and J. V. WARREN, An evaluation of the measurement of the cardiac output and of the so-called pulmonary blood volume by the dye-dilution method, *J. Lab. & Clin. Med.* **41**, 29 (1953).   [3

DURAS, F. P., Measurement of the circulation time with saccharin, *Lancet* 1, 303 (1944). [3

ELEK, S. R., and S. D. SOLARZ, The use of papaverine as an objective measure of circulation time, *Am. Heart J.* 24, 821 (1942). [3

EPSTEIN, B. S., and D. YOUNG, A correlation between roentgenographic changes in the lungs in left ventricular failure and the circulation rates, *Am. J. Roentgenol.* 50, 316 (1943). [3, 4

ESSER, K. H., and K. BERLINER, Duplicate measurements of circulation time made with the saccharin method, *Ann. Int. Med.* 19, 64 (1943). [3

FISHBACK, D. B., S. A. GUTTMAN, and E. B. ABRAMSON, An objective method of determining blood velocity (fluorescein method), *Am. J. M. Sc.* 203, 535 (1942). [3

FRANCO, A., and M. G. MARQUES, Digitalisation massive ou fractionnée dans l'insuffisance cardiaque congestive chronique avec fibrillation auriculaire, *Cardiologia* 20, 257 (1952). [3

GARCIA, J. E., and B. A. GOLDMAN, The combined use of strophanthin-K and digitalis in the treatment of congestive heart failure. A preliminary report, *Am. Heart J.* 26, 20 (1943). [3

GARGILL, S. L., The use of sodium dehydrocholate as a clinical test of the velocity of blood flow, *New England J. Med.* 209, 1089 (1933). [3

GASUL, B. M., J. J. MARINO, and J. R. CHRISTIAN, Fluorescein circulation time in normal and pathological conditions in infants and children, including various types of congenital malformations of the heart, *J. Pediat.* 34, 460 (1949). [3

GERNANDT, B., and G. NYLIN, The relation between circulation time and the amount of residual blood in the heart, *Am. Heart J.* 32, 411 (1946). [3

GIBSON, J. G. 2D, and W. A. EVANS, JR., Clinical studies of the blood volume. III. Changes in blood volume, venous pressure and blood velocity rate in chronic congestive heart failure, *J. Clin. Investigation* 16, 851 (1937). [3

GILBERT, R. A., and J. W. GOLDZIEHER, The mechanism and prevention of cardiovascular changes due to insulin, *Ann. Int. Med.* 25, 928 (1946). [3

GILLANDERS, A. D., Circulatory dynamics in emphysema, *Quart J. Med.* 18, 263 (1949). [3, 4

GILLANDERS, A. D., Nutritional heart disease, *Brit. Heart J.* 13, 177 (1951).

GODEL, R., and C. CHEHALE, Mesure de la vitesse de circulation appliquée à l'évolution et à la thérapeutique des cardiopathies. Application d'une methode nouvelle estimant simultanément l'activité circulatoire cardio-pulmonaire droite et gauche, *Presse méd.* 44, 48 (1936). [3, 4

GOLDBERG, S. J., The use of calcium gluconate as a circulation time test, *Am. J. M. Sc.* **192**, 36 (1936).   [3

GOLDBLOOM, A. A., and A. LIEBERSON, Clinical studies in circulatory adjustments. V. Clinical evaluation of cardiodynamic studies, *Am. J. M. Sc.* **197**, 182 (1939).   [3

GREENFIELD, I., Sodium succinate as a test of circulatory efficiency, *Ann. Int. Med.* **32**, 524 (1950).   [3

GROSS, D., The measurement of the lung-to-face time by amyl nitrite, *Am. Heart J.* **30**, 19 (1945).

GROSSMAN, J., R. C. WESTON, J. P. HALPERIN, and L. LEITER, The nature of the renal circulatory changes in chronic congestive failure as reflected by renal tubular maximal functions, *J. Clin. Investigation* **29**, 1320 (1950).   [3, 4

GRUBNER, R., S. SCHNUR, and J. H. CRAWFORD, The use of CO_2 inhalation as a test of circulation time, *J. Clin. Investigation* **18**, 395 (1939).
                                                     [3, 4

HAHN, W., and M. HETTLER, Die Kreislaufzeitbestimmung mit Farbstoffen, *Klin. Wchnschr.* **27**, 773 (1949).   [3

HARVEY, W. P., and C. A. FINCH, Dicumarol prophylaxis of thromboembolic disease in congestive heart failure, *New England J. Med.* **242**, 208 (1950).   [3

HELLER, B. I., and W. E. JACOBSON, Renal hemodynamics in heart disease, *Am. Heart J.* **39**, 188 (1950).   [3

HITZIG, W. M., The use of ether in measuring the circulation time from the antecubital veins to the pulmonary capillaries, *Am. Heart J.* **10**, 1080 (1934–35).   [3, 4

HITZIG, W. M., F. H. KING, and A. M. FISHBERG, Circulation time in failure of the left side of the heart, *Arch. Int. Med.* **55**, 112 (1935).
                                                     [3

HUSSEY, H. H., D. P. CYR, and S. KATZ, The comparative value of calcium gluconate, magnesium sulfate, and alpha lobeline hydrochloride as agents for measurement of the arm-to-tongue circulation time in 50 patients with and 50 patients without heart failure, *Ann. Int. Med.* **17**, 849 (1942).   [3

HUSSEY, H. H., and S. KATZ, The comparative value of ether and paraldehyde as agents for measurement of the arm-to-lung circulation time in fifty patients with, and fifty patients without heart failure, *Am. J. M. Sc.* **201**, 669 (1941).   [4

HUSSEY, H. H., J. J. WALLACE, and J. C. SULLIVAN, The value of combined measurements of the venous pressure and arm-to-tongue and arm-to-lung circulation times in the study of heart failure, *Am. Heart J.* **23**, 22 (1942).   [3, 4

JABLONS, B., and J. COHEN, Measurement of the circulation time (photoelectric method), *Proc. Soc. Exper. Biol. & Med.* **52,** 294 (1943). [3

JABLONS, B., J. COHEN, and M. Y. SWIRSKY, Clinical studies of circulation time with objective (photoelectric cell-dye) method, *New York State J. Med.* **44,** 398 (1944). [3

KAHLER, H., Ueber Veränderungen der Blutumlaufzeit, *Wien. Arch. f. inn. Med.* **19,** 1 (1930). [3

KELLEY, R. T., E. D. FRIES, and T. F. HIGGINS, The effects of hexamethonium on certain manifestations of congestive heart failure, *Circulation* **7,** 169 (1953). [3

KINSMAN, J. M., and J. W. MOORE, The hemodynamics of the circulation in hypertension, *Ann. Int. Med.* **9,** 649 (1935). [3

KINSMAN, J. M., J. W. MOORE, and W. F. HAMILTON, Studies on the circulation: An analysis of some problems of the circulation in man in the normal and in the pathological states, by the use of the injection method, *Kentucky State M. J.* **31,** 285 (1933). [3

KLEIN, O., and J. HEINEMAN, Zur Messung der Strömungsgeschwindigkeit des Blutes beim Menschen, *Zentralbl. f. inn. Med.* **50,** 490 (1929). [3

KOCH, E., Die Stromgeschwindigkeit des Blutes, *Deutsches Arch. f. klin. Med.* **140,** 39 (1922). [3

KOPELMAN, H., The circulation time as a clinical test, *Brit. Heart J.* **13,** 301 (1951). [3

KOPELMAN, H., and G. DE J. LEE, The intrathoracic blood volume in mitral stenosis and left ventricular failure, *Clin. Sc.* **10,** 383 (1951). [3

LANGE, K., and L. J. BOYD, The use of fluorescein to determine the adequacy of the circulation, *M. Clin. North America* **26,** 943 (1942). [3

LANGE, K., and L. J. BOYD, Objective methods to determine the speed of blood flow and their results (fluorescein and acetylene), *Am. J. M. Sc.* **206,** 438 (1943). [3

LEQUIME, J., Le débit cardiaque. Études expérimentales et cliniques, *Acta med. Scandinav., Supp. No. 107* (1940). [3

LESCHKE, E., Kreislaufzeit und Blutgeschwindigkeit. *München. med. Wchnschr.* **78,** 2117 (1931). [3

LIAN, C., and E. BARRAS, Mesure de la vitesse de la circulation chez l'homme (épreuve de la fluorescéine), *Bull. et mém. Soc. méd. d. hôp. de Paris* **46,** 175 (1930). [3

LIAN, C., and E. BARRAS, Intérêt clinique de la mesure de vitesse de la circulation par l'épreuve de la fluorescéine, *Bull. et mém. Soc. méd. d. hôp. de Paris* **46,** 179 (1930). [3

LIAN, C., and J. FACQUET, La mesure de la vitesse circulatoire dans l'insuffisance cardiaque, *Bull. et mém. Soc. méd. d. hôp. de Paris* **51,** 393 (1935). [3

LIAN, C., and J. FACQUET, La mesure de la vitesse circulatoire en dehors de l'insuffisance cardiaque, *Bull. et mém. Soc. méd. d. hôp. de Paris* **51**, 397 (1935).   [3

LIAN, C., and J. FACQUET, La mesure de la vitesse circulatoire avec l'éther, la saccharine, et la fluorescéine dans les principaux types d'insuffisance cardiaque, *Bull. et mém. Soc. méd. d. hôp. de Paris* **52**, 428 (1936).   [3, 4

LIAN, C., and J. FACQUET, La vitesse de circulation dans l'insuffisance ventriculaire droite autonome, *Bull. et mém. Soc. méd. d. hôp. de Paris* **58**, 189 (1942).   [3

LILIENFELD, A., and K. BERLINER, Duplicate measurements of circulation time made with the alpha lobeline method, *Arch. Int. Med.* **69**, 739 (1942).   [3

LOMBARDO, T. A., The effect of posture on the excretion of water and sodium by patients with congestive heart failure, *Circulation* **7**, 91 (1953).   [3

LUBIC, L. G., and N. J. SISSMAN, A modification of the fluorescein circulation time, *Am. Heart J.* **44**, 443 (1952).   [3

MACGREGOR, A. G., and E. J. WAYNE, Fluorescein test of circulation time in peripheral vascular disease, *Brit. Heart J.* **13**, 80 (1951).   [3

MANTERO, O., and G. BARLASSINA, Contributo allo studio della emodinamica renale nei cardiopatici mediante le prove selettive di funzionalità renale, *Minerva med.* **42**, 1049 (1951).   [3

McGUIRE, J., V. HAUENSTEIN, and R. SHORE, Cardiac output in heart disease determined by the direct Fick method, including comparative determinations by the acetylene method, *Arch. Int. Med.* **60**, 1034 (1937).   [3

McGUIRE, J., R. SHORE, V. HAUENSTEIN, and F. GOLDMAN, The cardiac output in compensation and decompensation in the same individual, *Am. Heart J.* **16**, 449 (1938).   [3

McGUIRE, J., R. SHORE, V. HAUENSTEIN, and F. GOLDMAN, Relation of cardiac output to congestive heart failure, *Arch. Int. Med.* **63**, 290 (1939).   [3

MENEELY, G. R., and J. L. CHESTNUT, A relation between the size of the heart and the velocity of the blood, *Am. Heart J.* **33**, 175 (1947).   [3

MENEELY, G. R. and N. L. KALTREIDER, A study of the volume of the blood in congestive heart failure. Relation to other measurements in fifteen patients, *J. Clin. Investigation* **22**, 521 (1943).   [3

MILLER, H. R., Velocity of blood flow in part of the pulmonary circulation, *Proc. Soc. Exper. Biol. & Med.* **31**, 942 (1934).   [4

MOTTA, G., Influenza della pressione venosa sul tempo di circolazione, *Cuore e circolaz.* **21**, 379 (1937).   [4

Moyer, J. H., S. I. Miller, A. B. Tashnek, and R. Bowman, The effect of theophylline with ethylenediamine (aminophylline) on cerebral hemodynamics in the presence of cardiac failure with and without Cheyne-Stokes respiration, *J. Clin. Investigation* **31**, 267 (1952). [3

Nathanson, M. H., and S. R. Elek, The influence of heart size on the circulation time, *Am. Heart J.* **33**, 464 (1947). [3

Neurath, O., Untersuchungen über die Bestimmung der Blutumlaufsgeschwindigkeit mit Magnesiumsulfat, *Ztschr. f. klin. Med.* **132**, 134 (1937). [3

Nylin, G., On the amount of, and changes in, the residual blood of the heart, *Am. Heart J.* **25**, 1598 (1943). [3

Nylin, G., Blood volume determinations with radioactive phosphorus, *Brit. Heart J.* **7**, 81 (1945*a*). [3

Nylin, G., The dilution curve of activity in arterial blood after intravenous injection of labeled corpuscles, *Am. Heart J.* **30**, 1 (1945*b*). [3

Nylin, G., and G. Malmström, Weitere Untersuchungen über die Bedeutung der Verlängerten Kreislaufzeit für die Kardiologie, *Cardiologia* **5**, 333 (1941). [3

Nylin, G., Studies of the changes in the amount of residual blood of the heart in man, *Cardiologia* **17**, 251 (1950).

Pearce, M. L., A. E. Lewis, and M. R. Kaplan, The factors influencing the circulation time, *Circulation* **5**, 583 (1952). [3

Piccione, F. V., and L. J. Boyd, The determination of blood velocity by lobeline, *J. Lab. & Clin. Med.* **26**, 766 (1941). [3

Porter, R. B., and R. S. Downs, Some physiological observations on the circulation during recovery from vitamin B_1 deficiency, *Ann. Int. Med.* **17**, 645 (1942).

Robb, G. P., and S. Weiss, The velocity of pulmonary and peripheral venous blood flow and related aspects of the circulation in cardiovascular disease. Their relation to clinical types of circulatory failure, *Am. Heart J.* **9**, 742 (1934). [3

Rocchini, G., Misure comparative della velocità circolatoria negli arti superiori ed inferiori, in condizioni normali e patologiche, *Cuore e circolaz.* **21**, 508 (1937). [3

Ross, D. N., Theophylline-ethylenediamine in the measurement of blood circulation-time, *Brit. Heart J.* **13**, 56 (1951). [3

Rubin, E. H., B. S. Kahn, and D. Pecker, Diffuse interstitial fibrosis of the lungs, *Ann. Int. Med.* **36**, 864 (1952).

Schalm, L., and W. A. H. Hoogenboom, Blood bilirubin in congestive heart failure, *Am. Heart J.* **44**, 571 (1952). [3

Sebastiani, A., Sulla determinazione della velocità di circolazione del sangue, *Cuore e circolaz.* **15**, 157 (1931). [3

SESSA, T., La velocità della corrente del sangue. II. Tempo di circolazione nei condizione pathologiche (cardiopatie), *Cuore e Circolaz.* **22**, 2 (1938).   [3

SOLOFF, L. A., J. ZATUCHNI, and L. TURNER, Aortic stenosis manifested as chronic cor pulmonale, *J. A. M. A.* **150**, 1111 (1952).   [3

STANOJÉVIC, L., Die Bestimmung der Kreislaufzeit mit Lobelin, *Ztschr. f. Kreislaufforsch.* **30**, 521 (1938).   [3

STANOYÉVITCH, L., and B. DJORDJEVITCH, Sur la détermination du temps de circulation par la lobeline, *Compt. rend. Soc. de biol.* **127**, 1362 (1938).   [3

STEWART, H. J., N. F. CRANE, R. F. WATSON, C. H. WHEELER, and J. E. DEITRICK, The cardiac output in congestive heart failure and in organic heart disease, *Ann. Int. Med.* **13**, 2323 (1940).   [3

STEWART, H. J., J. E. DEITRICK, N. F. CRANE, and C. H. WHEELER, Action of digitalis in uncompensated heart disease, *Arch. Int. Med.* **62**, 569 (1938).   [3

STEWART, H. J., J. E. DEITRICK, R. F. WATSON, C. H. WHEELER, and N. F. CRANE, The effect of valvular heart disease on the dynamics of the circulation. Observations before, during and after the occurrence of heart failure, *Am. Heart J.* **16**, 477 (1938).   [3

STEWART, H. J., W. F. EVANS, H. BROWN, and J. R. GERJUOY, Peripheral blood flow, rectal and skin temperature in congestive heart failure. The effects of rapid digitalization in this state, *Arch. Int. Med.* **77**, 643 (1946).   [3

STONE, D. J., A. SCHWARTZ, W. NEWMAN, J. A. FELTMAN, and F. J. LOVELOCK, Precipitation by pulmonary infection of acute anoxia, cardiac failure and respiratory acidosis in chronic pulmonary disease, *Am. J. Med.* **14**, 14 (1953).

STORSTEIN, O., Measurement of the venous pressure and of the circulation time, *Acta med. Scandinav.* **136**, 122 (1949).   [3

SUTTON, F. C., J. A. BRITTON, and J. G. CARR, Estimation of cardiopulmonary functional capacity by means of oxygen debt studies, *Am. Heart J.* **20**, 423 (1940).   [3

SWENSON, R. E., Parenteral vitamin B as an agent for determining the arm-to-tongue circulation time. Part I, *Am. Heart J.* **32**, 612 (1946).   [3

TARR, L., B. S. OPPENHEIMER, and R. V. SAGER, The circulation time in various clinical conditions determined by the use of sodium dehydrocholate, *Am. Heart J.* **8**, 766 (1932–33).   [3

TRIMARCHI, E., Sul metodo della lobelina per la misura della velocità circolatoria, *Riforma med.* **54**, 1407 (1938).   [3

VECCHI, E., Applicazione di un nuovo metodo per la determinazione della velocità di circolazione del grande e del piccolo circolo, *Cuore e circolaz.* **21**, 61 (1937). [3, 4

VOLGIN, O., and L. STANOJÉVIC, Vergleichende Untersuchungen der Bilirubinämie und Kreislaufszeit bei Dekompensation des Herzens, *Klin. Wchnschr.* **17**, 569 (1938). [3

WALL, H. C., Measurement of circulation time with calcium gluconate in patients receiving digitalis, with electrocardiographic studies, *Am. Heart J.* **18**, 228 (1939). [3

WEISS, S., G. P. ROBB, and H. L. BLUMGART, The velocity of blood flow in health and disease as measured by the effect of histamine on the minute vessels, *Am. Heart J.* **4**, 664 (1928–29). [3

WEISS, S., and R. W. WILKINS, The nature of the cardiovascular disturbances in nutritional deficiency states, *Ann. Int. Med.* **11**, 104 (1937).

WERKÖ, L., and H. LAGERLÖF, Studies on the circulation of blood in man. VII. The effect of a single intravenous dose of theophylline diethanolamine on the cardiac output, pulmonary blood volume and systemic and pulmonary blood pressures in hypertensive cardiovascular disease, *Scandinav. J. Clin. & Lab. Investigation* **1**, 181 (1949). [3

WOLLHEIM, E., Untersuchungen zur Hämodynamik unter Digitalis und Strophanthin, *Deutsche med. Wchnschr.* **75**, 482 (1950). [3

WINTERNITZ, M., J. DEUTSCH, and Z. BRÜLL, Eine klinisch brauchbare Bestimmungsmethode der Blutumlaufzeit mittels Decholininjektion, *Med. Klin.* **27**, 986 (1931). [3

WOLLHEIM, E., and K. LANGE, Kreislaufszeit und ihre Beziehung zu anderen Kreislaufgrössen. *Verhandl. d. deutsch. Gesellsch. f. inn. Med.* **43**, 134 (1931). [3

WOOD, P., Right and left ventricular failure. A study of circulation time and venous blood pressure, *Lancet* **2**, 15 (1936). [3

WOOD, P., The action of digitalis in heart failure with normal rhythm, *Brit. Heart J.* **2**, 132 (1940). [3

3. *Peripheral Circulation. Temperature Regulation*

Peripheral Circulation.—Data on peripheral blood flow may be obtained by various methods. These include studies of the gases in samples of blood taken from peripheral vessels (page 70), plethysmographic methods (Abramson *et al.*, 1942), and techniques based upon cutaneous temperature changes (Stewart *et al.*, 1946). Marked changes in blood flow through the extremities are not to be expected in patients with congestive failure, since the flow through resting muscle is small (Holling, 1939) and that in the skin amounts only to a few hundred cubic centimeters per minute for the whole body.

Few direct measurements of peripheral blood flow in patients with congestive failure have been reported. G. N. Stewart (1912, 1914) noted decreased flow in the hands, varying roughly with the degree of failure, in cardiac patients. Flow through the hands, however, is so strongly influenced by neurogenic factors which cannot always be controlled as to make these data of little value in themselves. H. J. Stewart (1946) found values that were in the normal range but low in relation to the elevated metabolic rates exhibited by his patients. On the other hand, the low oxygen content of the antecubital and femoral venous blood found by most observers in decompensated cardiacs show that the volume of flow is reduced in congestive failure (Harrop, 1919; Landt and Benjamin, 1941; Lundsgaard, 1918a,b,c; 5); Holling (1939) has demonstrated a parallelism between venous oxygen content and blood flow. The wide arteriovenous differences for carbon dioxide found in peripheral bloods by Pearce (1917, 1921) and Scott (1919) also indicate slow peripheral flow. In addition, the results of direct microscopy (page 47) also prove that the speed of flow is reduced. In patients with high-output failure the peripheral flow is probably increased, although few direct observations bearing on this point have been made. Weiss and Wilkins (1937) found a decreased peripheral arteriovenous oxygen difference in cardiac decompensation caused by beri-beri; it is probable that in this condition much or most of the blood is diverted through arteriovenous shunts and by-passes the capillaries — a condition that does not necessarily exist in other types of high-output failure.

Harrison and Pilcher (1929) concluded from their studies of blood gases that edema in cardiac patients causes an increase in the flow through the edematous areas, but their conclusions have been severely criticized by Weiss and Ellis (1935), who used the same methods. Abramson et al. (1943a) used a plethysmographic method, and also found evidence of increased flow through edematous limbs; however, some error in their method is suggested by the fact that it recorded increased flow in the presence of venous occlusion, whereas Friedland et al. (1941), who also used a plethysmographic method, found that venous stasis decreased blood flow through an extremity. The nature of the error in Abramson's work is probably elucidated by the observations of Wilkins and Bradley (1946) and Stanton *et al.* (1949), who found that the application of the cuff as required in plethysmographic methods might result in a temporary increase in blood flow if the latter was low initially. Rocchini (1937), who used fluorescein in his studies, claimed that the circulation through the edematous limbs of cardiac patients is slower than that through limbs free of edema. It is probable that edema has in itself no specific effect on blood flow.

During exercise the peripheral blood flow fails to increase in a normal manner and venous blood becomes markedly deoxygenated in patients in failure (Harris and Lipkin, 1931; Weiss and Ellis, 1935). Even in compensated cardiac patients the blood flow remains elevated longer after exercise than in normal subjects (Abramson *et al.*, 1942), implying an attempt to discharge an abnormally large oxygen debt; presumably a still larger "flow debt" would occur in the presence of congestive failure. It is significant that an increased "flow debt" also occurs when anoxia is induced in normal subjects who exercise while breathing low concentrations of oxygen (Abramson *et al.*, 1943*b*).

Temperature regulation.—Slight to moderate elevation of body temperature in the absence of evidences of infection is frequently observed in patients with severe congestive failure. Cohn and Steele (1934) studied this phenomenon and found a close parallelism between the presence of signs of marked failure and elevation of temperature, except that the latter might occur before the former became evident. Steele (1934) further reported that the difference between skin and rectal temperatures is abnormally great in cardiac patients, a finding not corroborated by Stewart *et al.* (1946); however, Stewart's patients had elevated metabolic rates and in proportion to the increase in heat production their cutaneous temperatures were low. Both Steele (1935) and Burch (1946*a,b*) observed that such patients eliminate two or three times as much heat as normally via the lungs.

These findings are not unexpected in view of the known marked reduction in peripheral blood flow (page 38) and the vasoconstriction (page 43) which ordinarily occur in severe failure. Diminution in blood flow to the periphery necessarily affects the dispersal of heat generated within the body, thereby giving rise to an elevation of body temperature. Steele (1937) was able to reproduce these conditions in normal subjects by slowing the peripheral circulation by means of tourniquets applied to the extremities. He suggested (1934) that this inability to disperse heat normally via the skin might be one cause of the hyperpnea exhibited by patients with cardiac decompensation. This view is supported by the clinical observation that many patients with severe congestive failure claim to experience increase of dyspnea when wrapped in blankets or placed in a warm, stuffy room (Burch, 1946c). It should be noted that other heat-dispersing mechanisms, namely, water loss through the skin and sweating in response to heating, are also impaired in patients with cardiac decompensation (Burch, 1946c; Kauf and Zak, 1927). D'Alton et al. (1948) found no diminution in sweating at ordinary temperatures. Vasodilatation is sluggish in patients with chronic cardiac decompensation in a hot, humid environment; an excessive rise in pulse rate occurs (Berenson and Burch, 1952).

Bibliography

Chapter I — Section 3

ABRAMSON, D. I., S. M. FIERST, and K. FLACHS, Effect of muscular exercise upon the peripheral circulation in patients with valvular heart disease, *J. Clin. Investigation* **21,** 747 (1942).

ABRAMSON, D. I., S. M. FIERST, and K. FLACHS, Rate of peripheral blood flow in the presence of edema, *Am. Heart J.* **25,** 328 (1943a).

ABRAMSON, D. I., H. LANDT, and J. E. BENJAMIN, Peripheral vascular response to acute anoxia, *Arch. Int. Med.* **71,** 583 (1943b).

BERENSON, C. S., and G. F. BURCH, The response of patients with congestive heart failure to a rapid elevation in atmospheric temperature and humidity, *Am. J. Med. Sc.* **223,** 45 (1952).

BURCH, G. E., Rate of water and heat loss from the respiratory tract of patients with congestive heart failure who were from a subtropical climate and resting in a comfortable atmosphere, *Am. Heart J.* **32,** 88 (1946a).

BURCH, G. E., Influence of variations in atmospheric temperature and humidity on the rates of water and heat loss from the respiratory tract of patients with congestive heart failure living in a subtropical climate, *Am. Heart J.* **32,** 191 (1946b).

BURCH, G. E., The influence of environmental temperature and relative humidity on the rate of water loss through the skin in congestive heart failure in a subtropical climate, *Am. J. M. Sc.* **211,** 181 (1946c).

COHN, A. E., and J. M. STEELE, Unexplained fever in heart failure, *J. Clin. Investigation* **13**, 853 (1934).

COSSIO, P., and I. BERCONSKY, The cyanosis in mitral stenosis, *Am. Heart J.* **17**, 1 (1939). [5

D'ALTON, C. J., R. C. DARLING, and E. SHEA, The insensible loss of water in congestive failure, *Am. J. Med. Sc.* **216**, 516 (1948).

DAUTREBANDE, L., Contribution à l'étude physiopathologique et thérapeutique des troubles circulatoires dans l'asystolie, *Arch. internat. de méd. expér.* **2**, 413 (1926). [5

FRIEDLAND, C. K., J. S. HUNT, and R. W. WILKINS, Effects of changes in venous pressure upon blood flow in the limbs, *Am. Heart J.* **25**, 631 (1941).

GRANT, S. B., Changes in the blood oxygen following therapeutic bleeding in cardiac patients, *J. Lab. & Clin. Med.* **9**, 160 (1923). [5

HARRIS, I., and I. J. LIPKIN, Cardiac output and oxygen utilization in some types of heart disease, *Edinburgh M. J.* **38**, 501 (1931).

HARRISON, T. R., and C. PILCHER, Studies in congestive heart failure. I. The effect of edema on oxygen utilization, *J. Clin. Investigation* **8**, 259 (1929–30).

HARROP, G. A., JR., The oxygen and carbon dioxide content of arterial and of venous blood in normal individuals and in patients with anemia and heart disease, *J. Exper. Med.* **30**, 241 (1919). [5

HEFTER, A. J., and D. F. OKUNEW, Ueber Veränderungen des peripheren Stoffwechsels im Zusammenhang mit den Blutkreislaufstörungen bei der Muskelarbeit, *Ztschr. f. d. ges. exper. Med.* **79**, 806 (1931). [5

HOLLING, H. E., Observations on the oxygen content of venous blood from the arm vein and on the oxygen consumption of resting human muscle, *Clin. Sc.* **4**, 103 (1939).

JANSEN, K., H. W. KNIPPING, and K. STROMBERGER, Klinische Untersuchungen über Atmung und Blutgase, *Beitr. z. Klin. d. Tuberk.* **80**, 304 (1932). [5

KAUF, E., and E. ZAK, Storungen des Wasserhaushaltes, insbesonders der Schweiss-Sekretion bei Kreislaufkranken, *Wien. klin. Wchnschr.* **40**, 1405 (1927).

LANDT, H., and J. E. BENJAMIN, Changes in the content of carbon dioxide in venous blood during rebreathing experiments. Comparison of change in persons with a normal heart and in patients with cardiac disease, *Arch. Int. Med.* **67**, 72 (1941). [5

LUNDSGAARD, C., Studies of oxygen in the venous blood. II. Studies of the oxygen unsaturation in the venous blood of a group of patients with circulatory disturbances, *J. Exper. Med.* **27**, 179 (1918a). [5

LUNDSGAARD, C., Studies of oxygen in the venous blood. III. Determinations on five patients with compensated circulatory disturbances, *J. Exper. Med.* **27,** 199 (1918*b*).   [5

LUNDSGAARD, C., Studies of oxygen in the venous blood. IV. Determinations on five patients with incompensated circulatory disturbances, *J. Exper. Med.* **27,** 219 (1918*c*).   [5

MEANS, J. H., and L. H. NEWBURGH, Studies of the blood flow by the method of Krogh and Lindhard, *Tr. A. Am. Physicians* **30,** 51 (1915).   [5

PEARCE, R. G., A possible explanation for the cyanosis and hyperpnea seen in pneumonia and cardiac decompensation, *J. Lab. & Clin. Med.* **2,** 867 (1917).

PEARCE, R. G., The cardiorespiratory mechanism in health and disease, *Arch. Int. Med.* **27,** 139 (1921).

RABINOWITCH, I. M., The output of the heart per beat in heart disease, *Arch. Int. Med.* **36,** 239 (1925).   [5

ROCCHINI, G., Misure comparative della velocità circolatoria negli arti superiori ed inferiori, in condizioni normali e patologiche, *Cuore e circolaz.* **21,** 508 (1937).

SCOTT, R. W., The total carbonate content of the arterial and venous plasma in patients with chronic heart disease. *Proc. Soc. Exper. Biol. & Med.* **17,** 19 (1919).

STANTON, J. R., E. D. FREIS, and R. W. WILKINS, The acceleration of linear flow in the deep veins of the lower extremity by local compression, *J. Clin. Investigation* **28,** 553 (1949).

STEELE, J. M., Fever in heart failure. Relations between the temperatures of the interior and the surface of the body, *J. Clin. Investigation* **13,** 869 (1934).

STEELE, J. M., Elimination of heat by evaporation of water from the lungs in heart failure, *J. Clin. Investigation* **14,** 706 (1935).

STEELE, J. M., Elevation of rectal temperature following mechanical obstruction to the peripheral circulation, *Am. Heart J.* **13,** 542 (1937).

STEWART, G. N., Studies on the circulation in man. The blood flow in the hands and feet in normal and pathological cases, *Harvey Lectures* **8,** 86 (1912–13).

STEWART, G. N., Studies on the circulation in man. X. The blood flow in the hands in diseases of the heart, *Arch. Int. Med.* **13,** 1 (1914).

STEWART, H. J., W. F. EVANS, H. BROWN, and J. R. GERJUOY, Peripheral blood flow, rectal and skin temperature in congestive heart failure. The effects of rapid digitalization in this state, *Arch. Int. Med.* **77,** 643 (1946).

WEISS, S., and L. B. ELLIS, Oxygen utilization and lactic acid production in the extremities during rest and exercise. In subjects with normal and in those with diseased cardiovascular systems, *Arch. Int. Med.* **55**, 665 (1935). [5

WEISS, S., and R. W. WILKINS, The nature of the cardiovascular disturbances in nutritional deficiency states, *Ann. Int. Med.* **11**, 104 (1937).

WILKINS, R. W., and S. E. BRADLEY, Changes in arterial and venous blood pressure and flow distal to a cuff inflated on the human arm, *Am. J. Physiol.* **147**, 260 (1946).

4. *Arterial Blood Pressure.*
Peripheral Resistance. Vasoconstriction

The arterial blood pressure shows no consistent change as a consequence of congestive failure, although a fall is often described in recovery (Seymour *et al.*, 1942; **6A**). This decrease in arterial pressure is difficult to interpret, since some lowering of blood pressure usually occurs when hypertensive patients and some normal subjects remain in bed over a period of some days. It is probable that cardiac decompensation has no consistent effect on arterial blood pressure; any tendency toward a fall consequent to lowered cardiac output is likely to be counteracted by vasoconstriction caused by sympathetic activity, the latter precipitated by anoxia, anxiety, or discomfort. The work of Henry *et al.* (1947) shows that vasoconstriction occurs in the extremities in normal subjects exposed to anoxia; the vasoconstriction is neurogenic in origin (Marsh and Van Liere, 1948). Other factors may be present since the over-all effect on the circulation of anoxia in normal subjects is lowering of total peripheral resistance. Evidence of vasoconstriction is afforded not only by the pallor the patients exhibit but also by the fact that reactive hyperemia is diminished (von Marsovsky, 1942). This cutaneous vasoconstriction may at times lead to a false diagnosis of shock.

On the other hand, some authors have found a lowered arterial pressure in congestive heart failure (Cournand, 1952; Eichna *et al.*, 1951, 1953); in these instances the decreased cardiac output evidently has a greater influence than the vasoconstriction. Since the cardiac output is low in decompensation and the arterial pressure is normal or slightly elevated, it is clear that the total peripheral resistance must be increased (Seymour *et al.*, 1942; Richards, 1945; Stead *et al.*, 1948; **6B**), which is additional evidence of vasoconstriction; the resistance falls to or toward normal in recovery (Seymour *et al.*, 1942; Harvey *et al.*, 1949; Lagerlöf and Werkö, 1949). The reported finding of renin (Merrill, 1946; Merrill *et al.*, 1946) in the renal venous blood in congestive failure may be important for an understanding of changes in blood pressure, although the amounts reported to be found are so large as to arouse skepticism; it should be noted that Mylon and Freedman (1949) found renin in the blood of only one patient of three studied in failure. The possible effects of VEM and VDM found in congestive failure (Mokotoff *et al.*, 1949; Shorr *et al.*, 1950; Edelman *et al.*, 1950) must also be borne in mind; the influence of these substances on the state of the arterial tree in cardiac decompensation has not been elucidated.

Maronde *et al.* (1950) found that in patients with severe pulmonary congestion a rise in blood pressure and pulse pressure occurs in inspiration, as opposed to the occurrence of this phenomenon in expiration normally. The significance of this observation is not known. Abnormal changes in arterial pressure occur with changes in position in cardiac decompensation (Howard and Leathart, 1951); the significance of this finding is not clear.

Bibliography

Chapter I — Section 4

BLOOMFIELD, R. A., B. RAPOPORT, J. P. MILNOR, W. K. LONG, J. G. MEBANE, and L. B. ELLIS, The effects of the cardiac glycosides upon the dynamics of the circulation in congestive heart failure. I. Ouabain, *J. Clin. Investigation* **27**, 588 (1948).   [6A

COURNAND, A., A discussion of the concept of cardiac failure in the light of recent physiologic studies in man, *Ann. Int. Med.* **37**, 649 (1952).   [6A

EDELMAN, I. S., B. W. ZWEIFACH, D. J. W. ESCHER, J. GROSSMAN, R. MOKOTOFF, R. E. WESTON, L. LEITER, and E. SHORR, Studies on VEM and VDM in blood in relation to renal hemodynamics and renal oxygen extraction in chronic congestive heart failure, *J. Clin. Investigation* **29**, 925 (1950).

EICHNA, L., S. J. FARBER, A. R. BERGER, D. P. EARLE, B. RADER, E. PELLEGRINO, R. E. ALBERT, J. D. ALEXANDER, H. TAUBE, and S. YOUNG-

WIRTH, The interrelationship of the cardiovascular, renal and electrolyte effects of intravenous digoxin in congestive heart failure, *J. Clin. Investigation* **30**, 1250 (1951).

EICHNA, L., S. J. FARBER, A. R. BERGER, D. P. EARLE, B. RADER, E. PELLEGRINO, R. E. ALBERT, J. D. ALEXANDER, H. TAUBE, and S. YOUNGWIRTH, Cardiovascular dynamics, blood volumes, renal functions and electrolyte excretions in the same patients during congestive heart failure and after recovery of cardiac decompensation, *Circulation* **7**, 674 (1953). [6A

FERRER, M. I., R. M. HARVEY, R. T. CATHCART, C. A. WEBSTER, D. W. RICHARDS, JR., and A. COURNAND, Some effects of digoxin upon the heart and circulation in man. Digoxin in chronic cor pulmonale, *Circulation* **1**, 161 (1950). [6A

GEISBÖCK, F., Die Bedeutung der Blutdruckmessung für die Praxis, *Deutsches Arch. f. klin. Med.* **83**, 363 (1905). [6A

HARRISON, T. R., Arterial and venous pressure factors in circulatory failure, *Physiol. Rev.* **18**, 86 (1938). [6A

HARVEY, R. M., M. I. FERRER, R. T. CATHCART, D. W. RICHARDS, JR., and A. COURNAND, Some effects of digoxin upon the heart and circulation in man. Digoxin in left ventricular failure, *Am. J. Med.* **7**, 439 (1949). [6A

HICKAM, J. B., W. H. CARGILL, and A. GOLDEN, Cardiovascular reactions to emotional stimuli. Effect on the cardiac output, arteriovenous oxygen difference, arterial pressure, and peripheral resistance, *J. Clin. Investigation* **27**, 291 (1948). [6A

HENRY, J. P., J. GOODMAN, and J. P. MEEHAN, Effects of acute anoxia on the capillary permeability of the human arm, *Am. J. Med.* **2**, 657 (1947).

HOWARD, P., and G. L. LEATHART, Changes of pulse pressure and heart rate induced by changes of posture in subjects with normal and failing hearts, *Clin. Sc.* **10**, 521 (1951).

KELLEY, R. T., E. D. FRIES, and T. F. HIGGINS, The effects of hexamethonium on certain manifestations of congestive heart failure, *Circulation* **7**, 169 (1953). [6A

LAGERLÖF, H., and L. WERKÖ, Studies on the circulation in man. V. The effect of cedilanid (lanatoside C) on cardiac output and blood pressure in the pulmonary circulation in patients with compensated and decompensated heart disease, *Acta Cardiol.* **4**, 1 (1949). [6A

LANG, G., and S. MANSWETOWA, Zur Frage der Veränderung des arteriellen Blutdrucks bei Herzkranken während der Kompensationsstörung, *Deutsches Arch. f. klin. Med.* **94**, 455 (1908). [6A

LEWIS, C. S., M. C. DAINES, A. J. SAMUELS, and H. H. HECHT, Cor pulmonale (pulmono-cardiac syndrome). A case report, *Dis. of Chest* **22**, 261 (1952). [6A

Loschkarewa, Zur Frage der Blutdrucksteigerung bei Herzinsufficienz, *Deutsches Arch. f. klin. Med.* **143,** 364 (1924).   [6A

Maronde, R. F., H. E. Martin, J. P. Meehan, and D. R. Drury, The effect of respiration on the arterial pulse in left ventricular failure, *Am. Heart J.* **40,** 930 (1950).

Marsh, D. F., and E. J. Van Liere, The effect of adrenergic blocking agents on the vasoconstriction produced by acute oxygen lack, *J. Pharmacol. & Exper. Therap.* **94,** 221 (1948).

Merrill, A. J., Edema and decreased renal blood flow in patients with chronic congestive heart failure. Evidence of "forward failure" as the primary cause of edema, *J. Clin. Investigation* **25,** 389 (1946).

Merrill, A. J., L. J. Morrison, and E. S. Brannon, Concentration of renin in renal venous blood in patients with chronic heart failure, *Am. J. Med.* **1,** 468 (1946).

Mokotoff, R., D. J. W. Escher, I. S. Edelman, J. Grossman, and L. Leiter, Studies on vasotropic principles of blood (VEM and VDM) and renal hemodynamics in chronic heart failure, *Federation Proc.* **8,** 112 (1949).

Mylon, E., and L. R. Freedman, On the occurrence of renin in the blood of hypertensive patients, *Am. Heart J.* **38,** 509 (1949).

Myer, J., and T. F. Mullen, Systolic blood pressure in cardiac decompensation and during compensation, *Am. Heart J.* **3,** 356 (1927–28).
                                                                    [6A

Richards, D. W., Jr., Cardiac output by the catheterization technique in various clinical conditions, *Federation Proc.* **4,** 215 (1945).
                                                                    [6, 6A

Seymour, W. B., W. H. Pritchard, L. P. Longley, and J. M. Hayman, Jr., Cardiac output, blood and interstitial fluid volumes, total circulating serum protein and kidney function during cardiac failure and after improvement, *J. Clin. Investigation* **21,** 229 (1942).   [6, 6A

Shorr, E., S. Baez, B. W. Zweifach, M. A. Payne, and A. Mazur, The antidiuretic action of the hepatic vasodepressor ferritin (VDM) and its occurrence in conditions associated with antidiuresis in man, *Tr. A. Am. Physicians* **63,** 39 (1950).

Stead, E. A., Jr., J. V. Warren, and E. S. Brannon, Effect of lanatoside C on the circulation of patients with congestive failure. A study using catheterization of the right side of the heart, *Arch. Int. Med.* **81,** 282 (1948).   [6A

von Marsovsky, P., Über die Funktionen der Arteriolen bei decompensierten Herzkranken, *Ztschr. f. Kreislaufforsch.* **34,** 446 (1942).

Werkö, L., The influence of positive pressure breathing on the circulation in man, *Acta med. Scandinav. Supp. No. 193* (1947).   [6A

5. *Venous Pressure. Venous Tone*

Venous engorgement is one of the cardinal signs of congestive failure. Measurements of the venous pressure by many workers, by direct or indirect methods, have corroborated this clinical finding (Gaertner, 1903; Clark, 1915; Eyster, 1926; Winsor and Burch, 1946; **7**). In addition to reports of changes in venous pressure in the extremities, pressures in the visceral veins, such as the coronary veins (Bing *et al.*, 1949), the jugular veins (Moyer *et al.*, 1952; Novack *et al.*, 1953), and the renal veins (page 160) have also been described as elevated. Most of these authors agree that the venous pressure is normal in patients with organic cardiac disease but without signs or symptoms of failure (exclusive of tricuspid disease and pericarditis), but Gaertner (1903) and Clark (1915) found it to be elevated in some such patients. A considerable degree of overlapping of venous pressure values may be found when normal individuals, compensated cardiac patients and patients in failure are studied (Altschule, 1938; **8**). When patients with congestive failure and high venous pressures sit up, the pressure in the veins falls, a phenomenon which does not occur in normal subjects (Winsor and Burch, 1946; Gitelson, 1951; Wollheim, 1950); the importance of this finding in regard to the genesis of orthopnea is apparent. Davis and Shock (1949) found a similar fall in normal subjects, while Winsor and Burch (1946), Wollheim (1950), and Gitelson (1951) did not. A single observation records the fact that tone of the small veins is normal in patients with elevated venous pressure (Capps, 1936).

The normal response to an increase in venous pressure is an increase in cardiac output (Altschule and Gilligan, 1938); decompensated patients who show increased venous pressure at rest have diminished cardiac outputs.

The rise in venous pressure frequently found in cardiac decompensation is due in part to the inability of the heart to take up and propel forward all the blood brought to it. This conclusion is supported by the loss of gradient between venous and right auricular pressures in chronic failure (page 62) and also by the striking and almost immediate rise in venous pressure which often occurs in patients with paroxysmal arrhythmias and rapid ventricular rates (page 360); vasoconstriction may, however, play a part in the latter phenomenon. The fact that the rise of venous pressure that follows exercise is greater and more prolonged in cardiac patients than in normal subjects (9; Schott, 1912: Harrison et al., 1932; White et al., 1925) also suggests the importance of impaired cardiac output; the increased venous return consequent to the pumping action of the exercising muscles is more than the weakened heart can propel forward. The right auricular pressure is found elevated in such instances (Hultgren, 1950); the mechanism of this change is discussed elsewhere (page 64). Brown et al. (1952) found no relation between the excessive rise in venous pressure after exercise and increased blood volume. It is to be noted, however, that even in normal subjects exercise in the anoxic state which occurs at high altitudes is associated with a greater than normal rise in venous pressure (Schneider, 1916); it is not unlikely, therefore, that excessively labored breathing also brings about elevated venous pressure. Pulmonary congestion causes changes within the lung which result in increased intrapleural pressure (page 78); the latter change impedes the entrance of blood into the thorax (Hooker, 1914; Holt, 1943, 1944; Prinzmetal and Kountz, 1935; Opdyke and Brecher, 1949, 1950), thereby tending to increase the venous pressure.

Still another factor making for a rise in venous pressure is increased blood volume. Several authors (Brandt, 1931; Wollheim, 1931; Gibson and Evans, 1937; Warren and Stead, 1944) who measured both have stressed the parallelism between the two in cardiac decompensation (page 6), and Starr (1940) reached the same conclusion by showing that after death the "static" pressure in the body of a decompensated cardiac patient is much above normal. Starr and Rawson (1940) studied the effects of lowered outputs in a model circulation and likewise found that the rise in venous pressure was related to an increase in the volume of fluid in the circulation. The work of Gibbons (1948), of Threefoot, Gibbons, and Burch (1947), of De Vries et al. (1950), and of Newman and Fishel (1950), shows that no regular temporal relation exists between increase in body weight and rise in venous pressure. The administration of sodium chloride elevates venous pressure (Davies, 1951; Lombardo, 1953; De Vries et al., 1950; Newman and Fishel, 1950).

Increases in intra-abdominal pressure cause a greater than normal rise in venous pressure in patients with cardiac decompensation (Zeus, 1941); abdominal distention of whatever origin should have an abnormally great effect on peripheral venous pressure in decompensated patients. This phenomenon must be borne in mind in interpreting the results of tests designed to reveal hepatic congestion by observation of the effects of pressing over the right upper quadrant upon the peripheral venous pressure. It is to be noted that this maneuver causes an excessive rise in venous pressure in patients with superior vena caval obstruction and no heart disease (Ballon, 1952).

The fall in venous pressure that occurs in cardiac decompensation and only slightly or not at all in normal subjects during sleep (Halmágyi et al., 1952), after vasodilators (Braun and Fryd, 1951), and after autonomic blocking agents (Kelley et al., 1953; Halmágyi et al., 1952) suggests that venoconstriction is present in chronic congestive failure. Emotion causes an excessive rise in venous pressure in cardiac decompensation (Borst and Molhuysen, 1952).

When the venous pressure is elevated in cardiac decompensation, it usually falls to or toward normal in recovery. Indeed, it often begins to decrease shortly after the patient is put to bed (Hussey, 1936), before the action of more specific therapy becomes effective. This phenomenon may be merely the consequence of relaxation, for straining raises the venous pressure (Meyer and Middleton, 1929; Liedholm, 1939; Adams, 1939; Chapman and Linton, 1945; Hamilton et al., 1944). Among the procedures that rapidly lower venous pressure are venesection (page 325), application of tourniquets to the extremities (page 322) and, in patients with pleural effusion, thoracentesis (page 512). The bearing of these findings on the relief of orthopnea and edema will be discussed in another place (page 260). Failure of the venous pressure to fall or a continuous rise during treatment may be a poor prognostic sign. An elevated venous pressure is found occasionally before dyspnea appears and often before edema and orthopnea become manifest. In many instances, however, marked signs of failure, such as râles in the chest, cyanosis, hepatic engorgement or even edema may be present without any elevation of venous pressure above the upper limit of the normal range (Winsor and Burch, 1946).

In addition to studies of the effects of exercise on venous pressure cited above, other procedures employing measurement of pressure in the veins have been suggested as tests of cardiac function. They are, however, difficult to interpret and therefore of doubtful value. These tests include the Valsalva maneuver (Meyer and Middleton, 1929; Liedholm, 1939), coughing (Lauson *et al.*, 1946), and sudden occlusion of both femoral arteries (Chiorazzo and Perini, 1938); abnormal responses are said to occur in patients with congestive failure. The finding of Gilbert and Goldzieher (1946) that epinephrine and insulin raise venous pressures in cardiac patients but not in normal subjects is clearly an error.

Bibliography

Chapter I — Section 5

ADAMS, J. C., Etiological factors in varicose veins of the lower extremities, *Surg., Gynec. & Obst.* **69,** 717 (1939).

ALBERT, R. E., and L. W. EICHNA, The response of the peripheral venous pressure to exercise in congestive heart failure, *Am. Heart J.* **43,** 395 (1952).   [7, 9

ALTSCHULE, M. D., The pathological physiology of chronic cardiac decompensation, *Medicine* **17,** 75 (1938).   [7, 8

ALTSCHULE, M. D., and D. R. GILLIGAN, The effects on the cardiovascular system of fluids administered intravenously in man. II. The dynamics of the circulation, *J. Clin. Investigation* **17,** 401 (1938).

BALLON, H. C., Superior vena caval obstruction, *Ann. Surg.* **136,** 39 (1952).

BARACH, A. L., and D. W. RICHARDS, JR., Effects of treatment with oxygen in cardiac failure, *Arch. Int. Med.* **48,** 325 (1931).   [7

BARNES, A. R., and J. KNUTSON, Evidence of hemodilution during diuresis produced by salyrgan in patients with congestive heart failure and a discussion on its possible clinical implications, *Tr. A. Am. Physicians* **62,** 169 (1949).   [7

BERGER, A. R., The value of direct venous pressure estimations in ambulatory cardiac patients, *Am. Heart J.* **13,** 440 (1937).   [7

BLANKENHORN, M. A., C. F. VILTER, I. M. SCHEINKER, and R. S. AUSTIN, Occidental beriberi heart disease, *J. A. M. A.* **131,** 717 (1946).   [7, 8

BLOOMFIELD, R. A., B. RAPOPORT, J. P. MILNOR, W. K. LONG, J. G. MEBANE, and L. B. ELLIS, The effects of the cardiac glycosides upon the dynamics of the circulation in congestive heart failure. I. Ouabain, *J. Clin. Investigation* **27,** 588 (1948).   [7

BLUMBERG, N., and E. M. SCHLOSS, The effect of circulatory factors on the bromsulphalein test in liver disease, *Am. J. M. Sc.* **213,** 470 (1947).   [7

BLUMGART, H. L., Venous pressures: their clinical significance, *M. Clin. North America* **8**, 1511 (1925). [7

BLUMGART, H. L., and S. WEISS, Studies on the velocity of blood flow. III. The velocity of blood flow and its relation to other aspects of the circulation in patients with rheumatic and syphilitic heart disease, *J. Clin. Investigation* **4**, 149 (1927). [7, 8

BLUMGART, H. L., and S. WEISS, Studies on the velocity of blood flow. IV. The velocity of blood flow and its relation to other aspects of the circulation in patients with arteriosclerosis and in patients with arterial hypertension, *J. Clin. Investigation* **4**, 173 (1927). [7, 8

BLUMGART, H. L., and S. WEISS, Clinical studies on the velocity of blood flow. IX. The pulmonary circulation time, the velocity of venous blood flow to the heart, and related aspects of the circulation in patients with cardiovascular disease, *J. Clin. Investigation* **5**, 343 (1927–28). [7, 8

BLUMGART, H. L., and S. WEISS, Clinical studies on the velocity of blood flow. X. The relation between the velocity of blood flow, the venous pressure and the vital capacity of the lungs in fifty patients with cardiovascular disease compared with similar measurements in fifty normal persons, *J. Clin. Investigation* **5**, 379 (1927–28). [7, 8

BOAS, E. P., and G. DOONEIEF, The mechanism of peripheral stasis in myocardial insufficiency, *Arch. Int. Med.* **33**, 407 (1924). [7, 8

BORST, J. G. G., The maintenance of an adequate cardiac output by the regulation of the urinary excretion of water and sodium chloride; an essential factor in the genesis of edema, *Acta med. Scandinav. Supp. No. 207* (1948). [7

BORST, J. G. G., and J. A. MOLHUYSEN, Exact determination of the central venous pressure by a simple clinical method, *Lancet* **2**, 304 (1952). [7, 9

BRAMS, W. A., and J. S. GOLDEN, The early response to venesection, with observations on so-called bloodless venesection, *Am. J. M. Sc.* **189**, 813 (1935). [7

BRANDT, F., Die Abhängigkeit des Venendruckes von der Grösse der zirkulierenden Blutmenge, zugleich ein Beitrag zur Frage seiner klinischen Bedeutung, *Ztschr. f. klin. Med.* **116**, 398 (1931). [7

BRAUN, K., and C. H. FRYD, The effect of priscol on the peripheral venous pressure, *Brit. Heart J.* **13**, 294 (1951). [7

BRIGDEN, W., and E. P. SHARPEY-SCHAFER, Postural changes in peripheral blood flow in cases with left heart failure, *Clin. Sc.* **9**, 93 (1950). [7

BROWN, E., J. HOPPER, JR., and J. D. LANGE, Venous pressure during exercise in man: relation to blood volume, cardiac competence and pulmonary pressure, *Federation Proc.* **11**, 17 (1952). [7, 9

BURWELL, C. S., and L. DEXTER, Beri-beri heart disease, *Tr. A. Am. Physicians* **60**, 59 (1947).   [7

CANDEL, S., and M. A. RABINOWITZ, Blood velocity rate and venous pressure in the prognosis of heart disease, *Ann. Int. Med.* **10**, 1000 (1937).   [7

CAPPS, R. B., A method for measuring tone and reflex constriction of the capillaries, venules and veins of the human hand with the results in normal and diseased states, *J. Clin. Investigation* **15**, 229 (1936).   [7

CHAPMAN, E. M., and R. R. LINTON, Mode of production of pulmonary emboli, *J. A. M. A.* **129**, 196 (1945).

CHIORAZZO, G., and D. PERINI, Osservazioni e ricerche sulla prova di Cardarelli-Katzenstein, con particolare riguardo al comportamento della pressione venosa periferica, *Cuore e circolaz.* **22**, 354 (1938).

CITRON, D., B. BERCU, R. LEMMER, and E. MASSIE, Congestive heart failure and hyponatremia: untoward effects of mercurial diuresis, *Ann. Int. Med.* **34**, 872 (1951).   [7

CLARK, A. H., A study of the diagnostic and prognostic significance of venous pressure observations in cardiac disease, *Arch. Int. Med.* **16**, 587 (1915).   [7

DAVIES, C. E., The effect of treatment on the renal circulation in heart-failure, *Lancet* **2**, 1052 (1951).   [7

DAVIS, J. O., and N. W. SHOCK, The effect of body position and reference level on the determination of venous and right auricular pressure, *Am. J. M. Sc.* **218**, 281 (1949).   [7

DAVISON, P. H., and R. GADDIE, The influence of intravenous digoxin on renal function in congestive cardiac failure, *Quart. J. Med.* **20**, 389 (1951).   [7

DEITCHMAN, M., and A. H. CANTER, Direct venous pressure in chronic right heart disease, *Mil. Surgeon* **110**, 402 (1952).   [7

DE VRIES, A., C. H. FRYD, and S. GITELSON, Observations on heart failure. The effect of withdrawal and administration of salt on body weight and venous pressure in heart failure, *Cardiologia* **15**, 368 (1950).   [7

DI PALMA, J. R., and P. E. KENDALL, The relationship between blood volume and blood specific gravity in the recovery from cardiac decompensation, *J. Lab. & Clin. Med.* **29**, 390 (1944).   [7

DRESDALE, D. T., M. SCHULTZ, and R. J. MICHTOM, Primary pulmonary hypertension. I. Clinical and hemodynamic study, *Am. J. Med.* **11**, 686 (1951).   [7

EARLE, D. P., JR., S. J. FARBER, J. D. ALEXANDER, and L. W. EICHNA, Effects of treatment on renal functions and electrolyte excretion in congestive heart failure, *J. Clin. Investigation* **28**, 778 (1949).   [7

EICHNA, L., S. J. FARBER, A. R. BERGER, D. P. EARLE, B. RADER, E. PELLE-GRINO, R. E. ALBERT, J. D. ALEXANDER, H. TAUBE, and S. YOUNG-

WIRTH, The interrelationship of the cardiovascular, renal and electrolyte effects of intravenous digoxin in congestive heart failure, *J. Clin. Investigation* **30**, 1250 (1951). [7

EICHNA, L., S. J. FARBER, A. R. BERGER, D. P. EARLE, B. RADER, E. PELLEGRINO, R. E. ALBERT, J. D. ALEXANDER, H. TAUBE, and S. YOUNGWIRTH, Cardiovascular dynamics, blood volumes, renal functions and electrolyte excretions in the same patients during congestive heart failure and after recovery of cardiac decompensation, *Circulation* **7**, 674 (1953). [7

EICHNA, L. W., and H. TAUBE, A comparison of the actions of four cardiac glycosides on a patient with congestive heart failure, *Am. Heart J.* **26**, 631 (1943). [7

EICHNA, L. W., and H. TAUBE, The effect of intravenously administered digoxin and ouabain on the systemic venous pressure of patients with congestive heart failure, *Am. Heart J.* **27**, 641 (1944). [7

EPSTEIN, B. S., and D. YOUNG, A correlation between roentgenographic changes in the lungs in left ventricular failure and the circulation rates, *Am. J. Roentgenol.* **50**, 316 (1943). [7,8

ERNSTENE, A. C., and H. L. BLUMGART, Orthopnea. Its relation to the increased venous pressure of myocardial failure, *Arch. Int. Med.* **45**, 593 (1930). [7

EVANS, J. M., H. J. ZIMMERMAN, J. G. WILMER, L. J. THOMAS, and C. B. ETHRIDGE, Altered liver function of chronic congestive heart failure, *Am. J. Med.* **13**, 705 (1952). [7

EVANS, W., Venous pressure, *New England J. Med.* **207**, 934 (1932). [7

EYSTER, J. A. E., Venous pressure and its clinical applications, *Physiol. Rev.* **6**, 281 (1926). [7

EYSTER, J. A. E., Venous pressure in cardiac decompensation, *J. A. M. A.* **89**, 428 (1927). [7

EYSTER, J. A. E., and W. S. MIDDLETON, Clinical studies on venous pressure, *Arch. Int. Med.* **34**, 228 (1924) [7

EYSTER, J. A. E., and W. S. MIDDLETON, Venous pressure as a guide to venesection in congestive heart failure, *Am. J. M. Sc.* **174**, 486 (1927). [7

FAHR, G., and I. ERSHLER, Capillary pressure in right heart failure, *Proc. Soc. Exper. Biol. & Med.* **37**, 701 (1938). [7

FARBER, S. J., J. D. ALEXANDER, E. D. PELLEGRINO, and D. P. EARLE, The effect of intravenously administered digoxin on water and electrolyte excretion and on renal function, *Circulation* **4**, 378 (1951). [7

FRANCO, A., and M. G. MARQUES, Digitalisation massive ou fractionnée dans l'insuffisance cardiaque congestive chronique avec fibrillation auriculaire, *Cardiologia* **20**, 257 (1952). [7

Frank, L., and M. Reh, Eine graphische Methode zur unblutigen Bestimmung des Venendruckes am Menschen, *Ztschr. f. exper. Path. u. Therap.* **10**, 241 (1912).   [7

Friedfeld, L., and A. M. Fishberg, The relation of the cerebrospinal and venous pressures in heart failure, *J. Clin. Investigation* **13**, 495 (1934).   [7

Frisk, A. R., L. Werkö, and G. Wrange, A new mercurial diuretic "diurgin," (Disodium salt of N-succinyl-, N¹ (8-carboxymethylmercaptomercuri-B-methoxy) propylcarbamide), *Acta med. Scandinav.* **144**, 85 (1952).   [7

Fuchs, L., Ueber die Messung des Venendruckes und ihre klinische Bedeutung, *Deutsches Arch. f. klin. Med.* **135**, 68 (1921).   [7

Gaertner, G., Die Messung des Drucks im rechten Vorhof, *München. med. Wchnschr.* **50**, 2038 (1903).   [7

Garcia, J. E., and B. A. Goldman, The combined use of strophanthin-K and digitalis in the treatment of congestive heart failure. A preliminary report, *Am. Heart J.* **26**, 20 (1943).   [7

Gibbons, T., The behavior of the venous pressure during various stages of chronic congestive failure, *Am. Heart J.* **35**, 553 (1948).   [7

Gibson, J. G., 2D, and W. A. Evans, Jr., Clinical studies of the blood volume. III. Changes in blood volume, venous pressure and blood velocity rate in chronic congestive heart failure, *J. Clin. Investigation* **16**, 851 (1937).   [7

Gilbert, R. A., and J. W. Goldzieher, The mechanism and prevention of cardiovascular changes due to insulin, *Ann. Int. Med.* **25**, 928 (1946).   [7

Gillanders, A. D., Circulatory dynamics in emphysema, *Quart. J. Med.* **18**, 263 (1949).   [7

Gillanders, A. D., Nutritional heart disease, *Brit. Heart J.* **13**, 177 (1951).   [7

Gitelson, S., The influence of body posture on the antecubital venous pressure, *Cardiologia* **19**, 163 (1951).   [7, 8

Goldbloom, A. A., and A. Lieberson, Clinical studies in circulatory adjustments. V. Clinical evaluation of cardiodynamic studies, *Am. J. M. Sc.* **197**, 182 (1939).   [7

Greene, J. A., W. D. Paul, and A. E. Feller, The action of theophylline with ethylenediamine on intrathecal and venous pressures in cardiac failure and on bronchial obstruction in cardiac failure and bronchial asthma, *J. A. M. A.* **109**, 1712 (1937).   [7

Grossman, J., R. C. Weston, J. P. Halperin, and L. Leiter, The nature of the renal circulatory changes in chronic congestive failure as reflected by renal tubular maximal functions, *J. Clin. Investigation* **29**, 1320 (1950).   [7

HALMÁGYI, D., B. FELKAI, J. IVÁNYI, and G. HETÉNYI, JR., The role of the nervous system in the maintenance of venous hypertension in heart failure, *Brit. Heart. J.* **14,** 101 (1952).   [7

HAMILTON, W. F., R. A. WOODBURY, and H. T. HARPER, JR., Arterial, cerebrospinal and venous pressures in man during cough and strain, *Am. J. Physiol.* **141,** 42 (1944).

HARRIS, I., E. W. JONES, and C. N. ALDRED, Blood pH and lactic acid in different types of heart disease, *Quart. J. Med.* **28,** 407 (1935).   [7, 8

HARRISON, T. R., W. G. HARRISON, JR., J. A. CALHOUN, and J. P. MARSH, Congestive heart failure. XVII. The mechanism of dyspnea on exertion, *Arch. Int. Med.* **50,** 690 (1932).   [9

HUSSEY, H. H., Clinical application of venous pressure measurement, *M. Ann. District of Columbia* **5,** 232 (1936).   [7

HUSSEY, H. H., J. J. WALLACE, and J. C. SULLIVAN, The value of combined measurements of the venous pressure and arm-to-tongue and arm-to-lung circulation times in the study of heart failure, *Am. Heart J.* **23,** 22 (1942).   [7

ISERI, L. T., A. J. BOYLE, and C. B. MYERS, Water and electrolyte balance during recovery from severe congestive failure on a 50 milligram sodium diet, *Am. Heart J.* **40,** 706 (1950).   [7

JAMES, A. H., The mechanism of pleural and ascitic effusions with a suggested method for the indirect estimation of portal venous pressure, *Clin. Sc.* **8,** 291 (1949).   [7

KARTUN, P., P. PARIS, J. NORY, and G. BOUSQUET, Action précoce sur la circulation de retour de l'injection intraveineuse d'un diurétique mercuriel, *Arch. d. mal. du cœur* **43,** 133 (1950).   [7

KELLEY, R. T., E. D. FRIES, and T. F. HIGGINS, The effects of hexamethonium on certain manifestations of congestive heart failure, *Circulation* **7,** 169 (1953).   [7

KINSMAN, J. M., and J. W. MOORE, The hemodynamics of the circulation in hypertension, *Ann. Int. Med.* **9,** 649 (1935).   [7

KROETZ, C., Die Koeffizienten des klinisch messbaren Venendruckes, *Deutsches Arch. f. klin. Med.* **139,** 325 (1922).   [7

LA DUE, J. S., and G. FAHR, The effect of the intravenous administration of lanatoside C upon the output, diastolic volume, and mechanical efficiency of the failing human heart, *Am. Heart J.* **25,** 344 (1943).   [7

LAUSON, H. D., R. M. BLOOMFIELD, and A. COURNAND, The influence of the respiration on the circulation in man, with special reference to pressures in the right auricle, right ventricle, femoral artery and peripheral veins, *Am. J. Med.* **1,** 315 (1946).   [7

LEQUIME, J., Le débit cardiaque. Études expérimentales et cliniques, *Acta med. Scandinav. Supp. No. 107* (1940).   [7

HARRISON, W. G., JR., The cisternal pressure in congestive heart failure and its bearing on orthopnea, *J. Clin. Investigation* **12**, 1075 (1933).
[7

HARRISON, W. G., JR., Cerebrospinal fluid pressure and venous pressure in cardiac failure, and the effect of spinal drainage in the treatment of cardiac decompensation, *Arch. Int. Med.* **53**, 782 (1934).   [7

HARVEY, W. P., and C. A. FINCH, Dicumarol prophylaxis of thrombo-embolic disease in congestive heart failure, *New England J. Med.* **242**, 208 (1950).
[7

HELLER, B. I., and W. E. JACOBSON, Renal hemodynamics in heart disease, *Am. Heart J.* **39**, 188 (1950).   [7

HERRMANN, G. R., Blood plasma proteins in patients with heart failure, *Ann. Int. Med.* **24**, 893 (1946).   [7

HITZIG, W. M., The use of ether in measuring the circulation time from the antecubital veins to the pulmonary capillaries, *Am. Heart J.* **10**, 1080 (1934–35).   [7

HOLT, J. P., The effect of positive and negative intrathoracic pressure on peripheral venous pressure in man, *Am. J. Physiol.* **139**, 208 (1943).

HOLT, J. P., The effect of positive and negative intrathoracic pressure on cardiac output and venous pressure in the dog, *Am. J. Physiol.* **142**, 594 (1944).

HOOKER, D. R., Observations on the venous blood pressure in man, *Am. J. Physiol.* **35**, 73 (1914).

HOOKER, D. R., and J. A. E. EYSTER, An instrument for the determination of venous pressure in man, *Bull. Johns Hopkins Hosp.* **19**, 274 (1908).
[7

HOWARD, P., and G. L. LEATHART, Changes of pulse pressure and heart rate induced by changes of posture in subjects with normal and failing hearts, *Clin. Sc.* **10**, 521 (1951).   [7

HULTGREN, H. N., The effect of increased venous return on the venous pressure of patients with congestive heart failure, *Am. Heart J.*, **39**, 593 (1950).   [7

LEMIERRE, A., and E. BERNARD, Recherches sur les indications et sur l'action physiologique de la soignée, *Presse méd.* **34**, 705 (1926). [7

LEVIN, E., La hipertensión venosa provocada como signo de insuficiencia cardiaca, *Semana méd.* **41**, 915 (1934).   [7, 8, 9

LIEDHOLM, K., Studien über das Verhalten des Venendrucks beim Valsal-vaschen Versuch, *Acta med. Scandinav.*, *Supp. No. 106* (1939). [7

LOMBARDO, T. A., The effect of posture on the excretion of water and sodium by patients with congestive heart failure, *Circulation* **7**, 91 (1953).   [7

MANTERO, O., and G. BARLASSINA, Contributo allo studio della emodinamica renale nei cardiopatici mediante le prove selettive di funzionalità renale, *Minerva med.* **42**, 1049 (1951). [7

MAXWELL, M. H., E. S. BREED, and I. L. SCHWARTZ, Renal venous pressure in chronic congestive heart failure, *J. Clin. Investigation* **29**, 342 (1950). [7

McGUIRE, J., V. HAUENSTEIN, and R. SHORE, Cardiac output in heart disease determined by the direct Fick method, including comparative determinations by the acetylene method, *Arch. Int. Med.* **60**, 1034 (1937). [7, 8

McGUIRE, J., R. SHORE, V. HAUENSTEIN, and F. GOLDMAN, The cardiac output in compensation and decompensation in the same individual, *Am. Heart J.* **16**, 449 (1938). [7

McGUIRE, J., R. SHORE, V. HAUENSTEIN, and F. GOLDMAN, Relation of cardiac output to congestive heart failure, *Arch. Int. Med.* **63**, 290 (1939). [7, 8

McMICHAEL, J., The output of the heart in congestive failure, *Quart. J. Med.* **7**, 331 (1938). [7

MELDOLESI, G., Studio clinico della pressione capillare nei suoi rapporti con la pressione arteriosa e con la pressione venosa, *Cuore e circolaz.* **10**, 20, 45 (1926). [7

MENEELY, G. R., and N. L. KALTREIDER, A study of the volume of the blood in congestive heart failure. Relation to other measurements in fifteen patients, *J. Clin. Investigation* **22**, 521 (1943). [7

MERKLEN, P., J. KABAKER, and J. WARTER, Étude de la pression du liquide céphalo-rachidien et de la manoeuvre de Queckenstedt au cours de l'asystolie. Rapports avec la tension veineuse. Influence du traitement par la digitale, *Paris méd.* **87**, 405 (1933). [7

MERRILL, A. J., Edema and decreased renal blood flow in patients with chronic congestive failure. Evidence of "forward failure" as the primary cause of edema, *J. Clin. Investigation* **25**, 389 (1946). [7

MEYER, O. O., and W. S. MIDDLETON, The influence of respiration on venous pressure, *J. Clin. Investigation* **8**, 1, (1929–30). [7

MOIA, B., M. R. MALINOW, and C. BAUDINO, Etudes segmentaires de la pression veineuse chez l'homme au moyen du cathéterisme cardiaque, *Acta cardiol.* **7**, 1 (1952). [7

MOORE, R. D., JR., The diagnostic value of venous pressure determinations in certain diseases, *South. M. J.* **30**, 1007 (1937). [7

MOTTA, G., Influenza della pressione venosa sul tempo di circolazione, *Cuore e circolaz.* **21**, 379 (1937). [7

MOYER, J. H., S. I. MILLER, A. B. TASHNEK, and R. BOWMAN, The effect of theophylline with ethylenediamine (aminophylline) on cerebral hemodynamics in the presence of cardiac failure with and without Cheyne-Stokes respiration, *J. Clin. Investigation* **31**, 267 (1952).

NEURATH, O., Untersuchungen über die Bestimmung der Blutumlaufsgeschwindigkeit mit Magnesiumsulfat, *Ztschr. f. klin. Med.* **132**, 134 (1937).
[7

NEWMAN, E. V., Function of the kidney and metabolic changes in cardiac failure, *Am. J. Med.* **7**, 490 (1949).
[7

NEWMAN, W., and L. FISHEL, Observations on the daily changes in venous pressure and weight in a case of chronic congestive heart failure, *Circulation* **1**, 706 (1950).
[7

NONNENBRUCH, W., Klinische Ödembeobachtungen (Die sog. Myodegeneratio cordis usw), *Deutsches Arch. f. klin. Med.* **191**, 113 (1943).
[7

NOVACK, P., B. GOLUBOFF, L. BORTIN, A. SOFFE, and H. A. SHENKIN, Studies of the cerebral circulation and metabolism in congestive heart failure, *Circulation* **7**, 724 (1953).

NYLIN, G., On the amount of, and changes in, the residual blood of the heart, *Am. Heart J.* **25**, 1598 (1943).
[7

NYLIN, G., Blood volume determinations with radioactive phosphorus, *Brit. Heart J.* **7**, 81 (1945).
[7

NYLIN, G., and G. MALMSTRÖM, Weitere Untersuchungen über die Bedeutung der verlängerten Kreislaufzeit für die Kardiologie, *Cardiologia* **5**, 333 (1941).
[7

OLMER, D., A.-X. JOUVE, and J. VAGUE, Une épreuve fonctionelle de la circulation de retour, *Presse méd.* **46**, 1233 (1938).
[7

OPDYKE, D. F., and G. A. BRECHER, Effect of intrapulmonic and intrathoracic pressure variations on left atrial pressure, *Federation Proc.* **8**, 121 (1949).

OPDYKE, D. F., and G. A. BRECHER, Effect of normal and abnormal changes of intrathoracic pressure on effective right and left atrial pressures, *Am. J. Physiol.* **160**, 556 (1950).

PERERA, G. A., The increased plasma volume in cardiac insufficiency: its correlation with right-sided failure, *J. Clin. Investigation* **24**, 708 (1945).
[7

PLA, J. C., L'hypertension veineuse, *Rev. sud-am. de méd. et de chir.* **1**, 283 (1930).
[9

POROT, M. A., Les fortes hypertensions céphalo-rachidiennes d'origine veineuse. Leur latence. La discordance manométrique et clinique, *Rev. neurol.* **1**, 1173 (1930).
[7

PORTER, R. B., and R. S. DOWNS, Some physiological observations on the circulation during recovery from vitamin B₁ deficiency, *Ann. Int. Med.* **17**, 645 (1942).
[7

PRENTICE, T. C., N. I. BERLIN, G. M. HYDE, R. J. PARSONS, J. H. LAW-RENCE, and S. PORT, Total red cell volume, plasma volume, and sodium space in congestive heart failure, *J. Clin. Investigation* **30**, 1471 (1951). [7, 8

PRINZMETAL, M., and W. B. KOUNTZ, Intrapleural pressure in health and disease and its influence on body function, *Medicine* **14**, 457 (1935).

REICHSMAN, F., and H. GRANT, Some observations on the pathogenesis of edema in cardiac failure, *Am. Heart J.* **32**, 438 (1946). [7

RELMAN, A. S., and F. H. EPSTEIN, Effect of tetraethylammonium on venous and arterial pressure in congestive heart failure, *Proc. Soc. Exper. Biol. & Med.* **70**, 11 (1948). [7

REVELEY, H. P., G. R. HERRMANN, and J. A. ORTIZ, Studies of factors in congestive heart failure during effective therapy, *Texas State J. Med.* **47**, 617 (1951). [7

RICHARDS, D. W., JR., Cardiac output by the catheterization technique, in various clinical conditions, *Federation Proc.* **4**, 215 (1945). [7

RICHARDS, D. W., JR., and A. L. BARACH, Prolonged residence in high oxygen atmospheres. Effects on normal individuals and on patients with chronic cardiac and pulmonary insufficiency, *Quart. J. Med.* **3**, 437 (1934). [7

ROBB, G. P., and S. WEISS, The velocity of pulmonary and peripheral venous blood flow and related aspects of the circulation in cardio-vascular disease. Their relation to clinical types of circulatory failure, *Am. Heart J.* **9**, 742 (1934). [7

ROBERTSON, H. F., and F. FETTER, The effect of venesection on arterial, spinal fluid, and venous pressures with especial reference to failure of the left and right heart, *J. Clin. Investigation* **14**, 305 (1935). [7

RUBIN, E. H., B. S. KAHN, and D. PECKER, Diffuse interstitial fibrosis of the lungs, *Ann. Int. Med.* **36**, 864 (1952). [8

SCHALM, L., and W. A. H. HOOGENBOOM, Blood bilirubin in congestive heart failure, *Am. Heart J.* **44**, 571 (1952). [7, 8

SCHNEIDER, E. C., The circulation of the blood in man at high altitudes. III. The effects of physical exertion on the pulse rate, arterial, and venous pressures, *Am. J. Physiol.* **40**, 380 (1916).

SCHOEN, R., and E. DERRA, Untersuchungen über die Bedeutung der Zyanose als klinisches Symptom (1), *Deutsches Arch. f. klin. Med.* **168**, 52 (1930). [7

SCHOTT, E., Die Erhöhung des Druckes im venösen System bei An-strengung als Mass für die Funktionstüchtigkeit des menschlichen Herzens, *Deutsches Arch. f. klin. Med.* **108**, 537 (1912). [7, 8, 9

SINCLAIR-SMITH, B., A. A. KATTUS, J. GENEST, and E. V. NEWMAN, The renal mechanism of electrolyte excretion and the metabolic balances of electrolytes and nitrogen in congestive cardiac failure; the effects of exercise, rest and aminophyllin, *Bull. Johns Hopkins Hosp.* **84,** 369 (1949). [7

SODEMAN, W. A., Direct venous pressure determinations by use of a new instrument, *Am. Heart J.* **43,** 687 (1952). [7

SOLOFF, L. A., J. ZATUCHNI, and L. TURNER, Aortic stenosis manifested as chronic cor pulmonale, *J. A. M. A.* **150,** 1111 (1952). [7, 8

STARR, I., Rôle of the "static blood pressure" in abnormal increments of venous pressure, especially in heart failure. II. Clinical and experimental studies, *Am. J. M. Sc.* **199,** 40 (1940).

STARR, I., and A. J. RAWSON, Role of the "static blood pressure" in abnormal increments of venous pressure, especially in heart failure. I. Theoretical studies on an improved circulation schema whose pumps obey Starling's law of the heart, *Am. J. M. Sc.* **199,** 27 (1940).

STEAD, E. A., JR., J. V. WARREN, and E. S. BRANNON, Effect of lanatoside C on the circulation of patients with congestive failure. A study using catheterization of the right side of the heart, *Arch. Int. Med.* **81,** 282 (1948). [7

STEWART, H. J., and A. E. COHN, Studies on the effect of the action of digitalis on the output of blood from the heart. III. Part 2, The effect on the output of hearts in heart failure with congestion in human beings, *J. Clin. Investigation* **11,** 933 (1932). [7

STEWART, H. J., N. F. CRANE, R. F. WATSON, C. H. WHEELER, and J. E. DEITRICK, The cardiac output in congestive heart failure and in organic heart disease, *Ann. Int. Med.* **13,** 2323 (1940). [7, 8

STEWART, H. J., J. E. DEITRICK, N. F. CRANE, and C. H. WHEELER, Action of digitalis in uncompensated heart disease, *Arch. Int. Med.* **62,** 569 (1938). [7, 8

STEWART, H. J., J. E. DEITRICK, R. F. WATSON, C. H. WHEELER, and N. F. CRANE, The effect of valvular heart disease on the dynamics of the circulation. Observations before, during and after the occurrence of heart failure, *Am. Heart J.* **16,** 477 (1938). [7, 8

STEWART, H. J., W. F. EVANS, H. BROWN, and J. R. GERJUOY, Peripheral blood flow, rectal and skin temperature in congestive heart failure. The effects of rapid digitalization in this state, *Arch. Int. Med.* **77,** 643 (1946). [7

STONE, D. J., A. SCHWARTZ, W. NEWMAN, J. A. FELTMAN, and F. J. LOVELOCK, Precipitation by pulmonary infection of acute anoxia, cardiac failure and respiratory acidosis in chronic pulmonary disease, *Am. J. Med.* **14,** 14 (1953). [7

STORSTEIN, O., Measurement of the venous pressure and of the circulation time, *Acta med. Scandinav.* **136,** 122 (1949). [7

Sutton, F. C., J. A. Britton, and J. G. Carr, Estimation of cardiopulmonary functional capacity by means of oxygen debt studies, *Am. Heart J.* **20**, 423 (1940). [7

Szekely, P., Venous pressure responses to exercise, *Am. Heart J.* **22**, 360 (1941). [7, 9

Taquini, A. C., J. C. Fasciolo, J. R. E. Suarez, and H. Chiodi, Respiration and circulation in pulmonary anoxemia, *Arch. Int. Med.* **82**, 534 (1948). [7

Taquini, A. C., and B. B. Lozada, Corazón pulmonar cronico con y sin insuficiencia cardiaca. Funciones respiratoria y circulatoria, *Medicina* **8**, 325 (1948). [7

Taylor, F. A., A. B. Thomas, and H. G. Schleiter, A direct method for the estimation of venous blood pressure, *Proc. Soc. Exper. Biol. & Med.* **27**, 867 (1930). [7

Tepper, W., Die Wirkung des Strophanthins auf den Venendruck bei kardialer Insuffiziens, *Deutsche med. Wchnschr.* **75**, 142 (1950). [7

Tetelbaum, A. G., S. I. Umanski, and M. I. Krynski, Ueber den Einfluss der körperlichen Belastung auf den Venendruck bei Gesunden und bei dekompensierten Herzkranken, *Wien. Arch. f. inn. Med.* **28**, 121 (1936). [7, 9

Threefoot, S., T. Gibbons, and G. Burch, Relationship of weight, venous pressure and radiosodium (Na^{22}) excretion in chronic congestive heart failure, *Proc. Soc. Exper. Biol. & Med.* **66**, 369 (1947). [7

Tornquist, H., Physiologische und klinische Studien über den Armvenendruck, *Ztschr. f. d. ges. exp. Med.* **81**, 227 (1932). [7

Tzanck, A., and P. Renault, Des rapports entre la tension veineuse et la tension du liquide céphalo-rachidien, *Compt. rend. Soc. de biol.* **96**, 157 (1927). [7

Villaret, M., F. St. Girons, and P. Grellety-Bosviel, Contribution à l'étude de la tension veineuse périphérique à l'état normal et pathologique, *J. méd. franç.* **10**, 359 (1921). [7

Villaret, M., F. St. Girons, and P. Grellety-Bosviel, La tension veineuse périphérique (P.V.) et ses modifications pathologiques, *Presse méd.* **31**, 318 (1923). [7

Volini, I. F., and R. O. Levitt, Studies on mercurial diuresis. II. The immediate effect on the venous blood pressure, *Am. Heart J.* **17**, 187 (1939). [7

Volini, I. F., and R. O. Levitt, Studies on mercurial diuresis. III. The alteration induced in the cerebrospinal fluid pressure, *Am. Heart J.* **19**, 566 (1940). [7

von Gonczy, V. I., J. Kiss, and Z. Enyedy, Ueber den Venendruck und dessen Tagesschwankungen, *Ztschr. f. d. ges. exper. Med.* **70**, 236 (1930). [7 von Nieuwenhuizen, C. L. C., Der venöse Blutdruck nach Arbeitsleistung. Eine Funktionsprüfung der Zirkulation, *Acta med. Scandinav.* **103**, 171 (1940). [9

von Tabora, D., Ueber den Aderlass bei Kreislaufstörungen und seinen unblutigen Ersatz, *München. med. Wchnschr.* **57**, 1265 (1910). [7

Warren, J. V., and E. A. Stead, Jr., Fluid dynamics in chronic congestive heart failure. An interpretation of the mechanisms producing the edema, increased plasma volume and elevated venous pressure in certain patients with prolonged congestive failure, *Arch. Int. Med.* **73**, 138 (1944). [7

Wartman, W. B., A study of the venous blood pressure in some common diseases, *Am. J. M. Sc.* **190**, 464 (1935). [7

Weiss, S., and R. W. Wilkins, The nature of the cardiovascular disturbances in nutritional deficiency states, *Ann. Int. Med.* **11**, 104 (1937). [7

White, H. L., P. S. Barker, and D. S. Allen, Venous pressure responses to exercise in patients with heart disease, *Am. Heart J.* **1**, 160 (1925–26). [7, 9

Winsor, T., and G. E. Burch, Use of the phlebomanometer: normal venous pressure values and a study of certain clinical aspects of venous hypertension in man, *Am. Heart J.* **31**, 387 (1946). [7

Wollheim, E., Die zirkulierende Blutmenge und ihre Bedeutung für Kompensation und Dekompensation des Kreislaufs, *Ztschr. f. klin. Med.* **116**, 269 (1931).

Wollheim, E., Untersuchungen zur Hämodynamik unter Digitalis und Strophanthin, *Deutsche med. Wchnschr.* **75**, 482 (1950). [7

Wood, P., Right and left ventricular failure. A study of circulation time and venous blood pressure, *Lancet* **2**, 15 (1936). [7

Wood, P., The action of digitalis in heart failure with normal rhythm, *Brit. Heart J.* **2**, 132 (1940). [7

Wood, W. B., and C. A. Janeway, Changes in plasma volume during recovery from congestive failure, *Arch. Int. Med.* **62**, 151 (1938). [7

Zeus, L., Beeinflussbarkeit des Venendruckes durch intraabdominelle Drucksteigerung, *Arch. f. Kreislaufforsch.* **8**, 330 (1941). [7

6. *Intracardiac and Pulmonary Vascular Pressures*

The right auricular pressure is high in congestive failure (McMichael and Sharpey-Schafer, 1944; Richards, 1945; Bloomfield *et al.*, 1946; 10) and the normal gradient between venous and intra-auricular pressure falls markedly, usually to an unmeasurably low value. The right auricular pressure falls during sleep (Halmágyi *et al.*, 1952) or after the injection of autonomic blocking agents or vasodilators (Halmágyi *et al.*, 1952; Kelley *et al.*, 1953).

The left auricular pressure was measured and found elevated by Staudacher (1932), who used an indirect method that was more ingenious than accurate. Although one mechanism for the rise in intraauricular pressures is the increase in intrapleural pressure that may occur in cardiac decompensation (page 78) probably the most important cause of the increased auricular pressures in cardiac decompensation is the rise in right ventricular (Bayliss *et al.*, 1950; Harvey *et al.*, 1949; **10A**) and left ventricular (Zimmerman, 1950) pressures. The ventricular systolic pressures must equal those of the pulmonary artery and aorta, respectively; accordingly, the right ventricular systolic pressure must be abnormally high since the pulmonary arterial pressure is usually elevated in cardiac decompensation (see below). The ventricular diastolic pressures also are elevated; normally the intraventricular pressure in diastole is zero or close to it. The findings of elevated diastolic pressure in failing hearts is difficult to explain completely. An excess of blood must be present in the ventricles owing to incomplete emptying in systole (Bing *et al.*, 1951; see also page 149). Some consideration must be given to the possibility that cardiac tone is abnormal, that is, not only does the failing ventricle contract inadequately but it also may not relax normally. Knowledge of cardiac tone, if the latter exists at all, is not satisfactory. At any rate, the increased intraventricular pressure of congestive failure must result in a rise in auricular pressure if filling of the ventricle is to occur.

The pulmonary arterial pressure, both systolic and diastolic, is elevated in congestive failure (Hickam and Cargill, 1948; Borden *et al.*, 1949; Dexter *et al.*, 1950; **10B**). The pulmonary vascular resistance is increased (Dow *et al.*, 1949; Lagerlöf and Werkö, 1949; Dexter *et al.*, 1950, 1951, 1952; Zimmerman, 1949, 1951; Fowler *et al.*, 1952; Lenègre *et al.*, 1953; Lewis *et al.*, 1952). Although the rise in pulmonary arterial pressure at first parallels that in pulmonary capillary pressure, the former shows disproportionately great elevations when the increase in the latter exceeds 100 percent. Changes of the magnitude described are largely the result of pulmonary arterial constriction. The findings of Motley *et al.* (1947), Riley *et al.* (1948), Werkö (1949), Doyle *et al.* (1952), and McGuire *et al.* (1951) show that anoxia may have this effect in normal man; a similar but exaggerated change occurs in congestive failure (Westcott *et al.*, 1951). This phenomenon, whose mechanism is unknown, has the effect of preventing excessive rises in pulmonary capillaries at a time when their permeability is increased, that is, during anoxia. The phenomenon is especially beneficial during exertion. In normal subjects exercise results in no change or in slight pulmonary vasodilatation (Dexter *et al.*, 1951; Hickam and Cargill, 1948; Riley *et al.*, 1948). In patients in failure, however, marked arteriolar constriction develops (Hickam and Cargill, 1948; Lenègre *et al.*, 1953; Lewis *et al.*, 1952), thereby minimizing the effects on filtration from the pulmonary capillaries of the rise in pulmonary venous pressure that probably occurs during exertion. Another effect of this vasoconstriction is to cause the expenditure of so much work against pressure as to prevent a rise in output by the right ventricle (page 10). The findings in mitral stenosis (page 408) are similar, even in the absence of anoxia. Understanding these reactions would be easier if it could be demonstrated that a reflex existed, which, when activated by increased pulmonary rigidity caused by congestion, edema, or other factors, resulted in pulmonary arteriolar constriction. That such a reflex exists is suggested by the work of Doyle *et al.* (1951) on the effects of infusions in man; intravenous infusions in normal subjects, by diluting the blood and raising capillary pressure in the lung, create a threat of pulmonary edema; arteriolar constriction results. The fact that the increase in pulmonary arterial pressure and pulmonary vascular resistance is reversed by autonomic blocking agents, in the absence of any fall in pulmonary capillary pressure, indicates that a neurogenic mechanism is involved (Fowler *et al.*, 1950; Kelley *et al.*, 1953; Halmágyi *et al.*, 1952).

The pulmonary capillary pressure is elevated in cardiac decompensation (Berglund *et al.*, 1949; Dexter *et al.*, 1950; Eliasch *et al.*, 1950; Fowler *et al.*, 1950; Lagerlöf and Werkö, 1949; **10C**); a tendency toward pulmonary edema therefore must be present in all cardiac patients in failure (page 312). An unexplained finding is the rise in capillary pressure during induced anoxia in congestive failure (Doyle *et al.*, 1952). The capillary pressure is normal in cor pulmonale (Dexter *et al.*, 1951; Fowler *et al.*, 1952).

Bibliography

Chapter I — Section 6

AHMED, S., R. I. S. BAYLISS, W. A. BRISCOE, and J. McMICHAEL, The action of G-strophanthin on the circulation in man, and a comparison with digoxin, *Clin. Sc.* **9**, 1 (1950).   [10

BALL, J. D., H. KOPELMAN, and A. C. WITHAM, Circulatory changes in mitral stenosis at rest and on exercise, *Brit. Heart J.* **14**, 363 (1952).
                                                                        [10A

BATTRO, A., H. BIDOGGIA, E. R. PIETRAFESA, and F. E. LABOURT, Intra-cardiac blood pressure in human subjects and its relation to the respiratory phases, *Am. Heart J.* **37**, 11 (1949).   [10A

BAYLISS, R. I. S., M. J. ETHERIDGE, A. L. HYMAN, H. G. KELLY, J. McMICHAEL, and E. A. S. REID, The effect of digoxin on the right ventricular pressure in hypertensive and ischaemic heart failure, *Brit. Heart J.* **12**, 317 (1950).   [10A

BERGLUND, H., H. LAGERLÖF, L. WERKÖ, and H. BUCHT, The relation between pulmonary capillary venous pressure, pulmonary blood volume, and vital capacity, *Tr. A. Am. Physicians* **62**, 124 (1949). [10C

BING, R. J., R. HEIMBECKER, and W. FALHOLT, An estimation of the residual volume of blood in the right ventricle of normal and diseased hearts in vivo, *Am. Heart J.* **42**, 483 (1951).

BLOOMFIELD, R. A., H. D. LAUSON, A. COURNAND, E. S. BREED, and D. W. RICHARDS, JR., Recording of right heart pressures in normal subjects and in patients with chronic pulmonary disease and various types of cardiocirculatory disease, *J. Clin. Investigation* **25**, 639 (1946).   [10, 10A

BORDEN, C. W., R. V. EBERT, R. H. WILSON, and H. S. WELLS, Studies of the pulmonary circulation. II. The circulation time from the pulmonary artery to the femoral artery and the quantity of blood in the lungs in patients with mitral stenosis and in patients with left ventricular failure, *J. Clin. Investigation* **28**, 1138 (1949).   [10A, 10B

BORDEN, C. W., R. V. EBERT, R. H. WILSON, and H. S. WELLS, Pulmonary hypertension in heart disease, *New England J. Med.* **242**, 529 (1950).   [10B

BORDEN, C. W., R. H. WILSON, R. V. EBERT, and H. S. WELLS, Pulmonary hypertension in chronic pulmonary emphysema, *Am. J. Med.* **8**, 701 (1950).   [10B

BROD, J., and Z. FEJFAR, The origin of oedema in heart failure, *Quart. J. Med.* **19**, 187 (1950).   [10

CASH, H. R., and H. A. ZIMMERMAN, An evaluation of the effect of Khellin on the pulmonary circulation in man, *Dis. of Chest* **21**, 137 (1952).   [10C

COURNAND, A., A discussion of the concept of cardiac failure in the light of recent physiologic studies in man, *Ann. Int. Med.* **37**, 649 (1952).   [10A, 10B

COURNAND, A., H. D. LAUSON, R. A. BLOOMFIELD, E. S. BREED, and E. DE F. BALDWIN, Recording of right heart pressures in man, *Proc. Soc. Exper. Biol & Med.* **55**, 34 (1944).   [10A

COURNAND, A., and H. A. RANGES, Catheterization of the right auricle in man, *Proc. Soc. Exper. Biol. & Med.* **46**, 462 (1941).   [10

DENOLIN, H., and J. LEQUIME, Les modifications circulatoires dans le coeur pulmonaire chronique, *Arch. d. mal. du cœur* **44**, 391 (1951).   [10B

DEXTER, L., J. W. DOW, F. W. HAYNES, J. L. WHITTENBERGER, B. G. FERRIS, W. T. GOODALE, and H. K. HELLEMS, Studies of the pulmonary circulation in man at rest. Normal variations and the interrelations between increased pulmonary blood flow, elevated pulmonary arterial pressure, and high pulmonary "capillary" pressures, *J. Clin. Investigation* **29**, 602 (1950).   [10B, 10C

DEXTER, L., B. M. LEWIS, F. W. HAYNES, R. GORLIN, and H. E. J. HOUSSAY, Chronic cor pulmonale without hypoxia, *Bull. New England Med. Center* **14**, 69 (1952).   [10B

DEXTER, L., J. L. WHITTENBERG, R. GORLIN, B. M. LEWIS, F. W. HAYNES, and R. J. SPIEGL, The effect of chronic pulmonary disease (cor pulmonale and hypoxia) on the dynamics of the circulation in man, *Tr. A. Am. Physicians* **64**, 226 (1951).   [10B

DEXTER, L., J. L. WHITTENBERGER, F. W. HAYNES, W. T. GOODALE, R. GORLIN, and C. G. SAWYER, Effect of exercise on circulatory dynamics of normal individuals, *J. Appl. Physiol.* **3**, 439 (1951).

DRESDALE, D. T., M. SCHULTZ, and R. J. MICHTOM, Primary pulmonary hypertension. I. Clinical and hemodynamic study, *Am. J. Med.* **11**, 686 (1951).   [10, 10B

DOW, J. W., L. DEXTER, F. W. HAYNES, J. L. WHITTENBERGER, and B. G. FERRIS, Pulmonary circulatory dynamics in mitral stenosis and left heart failure, *J. Clin. Investigation* **28**, 778 (1949).   [10B, 10C

DOYLE, J. T., J. S. WILSON, E. H. ESTES, and J. V. WARREN, The effect of intravenous infusions of physiologic saline solution on the pulmonary arterial and pulmonary capillary pressure in man, *J. Clin. Investigation* **30**, 345 (1951).

DOYLE, J. T., J. S. WILSON, and J. V. WARREN, The pulmonary vascular responses to short-term hypoxia in human subjects, *Circulation* **5**, 263 (1952).   [10B, 10C

EICHNA, L., S. J. FARBER, A. R. BERGER, D. P. EARLE, B. RADER, E. PELLE-
GRINO, R. E. ALBERT, J. D. ALEXANDER, H. TAUBE, and S. YOUNG-
WIRTH, The interrelationship of the cardiovascular, renal and electro-
lyte effects of intravenous digoxin in congestive heart failure, *J. Clin.
Investigation* 30, 1250 (1951). [10, 10B

EICHNA, L., S. J. FARBER, A. R. BERGER, D. P. EARLE, B. RADER, E. PELLE-
GRINO, R. E. ALBERT, J. D. ALEXANDER, H. TAUBE, and S. YOUNG-
WIRTH, Cardiovascular dynamics, blood volumes, renal functions and
electrolyte excretions in the same patients during congestive heart
failure and after recovery of cardiac decompensation, *Circulation* 7,
674 (1953). [10, 10B

ELIASCH, H., H. LAGERLÖF, and L. WERKÖ, Diagnos av adhesiv pericardit
med sarskild hansyn till hjartkatetrisering, *Nord. med.* 44, 1128
(1950). [10, 10A, 10B, 10C

FERRER, M. I., R. M. HARVEY, R. T. CATHCART, A. COURNAND, and D. W.
RICHARDS, JR., Hemodynamic studies in rheumatic heart disease,
Circulation 6, 688 (1952). [10A, 10B

FERRER, M. I., R. M. HARVEY, R. T. CATHCART, C. A. WEBSTER, D. W.
RICHARDS, JR., and A. COURNAND, Some effects of digoxin upon the
heart and circulation in man. Digoxin in chronic cor pulmonale,
Circulation 1, 161 (1950). [10A, 10B

FOWLER, N. O., Cardiac catheterization in the diagnosis of adult heart
disease, *Ann. Int. Med.* 38, 478 (1953). [10, 10B, 10C

FOWLER, N. O., R. N. WESTCOTT, V. D. HAUENSTEIN, R. C. SCOTT, and
J. McGUIRE, Observations on autonomic participation in pulmonary
arteriolar resistance in man, *J. Clin Investigation* 29, 1387 (1950).
[10B, 10C

FOWLER, N. O., R. N. WESTCOTT, R. C. SCOTT, and E. HESS, The cardiac
output in chronic cor pulmonale, *Circulation* 6, 888 (1952).
[10, 10A, 10B

FRISK, A. R., L. WERKÖ, and G. WRANGE, A new mercurial diuretic
"diurgin." (Disodium salt of N-succinyl-, N^1 (8-carboxymethylmer-
captomercuri-B-methoxy) propylcarbamide), *Acta med. Scandinav.*
144, 85 (1952). [10, 10B, 10C

GELFAND, M. L., Chronic cor pulmonale in long-standing bronchial asthma,
Am. J. Med. 10, 27 (1951). [10A, 10B

GILROY, J. C., and V. H. WILSON, On the relationship of pulmonary hypertension to anoxaemia in cases of respiratory disease with cor
pulmonale, *South African J. M. Sc.* 16, 1 (1951). [10B

GRAY, F. D., M. H. WILLIAMS, JR., and F. C. GRAY, The circulatory and
ventilatory changes in chronic pulmonary disease as affected by
Lanatoside C, *Am. Heart J.* 44, 517 (1952). [10, 10A, 10B, 10C

HALMÁGYI, D., B. FELKAI, J. IVÁNYI, and G. HETÉNYI, JR., The role of the nervous system in the maintenance of venous hypertension in heart failure, *Brit. Heart J.* **14,** 101 (1952). [10

HALMÁGYI, D., B. FELKAI, J. IVÁNYI, T. ZSÓTÉR, M. TENYI, and S. SZÜCS, The role of the nervous system in the maintenance of pulmonary arterial hypertension in heart failure, *Brit. Heart J.* **15,** 15 (1953). [10B

HANSEN, A. T., P. ESKILDSEN, and H. GÖTZSCHE, Pressure curves from the right auricle and the right ventricle in chronic constrictive pericarditis, *Circulation* **3,** 881 (1951). [10, 10A

HARVEY, R. M., M. I. FERRER, R. T. CATHCART, D. W. RICHARDS, JR., and A. COURNAND, Some effects of digoxin upon the heart and circulation in man. Digoxin in left ventricular failure, *Am. J. Med.* **7,** 439 (1949). [10A, 10B

HARVEY, R. M., M. I. FERRER, D. W. RICHARDS, JR., and A. COURNAND, Influence of chronic pulmonary disease on the heart and circulation, *Am. J. Med.* **10,** 719 (1951). [10A, 10B

HICKAM, J. B., and W. H. CARGILL, Effect of exercise on cardiac output and pulmonary arterial pressure in normal persons and in patients with cardiovascular disease and pulmonary emphysema, *J. Clin. Investigation* **27,** 10 (1948). [10, 10B

HICKAM, J. B., W. H. CARGILL, and A. GOLDEN, Cardiovascular reactions to emotional stimuli. Effect on the cardiac output, arteriovenous oxygen difference, arterial pressure, and peripheral resistance, *J. Clin. Investigation* **27,** 291 (1948). [10, 10B

HOWARTH, S., J. MCMICHAEL, and E. P. SHARPEY-SCHAFER, Effects of venesection in low output heart failure, *Clin. Sc.* **6,** 41 (1946). [10

HOWARTH, S., J. MCMICHAEL, and E. P. SHARPEY-SCHAFER, The effects of oxygen, venesection and digitalis in chronic heart failure from disease of the lungs, *Clin. Sc.* **6,** 187 (1947). [10

HULTGREN, H. N., The effect of increased venous return on the venous pressure of patients with congestive heart failure, *Am. Heart J.* **39,** 593 (1950). [10

KARTUN, P., P. PARIS, J. NORY, and G. BOUSQUET, Action précose sur la circulation de retour de l'injection intraveineuse d'un diurétique mercuriel, *Arch. d. mal. du cœur* **43,** 133 (1950). [10A

KELLEY, R. T., E. D. FRIES, and T. F. HIGGINS, The effects of hexamethonium on certain manifestations of congestive heart failure, *Circulation* **7,** 169 (1953). [10, 10A, 10B

KELLY, H. G., and R. I. S. BAYLISS, Influence of heart-rate on cardiac output. Studies with digoxin and atropin, *Lancet* **2,** 1071 (1949). [10

LAGERLÖF, H., and L. WERKÖ, Studies on the circulation of blood in man. VI. The pulmonary capillary venous pressure pulse in man, *Scandinav. J. Clin. & Lab. Investigation* **1**, 147 (1949). [10C

LAGERLÖF, H., and L. WERKÖ, Studies on the circulation in man. V. The effect of cedilanid (lanatoside C) on cardiac output and blood pressure in the pulmonary circulation in patients with compensated and decompensated heart disease, *Acta cardiol.* **4**, 1 (1949). [10, 10A, 10B, 10C

LENÈGRE, J., and P. MAURICE, Recherches sur la pression sanguine dans la petite circulation chez l'homme, *Acta cardiol.* **2**, 1 (1947). [10A

LENÈGRE, J., L. SCÉBAT, H. BESSON, F. BENCHEMOUL, and J. DAMIEN, Etude de la pression capillaire pulmonaire dans différents types de cardiopathies, *Arch. d. mal du cœur* **46**, 1 (1953). [10B, 10C

LEWIS, C. S., M. C. DAINES, A. J. SAMUELS, and H. H. HECHT, Cor pulmonale (pulmono-cardiac syndrome). A case report, *Dis. of Chest* **22**, 261 (1952). [10B

LEWIS, C. S., A. J. SAMUELS, M. C. DAINES, and H. H. HECHT, Chronic lung disease, polycythemia and congestive heart failure. Cardiorespiratory, vascular and renal adjustments in cor pulmonale, *Circulation* **6**, 874 (1952). [10B

McGUIRE, J., R. N. WESTCOTT, and N. O. FOWLER, Anoxia and human pulmonary vascular resistance, *Tr. A. Am. Physicians* **64**, 404 (1951). [10B

McMICHAEL, J., and E. P. SHARPEY-SCHAFER, The action of intravenous digoxin in man, *Quart. J. Med.* **13**, 123 (1944). [10

MERRILL, A. J., Edema and decreased renal blood flow in patients with chronic congestive failure. Evidence of "forward failure" as the primary cause of edema, *J. Clin. Investigation* **25**, 389 (1946). [10

MOIA, B., M. R. MALINOW, and C. BAUDINO, Etudes segmentaires de la pression veineuse chez l'homme au moyen du cathéterisme cardiaque, *Acta cardiol.* **7**, 1 (1952). [10

MOTLEY, H. L., A. COURNAND, L. WERKÖ, A. HIMMELSTEIN, and D. DRESDALE, The influence of short periods of anoxia upon pulmonary artery pressures in man, *Am. J. Physiol.* **150**, 315 (1947).

MOUNSEY, J. P. D., L. W. RITZMAN, N. J. SELVERSTONE, W. A. BRISCOE, and G. A. McLEMORE, Circulatory changes in severe pulmonary emphysema, *Brit. Heart J.* **14**, 153 (1952). [10A

MYERS, J. D., and J. B. HICKAM, An estimation of the hepatic blood flow and splanchnic oxygen consumption in heart failure, *J. Clin. Investigation* **27**, 620 (1948). [10

PUGH, L. C. G., and C. L. WYNDHAM, The circulatory effects of mercurial diuretics in congestive heart failure, *Clin. Sc.* **8**, 10 (1949). [10

RICHARDS, D. W., JR., Cardiac output by the catheterization technique in various clinical conditions, *Federation Proc.* **4,** 215 (1945).
[10, 10A

RICHARDS, D. W., JR., A. COURNAND, R. C. DARLING, W. H. GILLESPIE, and E. D. BALDWIN, Pressure of blood in the right auricle in animals and in man: under normal conditions and in right heart failure, *Am. J. Physiol.* **136,** 115 (1942).
[10

RILEY, R. L., A. HIMMELSTEIN, H. L. MOTLEY, H. M. WEINER, and A. COURNAND, Studies of the pulmonary circulation at rest and during exercise in normal individuals and in patients with chronic pulmonary disease, *Am. J. Physiol.* **152,** 372 (1948).

SCÉBAT, L., J. LENÈGRE, B. RANSON-BITKER, F. BENCHEMOUL, and J. DAMIEN, Etude des gaz du sang et du débit cardiaque dans les différents types de cardiopathies, *Arch. d. mal. du cœur* **46,** 18 (1953).
[10, 10B, 10C

SCÉBAT, L., P. MAURICE, and J. LENÈGRE, L'action d'un diuretique mercuriel sur la pression sanguine des cavités droites du coeur chez les cardiaques, *Arch d. mal. du cœur* **42,** 1149 (1949).   [10, 10A

SHARPEY-SCHAFER, E. P., Cardiac output in severe anaemia, *Clin. Sc.* **5,** 125 (1944).
[10

SHARPEY-SCHAFER, E. P., 2-Thiouracil in the treatment of congestive heart failure, *Brit. M. J.* **2,** 888 (1946).
[10

SHERLOCK, S., The liver in heart failure. Relation of anatomical, functional, and circulatory changes, *Brit. Heart J.* **13,** 273 (1951).   [10

SICOT, J-R., F. JOLY, and J. CARLOTTI, Les courbes de pression ventriculaires et vasculaires chez l'homme, *Semaine d. Hôp. de Paris* **27,** 38 (1951).   [10A, 10B

STAUDACHER, W., Ueber oszillatorische Druckmessung am linken Vorhof des Menschen. II Mitt. Der Vorhofdruck des Insuffizienten und des ventilgestorten Herzens, *Ztschr. f. d. ges. exper. Med.* **84,** 548 (1932).

VAN LINGEN, B., J. H. GEAR, and J. WHIDBOURNE, Ballistocardiographic patterns in congestive cardiac failure before and after the intravenous administration of digitalis, *South African J. Clin. Sc.* **2,** 239 (1951).

VON EULER, U. S., and G. LILJESTRAND, Studies on the pulmonary arterial blood-pressure, *Acta physiol. Skandinav., Supp.* **53,** 21 (1948).

WERKÖ, L., The influence of positive pressure breathing on the circulation in man, *Acta med. Scandinav. Supp. No. 193* (1947).   [10A

WERKÖ, L., and H. LAGERLÖF, Studies on the circulation in man. IV. Cardiac output and blood pressure in the right auricle, right ventricle and pulmonary artery in patients with hypertensive cardiovascular disease, *Acta med. Scandinav.* **133,** 427 (1949).   [10, 10A, 10B, 10C

WERKÖ, L., and H. LAGERLÖF, Studies on the circulation of blood in man. VII. The effect of a single intravenous dose of theophylline diethanolamine on the cardiac output, pulmonary blood volume and systemic and pulmonary blood pressures in hypertensive cardiovascular disease, *Scandinav. J. Clin. & Lab. Investigation* **1,** 181 (1949). [10, 10B, 10C

WESTCOTT, R. N., N. O. FOWLER, R. C. SCOTT, V. D. HAUENSTEIN, and J. McGUIRE, Anoxia and human pulmonary vascular resistance, *J. Clin. Investigation* **30,** 957 (1951). [10B

WOOD, P., and J. PAULETT, The effect of digitalis on the venous pressure, *Brit. Heart J.* **11,** 83 (1949). [10

ZIMMERMAN, H. A., Left ventricular pressures in patients with aortic insufficiency studied by intracardiac catheterization, *J. Clin. Investigation* **29,** 1601 (1950). [10, 10A, 10B

ZIMMERMAN, H., A study of the pulmonary circulation in man, *Dis. of Chest* **20,** 46 (1951). [10, 10A, 10B

7. Cutaneous Capillaries and Capillary Pressure

Engorgement of the tissue capillaries, often to the point of hemorrhage, is the usual postmortem finding in congestive failure. The degree of congestion that exists during life in such patients cannot be estimated accurately from the sections of fixed tissues, since some of the changes may be agonal or postmortem. Direct observation of the capillaries of the nail folds of patients with congestive failure has been possible for many years, and the findings of all observers (Crawford, 1926, 1927; **11**) are in substantial agreement. The visible capillaries are increased in number, consistently show dilatation of the venous limb and may exhibit slight narrowing of the arterial limb. The blood in them is dark, moves slowly and may be motionless for abnormally long periods of time; the column of moving blood often appears granular or segmented. It is to be noted also that the small venules of the subpapillary region are likewise abnormally numerous and prominent. Hisinger-Jägerskiöld (1923) found these changes only in patients with peripheral failure and not in those in whom the signs of congestion were limited to the lungs; the latter patients showed only cutaneous capillary constriction. The reason for the dilatation of the venous limb of the capillaries is made clear by the observations of Krogh (1929) and of Landis (1928), who showed that anoxemia causes capillary dilatation. In congestive failure the effects of anoxemia are naturally most marked at the venous end of the capillary.

It is to be expected that the capillary pressure will always be higher than the venous, so that a finding of elevated venous pressure carries with it the implication in general that the capillary pressure is also elevated, as direct measurements show (Eichna and Bordley, 1939, 1942). Earlier measurements of capillary pressure in patients with congestive failure by indirect methods gave variable results (Meldolesi, 1926; Boas and Dooneief, 1924); these methods are demonstrably inaccurate (Eichna and Bordley, 1939). More recently measurements have been made by means of direct micro-injection of the cutaneous capillaries in patients in failure. Those with edema were observed to have high values (Fahr and Ershler, 1938, 1941), while those without edema had capillary pressures within the normal range. High pressures fell to normal in recovery, according to these authors. However, their finding that the capillary pressure may be found to be abnormally high, even when the venous pressure was not outside the normal range, invites skepticism.

Bibliography

Chapter I — Section 7

BOAS, E. P., and G. DOONEIEF, The mechanism of peripheral stasis in myocardial insufficiency. Capillary and venous pressures, *Arch. Int. Med.* **33,** 407 (1924).

CRAWFORD, J. H., Studies on human capillaries. III. Observations in cases of auricular fibrillation, *J. Clin. Investigation* **2,** 365 (1926).   [11

CRAWFORD, J. H., Studies on human capillaries. V. Observations in cases of heart disease with regular rhythm, *J. Clin. Investigation* **4,** 317 (1927).   [11

EICHNA, L. W., and J. BORDLEY, III, Capillary blood pressure in man. Comparison of direct and indirect methods of measurement, *J. Clin. Investigation* **18,** 695 (1939).

EICHNA, L. W., and J. BORDLEY, Capillary blood pressure in man. Direct measurements in the digits of normal and hypertensive subjects during vasoconstriction and vasodilatation variously induced, *J. Clin. Investigation* **21,** 711 (1942).

FAHR, G., and I. ERSHLER, Capillary pressure in right heart failure, *Proc. Soc. Exper. Biol. & Med.* **37,** 701 (1938).

FAHR, G., and I. ERSHLER, Studies of the factors concerned in edema formation. II. The hydrostatic pressure in the capillaries during edema formation in right heart failure, *Ann. Int. Med.* **15**, 799 (1941).

FREEDLANDER, S. O., and C. H. LENHART, Clinical observations on the capillary circulation, *Arch. Int. Med.* **29**, 12 (1922). [11

HISINGER-JÄGERSKIÖLD, E., Klinische Kapillarstudien bei Blutkrankheiten und Zirkulationsstörungen, *Acta med. Scandinav.* **58**, 231 (1923). [11

JÜRGENSEN, E., Mikrokapillarbeobachtungen. Ein Beitrag zur pathologischen Physiologie des Kreislaufsystems, *Deutsches Arch. f. klin. Med.* **132**, 204 (1920). [11

KROGH, A., *The anatomy and physiology of capillaries* (New Haven, 1929), pp. 230–332.

LANDIS, E. M., Micro-injection studies of capillary permeability. III. The effect of lack of oxygen on the permeability of the capillary wall to fluid and to the plasma proteins, *Am. J. Physiol.* **83**, 528 (1928).

MELDOLESI, G., Studio clinico della pressione capillare nei suoi rapporti con la pressione arteriosa e con la pressione venosa, *Cuore e circolaz.* **10**, 20, 45 (1926).

SCHILLER, M., Capillaruntersuchungen bei Schulkindern. (Unter besonderer Berücksichtigung der Frage: Sind Beziehungen zwischen Intelligenz und Capillarbild vorhanden?), *Ztschr. f. d. ges. Neurol. u. Psychiat.* **151**, 700 (1934). [11

SCHUR, H., Mikroskopische Hautstudien am Lebenden, *Wien. klin. Wchnschr.* **32**, 1201 (1919). [11

SECHER, K., Klinische Kapillaruntersuchungen, *Acta med. Scandinav.* **56**, 295 (1922). [11

WEISS, E., Beobachtungen und mikrophotographische Darstellung der Hautkapillaren am lebenden Menschen, *Deutsches Arch. f. klin. Med.* **119**, 1 (1916). [11

8. *Cerebrospinal Fluid Pressure*

The relation between venous and spinal fluid pressures is well established. Accordingly, it is to be expected that patients with a high venous pressure associated with congestive failure will also show elevation of the spinal fluid pressure; many observations confirming this relationship in heart disease have been recorded (Lamache, 1926; Harrison, 1933, 1934; **12**). Pulsations in the spinal fluid manometer are more marked than normal (Hamilton *et al.*, 1944). The cisternal pressure has also been measured by Harrison (1933, 1934), who found it to be elevated. The spinal fluid pressure parallels the venous pressure and is always somewhat the higher of the two. With recovery from failure the two measurements fall to or toward normal levels, though the actual or percentage decrease is not necessarily the same in both. Patients with considerably elevated spinal fluid pressure consequent to cardiac decompensation show none of the symptoms or signs usually associated with similarly increased intracranial pressure due to primary intracranial disease, such as headache, projectile vomiting, slow pulse or papilledema. This fact suggests that factors in addition to the cerebrospinal fluid pressure itself may be important in the genesis of these signs and symptoms in primary intracranial disorders.

Tzanck and Renault (1927) and Robertson and Fetter (1935) recorded the effect of venesection in lowering the spinal fluid pressure as well as the venous pressure. Similar observations on the effect of mercurial diuretics have been recorded by Volini and Levitt (1940). Harrison (1933, 1934) observed improvement in orthopnea in most instances after spinal drainage; he reported (1934) that the peripheral venous pressure also usually decreased significantly after this procedure. The observation that respiratory distress is relieved by removal of spinal fluid has been corroborated by others (Altschule, 1933; Volini and Levitt, 1940). Robertson and Fetter (1935) felt that withdrawal of spinal fluid performed simultaneously with venesection was more effective in relieving orthopnea than was the latter alone. Harrison (1934), however, was unable to correlate the relief of orthopea with lowering of the venous pressure in his patients, and felt that orthopnea was due to increased intracranial pressure. Patients with increased intracranial pressure due to primary intracranial disease do not have dyspnea or orthopnea, however, nor does lumbar puncture alter their respiratory dynamics in any consistent manner.

The reason for the temporary relief of respiratory distress in congestive failure after spinal puncture is probably a transitory increase in blood flow through the cerebral respiratory centers; high intracranial pressure has been shown to cause a decrease in cerebral blood flow in man (Shenkin et al., 1946; Kety et al., 1948). The reason for the reported decrease in peripheral venous pressure following spinal puncture is obscure.

It is of interest that increased intracranial pressure has been found to cause pulmonary veno- and arteriolar constriction in dogs (Campbell *et al.*, 1949).

Bibliography

Chapter I — Section 8

ALTSCHULE, M. D., Relief of dyspnea after spinal fluid drainage, *Unpublished data* (1933).

CAMPBELL, G. S., F. J. HADDY, W. L. ADAMS, and M. B. VISSCHER, Circulatory changes and pulmonary lesions in dogs following increased intracranial pressure, and the effects of atropine upon such changes, *Am. J. Physiol.* **158**, 96 (1949).

FRIEDFELD, L., and A. M. FISHBERG, The relation of the cerebrospinal and venous pressures in heart failure, *J. Clin. Investigation* **13**, 495 (1934). [12

GREENE, J. A., W. D. PAUL, and A. E. FELLER, The action of theophylline with ethylenediamine on intrathecal and venous pressures in cardiac failure and on bronchial obstruction in cardiac failure and bronchial asthma, *J. A. M. A.* **109**, 1712 (1937). [12

HAMILTON, W. F., R. A. WOODBURY, and H. T. HARPER, JR., Arterial, cerebrospinal and venous pressures in man during cough and strain, *Am. J. Physiol.* **141**, 42 (1944). [12

HARRISON, W. G., JR., The cisternal pressure in congestive heart failure and its bearing on orthopnea. *J. Clin. Investigation* **12**, 1075 (1933). [12

HARRISON, W. G., JR., Cerebrospinal fluid pressure and venous pressure in cardiac failure, and the effect of spinal drainage in the treatment of cardiac decompensation, *Arch. Int. Med.* **53**, 782 (1934). [12

LAMACHE, A., Étude sur la tension du liquide céphalo-rachidien, *Thèse de Fac. de méd.* Paris (1926). [12

KETY, S. S., H. A. SHENKIN, and C. F. SCHMIDT, The effects of increased intracranial pressure on cerebral circulatory functions in man, *J. Clin. Investigation* **27**, 493 (1948).

MERKLEN, P., J. KABAKER, and J. WARTER, Étude de la pression du liquide céphalo-rachidien et de la manoeuvre de Queckenstedt au cours de l'asystolie. Rapports avec la tension veineuse. Influence du traitement par la digitale, *Paris méd.* **87**, 405 (1933). [12

PLANQUES, RISER, and R. SOREL, La pression rachidienne chez les hypertendus artériels, *Presse méd.* **41**, 513 (1933). [12

POROT, M. A., Les fortes hypertensions céphalo-rachidiennes d'origine veineuse. Leur latence. La discordance manométrique et clinique, *Rev. neurol.* **1**, 1173 (1930). [12

ROBERTSON, H. F., and F. FETTER, The effect of venesection on arterial, spinal fluid, and venous pressures with especial reference to failure of the left and right heart, *J. Clin. Investigation* **14**, 305 (1935).   [12

SHENKIN, H. A., S. S. KETY, F. C. GRANT, and C. F. SCHMIDT, Cerebral blood flow and metabolism in patients with increased intracranial pressure, *Am. J. M. Sc.* **212**, 755 (1946).

TZANCK, A., and P. RENAULT, Des rapports entre la tension veineuse et la tension du liquide céphalo-rachidien, *Compt. rend. Soc. de biol.* **96**, 157 (1927).   [12

VOLINI, I. F., and R. O. LEVITT, Studies on mercurial diuresis. III. The alteration induced in the cerebrospinal fluid pressure, *Am. Heart J.* **19**, 566 (1940).   [12

9. *Lung Volume. Pulmonary Elasticity and Distensibility. Intrapleural Pressure*

Many authors, chiefly clinicians, have ascribed the dyspnea of heart disease to a reduction in vital capacity. As Christie and Meakins (1934) have emphasized, this erroneous concept is based on loose thinking consequent to lack of appreciation of the significance of the various subdivisions of the total lung volume. It is, therefore, essential to understand clearly the terminology bearing on this subject.

Functional residual (subtidal) air is the volume of air remaining in the lungs after normal expiration. It is the sum of the residual and reserve (supplemental) airs, and is largely a measure of the space available for respiratory exchange; it must be changed by mixing with and diffusion from the tidal air. A subdivision of the total lung volume having approximately the same significance is the *mid capacity*, a measure used by some continental authors; it consists of the functional residual air plus half the tidal air volume.

Residual air is the volume of air remaining in the lungs after maximal forced expiration.

Reserve (supplemental) air is the air which, after normal expiration, is expelled by maximal forced expiration. It is a measure of the elasticity of the lungs and in individual subjects varies with the intrapleural negative pressure, decreasing as the pressure approaches the atmospheric.

Complemental air is the air which, after normal inspiration, is taken in by maximal forced inspiration, and is therefore a measure of the expansibility of the lungs and of the thoracic cage.

Vital capacity is the sum of the reserve, complemental and tidal air volumes and, since it measures all at the same time, may have no precise significance in some circumstances. Variations in vital capacity and the large effects of practice in the maneuver have been studied by Mills (1949); Gross (1942) has discussed the influence of the patient's attitude. Bahnson (1952) showed that voluntary breathholding may increase the vital capacity if the intrapulmonary pressure is elevated.

Total capacity is the sum of the residual, reserve, and complemental air volumes.

Some of these subdivisions of the lung volume are measured easily and with accuracy; these include the reserve and complemental airs and the vital capacity. On the other hand, the residual and functional residual airs are measured by means of fairly complicated techniques, some of which do not yield accurate data in subjects in whom mixing in the lungs is impaired, including patients with cardiac decompensation.

Although a number of authors have measured the functional residual air and the mid capacity in patients with congestive failure (13), the data in most instances are not acceptable, having been obtained by the use of methods that do not give accurate results in patients with abnormal lungs. The more reliable data of Binger (1923), Christie and Meakins (1934), Poli (1938*a,b*), Altschule *et al.* (1943), Fowler *et al.* (1952), and Richards *et al.* (1951) indicate no great change in functional residual air in chronic congestive failure, except possibly in severe decompensation (Binger, 1923; Fowler *et al.*, 1952; Wilson *et al.*, 1950; Richards *et al.*, 1951), where it may be decreased significantly. Accordingly, it appears that, with possible exceptions in patients with very severe failure, the space available for breathing is not decreased.

Reported measurements of the *residual* air are also numerous (14) but many are unacceptable. The more reliable data of Binger (1923), Christie and Meakins (1934), Kaltreider and McCann (1937), Poli (1938*a,b*), Altschule *et al.* (1943), Richards *et al.* (1951), and Wilson *et al.* (1950) show that the residual air is usually increased in patients with chronic congestive failure, although Binger (1923) found that it might be decreased in severe failure; increase in residual air indicates that a state of mild secondary pulmonary emphysema is common in myocardial insufficiency.

All authors agree that the *reserve* air is reduced in this condition (Binger, 1923; Christie and Meakins, 1934; **15**). This finding indicates a loss of elasticity, which actually has been demonstrated by more direct methods as well (Christie and Meakins, 1934; Christie and McIntosh, 1934; Paine, 1940). The loss of elasticity, together with generalized muscular weakness, serves to explain the reduced expiratory velocity and pressure manifested by cardiac patients (Gross, 1943; Plotz, 1947; Heyer, 1946). The diminution in reserve air is paralleled by changes in the intrapleural pressure, the latter becoming less negative (Christie and Meakins, 1934; Christie and McIntosh, 1934; Paine, 1940); the conclusion of Poli (1936, 1938a, b) that it becomes more negative cannot be accepted. The loss of most or all of the intrapleural negative pressure impairs the effectiveness of inspiration and also impedes venous return; the latter change tends to elevate peripheral venous pressure (page 35). The reserve air does not change during exertion (Décourt et al., 1951).

The *complemental* air is diminished—often markedly—in chronic congestive failure (Binger, 1923; Siebeck, 1910; **16**). Accordingly, the distensibility of the lungs must be greatly impaired because of increased rigidity, as has indeed been demonstrated by more direct methods (Christie and Meakins, 1934; Christie and McIntosh, 1934). This in itself makes inspiration more difficult and also limits the increase in tidal air volume that normally occurs in response to work (page 90). The complemental air does not change during exertion in cardiac decompensation (Décourt et al., 1951).

The *vital capacity* (Peabody and Wentworth, 1917; Rubow, 1908; Siebeck, 1910; **17**) and total capacity (**13, 14**) are both diminished, since both are derived from the reserve and complemental airs, the vital capacity entirely and the total capacity largely. The vital capacity may increase after hexamethonium (Kelley et al., 1953) but not after epinephrine (Gottsegen, 1951) in cardiac decompensation.

The mechanisms underlying the aforementioned changes in the lungs have been studied in experiments on animals by Romanoff (1911), Drinker, Peabody and Blumgart (1922) and Mack et al. (1947). The first two showed that congestion causes encroachment by the engorged vessels on the air spaces, thus supporting von Basch's earlier theoretical analysis. Increased rigidity of the lung was also found by Romanoff (1911) and by Mack et al. (1947); that engorgement with blood increases the rigidity of tissues is well known. On the other hand Berglund et al. (1949) and Borden et al. (1949) found no relation between the calculated pulmonary blood volume and the measured vital capacity in patients with cardiac decompensation; it would perhaps have been more informing to have studied the possible relation between pulmonary blood volume and complemental air. Borden et al. (1950) found no relation between vital capacity and pulmonary arterial pressure, but Berglund et al. (1949) observed that pulmonary capillary pressure and vital capacity vary inversely in congestive failure. Intravenous infusions cause negligible changes in subdivisions of the lung volume (Altschule et al., 1942; Doyle et al., 1951); such infusions, while they cause increases in capillary pressure (Doyle et al., 1951) never cause it to rise above the normal range. Increases in blood volume by themselves, as in polycythemia vera, do not lower the vital capacity (Altschule et al., 1940). It is probable that the abnormally high pressures in the small pulmonary vessels rather than the volume of blood contained within the latter constitute the most important cause of the changes in lung volume characteristic of cardiac decompensation. Calculated pulmonary blood-volume values are usually high in chronic congestive failure, but there are exceptions to this rule (Berglund et al., 1949; Borden et al., 1949; Doyle et al., 1952, 1953; Kopelman and Lee, 1951); the method used is not highly sensitive. Anoxia itself does not increase the pulmonary blood volume in normal subjects (Doyle et al., 1952) and the vital capacity likewise is unchanged (Rahn and Hammond, 1952).

Attempts to correlate vital capacity with severity of dyspnea obviously cannot succeed, since many mechanisms participate in the genesis of that symptom; indeed, as a symptom, dyspnea is not measurable. Similarly, the use of various ratios, such as respiratory minute volume to vital capacity (Harrison et al., 1931, 1932), maximal respiration to vital capacity, maximal tidal air to vital capacity, or vital capacity to total capacity, is not valid. The ratios of residual air to total capacity and of functional residual air to total capacity have also been employed. All of these ratios are objectionable because there is no way in which the cerebral cortex of the dyspneic patient becomes aware of them, whereas abnormality of one of the factors previously discussed might make its presence known by lessened efficiency of breathing or by changes in blood gases. The data of all authors show a great deal of overlapping of values for vital capacity in the dyspneic and nondyspneic groups of cardiac patients. A general relation between vital capacity and exercise tolerance of course exists (Gardam, 1950). McMichael (1939) found a better correlation between the degree of hyperventilation and fall in cardiac output than between the former and decrease in vital capacity.

The validity of the application of methods for measuring the residual air to exercising patients has not been established; the vital capacity can, however, be measured during or immediately after exercise. Although a number of authors have described a slight reduction in vital capacity in normal subjects during severe exertion (18), Levine and Wilson (1919), Harrison *et al.* (1932) and Iglauer and Altschule (1938) found only insignificant changes, which the last named ascribed to difficulty in holding the breath long enough for performing maximal inspiration and expiration while dyspneic. Measurements of vital capacity in cardiac patients made dyspneic by exertion reveal no change from the control values (Alt *et al.*, 1930; Harrison *et al.*, 1932). These findings strongly suggest that exertion causes no great increase in pulmonary congestion. Some increase probably does occur, for Bolt *et al.* (1950) did observe some decrease in vital capacity after exertion in patients with congestive failure. The exacerbation of pulmonary congestion that might occur during exercise is limited by the fact that right ventricular output cannot increase much or at all during exercise in patients with congestive failure (page 10).

Bibliography

Chapter I — Section 9

ALSEVER, J. B. and S. A. LEVINE, The immediate effect of mercurial diuretics on the vital capacity of the lungs, *Am. Heart J.* **15**, 201 (1938)   **[17**

ALT, H. L., G. L. WALKER, and W. C. SMITH, The cardiac output in heart disease. II. Effect of exercise on the circulation in patients with chronic rheumatic valvular disease, subacute rheumatic fever and complete heart block, *Arch. Int. Med.* **45,** 958 (1930).

ALTSCHULE, M. D., D. R. GILLIGAN, and N. ZAMCHECK, The effects on the cardiovascular system of fluids administered intravenously in man. IV. The lung volume and pulmonary dynamics, *J. Clin. Investigation* **21,** 365 (1942).

ALTSCHULE, M. D., M. C. VOLK, and H. HENSTELL, Cardiac and respiratory function at rest in patients with uncomplicated polycythemia vera, *Am. J. M. Sc.* **200,** 478 (1948).

ALTSCHULE, M. D., N. ZAMCHECK, and A. IGLAUER, The lung volume and its subdivisions in the upright and recumbent positions in patients with congestive failure. Pulmonary factors in the genesis of orthopnea, *J. Clin. Investigation* **22,** 805 (1943).   [13, 14, 15, 16, 17

ARNETT, J. H., Vital capacity of the lungs: changes occurring in health and disease, *J. Clin. Investigation* **14,** 543 (1935).   [17

BAHNSON, H. T., Effect of a brief period of voluntary increased pulmonary pressure upon vital capacity, *J. Appl. Physiol.* **5,** 273 (1952).

BENDIXEN, H., Zur Funktionsprüfung des Herzens durch Dyspnoeversuche, *Ztschr. f. klin. Med.* **115,** 271 (1931).   [17

BERGLUND, H., H. LAGERLÖF, L. WERKÖ, and H. BUCHT, The relation between pulmonary capillary venous pressure, pulmonary blood volume, and vital capacity, *Tr. A. Am. Physicians* **62,** 124 (1949).   [17

BINGER, C. A. L., The lung volume in heart disease, *J. Exper. Med.* **38,** 445 (1923).   [13, 14, 15, 16, 17

BITTORF, A., and J. FORSCHBACH, Untersuchungen über die Lungenfullung bei Krankheiten, *Ztschr. f. klin. Med.* **70,** 474 (1910).
          [13, 14, 15, 16, 17

BLUMGART, H. L., and S. WEISS, Studies on the velocity of blood flow. III. The velocity of blood flow and its relation to other aspects of the circulation in patients with rheumatic and syphilitic heart disease, *J. Clin. Investigation* **4,** 149 (1927).   [17

BLUMGART, H. L., and S. WEISS, Studies on the velocity of blood flow. IV. The velocity of blood flow and its relation to other aspects of the circulation in patients with arteriosclerosis and in patients with arterial hypertension, *J. Clin. Investigation* **4,** 173 (1927).   [17

BLUMGART, H. L., and S. WEISS, Clinical studies on the velocity of blood flow. IX. The pulmonary circulation time, the velocity of venous blood flow to the heart, and related aspects of the circulation in patients with cardiovascular disease, *J. Clin. Investigation* **5,** 343 (1927–28).
          [17

BLUMGART, H. L., and S. WEISS, Clinical studies on the velocity of blood flow. X. The relation between the velocity of blood flow, the venous pressure and the vital capacity of the lungs in fifty patients with cardiovascular disease compared with similar measurements in fifty normal persons, *J. Clin. Investigation* **5**, 379 (1927–28). [17

BOHR, C., Die Funktionellen Änderungen in der Mittelage und Vitalkapazität der Lungen. Normales und pathologisches Emphysem, *Deutsches Arch. f. klin. Med.* **88**, 305 (1906–07). [18

BOLT, W., H. VALENTIN, and H. NEURATH, Herzleistungsbreite der kardialen Linkinsuffizienz, *Ztschr. f. Kreislaufforsch.* **39**, 718 (1950). [17

BORDEN, C. W., R. V. EBERT, R. H. WILSON, and H. S. WELLS, Studies of the pulmonary circulation. II. The circulation time from the pulmonary artery to the femoral artery and the quantity of blood in the lungs in patients with mitral stenosis and in patients with left ventricular failure, *J. Clin. Investigation* **28**, 1138 (1949). [17

BORDEN, C. W., R. V. EBERT, R. H. WILSON, and H. S. WELLS, Pulmonary hypertension in heart disease, *New England J. Med.* **242**, 529 (1950). [17

BRITTINGHAM, H. H., and P. D. WHITE, Cardiac functional tests, *J. A. M. A.* **79**, 1901 (1922). [17

BURWELL, C. S., and L. DEXTER, Beri-beri heart disease, *Tr. A. Am. Physicians* **60**, 59 (1947). [17

CAMPBELL, M., Vital capacity in heart disease, *Guy's Hosp. Rep.* **9**, 70 (1929). [17

CAMPBELL, M., The respiratory exchange during exercise in heart disease. III, *Quart. J. Med.* **27**, 369 (1934). [17

CHRISTIE, C. D., and A. J. BEAMS, Orthopnea, *Arch. Int. Med.* **31**, 85 (1923). [17

CHRISTIE, R. V., and J. C. MEAKINS, The intrapleural pressure in congestive heart failure and its clinical significance, *J. Clin. Investigation* **13**, 323 (1934). [13, 14, 15, 17

CHRISTIE, R. V., and C. A. McINTOSH, The measurement of the intrapleural pressure in man and its significance, *J. Clin. Investigation* **13**, 279 (1934).

DE CARNASCO, H. O., and W. VORWERK, Beitrag zur Lungen- und Herzfunktionsprüfung, *Arch. f. exper. Path. u. Pharmakol.* **184**, 156 (1936). [17

DÉCOURT, L. V., B. TRANCHESI, E. BARBATO, and R. MACRUZ, Volumes respiratórios e estase pulmonar nos cardiácos, *Arq. brasil. cardiol.* **4**, 391 (1951). [15, 16, 17

DOYLE, J. T., J. S. WILSON, E. H. ESTES, and J. V. WARREN, The effect of intravenous infusions of physiologic saline solution on the pulmonary arterial and pulmonary capillary pressure in man, *J. Clin. Investigation* **30**, 345 (1951).

DOYLE, J. T., J. S. WILSON, C. LÉPINE, and J. V. WARREN, An evaluation of the measurement of the cardiac output and of the so-called pulmonary blood volume by the dye-dilution method, *J. Lab. & Clin. Med.* **41**, 29 (1953).

DOYLE, J. T., J. S. WILSON, and J. V. WARREN, The pulmonary vascular responses to short-term hypoxia in human subjects, *Circulation* **5**, 263 (1952).

DRINKER, C. K., F. W. PEABODY, and H. L. BLUMGART, The effect of pulmonary congestion on the ventilation of the lungs, *J. Exper. Med.* **35**, 77 (1922).

ENGELHARD, A., Der Wert der Spirometrie für die Klinik der Herzkrankheiten mit Lungenstauung und ihr Ausbau zur einer Funktionsprüfung, *Deutsches Arch. f. klin. Med.* **156**, 1 (1927). [15, 16, 17

ERNSTENE, A. C., and H. L. BLUMGART, Orthopnea, Its relation to the increased venous pressure of myocardial failure, *Arch. Int. Med.* **45**, 593 (1930). [17

FOWELL, D. M., A. P. BRIGGS, N. C. WHEELER, J. A. WINSLOW, JR., J. W. REMINGTON, and W. F. HAMILTON, Renal and circulatory factors in congestive failure of the circulation, *Federation Proc.* **7**, 35 (1948). [17

FOWLER, W. S., E. R. CORNISH, JR., and S. KETY, Lung function studies. VIII. Analysis of alveolar ventilation by pulmonary N_2 clearance curves, *J. Clin. Investigation* **31**, 40 (1952). [13

FRIEDMAN, B., G. CLARK, H. RESNIK, JR., and T. R. HARRISON, Effect of digitalis on the cardiac output of persons with congestive heart failure, *Arch. Int. Med.* **56**, 710 (1935). [17

GARDAM, J. D., Vital capacity in adults with heart disease in relation to age, degree of cardiac enlargement and type of valvular lesion, *Am. J. M. Sc.* **219**, 76 (1950). [17

GORDON, B., S. A. LEVINE, and A. WILMAERS, Observations on a group of marathon runners, with special reference to the circulation, *Arch. Int. Med.* **33**, 425 (1924). [18

GOTTSEGEN, G., Vitalkapazität und Herzinsuffizienz. II Mitt. Ueber Adrenalin und Stophanthineffekte, *Cardiologia* **19**, 174 (1951). [17

GROSS, D., Investigaciones patofisiologicas sobre capacidad vital, *Rev. méd. latino-am.* **27**, 320 (1942). [17

GROSS, D., Investigations concerning vital capacity, *Am. Heart J.* **25**, 335 (1943). [17

HARRISON, T. R., B. FRIEDMAN, G. CLARK, and H. RESNIK, The cardiac output in relation to cardiac failure, *Arch. Int. Med.* **54**, 239 (1934). [17

HARRISON, T. R., S. HARRIS, JR., and J. A. CALHOUN, Studies in congestive failure. XVI. The clinical value of the ventilation test in the estimation of cardiac function, *Am. Heart J.* **7,** 157 (1931–32).   [17

HARRISON, T. R., W. G. HARRISON, JR., J. A. CALHOUN, and J. P. MARSH, Congestive heart failure. XVII. The mechanism of dyspnea on exertion, *Arch. Int. Med.* **50,** 690 (1932).

HARRISON, T. R., F. C. TURLEY, E. JONES, and J. A. CALHOUN, Congestive heart failure. X. The measurement of ventilation as a test of cardiac function, *Arch. Int. Med.* **48,** 377 (1931).   [17

HARRISON, W. G., JR., The cisternal pressure in congestive heart failure and its bearing on orthopnea, *J. Clin. Investigation* **12,** 1075 (1933).
    [17

HARVEY, W. P., and C. A. FINCH, Dicumarol prophylaxis of thromboembolic disease in congestive heart failure, *New England J. Med.* **242,** 208 (1950).   [17

HASSELBALCH, K. A., Ueber die Totalkapazität der Lungen, *Deutsches Arch. f. klin. Med.* **93,** 64 (1908).   [18

HELLER, B. I., and W. E. JACOBSON, Renal hemodynamics in heart disease, *Am. Heart J.* **39,** 188 (1950).   [17

HEWLETT, A. W., The vital capacities of patients with cardiac complaints, *Heart* **11,** 195 (1924).   [17

HEYER, H. E., Abnormalities of the respiratory pattern in patients with cardiac dyspnea, *Am. Heart J.* **32,** 457 (1946).   [17

IGLAUER, A., and M. D. ALTSCHULE. Effect of exertion on vital capacity of normal subjects, *Proc. Soc. Exper. Biol. & Med.* **39,** 512 (1938).

IHAYA, H., Studien über die Alveolarluft, Blutgase, Vitalkapazität und Minuten- und Schlagvolumen des Herzens bei Beriberi, Herzklappenfehler und Pleuritis, *Mitt. d. med. Gesellsch. zu Tokyo* **48,** 2167 (1934).   [17

JANSEN, K., H. W. KNIPPING, and K. STROMBERGER, Klinische Untersuchungen über Atmung und Blutgase, *Beitr. z. Klin. d. Tuberk.* **80,** 304 (1932).   [17

JOANNIDES, M., The effect of dyspnea variously produced on the vital capacity of the lungs, *Arch. Int. Med.* **33,** 145 (1924).   [18

KALTREIDER, N. L., and W. S. McCANN, Respiratory response during exercise in pulmonary fibrosis and emphysema, *J. Clin. Investigation* **16,** 23 (1937).   [14, 17

KATZ, L. N., W. W. HAMBURGER, and S. H. RUBINFELD, Observations on the effects of oxygen therapy. II. Changes in the circulation and respiration, *Am. J. M. Sc.* **184,** 810 (1932).   [17

KELLEY, R. T., E. D. FRIES, and T. F. HIGGINS, The effects of hexamethonium on certain manifestations of congestive heart failure, *Circulation* **7,** 169 (1953).   [17

KINSMAN, J. M., and J. W. MOORE, The hemodynamics of the circulation in hypertension, *Ann. Int. Med.* **9**, 649 (1935).   [17

KNIPPING, H. W., W. LEWIS, and A. MONCRIEFF, Ueber die Dyspnoe, *Beitr. z. Klin. d. Tuberk.* **79**, 1 (1932).   [15, 16, 17

KOPELMAN, H., and G. de J. LEE, The intrathoracic blood volume in mitral stenosis and left ventricular failure, *Clin. Sc.* **10**, 383 (1951).
[17

LEVINE, S. A., and F. N. WILSON, Observations on the vital capacity of the lungs in cases of irritable heart, *Heart* **7**, 53 (1919).

LOMBARDO, T. A., The effect of posture on the excretion of water and sodium by patients with congestive heart failure, *Circulation* **7**, 91 (1953).   [17

LUNDSGAARD, C., Determination and interpretation of changes in lung volumes in certain heart lesions, *J. A. M. A.* **80**, 163 (1923).   [13, 14

LUNDSGAARD, C., and K. SCHIERBECK, Untersuchungen über die Volumina der Lungen. III. Die Verhältnisse bei Patienten mit Herzleiden (Mitralfehlern). Ein Beitrag zur pathologischen Physiologie der cardiogenen Lungenaffektionen, *Acta med. Scandinav.* **58**, 495 (1923).
[13, 14, 17

MACK, I., M. GROSSMAN, and L. N. KATZ, The effect of pulmonary congestion on distensibility of the lung, *Federation Proc.* **6**, 161 (1947).

MATHIEU, L., GRILLIAT, and PILLOT, Considérations diagnostiques sur la fonction ventilatoire des cardiaques, *Arch. d. mal. du cœur* **45**, 21 (1952).   [17

McCLURE, C. W., and F. W. PEABODY, Relation of vital capacity of lungs to clinical condition of patients with heart disease, *J. A. M. A.* **69**, 1954 (1917).   [17

McGUIRE, J., V. HAUENSTEIN, and R. SHORE, Cardiac output in heart disease determined by the direct Fick method, including comparative determinations by the acetylene method, *Arch. Int. Med.* **60**, 1034 (1937).   [17

McGUIRE, J., R. SHORE, V. HAUENSTEIN, and F. GOLDMAN, The cardiac output in compensation and decompensation in the same individual, *Am. Heart J.* **16**, 449 (1938).   [17

McGUIRE, J., R. SHORE, V. HAUENSTEIN, and F. GOLDMAN, Relation of cardiac output to congestive heart failure, *Arch. Int. Med.* **63**, 290 (1939).   [17

McMICHAEL, J., Hyperpnoea in heart failure, *Clin. Sc.* **4**, 19 (1939). [17

MENEELY, G. R., and N. L. KALTREIDER, A study of the volume of the blood in congestive heart failure. Relation to other measurements in fifteen patients, *J. Clin. Investigation* **22**, 521 (1943).   [17

MILLS, J. N., Variability of the vital capacity of the normal human subject, *J. Physiol.* **110**, 76 (1949).

NEURATH, O., Untersuchungen über die Bestimmung der Blutumlaufsgeschwindigkeit mit Magnesiumsulfat, *Ztschr. f. klin. Med.* **132,** 134 (1937). [17

PAINE, J. R., The clinical measurement of pulmonary elasticity. A comparison of the methods of Christie and McIntosh and of Neergaard and Wirz, *J. Thoracic Surg.* **9,** 550 (1940).

PEABODY, F. W., and C. C. STURGIS, Clinical studies on respiration. IX. The effect of exercise on the metabolism, heart rate, and pulmonary ventilation of normal subjects and patients with heart disease, *Arch. Int. Med.* **29,** 277 (1922). [17

PEABODY, F. W., and J. A. WENTWORTH, Clinical studies of the respiration. IV. The vital capacity of the lungs and its relation to dyspnea, *Arch. Int. Med.* **20,** 443 (1917). [17

PETERS, J. P., JR., and D. P. BARR, Studies of the respiratory mechanism in cardiac dyspnea. II. A note on the effective lung volume in cardiac dyspnea, *Am. J. Physiol.* **54,** 335 (1920). [17

PLESCH, J., Die pathologische Physiologie des Lungenvolumens und seine Beziehung zum Kreislauf, *Ztschr. f. exper. Path. u. Pharmakol.* **13,** 165 (1913). [14, 15, 16, 17

PLOTZ, M., Bronchial spasm in cardiac asthma, *Ann. Int. Med.* **26,** 521 (1947). [17

POLI, E., Patogenesi dell'idrotorace nei cardiopatici, *Cuore e circolaz.* **20,** 635 (1936).

POLI, E., Ricerche di fisiomeccanica respiratoria nei cardiopatici, *Arch. per le sc. med.* **65,** 803 (1938a). [13, 14, 15, 16, 17

POLI, E., Hypotensiver Pneumothorax und dekompensierte Herzkrankheiten mit Lungenstauung, *Klin. Wchnschr.* **17,** 919 (1938b). [13, 14, 15, 16

PORTER, R. B., and R. S. DOWNS, Some physiological observations on the circulation during recovery from vitamin B_1 deficiency, *Ann. Int. Med.* **17,** 645 (1942). [17

RABINOWITCH, I. M., The output of the heart per beat in heart disease, *Arch. Int. Med.* **36,** 239 (1925). [17

RAHN, H., and D. HAMMOND, Vital capacity at reduced barometric pressure, *J. Appl. Physiol.* **4,** 715 (1952).

RICHARDS, D. G. B., A. G. W. WHITFIELD, W. M. ARNOTT, and J. A. H. WATERHOUSE, The lung volume in low output cardiac syndromes, *Brit. Heart J.* **13,** 381 (1951). [13, 14, 15, 16, 17

RICHARDS, D. W., JR., and A. L. BARACH, Prolonged residence in high oxygen atmospheres. Effects on normal individuals and on patients with chronic cardiac and pulmonary insufficiency, *Quart. J. Med.* **3,** 437 (1934). [17

ROBB, G. P., and S. WEISS, The role of the pulmonary circulation in the dyspnoea of circulatory failure and of hyperthyroidism, *J. Clin. Investigation* **11**, 823 (1932).   [14, 17

ROBB, G. P., and S. WEISS, The velocity of pulmonary and peripheral venous blood flow and related aspects of the circulation in cardiovascular disease. Their relation to clinical types of circulatory failure, *Am. Heart J.* **9**, 742 (1934).   [17

ROMANOFF, M., Experimente über Beziehungen zwischen Atmung und Kreislauf, *Arch. f. exper. Path. u. Pharmakol.* **64**, 183 (1911).

RUBOW, V., Untersuchungen über die Atmung bei Herzkrankheiten. Ein Beitrag zum Studium der Pathologie des kleinen Kreislaufes, *Deutsches Arch. f. klin. Med.* **92**, 255 (1908).   [13, 14, 15, 16, 17, 18

SCHALM, L., and W. A. H. HOOGENBOOM, Blood bilirubin in congestive heart failure, *Am. Heart J.* **44**, 571 (1952).   [17

SIEBECK, R., Über die Beeinflussung der Atemmechanik durch krankhafte Zustände des Respirations- und Kreislaufapparates, *Deutsches Arch. f. klin. Med.* **100**, 204 (1910).   [13, 14, 15, 16, 17, 18

SIEBECK, R., Die funktionelle Bedeutung der Atemmechanik und die Lungenventilation bei kardialer Dyspnoe, *Deutsches Arch. f. klin. Med.* **107**, 252 (1912).   [13

STEWART, H. J., and A. E. COHN, Studies on the effect of the action of digitalis on the output of blood from the heart. III. Part 2. The effect on the output of hearts in heart failure with congestion, in human beings, *J. Clin. Investigation* **11**, 933 (1932).   [17

STEWART, H. J., N. F. CRANE, R. F. WATSON, C. H. WHEELER, and J. E. DEITRICK, The cardiac output in congestive heart failure and in organic heart disease, *Ann. Int. Med.* **13**, 2323 (1940).   [17

STEWART, H. J., J. E. DEITRICK, N. F. CRANE, and C. H. WHEELER, Action of digitalis in uncompensated heart disease, *Arch. Int. Med.* **62**, 569 (1938).   [17

SUTTON, F. C., J. A. BRITTON, and J. G. CARR, Estimation of cardiopulmonary functional capacity by means of oxygen debt studies, *Am. Heart J.* **20**, 423 (1940).   [17

TAQUINI, A. C., and B. B. LOZADA, Corazón pulmonar cronico con y sin insuficiencia cardiaca. Funciones respiratoria y circulatoria, *Medicina* **8**, 325 (1948).   [13, 17

WEISS, S., G. P. ROBB, and H. L. BLUMGART, The velocity of blood flow in health and disease as measured by the effect of histamine on the minute vessels, *Am. Heart J.* **4**, 664 (1928–29).   [17

WEISS, S., and R. W. WILKINS, The nature of the cardiovascular disturbances in nutritional deficiency states, *Ann. Int. Med.* **11**, 104 (1937).   [17

WERKÖ, L., and H. LAGERLÖF, Studies on the circulation of blood in man. VII. The effect of a single intravenous dose of theophylline diethanol-amine on the cardiac output, pulmonary blood volume and systemic and pulmonary blood pressures in hypertensive cardiovascular disease, *Scandinav. J. Clin. & Lab. Investigation* **1**, 181 (1949).   [17

WILSON, R. H., C. W. BORDEN, R. V. EBERT, and H. S. WELLS, A comparison of the effect of voluntary hyperventilation in normal persons, patients with pulmonary emphysema, and patients with cardiac disease, *J. Lab. & Clin. Med.* **36**, 119 (1950).   [13, 14, 15, 16, 17

10. *Respiratory Dynamics. Mixing in the Lungs*

The earliest clinical evidences of congestive failure are in most instances associated with altered respiratory dynamics during exertion; as the severity of decompensation becomes more marked. these changes become apparent even when the patient is at rest.

The alterations of pulmonary function that occur in moderately or severely decompensated cardiac patients at rest include increased respiratory rate (Campbell, 1934; Harrison *et al.*, 1932; Peabody, 1917; **19**) and respiratory minute volume (Beddard and Pembrey, 1908; Espersen, 1941; McMichael, 1939; **20**). Oxygen consumption is often increased in patients with cardiac decompensation (page 214), but the increase in respiratory minute volume is proportionately greater, often very much so (Herbst, 1928; Jansen *et al.*, 1932; **21**). Respiration is usually found to be shallow (Campbell, 1934; Knipping *et al.*, 1932*a, b*; Peabody, 1917; **22**), although Boyer and Bailey (1943) found it normal in depth and Thiel (1930) described it as increased. The shallowness of the respiration is reflected in the low carbon dioxide content of expired air (Barr and Peters, 1920; Boyer and Bailey, 1943; Campbell and Poulton, 1927; Apjohn, 1830).

The decrease in tidal air volume is really more serious than the measurements indicate. For instance, a patient whose tidal air volume is normally 500 cc. and in whom it falls to 350 cc. during a period of decompensation apparently has a decrease in tidal air of only 30 per cent. Actually, however, since somewhat more than 100 cc. of inspired air is used to wash out the airways that do not function in respiratory exchange, the figures for effective tidal air would be less than 400 cc. in the normal and 250 cc. in the decompensated state, a difference of 40 percent or more. The increase in respiratory minute volume at rest is therefore more apparent than real, and in many instances the *effective* minute volume respiration must be smaller or at least no larger than normal. Expiration is prolonged (Thiel, 1930; Gross, 1943; Heyer, 1946; Plotz, 1947; Gottsegen, 1951) and the velocity and pressure of expiration are low. Shallowness of respiration in congestive failure is the consequence of several factors. (i) Increased rigidity of the lungs makes inspiration more laborious and prolongs expiration; the latter is normally purely passive, but in some cardiac patients active muscular effort is required. (ii) The lessened negativity of the intrapleural pressure which obtains in chronic cardiac decompensation makes inspiration less effective. (iii) The diaphragm is often flattened in congestive failure, so that its excursions are limited. (iv) Reflexes from the congested lung and elsewhere may cause rapid shallow respiration (page 97). (v) The movements of the diaphragm may be limited by pleural effusions or abdominal distention. Accordingly, it is to be expected that factors that normally might increase tidal air volume, such as anoxia (Graybiel *et al.*, 1937) or hypercarbia (Peabody, 1915, 1917), will, in decompensated cardiacs, act largely by increasing the rate instead, as these authors have shown.

Effect of exercise.—The respiratory rate shows a greater than normal rise during exercise in cardiac patients (Kaltreider and McCann, 1937; Bendixen, 1931; Dennig and Prodger, 1933; Engelhard, 1927; Harrison *et al.*, 1932), as does the respiratory minute volume also (Campbell, 1934; Cullen *et al.*, 1931; Nielsen, 1937; Peabody and Sturgis, 1922; **23**); both return to normal after cessation of exercise more slowly than normal. With excessively severe exercise, the rise in respiratory minute volume may be abnormally low during effort but remains elevated for a greatly prolonged time (Landen and Ehringhaus, 1941); the total respiratory effort during and after such exercise is increased. The increase in respiratory minute volume is far in excess of the rise in oxygen consumption consequent to work, so that the ratio of respiratory minute volume to oxygen consumption, which is high in cardiac patients at rest, becomes larger (Herbst, 1928; Kaltreider and McCann, 1937; Knipping and Moncrieff, 1932; Wahlund, 1948; Denolin and Lequime, 1951; Zaeper *et al.*, 1939). The increase in minute volume respiration that occurs is largely the result of a rise in rate, for decompensated patients show a marked limitation of the degree to which the tidal air can increase during exercise (Bendixen, 1931; Campbell, 1934; Campbell and Sale, 1927; Dennig and Prodger, 1933; Mathieu et al., 1952; Kaltreider and McCann, 1937). Bendixen (1931) and Décourt et al. (1951) claimed that the ratio of maximal tidal air to vital capacity was normal in exercise in congestive failure, suggesting that the restriction of tidal air in exercise was merely a reflection of a lessened vital capacity. However, Campbell (1934) found it larger, and Engelhard (1927) smaller, than normal, so that attempts to attribute the lowered tidal air volumes of exercise in cardiacs solely to reduction of the vital capacity do not appear to be warranted. Increased rigidity of the lungs (page 78) explains the limited increase of tidal volume during exercise in cardiac patients in failure; the activity of reflexes arising in congested lungs and causing rapid shallow respiration does not appear to increase during exercise, but such reflexes may originate elsewhere. The maximal possible ventilation is of course considerably decreased in decompensated cardiacs (Jansen et al., 1932; Battro and Labourt, 1943; de Carrasco and Vorwerk, 1936; Engelhard, 1927; Wilson et al., 1950; Mathieu et al., 1952; Décourt et al., 1951), thereby limiting their activity greatly, for the difference between their high respiratory minute volumes at rest and their low maximal respiratory volume is small, that is, the "ventilation reserve" is low. Quantitative interpretations of the measured maximal ventilation should be made with caution; uncontrolled factors may introduce errors (Georg, 1952; Bernstein et al., 1952).

Cardiac patients with more severe degrees of dyspnea usually have a larger respiratory minute volume at rest and on exertion than those in whom dyspnea is less marked, but the correlation is poor. In general, the increase in respiratory minute volume which occurs at rest or during exertion in congestive failure is associated with the feeling of shortness of breath, but it does not explain the sensation of dyspnea; when increases of respiratory minute volume comparable to those observed in congestive failure are induced in normal subjects by exertion or inhalation of carbon dioxide, the subjects do not become dyspneic (Harrison et al., 1931; Peabody, 1917).

The abnormally great increase in respiratory activity manifested during exercise by decompensated cardiac patients may be consequent to a number of factors. Authors who ascribe dyspnea entirely to pulmonary congestion relate the increased respiration of cardiacs during exertion to the changes in the lungs, and point to the fact that patients with primary pulmonary disease also have an abnormally great respiratory response to exercise. Actually, however, the degree of increase in respiratory minute volume in decompensated cardiacs far exceeds that which occurs when patients with severe pulmonary disease exercise, so that other factors must be more important. The absence of further increase in circulation time (page 26) and of large additional decreases in vital capacity in exercising cardiac patients (page 80) suggests that increased congestion of the lungs is not severe. It is doubtful whether increased activity of reflexes from congested lungs during exertion is of importance, since the lungs do not appear to become more congested. Nor do reflexes arising in the great veins appear to be a factor (page 98). The large and persistent increase in respiration on exercise in congestive failure strikingly resembles the high and long curve of rise in blood lactic acid level which also occurs (page 121); the lactic acidosis is due to both arterial anoxia and lowered cardiac output. The importance of anoxia in the exertional hyperventilation of congestive failure is emphasized by the fact that patients with this disorder when made anoxic at rest hyperventilate more than do normal subjects under the same conditions (Graybiel et al., 1937; Landt and Benjamin, 1941). Inhalation of oxygen during exertion prevents excessive hyperventilation in congestive failure (Bolt et al., 1950; Rothkopf and Linxweiler, 1940). In addition, even normal subjects hyperventilate abnormally when performing work under anoxic conditions (Clark-Kennedy and Owen, 1926; Asmussen and Chiodi, 1941; Bruce et al., 1952; Nielsen, 1936). Impaired dispersal of the excess heat produced during exertion may be an additional factor causing increase in respiration. The breath-holding time is low in cardiac decompensation (Friedman, 1947); however, the fact that it may be lengthened by previous forced hyperventilation suggests that anoxia alone is not the mechanism responsible and that carbon dioxide is a factor.

Mixing. — Mixing in the lungs is abnormal in about half the cases reported (Bruns, 1910; Siebeck, 1912; Cournand et al., 1941; Comroe and Fowler, 1951; Fowler et al., 1952).

Bibliography

Chapter I — Section 10

Apjohn, J., Experiments relative to the acid carbonic of expired air in health and disease, *Dublin Hosp. Rep.* **5**, 525 (1830).

Asmussen, E., and H. Chiodi, The effect of hypoxemia on ventilation and circulation in man, *Am. J. Physiol.* **132**, 426 (1941).

Barach, A. L., The therapeutic use of oxygen in heart disease, *Ann. Int. Med.* **5**, 428 (1931). [20

Barach, A. L., and D. W. Richards, Jr., Effects of treatment with oxygen in cardiac failure, *Arch. Int. Med.* **48**, 325 (1931). [20

Barr, D. P., and J. P. Peters, Jr., Studies of the respiratory mechanism in cardiac dyspnea. III. The effective ventilation in cardiac dyspnea, *Am. J. Physiol.* **54**, 345 (1920). [19, 20, 22

Battro, A., and F. E. Labourt, Consideraciones sobre la determinacion de la ventilacion maxima, la reserva pulmonar y la hiperpnea de los cardiacos, *Rev. argent. de cardiol.* **10**, 83 (1943).

Beddard, A. P., and M. S. Pembrey, Observations on pulmonary ventilation in disease, *Brit. M. J.* **2**, 580 (1908). [20

Bendixen, H., Zur Funktionsprüfung des Herzens durch Dyspnoeversuche, *Ztschr. f. klin. Med.* **115**, 271 (1931).

Bernstein, L., J. L. D'Silva, and D. Mendel, The effect of the rate of breathing on the maximum breathing capacity determined with a new spirometer, *Thorax* **7**, 255 (1952).

Bolt, W., H. Valentin, and H. Neurath, Herzleistungsbreite der kardialen Linksinsuffizienz, *Ztschr. f. Kreislaufforsch.* **39**, 718 (1950). [20, 23

Boyer, P. K., and C. V. Bailey, Concentration of carbon dioxide in expired air in heart disease, *Arch. Int. Med.* **71**, 529 (1943). [19, 20

Bruce, R. A., F. W. Lovejoy, Jr., P. N. G. Yu, and M. E. McDowell, Observations of cardiorespiratory performance in normal subjects under unusual stress during exercise, *Arch. Indust. Hyg. & Occupat. Med.* **6**, 105 (1952).

Bruns, O., Die Bedeutung der spirometrischen Untersuchung von Emphysematiken und Herzkranken, *Med. Klin.* **6**, 1524 (1910).

Campbell, M., The respiratory exchange during exercise in heart disease III, *Quart. J. Med.* **27**, 369 (1934). [19, 20, 22, 23

Campbell, J. M. H., G. H. Hunt, and E. P. Poulton, An examination of the blood gases and respiration in disease, with reference to the cause of breathlessness and cyanosis, *J. Path. & Bact.* **26**, 234 (1923). [20, 22

CAMPBELL, J. M. H., and E. P. POULTON, The effect on breathless subjects of residence in an oxygen chamber, *Quart. J. Med.* **20**, 141 (1926–27).
[20

CAMPBELL, J. M. H., and F. J. SALE, Effect of exercise on respiratory exchange in heart disease. II, *Arch. Int. Med.* **40**, 237 (1927).   [23

CHRISTIE, R. V., and J. C. MEAKINS, The intrapleural pressure in congestive heart failure and its clinical significance, *J. Clin. Investigation* **13**, 323 (1934).   [20, 22

CLARK-KENNEDY, A. E., and T. OWEN, The limitation of muscular effort and its relation to cardiac failure, *Quart. J. Med.* **20**, 383 (1926).

COMROE, J. H., and W. S. FOWLER, Lung function studies. VI. Detection of uneven alveolar ventilation during a single breath of oxygen, *Am. J. Med.* **10**, 408 (1951).

COURNAND, A., E. D. BALDWIN, R. C. DARLING, and D. W. RICHARDS, JR., Studies on intrapulmonary mixture of gases. IV. The significance of the pulmonary emptying rate and a simplified open circuit measurement of residual air, *J. Clin. Investigation* **20**, 681 (1941).

CULLEN, G. E., T. R. HARRISON, J. A. CALHOUN, W. E. WILKINS, and M. M. TIMS, Studies in congestive heart failure. XIII. The relation of dyspnea of exertion to the oxygen saturation and acid-base condition of the blood, *J. Clin. Investigation* **10**, 807 (1931).   [20, 23

DE CARRASCO, H. O., and W. VORWERK, Beitrag zur Lungen- und Herzfunktionsprüfung, *Arch. f. exper. Path. u. Pharmakol* **184**, 156 (1936).

DENNIG, H., and S. H. PRODGER, Herzkranke bei Arbeit, *Deutsches Arch. f. klin. Med.* **175**, 170 (1933).   [23

DENOLIN, H., and J. LEQUIME, Les modifications circulatoires dans le coeur pulmonaire chronique, *Arch. d. mal. du cœur* **44**, 391 (1951).
[23

ENGELHARD, A., Der Wert der Spirometrie für die Klinik der Herzkrankheiten mit Lungenstauung und ihr Ausbau zur einer Funktionsprüfung, *Arch. f. klin. Med.* **156**, 1 (1927).

EPPINGER, H., F. KISCH, and H. SCHWARZ, Arbeit und Kreislauf, *Klin. Wchnschr.* **4**, 1101 (1925).   [20, 21

ESPERSEN, T., Studies of the cardiac output and related circulatory functions, especially in patients with congestive heart failure, *Acta med. Scandinav.* **108**, 153 (1941).   [20

ESPERSEN, T., Congestive heart failure, oxygen consumption and lung ventilation, *Acta med. Scandinav.* **108**, 183 (1941).   [20

FOWLER, W. S., E. R. CORNISH, JR., and S. KETY, Lung function studies. VIII. Analysis of alveolar ventilation by pulmonary N_2 clearance curves, *J. Clin. Investigation* **31**, 40 (1952).

FRIEDMAN, M., Studies concerning the etiology and pathogenesis of neurocirculatory asthenia. V. The introduction of a new test for the diagnosis and assessment of the syndrome, *Psychosom. Med.* **9,** 242 (1947).

GEORG, J., Pulmonary function tests, *Scandinav. J. Clin. & Lab. Investigation* **4,** 327 (1952).

GOTTSEGEN, G., Vitalkapazität und Herzinsuffizienz. II Mitt. Ueber Adrenalin und Stophanthineffekte, *Cardiologia* **19,** 174 (1951).

GRASSMANN, W., and F. HERZOG, Die Wirkung von Digitalis (Strophanthin) auf das Minuten- und Schlagvolumen des Herzkranken, *Arch. f. exper. Path. u. Pharmakol,* **163,** 97 (1932). [20

GRAYBIEL, A., W. MISSIURO, D. B. DILL, and H. T. EDWARDS, Experimentally induced asphyxiation in cardiac patients, with especial reference to certain hazards in air travel and to the use of asphyxiation as a cardiac functional test, *J. Aviation Med.* **8,** 178 (1937).

GROSS, D., Investigations concerning vital capacity, *Am. Heart J.* **25,** 335 (1943).

GROSSMAN, J., R. E. WESTON, and L. LEITER, A method for determining cardiac output by the direct Fick principle without gas analysis, *J. Clin. Investigation* **32,** 161 (1953). [21

HARRIS, I., and I. J. LIPKIN, Cardiac output and oxygen utilization in some types of heart disease, *Edinburgh M. J.* **38,** 501 (1931). [23

HARRISON, T. R., B. FRIEDMAN, and H. RESNIK, Mechanism of acute experimental heart failure, *Arch. Int. Med.* **57,** 927 (1936). [20

HARRISON, T. R., W. G. HARRISON, JR., J. A. CALHOUN, and J. P. MARSH, Congestive heart failure. XVII. The mechanism of dyspnea on exertion, *Arch. Int. Med.* **50,** 690 (1932). [19, 20, 23

HARRISON, T. R., and C. PILCHER, Studies in congestive failure. II. The respiratory exchange during and after exercise, *J. Clin. Investigation* **8,** 291 (1929–30). [20, 23

HARRISON, T. R., F. C. TURLEY, E. JONES, and J. A. CALHOUN, Congestive heart failure. X. The measurement of ventilation as a test of cardiac function, *Arch. Int. Med.* **148,** 377 (1931). [20

HERBST, R., Der Gasstoffwechsel als Mass der körperlichen Leistungsfähigkeit. III. Untersuchungen am Herzkranken, *Deutsches Arch. f. klin. Med.* **162,** 257 (1928). [20, 21

HEYER, H. E., Abnormalities of the respiratory pattern in patients with cardiac dyspnea, *Am. Heart J.* **32,** 457 (1946).

JANSEN, K., H. W. KNIPPING, and K. STROMBERGER, Klinische Untersuchungen über Atmung und Blutgase, *Beitr. z. Klin. d. Tuberk.* **80,** 304 (1932). [20, 21

KALTREIDER, N. L., and W. S. McCANN, Respiratory response during exercise in pulmonary fibrosis and emphysema, *J. Clin. Investigation* **16,** 23 (1937). [19, 20, 23

KATZ, L. N., W. W. HAMBURGER, and S. H. RUBINFELD, Observations on the effects of oxygen therapy. II. Changes in the circulation and respiration, *Am. J. M. Sc.* **184**, 810 (1932). [20

KININMONTH, J. G., The circulation rate in some pathological states, with observations on the effect of digitalis, *Quart. J. Med.* **21**, 277 (1928). [20

KNIPPING, H. W., W. LEWIS, and A. MONCRIEFF, Ueber die Dyspnoe, *Beitr. z. Klin. d. Tuberk.* **79**, 1 (1932a). [19, 20, 21, 22

KNIPPING, H. W., and A. MONCRIEFF, The ventilation equivalent for oxygen, *Quart. J. Med.* **1**, 17 (1932b). [20, 21, 23

LANDEN, H. C., and H. EHRINGHAUS, Beitrag zur Arbeitsatmung des Herzkranken, *Ztschr. f. d. ges. exper. Med.* **109**, 242 (1941). [23

LANDT, H., and J. E. BENJAMIN, Changes in the content of carbon dioxide in venous blood during rebreathing experiments. Comparison of change in persons with a normal heart and in patients with cardiac disease, *Arch, Int. Med.* **67**, 72 (1941).

LIAN, C., BARAIGE, DANHIER, and J. DESCLAUX, Le coefficient de ventilation pulmonaire d'effort (épreuve fonctionelle d'aptitude respiratoire à l'effort), *Presse méd.* **48**, 993 (1940). [23

McMICHAEL, J., Hyperpnoea in heart failure, *Clin. Sc.* **4**, 19 (1939). [20, 21

NIELSEN, H. E., Clinical investigations into the cardiac output of patients with compensated heart disease during rest and during muscular work, *Acta med. Scandinav.* **91**, 223 (1937). [23

NIELSEN, M., Untersuchungen über die Atemregulation beim Menschen, *Skandinav. Arch. f. Physiol.* **74**, Supp. 10, 85 (1936).

NYLIN, G., Clinical tests of the function of the heart, *Acta med. Scandinav. Supp. No. 52*, 1 (1933). [23

PEABODY, F. W., Clinical studies on the respiration. I. The effect of carbon dioxide in the inspired air on patients with cardiac disease, *Arch. Int. Med.* **16**, 846 (1915).

PEABODY, F. W., Clinical studies of the respiration. III. A mechanical factor in the production of dyspnea in patients with cardiac disease, *Arch. Int. Med.* **20**, 433 (1917). [19, 22

PEABODY, F. W., and C. C. STURGIS, Clinical studies on respiration. IX. The effect of exercise on the metabolism, heart rate, and pulmonary ventilation of normal subjects and patients with heart disease, *Arch. Int. Med.* **29**, 277 (1922). [22, 23

PEABODY, F. W., J. A. WENTWORTH, and B. I. BARKER, Clinical Studies on the respiration. V. The basal metabolism and the minute volume of the respiration of patients with cardiac disease, *Arch. Int. Med.* **20**, 468 (1917). [19, 20, 22

PEARCE, R. G., The cardiorespiratory mechanism in health and disease, *Arch. Int. Med.* **27**, 139 (1921).   [20

PLESCH, J., Die pathologische Physiologie des Lungenvolumens und seine Beziehung zum Kreislauf, *Ztschr. f. exper. Path. u. Pharmakol.* **13**, 165 (1913).   [19

PLOTZ, M., Bronchial spasm in cardiac asthma, *Ann. Int. Med.* **26**, 521 (1947).

POLI, E., Ricerche di fisiomeccanica respiratoria nei cardiopatici, *Arch. per le sc. med.* **65**, 803 (1938).   [19, 20, 22

RICHARDS, D. W., JR., and A. L. BARACH, Prolonged residence in high oxygen atmospheres. Effects on normal individuals and on patients with chronic cardiac and pulmonary insufficiency, *Quart. J. Med.* **3**, 437 (1934).   [20

RIGONI, M., Il ricambio respiratorio, la portata circolatoria e la gittata systolica nelle cardiopatie compensate e nello scompenso di circolo. I. Metabolismo basale, ventilazione polmonare e tensione dei gas alveolari, *Cuore e circolaz.* **21**, 157 (1937).   [20, 21

ROTHKOPF, H., and K. LINXWEILER, Ueber Zusatzgutachten zur Beurteilung von Lunge, Herz und Kreislauf mit Hilfe von Spirographie und Ergometrie, *Beitr. z. Klin. d. Tuberk.* **94**, 309 (1940).   [23

SIEBECK, R., Die funktionelle Bedeutung der Atemmechanik und die Lungenventilation bei kardialer Dyspnoe, *Deutsches Arch. f. klin. Med.* **107**, 252 (1912).

TAQUINI, A. C., and B. B. LOZADA, Corazón pulmonar cronico con y sin insuficiencia cardiaca. Funciones respiratoria y circulatoria, *Medicina* **8**, 325 (1948).   [20

THIEL, K., Pneumotachographische Studien. II. Die kardiale Dyspnoe, *Deutsches Arch. f. klin. Med.* **167**, 208 (1930).   [19, 20

THOMAS, D., Das sogennante erregbare Soldatenherz, *Deutsche med. Wchnschr.* **66**, 989 (1940).   [23

WAHLUND, H., Determination of the physical working capacity. A physiological and clinical study with special reference to standardization of cardio-pulmonary function tests, *Acta med. Scandinav. Suppl.*, 215 (1948).   [19, 20, 21

WERKÖ, L., and H. LAGERLÖF, Studies on the circulation in man. VII. The effect of a single intravenous dose of theophylline diethanolamine on the cardiac output, pulmonary blood volume and systemic and pulmonary blood pressures in hypertensive cardiovascular disease, *Scandinav. J. Clin. & Lab. Investigation* **1**, 181 (1949).   [20

WILSON, R. H., C. W. BORDEN, R. V. EBERT, and H. S. WELLS, A comparison of the effect of voluntary hyperventilation in normal persons, patients with pulmonary emphysema, and patients with cardiac disease, *J. Lab. & Clin. Med.* **36**, 119 (1950).

ZAEPER, G., Ueber Bedeutung und Verwertung arbeitsphysiologischer Erkenntnisse in der Klinik der Lungen- und Kreislauferkrankungen, *Deutsches Arch. f. klin. Med.* **186**, 1 (1940).   [23

ZAEPER, G., H. HAEBISCH, A. CRANEFOD, and W. WOLF, Zur Charakterisierung bestimmter Formen von cardialer Arbeitsinsufficienz durch Arbeitatmung, *Klin. Wchnschr.* **18**, 270 (1939).   [23

11. *Reflexes from the Lungs and Great Veins*

Drinker, Peabody and Blumgart (1922) found that congestion of the lungs induced in animals by clamping the pulmonary veins was associated with an immediate increase in respiratory rate. Underhill (1921) and Haggart and Walker (1923) also noted immediate increases in respiration when branches of the pulmonary artery were ligated, even though no change in cardiac output occurred; a marked increase in pulmonary arterial pressure was noted in these experiments. Heymans and Heymans (1927) reported that in dogs whose isolated heads were maintained by means of cross circulation with other dogs, the production of increased pressure in the heart and lungs gave rise to hyperpnea of the heads connected to their respective lungs only by nerve pathways, at least under some conditions. All these results suggest that the respiratory changes observed might have been consequent to some reflex from the pulmonary vascular bed. The fact that such reflexes exist was not, however, established until 1929, when Churchill and Cope (1929) reported experiments in which engorgement of the pulmonary vessels was induced in a lung completely isolated from the body except for its nerves. These observers clamped the artery and vein to that lung and then injected varying amounts of fluid into the pulmonary vessels; rapid shallow respiration resulted, which could be terminated by withdrawal of the injected fluid. The results of these experiments were corroborated by Harrison, Calhoun *et al.* (1932), who also showed that the response was abolished by section of the vagus nerve. Daly *et al.* (1937) also showed that the hyperpnea induced by increasing pulmonary inflow likewise was abolished by vagal section. The work of Aviado *et al.* (1951) indicates that the reflex is activated by sensitive structures in the neighborhood of venules. The work of Walsh (1946) suggests that fibers attached to vessels, and not fibers sensitive to parenchymal stretching, are involved. Whether this reflex remains active during long periods of continuous stimulation is not known. It must be borne in mind that raising pulmonary arterial or capillary pressures slightly in normal man by means of intravenous infusions does not cause dyspnea (Doyle *et al.*, 1951).

It has been supposed for many years that the abnormal rigidity of the lungs that develops in patients with congestive failure is in itself a cause of dyspnea or at least hyperpnea. Many authors have expressed the belief that this impaired collapsibility of the lungs activates the Hering-Breuer reflex, thereby causing rapid shallow breathing. This point of view has been stressed chiefly by Christie (1938). Recent work in animals by Bülbring and Whitteridge (1945) appears to negate this concept, although other work supports it (Larrabee and Knowlton, 1946). It is impossible at present to arrive at a definite conclusion regarding the role of the Hering-Breuer reflex in the respiratory disturbances of cardiac decompensation.

The role of reflexes from the lungs in the genesis of dyspnea and hyperpnea of congestive failure is difficult to evaluate in general. That they are important in causing the respiratory manifestations associated with rapidly developing engorgement and edema in acute pulmonary edema seems to be established (page 319). In chronic cardiac decompensation, however, there is no certainty as to the part they play in dyspnea at rest. The *increased* dyspnea of exertion does not appear to depend primarily on pulmonary reflexes, for there is no evidence that greatly *increased* congestion of the lungs occurs during exercise (page 80).

Distention of the auricle was described by Harrison, Harrison *et al.*, (1932*a*, *b*) as a cause of reflex hyperventilation, but their experiments in animals have been criticized because slowing of the circulation through the brain probably also occurred. The results of Megibow *et al.* (1943) similarly do not establish the role of such mechanisms in dyspnea. The administration of large intravenous infusions in normal man may distend the veins and auricles greatly without giving rise to dyspnea or hyperpnea (Altschule and Gilligan, 1938; Altschule, Gilligan and Zamcheck, 1942; Warren *et al.*, 1948).

The above discussion deals with reflexes arising from changes in intravascular pressure or from parenchymal stretching in the lungs.

Reflexes activated by anoxia are generally considered only in relation to extrapulmonary structures, such as the carotid bodies. The work of Heymans and Heymans (1927) raises the possibility that structures sensitive to oxygen lack exist in the lungs as well, although the later work of Aviado et al. (1951) does not support any such concept.

Bibliography

Chapter I — Section 11

ALTSCHULE, M. D., and D. R. GILLIGAN, The effects on the cardiovascular system of fluids administered intravenously in man. II. The dynamics of the circulation, *J. Clin. Investigation* **17**, 401 (1938).

ALTSCHULE, M. D., D. R. GILLIGAN, and N. ZAMCHECK, The effects on the cardiovascular system of fluids administered intravenously in man. IV. The lung volume and pulmonary dynamics, *J. Clin. Investigation* **21**, 365 (1942).

AVIADO, D. M., JR., T. H. LI, W. KALOW, C. F. SCHMIDT, G. L. TURNBULL, G. W. PESKIN, M. E. HESS, and A. J. WEISS, Respiratory and circulatory reflexes from the perfused heart and pulmonary circulation of the dog, *Am. J. Physiol.* **165**, 261 (1951).

BÜLBRING, E., and D. WHITTERIDGE, The activity of vagal stretch endings during congestion in perfused lungs, *J. Physiol.* **103**, 477 (1945).

CHRISTIE, R. V., Dyspnoea: a review, *Quart. J. Med.* **31**, 421 (1938).

CHURCHILL, E. D., and O. COPE, The rapid shallow breathing resulting from pulmonary congestion and edema, *J. Exper. Med.* **49**, 531 (1929).

DALY, I. DE B., G. LUDANY, A. TODD, and E. B. VERNEY, Sensory receptors in the pulmonary vascular bed, *Quart. J. Exper. Physiol.* **27**, 123 (1937).

DOYLE, J. T., J. S. WILSON, E. H. ESTES, and J. V. WARREN, The effect of intravenous infusions of physiologic saline solution on the pulmonary arterial and pulmonary capillary pressure in man, *J. Clin. Investigation* **30**, 345 (1951).

DRINKER, C. K., F. W. PEABODY, and H. L. BLUMGART, The effect of pulmonary congestion on the ventilation of the lungs, *J. Exper. Med.* **35**, 77 (1922).

HAGGART, G. E., and A. M. WALKER, The physiology of pulmonary embolism as disclosed by quantitative occlusion of the pulmonary artery, *Arch. Surg.* **6**; 764 (1923).

HARRISON, T. R., J. A. CALHOUN, G. E. CULLEN, W. E. WILKINS, and C. Pilcher, Studies in congestive heart failure. XV. Reflex versus chemical factors in the production of rapid breathing, *J. Clin. Investigation* **11**, 133 (1932).

HARRISON, T. R., W. G. HARRISON, JR., J. A. CALHOUN, and J. P. MARSH, Congestive heart failure. XVII. The mechanism of dyspnea on exertion, *Arch. Int. Med.* **50**, 690 (1932a).

HARRISON, T. R., W. G. HARRISON, JR., and J. P. MARSH, Reflex stimulation of respiration from increase in venous pressure, *Am. J. Physiol.* **100**, 417 (1932b).

HEYMANS, J.-F., and C. HEYMANS, Stimulation et inhibition réflexes des mouvements respiratoires de la tête "isolée" du chien B dont le coeur-poumon "isolée" est perfusé par un chien C, *Compt. rend. Soc. de biol.* **95**, 1118 (1927).

LARRABEE, M. G., and G. C. KNOWLTON, Excitation and inhibition of phrenic motoneurones by inflation of the lungs, *Am. J. Physiol.* **147**, 90 (1946).

MEGIBOW, R. S., L. N. KATZ, and M. FEINSTEIN, Kinetics of respiration in experimental pulmonary embolism, *Arch. Int. Med.* **71**, 536 (1943).

UNDERHILL, S. W. F., An investigation into the circulation through the lungs, *Brit. M. J.* **2**, 779 (1921).

WALSH, E. G., Vagal nerve fibre activity following multiple pulmonary embolism, *J. Physiol.* **106**, 466 (1946).

WARREN, J. V., E. S. BRANNON, H. S. WEEMS, and E. A. STEAD, JR., Effect of increasing the blood volume and right atrial pressure on the circulation of normal subjects by intravenous infusion, *Am. J. Med.* **4**, 193 (1948).

12. *Arterial and Venous Blood Oxygen. Arteriovenous Oxygen Difference*

Many observers who have studied the arterial blood oxygen saturation in patients with chronic cardiac decompensation (Harrop, 1919; 24) report values that are somewhat below normal in some or many of their patients; a few describe consistently normal values (Eppinger et al., 1926; 25). When a diminished arterial oxygen saturation occurs in uncomplicated congestive failure, the values usually lie above 85 per cent. During exercise little or no change in arterial blood oxygen saturation occurs in patients with cardiac failure (Himwich and Loebel, 1927; Cullen et al., 1931; Eppinger et al., 1926); patients with severe pulmonary disease usually show a fall. The decreases in saturation below the normal lower limit of 94 per cent which are found in patients with cardiac decompensation, though apparently small, are of importance, since they occur in a portion of the dissociation curve where small changes in saturation are associated with large changes in tension. In normal individuals the circulatory response to anoxia is increased cardiac output and more rapid blood flow (Asmussen and Chiodi, 1941; Davis, 1944; **26**) in all parts of the body except possibly the hands (Abramson *et al.*, 1943; Freeman *et al.*, 1936; Gellhorn and Steck, 1938), so that at least a partial compensation occurs and the effects of anoxia are mitigated. In decompensated cardiac patients, however, no such increase in blood flow occurs, to judge from the results of the work of Landt and Benjamin (1938), Doyle *et al.* (1952), Grossman *et al.* (1953), and Westcott *et al.* (1951). If an increase in cardiac output did occur, it would constitute an additional source of strain in patients with hearts already damaged. Moreover, it appears that the respiratory center in cardiac patients in failure is hypersensitive to oxygen lack (Landt and Benjamin, 1941; Graybiel *et al.*, 1937) and therefore small changes in arterial blood oxygen saturation should aggravate dyspnea. Additional evidence of the importance of the apparently mild degree of arterial anoxemia that occurs in cardiac decompensation is afforded by data on the effects of oxygen therapy. Relief of symptoms, when it occurs, is usually associated with an elevation of the level of arterial blood oxygen saturation to or toward normal (Barach and Richards, 1931; Barach and Woodwell, 1921*a*; Cohn *et al.*, 1932; Richards and Barach, 1934; Schoen and Derra, 1930; Penneys, 1952); venous blood oxygen content also rises (Barach and Woodwell, 1921*a*).

Pulmonary factors are for the most part responsible for lowered arterial blood oxygen saturations in patients with cardiac decompensation not associated with congenital heart disease. These factors include inefficient respiration, impaired mixing in the lungs, edema of the alveolar walls and, in some instances of severe mitral stenosis, organic changes in the alveoli (page 412). Tachypnea, of whatever origin, may also lower the arterial blood oxygen saturation (Meakins, 1920, 1922; Meakins and Davies, 1920; Barach and Woodwell, 1921*b*). Hellems *et al.* (1949) reported the finding of normal oxygen saturation of pulmonary capillary blood in two patients with cardiac decompensation; further studies are desirable.

The strikingly low oxygen content of the peripheral venous blood in chronic congestive failure has been known for several decades and has been observed by many authors (Harrop, 1919; Lundsgaard, 1918*a,b,c*; **27**); Harrison and Pilcher (1929) found no deviation from the normal. Low jugular venous blood saturations were found by McMichael (1939), Himwich and Fazekas (1944), Moyer *et al.* (1952), and Raab (1931). These observations may be significant with respect to the origin of dyspnea. Novack *et al.* (1953) found normal jugular oxygen contents in patients partially treated but still in failure. The renal (page 160) and hepatic (page 194) venous oxygen contents are likewise low in untreated cardiac decompensation. The lowered venous blood oxygen levels are consequent to decreased cardiac output relative to the oxygen consumption of the tissues. During exercise the inability of the cardiac output to increase in proportion to the increased needs of the body (page 10) results in a further fall in oxygen content of the venous blood; this is particularly striking in the exercising limb, where the levels may approach zero (Weiss and Ellis, 1935).

The fall in venous blood oxygen is more constantly found and more marked than in the arterial blood oxygen; consequently the arteriovenous oxygen difference is increased. The venous blood oxygen level is a better indicator of the state of the tissues than is the arterial.

Bibliography

Chapter I — Section 12

ABRAMSON, D. I., H. LANDT, and J. E. BENJAMIN, Peripheral vascular response to acute anoxia, *Arch. Int. Med.* **71**, 583 (1943).   [26

ANGELINO, P. F., and A. ACTIS-DATO, La gasometria del sangue venoso renale e le pressioni venose renale studiate mediante cateterismo in soggetti normali, cardiopatici e in altre forme morbose, *Cuore e circolaz.* **35**, 283 (1951).   [24

ASMUSSEN, E., and H. CHIODI, The effect of hypoxemia on ventilation and circulation in man, *Am. J. Physiol.* **132**, 426 (1941).   [26

ASMUSSEN, E., and F. C. CONSOLAZIO, The circulation in rest and work on Mount Evans (4300 m.), *Am. J. Physiol.* **132**, 555 (1941).   [26

BARACH, A. L., The therapeutic use of oxygen in heart disease, *Ann. Int. Med.* **5**, 428 (1931).   [24

BARACH, A. L., and D. W. RICHARDS, JR., Effects of treatment with oxygen in cardiac failure, *Arch. Int. Med.* **48**, 325 (1931).   [24

BARACH, A. L., and M. N. WOODWELL, Studies in oxygen therapy with determinations of the blood gases. I. In cardiac insufficiency and related conditions, *Arch. Int. Med.* **28**, 367 (1921a).   [24

BARACH, A. L., and M. N. WOODWELL, Studies in oxygen therapy. III. In an extreme type of shallow breathing occurring in lethargic encephalitis, *Arch. Int. Med.* **28**, 421 (1921b).

BLEGEN, E., and K. AAS, Renal blood flow and glomerular filtration rate in patients with valvular heart disease, *Acta med. Scandinav.* **138**, 391 (1950).   [26

BRIGGS, A. P., D. M. FOWELL, W. F. HAMILTON, J. W. REMINGTON, N. C. WHEELER, and J. A. WINSLOW, Renal and circulatory factors in the edema formation of congestive heart failure, *J. Clin. Investigation* **27**, 810 (1948).   [24, 27

BROD, J., and Z. FEJFAR, The origin of oedema in heart failure, *Quart. J. Med.* **19**, 187 (1950).   [24

CAMPBELL, J. M. H., G. H. HUNT, and E. P. POULTON, An examination of the blood gases and respiration in disease, with reference to the cause of breathlessness and cyanosis, *J. Path. & Bact.* **26**, 234 (1923).   [24

CHRISTIE, R. V., and J. C. MEAKINS, The intrapleural pressure in congestive heart failure and its clinical significance, *J. Clin. Investigation* **13**, 323 (1934).   [24

COBET, R., Ueber die Wasserstoffzahl des Blutes bei Herzkranken, *Deutsches Arch. f. klin. Med.* **144**, 126 (1924).   [24

COHN, D. J., L. N. KATZ, S. SOSKIN, and W. W. HAMBURGER, Observations on the effects of oxygen therapy. III. Blood chemical changes, *Am. J. M. Sc.* **184**, 818 (1932).   [24

COSSIO, P., and I. BERCONSKY, The cyanosis in mitral stenosis, *Am. Heart J.* **17**, 1 (1939).   [24, 27

COURNAND, A., E. D. BALDWIN, R. C. DARLING, and D. W. RICHARDS, JR., Studies on intrapulmonary mixture of gases. IV. The significance of the pulmonary emptying rate and a simplified open circuit measurement of residual air, *J. Clin. Investigation* **20**, 681 (1941).   [24

CULLEN, G. E., T. R. HARRISON, J. A. CALHOUN, W. E. WILKINS, and M. M. TIMS, Studies in congestive heart failure. XIII. The relation of dyspnea of exertion to the oxygen saturation and acid-base condition of the blood, *J. Clin. Investigation* **10**, 807 (1931).   [25

DAUTREBANDE, L., Contribution à l'étude physiopathologique et thérapeutique des troubles circulatoires dans l'asystolie, *Arch. internat. de méd. expér.* **2**, 413 (1926).   [27

DAVIS, B. D., The indirect measurement of mean venous oxygen tension during anoxia, *J. Clin. Investigation* **23**, 666 (1944).   [26

DOYLE, J. T., J. S. WILSON, and J. V. WARREN, The pulmonary vascular responses to short-term hypoxia in human subjects, *Circulation* **5**, 263 (1952).   [26

EICHNA, L., S. J. FARBER, A. R. BERGER, D. P. EARLE, B. RADER, E. PELLE- GRINO, R. E. ALBERT, J. D. ALEXANDER, H. TAUBE, and S. YOUNG- WIRTH, The interrelationship of the cardiovascular, renal and electro- lyte effects of intravenous digoxin in congestive heart failure, *J. Clin. Investigation* **30**, 1250 (1951).   [24

EICHNA, L., S. J. FARBER, A. R. BERGER, D. P. EARLE, B. RADER, E. PELLE- GRINO, R. E. ALBERT, J. D. ALEXANDER, H. TAUBE, and S. YOUNG- WIRTH, Cardiovascular dynamics, blood volumes, renal functions and electrolyte excretions in the same patients during congestive heart failure and after recovery of cardiac decompensation, *Circulation* **7**, 674 (1953).   [24

EDELMAN, I. S., B. W. ZWEIFACH, D. J. W. ESCHER, J. GROSSMAN, R. MOKOTOFF, R. E. WESTON, L. LEITER, and E. SHORR, Studies on VEM and VDM in blood in relation to renal hemodynamics and renal oxygen extraction in chronic congestive heart failure, *J. Clin. Investigation* **29**, 925 (1950).   [24, 26

EPPINGER, H., F. KISCH, and H. SCHWARZ, Der Einfluss körperlicher Arbeit auf die Sauerstoffsättigung und auf die aktuelle Reaktion des Arte- rienblutes bei Kreislaufkranken, *Klin. Wchnschr.* **5**, 1316 (1926).   [25

ERSHLER, I., C. E. KOSSMAN, and M. S. WHITE, Venous pressure and cir- culation time during acute progressive anoxia in man, *Am. J. Physiol.* **138**, 593 (1943).   [26

EVANS, J. M., H. J. ZIMMERMAN, J. G. WILMER, L. J. THOMAS, and C. B. ETHRIDGE, Altered liver function of chronic congestive heart failure, *Am. J. Med.* **13**, 705 (1952).   [24

EWIG, W., and K. HINSBERG, Kreislaufstudien. II, *Ztschr. f. klin. Med.* **115**, 693 (1931).   [25

FISHMAN, A. P., M. H. MAXWELL, C. H. CROWDER, and P. MORALES, Kidney function in cor pulmonale. Particular consideration of changes in renal hemodynamics and sodium excretion during variation in level of oxygenation, *Circulation* **3**, 703 (1951).   [26

FOWLER, N. O., Cardiac catheterization in the diagnosis of adult heart disease, *Ann. Int. Med.* **38**, 478 (1953).   [25

FRASER, F. R., Goulstonian lectures on cardiac dyspnoea, *Lancet* **1**, 529, 589, 643 (1927).   [24

FRASER, F. R., C. F. HARRIS, R. HILTON, and G. C. LINDER, Arterial carbon dioxide pressure in cardiac dyspnoea, *Quart. J. Med.* **22**, 1 (1928).   [24

FREEMAN, N. W., J. L. SHAW, and J. C. SNYDER, The peripheral blood flow in surgical shock. The reduction in circulation through the hand resulting from pain, fear, cold, and asphyxia, with quantitative measurements of the volume flow of blood in clinical cases of surgical shock, *J. Clin. Investigation* **15**, 651 (1936).

GELLHORN, E., and I. E. STECK, The effect of the inhalation of gases with a low oxygen and an increased carbon dioxide tension on the peripheral blood flow in man, *Am. J. Physiol.* **124**, 735 (1938).

GIBBS, F. A., E. L. GIBBS, and W. G. LENNOX, Changes in human cerebral blood flow consequent on alterations in blood gases, *Am. J. Physiol.* **111**, 557 (1935).   [26

GODFREY, L., H. S. POND, and F. C. WOOD, The Millikan oximeter in the recognition and treatment of anoxemia in clinical medicine, *Am. J. Med. Sc.* **216**, 523 (1948).   [24

GRANT, S. B., Changes in the blood oxygen following therapeutic bleeding in cardiac patients, *J. Lab. & Clin. Med.* **9**, 160 (1923).   [24, 27

GRAYBIEL, A., W. MISSIURO, D. B. DILL, and H. T. EDWARDS, Experimentally induced asphyxiation in cardiac patients, with especial reference to certain hazards in air travel and to the use of asphyxiation as a cardiac functional test, *J. Aviation Med.* **8**, 178 (1937).

GROSSMAN, J., R. E. WESTON, and L. LEITER, A method for determining cardiac output by the direct Fick principle without gas analysis, *J. Clin. Investigation* **32**, 161 (1953).   [26

HARRISON, T. R., and C. PILCHER, Studies in congestive heart failure. I. The effect of edema on oxygen utilization, *J. Clin. Investigation* **8**, 259 (1929).   [25

HARROP, G. A., JR., The oxygen and carbon dioxide content of arterial and of venous blood in normal individuals and in patients with anemia and heart disease, *J. Exper. Med.* **30**, 241 (1919).   [24, 27

HEFTER, A. J., and D. F. OKUNEW, Ueber Veränderungen des peripheren Stoffwechsels im Zusammenhang mit den Blutkreislaufstörungen bei der Muskelarbeit, *Ztschr. f. d. ges. exper. Med.* **79**, 806 (1931).
                                                                              [25, 27

HELLEMS, H. K., F. W. HAYNES, and L. DEXTER, Pulmonary "capillary" pressure in man, *J. Appl. Physiol.* **2**, 24 (1949).   [24

HICK, F. K., A. W. CHRISTIAN, and P. W. SMITH, Criteria of oxygen want, with especial reference to neurocirculatory asthenia, *Am. J. M. Sc.* **194**, 800 (1937).   [24

HIMWICH, H. E., and J. E. FAZEKAS, The oxygen content of cerebral blood in patients with acute symptomatic psychoses and acute destructive brain lesions, *Am. J. Psychiat.* **100**, 648 (1944).

HIMWICH, H. E., and R. O. LOEBEL, The oxygen saturation of hemoglobin in the arterial blood of exercising patients, *J. Clin. Investigation* **5**, 113 (1927–28).   [24

HÜRTER, Untersuchungen am arteriellen menschlichen Blute, *Deutsches Arch. f. klin. Med.* **108**, 1 (1912).   [24

IHAYA, H., Studien über die Alveolarluft, Blutgase, Vitalkapazität und Minuten- und Schlagvolumen des Herzens bei Beriberi, Herzklappen-fehler und Pleuritis, *Mitt. d. med. Gesellsch. zu Tokyo* **48**, 2167 (1934).   [24

JANSEN, K., H. W. KNIPPING, and K. STROMBERGER, Klinische Unter-suchungen über Atmung und Blutgase, *Beitr. z. Klin. d. Tuberk.* **80**, 304 (1932).   [24, 27

KETY, S. S., and C. F. SCHMIDT, Effects of alterations in the arterial ten-sions of carbon dioxide and oxygen on cerebral blood flow and cerebral oxygen consumption of normal young men, *Federation Proc.* **5**, 55 (1946).   [26

KEYS, A., J. P. STAPP, and A. VIOLANTE, Responses in size, output and efficiency of the human heart to acute alteration in the composition of inspired air, *Am. J. Physiol.* **138**, 763 (1943).   [26

KORNFELD, F., Ueber Blutgase und Blutreaktion bei Dyspnoischen Zu-standen, *Ztschr. f. d. ges. exp. Med.* **38**, 289 (1923).   [24

KROETZ, C., Gasanalytische Untersuchungen über die Endothelfunktion der Lungen, *Verhandl. d. deutsch. Gesell. f. inn. Med.* **41**, 449 (1929).
                                                                            [24

KROETZ, C., Physiologische und pathologische Schwankungen der Sauer-stoffdurchlässigkeit der Lungen, *Verhandl. d. deutsch. Gesellsch. f. inn. Med.* **43**, 105 (1931).

LANDT, H., and J. E. BENJAMIN, Respiratory changes produced in the cardiac patient by rebreathing experiments as compared with those of the normal individual, *Am. Heart J.* **15**, 83 (1938).   [26

LANDT, H., and J. E. BENJAMIN, Changes in the content of carbon dioxide in venous blood during rebreathing experiments. Comparison of change in persons with a normal heart and in patients with cardiac disease, *Arch. Int. Med.* **67**, 72 (1941).   [27

LENNOX, W. G., and E. L. GIBBS, The blood flow in the brain and the leg of man, and the changes induced by alteration of the blood gases, *J. Clin. Investigation* **11**, 1155 (1932).   [26

LUNDSGAARD, C., Studies of oxygen in the venous blood. II. Studies of the oxygen unsaturation in the venous blood of a group of patients with circulatory disturbances, *J. Exper. Med.* **27**, 179 (1918a).   [27

LUNDSGAARD, C., Studies of oxygen in the venous blood. III. Determina-tions on five patients with compensated circulatory disturbances, *J. Exper. Med.* **27**, 199 (1918b).   [27

LUNDSGAARD, C., Studies of oxygen in the venous blood. IV. Determinations on five patients with incompensated circulatory disturbances, *J. Exper. Med.* **27,** 219 (1918*c*).   **[27**

MCGUIRE, J., R. N. WESTCOTT, and N. O. FOWLER, Anoxia and human pulmonary vascular resistance, *Tr. A. Am. Physicians* **64,** 404 (1951).
      [26

MCMICHAEL, J., Hyperpnoea in heart failure, *Clin. Sc.* **4,** 19 (1939).

MEAKINS, J., Harmful effects of shallow breathing with special reference to pneumonia, *Arch. Int. Med.* **25,** 1 (1920).

MEAKINS, J., The influence of circulatory disturbances on the gaseous exchange of the blood. I. The oxygen saturation of the arterial blood in tachycardia, *Heart,* **9,** 185 (1922).

MEAKINS, J., L. DAUTREBANDE, and W. J. FETTER, The influence of circulatory disturbances on the gaseous exchange of the blood. IV. The blood gases and circulation rate in cases of mitral stenosis, *Heart* **10,** 153 (1923).   **[25**

MEAKINS, J., and M. B. DAVIES, Observations on the gases in human arterial and venous blood, *J. Path. & Bact.* **23,** 451 (1920).

MEANS, J. H., and L. H. NEWBURGH, Studies of the blood flow by the method of Krogh and Lindhard, *Tr. A. Am. Physicians* **30,** 51 (1915).
      [27

MENEELY, G. R., and N. L. KALTREIDER, A study of the volume of blood in congestive heart failure. Relation to other measurements in fifteen patients, *J. Clin. Investigation* **22,** 521 (1943).   **[24**

MOYER, J. H., S. I. MILLER, A. B. TASHNEK, and R. BOWMAN, The effect of theophylline with ethylenediamine (aminophylline) on cerebral hemodynamics in the presence of cardiac failure with and without Cheyne-Stokes respiration, *J. Clin. Investigation* **31,** 267 (1952).

MYERS, J. D., and J. B. HICKAM, An estimation of the hepatic blood flow and splanchnic oxygen consumption in heart failure, *J. Clin. Investigation* **27,** 620 (1948).   **[24**

MYERSON, A., J. LOMAN, H. T. EDWARDS, and D. B. DILL, The composition of blood in the artery, in the internal jugular vein and in the femoral vein during oxygen want, *Am. J. Physiol.* **98,** 373 (1931).   **[26**

NOVACK, P., B. GOLUBOFF, L. BORTIN, A. SOFFE, and H. A. SHENKIN, Studies of the cerebral circulation and metabolism in congestive heart failure, *Circulation* **7,** 724 (1953).

PENNEYS, R., Studies with the Millikan oximeter at the bedside of patients with cardiac and pulmonary disease, *Bull. Johns Hopkins Hosp.* **90,** 192 (1952).   **[24**

PETERS, J. P., JR., and D. P. BARR, II. The carbon dioxide absorption curve and carbon dioxide tension of the blood in cardiac dyspnea, *J. Biol. Chem.* **45,** 537 (1921).   **[25**

PLATTS, M. M., The arterial blood gases in pulmonary heart failure, *Clin. Sc.* **12,** 63 (1953). [24

RAAB, W., Hirnblutuntersuchungen bei Hypertonie, *Ztschr. f. klin. Med.* **115,** 577 (1931).

RABINOWITCH, I. M., The output of the heart per beat in heart disease, *Arch. Int. Med.* **36,** 239 (1925). [24, 27

RASMUSSEN, H., and O. STORSTEIN, Studies in oxygen therapy. Part I. On the frequency of anoxemia, its occurrence in medical diseases and its relation to cyanosis, *Acta med. Scandinav.* **141,** 43 (1951). [24

RICHARDS, D. W., JR., Cardiac output by the catheterization technique in various clinical conditions, *Federation Proc.* **4,** 215 (1945). [24

RICHARDS, D. W., JR., and A. L. BARACH, Prolonged residence in high oxygen atmospheres. Effects on normal individuals and on patients with chronic cardiac and pulmonary insufficiency, *Quart. J. Med.* **3,** 437 (1934). [24

SCÉBAT, L., J. LENÈGRE, B. RANSON-BITKER, F. BENCHEMOUL, and J. DAMIEN, Etude des gaz du sang et du débit cardiaque dans les différents types de cardiopathies, *Arch. d. mal. du cœur* **46,** 18 (1953). [24

SCHALM, L., and W. A. H. HOOGENBOOM, Blood bilirubin in congestive heart failure, *Am. Heart J.* **44,** 571 (1952). [24

ROUGIER, G., and L. CABANES, Sur le débit cardiaque en altitude, *Compt. rend. Soc. de biol.* **143,** 1185 (1949). [26

SCARBOROUGH, W. R., R. PENNEYS, C. B. THOMAS, B. M. BAKER, and R. E. MASON, The cardiovascular effect of induced controlled anoxemia, *Circulation* **4,** 190 (1951). [26

SCHOEN, R., and E. DERRA, Untersuchungen über die Bedeutung der Zyanose als klinisches Symptom (I), *Deutsches Arch. f. klin. Med.* **168,** 52 (1930). [24

SCHWARTZ, B. A., and D. STATS, Oxygen saturation of sternal marrow blood in polycythemia, *J. Clin. Investigation* **28,** 736 (1949). [24

SHARPEY-SCHAFER, E. P., 2-Thiouracil in the treatment of congestive heart failure, *Brit. M. J.* **2,** 888 (1946). [24, 27

SHERLOCK, S., The liver in heart failure. Relation of anatomical, functional, and circulatory changes, *Brit. Heart J.* **13,** 273 (1951). [24

STARR, I., and M. MCMICHAEL, Oxygen transport, circulation and respiration in healthy subjects at simulated altitudes of 16,000–18,000 feet, *J. Appl. Physiol.* **1,** 430 (1948). [26

STEAD, E. A., JR., J. V. WARREN, and E. S. BRANNON, Cardiac output in congestive heart failure. An analysis of the reasons for the lack of close correlation between the symptoms of heart failure and the resting cardiac output, *Am. Heart J.* **35,** 529 (1948). [24

STEAD, E. A., JR., J. V. WARREN, and E. S. BRANNON, Effect of lanatoside C on the circulation of patients with congestive failure. A study using catheterization of the right side of the heart, *Arch. Int. Med.* **81**, 282 (1948). [24

WEISS, S., and L. B. ELLIS, Oxygen utilization and lactic acid production in the extremities during rest and exercise, in subjects with normal and in those with diseased cardiovascular systems, *Arch. Int. Med.* **55**, 665 (1935). [27

WESTCOTT, R. N., N. O. FOWLER, R. C. SCOTT, V. D. HAUENSTEIN, and J. McGUIRE, Anoxia and human pulmonary vascular resistance, *J. Clin. Invest.* **30**, 957 (1951). [26

WEZLER, K., and E. FRANK, Der Kreislauf im Sauerstoffmangel bei Behaglichkeitstemperatur, *Arch. f. d. ges. Physiol.* **250**, 249 (1948). [26

WILSON, R. H., C. W. BORDEN, R. V. EBERT, and H. S. WELLS, A comparison of the effect of voluntary hyperventilation in normal persons, patients with pulmonary emphysema, and patients with cardiac disease, *J. Lab. & Clin. Med.* **36**, 119 (1950). [24

13. *Alveolar Air and Arterial and Venous Blood Carbon Dioxide Content. Carbonic Anhydrase. Arterial and Venous Blood pH. Electrolyte Patterns*

A decrease in alveolar air carbon dioxide content or tension has been noted in patients with cardiac decompensation by many authors (Dautrebande, 1928; Peabody *et al.*, 1916; **28**). This decrease parallels the increase in respiratory minute volume and thereby is related to the degree of dyspnea to some extent. Indeed, it is caused by hyperventilation out of proportion to carbon dioxide production in the body, and indicates central respiratory stimulation. As Pearce (1917, 1921) and Dautrebande (1928) pointed out, circulatory insufficiency may cause it; however, central stimulation by other mechanisms, such as reflexes, anoxia, cortical influences, and the direct effect of fever on the medullary centers, may act likewise. Lowering of alveolar carbon dioxide content is not diagnostic, but it does distinguish cardiac dyspnea from that due to diffuse pulmonary disease (in the absence of fever).

Since the free carbonic acid of the arterial blood varies as the alveolar carbon dioxide tension, the former must also be diminished in cardiac decompensation. A large number of observers have recorded measurements of arterial whole blood carbon dioxide content or tension, and arterial plasma bicarbonate in patients with congestive failure; the values reported are usually low in the normal range or below it (Cobet, 1924; Fraser, 1927; **29**), the degree of lowering varying with the severity of hyperventilation. The carbon dioxide content of arterial blood is above normal in only a small minority of patients with chronic cardiac decompensation; these have either diffuse primary pulmonary disease as well (Campbell et al., 1923; Fraser, 1927; Fraser et al., 1928; Peters et al., 1927a,b; Winkler and Crankshaw, 1938) or else very severe uncomplicated congestive failure with extreme degrees of pulmonary engorgement and edema (Campbell et al., 1923; Fraser, 1927). In either of these conditions the diffusion of carbon dioxide across the alveolar walls may be impeded. The concept that an increased gradient regularly exists (Kroetz, 1931) does not appear to be well founded.

Changes in venous whole blood carbon dioxide tension and in venous serum bicarbonate at rest are variable (Pearce, 1921; Pilcher et al., 1930; Scott, 1919; **30**); in most instances the values are in the normal range. When cardiac decompensation is extreme, however, the venous blood carbon dioxide content may be somewhat lowered (Scott, 1919; Peters, 1917), but not to the extent to which the arterial level is depressed. McMichael (1939) found the jugular venous carbon dioxide tension elevated in dyspneic patients; Moyer et al. (1952) and Novack et al. (1953) did not observe this change in their patients.

Since the pH of the blood depends on the ratio of bicarbonate to carbonic acid, it is clear that a variety of changes can occur in the blood of patients with cardiac decompensation. The arterial blood pH is within the normal range or somewhat elevated (Fraser et al., 1928; **31**), depending apparently on the severity of hyperventilation. In severe hyperventilation there is marked lowering of the alveolar air carbon dioxide tension with a corresponding fall in carbonic acid content of the arterial blood. The ratio of bicarbonate to carbonic acid is increased and the arterial pH usually rises.

That more patients with severe congestive failure do not manifest this trend toward arterial alkalosis may be due to the increases in blood lactic acid frequently present (page 86). A small group of patients, consisting principally of those with additional diffuse organic pulmonary disease, show carbon dioxide retention with a consequent lowering of arterial blood pH due to this factor in itself. The venous blood pH is usually normal, although in occasional instances it may lie a little above or below the normal range (Peabody, 1914; Fraser et al., 1922; Harris et al., 1935; Peters and Barr, 1921; Pilcher et al., 1930; Shiskin, 1937; Sonne and Jarlöv, 1918). However, the difference between arterial and venous blood pH is greater than normal.

It is clear that the above-described changes in arterial blood are the consequences rather than the causes of hyperventilation and dyspnea at rest. Lowering of arterial carbon dioxide content and hydrogen ion concentration appears to provide a compensatory mechanism for stasis; a means is provided whereby each unit of blood passing through the tissues may take up more carbon dioxide. The discussion of Pearce in 1921 is still pertinent in this respect; of particular interest in regard to cardiac decompensation is his general conclusion that if the venous blood carbon dioxide is high relative to the alveolar, then the circulation must be inadequate. Arterial acidosis is not a cause of dyspnea in chronic congestive failure, at least at rest, but a tendency toward *tissue* acidosis, consequent to carbon dioxide retention secondary to stasis, apparently is partly responsible for the hyperventilation of cardiac decompensation; Peabody (1915) pointed out that the respiratory response to inhalation of carbon dioxide is similar in patients with congestive failure to that shown by patients with uremic acidosis. The observation of Friedman (1947) that voluntary hyperventilation increases the low breath-holding time found in cardiac decompensation also suggests that tissue hypercarbia may be a factor in cardiac dyspnea. It should be noted that anoxia sensitizes the respiratory center to carbon dioxide in man (Nielsen and Smith, 1952).

A number of authors have studied the carbon dioxide carrying power of the arterial and venous blood by measuring part or all of the dissociation curve (Fraser, 1927; Meneely and Kaltreider, 1943; 32). Although the results are usually within the normal range, in some instances the curve is somewhat low and in others, apparently normal, some rise occurs in recovery. Meakins, Dautrebande and

Fetter (1923) determined the carbon dioxide dissociation curves of both arterial and venous blood in the same decompensated patients and found normal values for the former, but a lowering of the latter. They ascribed this depression of the venous curve to loss of base to the tissues consequent to stasis (Dautrebande, Davies and Meakins, 1923). It is difficult to understand, however, how this lost base returns to the arterial blood so as to restore the curve of that blood to normal. Their findings are also difficult to interpret in the light of those of other workers who found a depression of the arterial carbon dioxide dissociation curve.

Fraser, Graham, and Hilton (1924) corroborated the observations of Meakins *et al.* (1923) on the lowering of the venous curve as compared to the arterial, but in their experience this change was not limited to patients in whom stasis existed. They pointed out that the arterial blood dissociation curve and pH were the result of the passage of *mixed* venous blood through the lungs and that comparing arterial with venous blood taken from one part of the body, usually the arm, did not permit one to draw conclusions concerning the relation between the arterial and *mixed* venous blood.

The cause of the slight lowering of the blood carbon dioxide curves that may occur in congestive failure is not established, but it is not unlikely that lactic acidosis may play a part in some instances. Not to be overlooked in this connection is the possibility that the administration of excessive amounts of ammonium chloride may also be a factor (page 273). In the presence of moderate or severe acidosis a shift in the oxygen dissociation curve to the right should occur. Lewis *et al.* (1913) found this change in the venous blood in some of their patients, but Meakins *et al.* (1923) could not corroborate this observation when they studied arterial blood; available data indicate that significant acidosis does not occur at rest in cardiac decompensation.

After exercise, the carbon dioxide capacity of the blood (Schmitz and Preston, 1927; Groag and Schwartz, 1927; Harris *et al.*, 1935) and the pH (Dennig and Prodger, 1933; Eppinger *et al.*, 1926; Harris *et al.*, 1935; Pilcher *et al.*, 1930) usually fall abnormally in cardiac patients. This shift toward acidosis has been correlated with elevated blood lactic acid levels by Harris, Jones and Aldred (1935). Although the carbon dioxide content of arterial blood (Cullen *et al.*,

1931) falls in exercising cardiac patients, the tension rises slightly and so the pH falls.

In spite of the fact that changes in blood carbon dioxide content which occur in congestive failure appear to be insignificant, since the venous blood carbon dioxide level is usually in the normal range, there exists the possibility that immeasurably small changes in tissue tensions of that gas are important in the genesis of dyspnea. A number of authors have shown that raising the carbon dioxide content of the alveolar air produces in cardiac patients very much more discomfort and hyperventilation than in normal subjects (Engelhard, 1927; Peabody, 1915, 1917; Peters and Barr, 1920; Pilcher *et al.*, 1930); this increased dyspnea is due in part to the fact that cardiacs breathing carbon dioxide cannot enlarge their tidal air volumes normally and consequently increase the rate of respiration excessively. On the other hand, increased carbon dioxide itself is also a factor, for the rise in respiratory minute volume exhibited by cardiac patients breathing increased amounts of carbon dioxide is greater than that seen in normal subjects breathing air of the same content (Peabody, 1915, 1917; Pilcher *et al.*, 1930); the blood pH is possibly lowered more in cardiac patients at the same time (Pilcher *et al.*, 1930). This finding suggests that the elimination of the low alveolar air (and arterial) carbon dioxide contents that results when cardiac patients breathe high concentrations of that gas removes an important mechanism which compensates for the fact that diminished blood flow does not remove tissue carbon dioxide adequately.

The question arises whether the rate of conversion of carbon dioxide to and from bicarbonate is normal in patients with cardiac decompensation. This reaction is catalyzed by carbonic anhydrase. Carbonic anhydrase activity of each unit of blood is normal in congestive failure (Altschule and Lewis, 1949; Hodgson, 1936; Lambie, 1938); however, the blood volume is probably increased (page 147) and so the total circulating carbonic anhydrase must be increased in proportion.

Deviations from the normal plasma bicarbonate content are associated with changes in serum chloride level. Peters, Bulger, and Eisenman (1927*a,b*) studied this problem and found that their cardiac patients could be divided into three groups: (i) patients with low bicarbonate and high chloride levels; (ii) patients with high bicarbonate and low chloride levels (these patients usually have some associated diffuse pulmonary disease); (iii) patients with low bicarbonate and chloride levels. The third group is a small one and includes patients in whom there is probably an element of renal insufficiency accounting for the loss of plasma base. The data of other authors (Atchley *et al.*, 1923; Gilligan *et al.*, 1934; Winkler and Crankshaw, 1938; Borst, 1948) may be grouped in the same manner. Many authors (page 276) have also observed that diuresis is often associated with a lowering of plasma chloride and an elevation of bicarbonate concentration.

Bibliography

Chapter I — Section 13

ALTSCHULE, M. D., and H. D. LEWIS, Activity of carbonic anhydrase in the blood. Study of patients with dyspnea consequent to chronic cardiac and pulmonary disease, *Arch. Int. Med.* **83,** 547 (1949).

ANGELINO, P. F., and A. ACTIS-DATO, La gasometria del sangue venoso renale e le pressioni venose renale studiate mediante cateterismo in soggetti normali, cardiopatici e in altre forme morbose, *Cuore e circolaz.* **35,** 283 (1951). [29

ATCHLEY, D. W., R. F. LOEB, E. M. BENEDICT, and W. W. PALMER, Physical and chemical studies of human blood serum. III. A study of miscellaneous disease conditions, *Arch. Int. Med.* **31,** 616 (1923).

BARACH, A. L., The therapeutic use of oxygen in heart disease, *Ann. Int. Med.* **5,** 428 (1931). [29

BARACH, A. L., and D. W. RICHARDS, JR., Effects of treatment with oxygen in cardiac failure, *Ann. Int. Med.* **48,** 325 (1931). [29, 31, 32

BARACH, A. L., and M. N. WOODWELL, Studies in oxygen therapy with determinations of the blood gases. I. In cardiac insufficiency and related conditions, *Ann. Int. Med.* **28,** 367 (1921). [29

BARR, D. P., and J. P. PETERS, JR., Studies of the respiratory mechanism in cardiac dyspnea. III. The effective ventilation in cardiac dyspnea, *Am. J. Physiol.* **54,** 345 (1920). [28

BEDDARD, A. P., and M. S. PEMBREY, Observations on pulmonary ventilation in disease, *Brit. M. J.* **2,** 580 (1908). [28

BERGNER, G. E., J. H. HUTCHINSON, J. W. KOEHLER, and E. L. CZEBRIN-SKI, Metabolic problems arising in the management of congestive heart failure, *Arch. Int. Med.* **88,** 387 (1951). [30

BORST, J. G. G., The maintenance of an adequate cardiac output by the regulation of the urinary excretion of water and sodium chloride; an essential factor in the genesis of edema, *Acta med. Scandinav. Supp. No.* 207 (1948).

CAMPBELL, J. M. H., G. H. HUNT, and E. P. POULTON, An examination of the blood gases and respiration in disease, with reference to the cause of breathlessness and cyanosis, *J. Path. & Bact.* **26,** 234 (1923).
[29, 31, 32

COBET, R., Ueber die Wasserstoffzahl des Blutes bei Herzkranken *Deutsches Arch. f. klin. Med.* **144,** 126 (1924).   [28, 29, 31

COSSIO, P., and I. BERCONSKY, The cyanosis in mitral stenosis, *Am. Heart J.* **17,** 1 (1939).   [28

CULLEN, G. E., T. R. HARRISON, J. A. CALHOUN, W. E. WILKINS, and M. M. TIMS, Studies in congestive heart failure. XIII. The relation of dyspnea of exertion to the oxygen saturation and acid-base condition of the blood, *J. Clin. Investigation* **10,** 807 (1931).   [29, 30

DAUTREBANDE, L., Physiopathologie du ralentissement circulatoire. Ses rapports avec le débit cardiaque, *Arch. d. mal. du cœur* **21,** 296 (1928).   [28, 29, 30, 31, 32

DAUTREBANDE, L., H. W. DAVIES, and J. MEAKINS, The influence of circulatory changes on the gaseous exchanges of the blood. III. An experimental study of circulatory stasis, *Heart* **10,** 133 (1923).

DENNIG, H., and S. H. PRODGER, Herzkranke bei Arbeit, *Deutsches Arch. f. klin. Med.* **175,** 170 (1933).

ENGELHARD, A., Der Wert der Spirometrie für die Klinik der Herzkrankheiten mit Lungenstauung und ihr Ausbau zur einer Funktionsprüfung, *Deutsches Arch. f. klin. Med.* **156,** (1927).

EPPINGER, H., F. KISCH, and H. SCHWARZ, Der Einfluss körperlicher Arbeit auf die Sauerstoffsättigung und auf die aktuelle Reaktion des Arterienblutes bei Kreislaufkranken, *Klin. Wchnschr.* **5,** 1316 (1926).

FITZGERALD, M. P., The alveolar carbonic acid pressure in diseases of the blood and in diseases of the respiratory and circulatory systems, *J. Path. & Bact.* **14,** 328 (1909).   [28

FRASER, F. R., Goulstonian lectures on cardiac dyspnoea, *Lancet* **1,** 529, 589, 643 (1927).   [29, 31, 32

FRASER, F. R., G. GRAHAM, and R. HILTON, A comparison of blood curves constructed with arterial and with venous blood, *J. Physiol.* **54,** 221 (1924).

FRASER, F. R., C. F. HARRIS, R. HILTON, and G. C. LINDER, Arterial carbon dioxide pressure in cardiac dyspnoea, *Quart. J. Med.* **22,** 1 (1928)
[29, 31, 32

FRASER, F. R., J. P. ROSS, and N. B. DREYER. The reaction of the blood in relation to dyspnoea, *Quart. J. Med.* **15,** 195 (1922).   [31

116   CHRONIC CARDIAC DECOMPENSATION

FRIEDMAN, M., Studies concerning the etiology and pathogenesis of neuro-circulatory asthenia. V. The introduction of a new test for the diagnosis and assessment of the syndrome, *Psychosom. Med.* **9**, 242 (1947).

GILLIGAN, D. R., M. C. VOLK, and H. L. BLUMGART, Observations on the chemical and physical relation between blood serum and body fluids. I. The nature of edema fluids and evidence regarding the mechanism of edema formation, *J. Clin. Investigation* **13**, 365 (1934).

GROAG, B., and H. SCHWARTZ, Der Einfluss der Muskelarbeit auf die Blut-milchsäure, Alkalireserve, Azidität des Harns usw. bei Kreislaufkranken, *Arch. f. exper. Path. u. Pharmakol.* **121**, 23 (1927).

HARRIS, I., E. W. JONES, and C. N. ALDRED, Blood pH and lactic acid in different types of heart disease, *Quart. J. Med.* **28**, 407 (1935).   [32

HARROP, G. A., JR., The oxygen and carbon dioxide content of arterial and of venous blood in normal individuals and in patients with anemia and heart disease, *J. Exper. Med.* **30**, 241 (1919).   [29, 30

HEFTER, A. J., and D. F. OKUNEW, Ueber Veränderungen des peripheren Stoffwechsels im Zusammenhang mit den Blutkreislaufstörungen bei der Muskelarbeit, *Ztschr. f. d. ges. exper. Med.* **79**, 806 (1931).   [29

HODGSON, T. H., The carbonic anhydrase content of blood in pathological states in man, *Brit. J. Exper. Path.* **17**, 75 (1936).

HÜRTER, Untersuchungen am arteriellen menschlichen Blute, *Deutsches Arch. f. klin. Med.* **108**, 1 (1912).   [29

IHAYA, H., Studien über die Alveolarluft, Blutgase, Vitalkapazität und Minuten- und Schlagvolumen des Herzens bei Beriberi, Herzklappenfehler und Pleuritis, *Mitt. d. med. Gesellsch. zu Tokyo* **48**, 2167 (1934).   [28

JANSEN, K., H. W. KNIPPING, and K. STROMBERGER, Klinische Untersuchungen über Atmung und Blutgase, *Beitr. z. Klin. d. Tuberk.* **80**, 304 (1932).   [29, 30

KORNFELD, F., Ueber Blutgase und Blutreaktion bei dyspnoischen Zuständen, *Ztschr. f. d. ges. exper. Med.* **38**, 289 (1923).   [29, 31, 32

KROETZ, C., Physiologische und pathologische Schwankungen der Sauerstoffdurchlässigkeit der Lungen, *Verhandl. d. deutsch. Gesellsch. f. inn. Med.* **43**, 105 (1931).   [28, 29

LAMBIE, C. G., Observations on the carbonic anhydrase of the blood in anaemia and in other pathological conditions, *Edinburgh M. J.* **45**, 373 (1938).

LANDT, H., and J. E. BENJAMIN, Changes in the content of carbon dioxide in venous blood during rebreathing experiments. Comparison of change in persons with a normal heart and in patients with cardiac disease, *Arch. Int. Med.* **67**, 72 (1941).   [30

LEWIS, T., J. H. RYFFEL, C. G. L. WOLF, T. COTTON, and J. BARCROFT, Observations relating to dyspnea in cardiac and renal patients, *Heart* **5**, 45 (1913). [28

MCMICHAEL, J., Hyperpnoea in heart failure, *Clin. Sc.* **4**, 19 (1939).

MEAKINS, J., L. DAUTREBANDE, and W. J. FETTER, The influence of circulatory disturbances on the gaseous exchange of the blood. IV. The blood gases and circulation rate in cases of mitral stenosis, *Heart* **10**, 153 (1923). [28, 29, 31, 32

MENEELY, G. R., and N. L. KALTREIDER, A study of the volume of the blood in congestive heart failure. Relation to other measurements in fifteen patients, *J. Clin. Investigation* **22**, 521 (1943). [29, 32

MOKOTOFF, R., G. ROSS, and L. LEITER, The electrolyte content of skeletal muscle in congestive heart failure; a comparison of results with inulin and chloride as reference standards for extracellular water, *J. Clin. Investigation* **31**, 291 (1952). [30

MOYER, J. H., S. I. MILLER, A. B. TASHNEK, and R. BOWMAN, The effect of theophylline with ethylenediamine (aminophylline) on cerebral hemodynamics in the presence of cardiac failure with and without Cheyne-Stokes respiration, *J. Clin. Investigation* **31**, 267 (1952). [29, 30

NIELSEN, M., and H. SMITH, Studies on the regulation of respiration in acute hypoxia. With an appendix on respiratory control during prolonged hypoxia, *Acta physiol. Scandinav.* **24**, 293 (1952).

NOVACK, P., B. GOLUBOFF, L. BORTIN, A. SOFFE, and H. A. SHENKIN, Studies of the cerebral circulation and metabolism in congestive heart failure, *Circulation* **7**, 724 (1953). [29

PEABODY, F. W., Studies on acidosis and dyspnea in renal and cardiac disease, *Arch. Int. Med.* **14**, 236 (1914). [28

PEABODY, F. W., Clinical studies on the respiration. I. The effect of carbon dioxide in the inspired air on patients with cardiac disease, *Arch. Int. Med.* **16**, 846 (1915). [28

PEABODY, F. W., Clinical studies on the respiration. III. A mechanical factor in the production of dyspnea in patients with cardiac disease, *Arch. Int. Med.* **20**, 433 (1917).

PEABODY, F. W., A. L. MEYER, and E. F. DUBOIS, Clinical calorimetry. XVI. The basal metabolism of patients with cardiac and renal disease, *Arch. Int. Med.* **17**, 980 (1916). [28

PEARCE, R. G., A possible explanation for the cyanosis and hyperpnea seen in pneumonia and cardiac decompensation, *J. Lab. & Clin. Med.* **2**, 867 (1917). [28, 30, 32

PEARCE, R. G., The cardiorespiratory mechanism in health and disease, *Arch. Int. Med.* **27**, 139 (1921). [28, 30

PETERS, J. P., JR., Carbon dioxide acidosis, the cause of cardiac dyspnea, *Am. J. Physiol.* **43**, 113 (1917).   [28, 30

PETERS, J. P., JR., and D. P. BARR, Studies of the respiratory mechanism in cardiac dyspnea. I. The low alveolar carbon dioxide of cardiac dyspnea, *Am. J. Physiol.* **54**, 307 (1920).   [28, 30

PETERS, J. P., JR., and D. P. BARR, II. The carbon dioxide absorption curve and carbon dioxide tension of the blood in cardiac dyspnea, *J. Biol. Chem.* **45**, 537 (1921).   [28, 30, 32

PETERS, J. P., JR., H. A. BULGER, and A. J. EISENMAN, Total acid-base equilibrium of plasma in health and disease. VIII. Bicarbonate and chloride in the serum of patients with heart failure, *J. Clin. Investigation* **3**, 497 (1926–27a).   [29

PETERS, J. P., JR., H. A. BULGER, and A. J. EISENMAN, Total acid-base equilibrium of plasma in health and disease. IX. High serum bicarbonate in heart failure. Asphyctic anoxemia, *J. Clin. Investigation* **3**, 511 (1926–27b).

PILCHER, C., G. CLARK, and T. R. HARRISON, Studies in congestive heart failure. III. The buffering power of the blood and tissues, *J. Clin. Investigation* **8**, 317 (1929–30).   [29, 30

PLATTS, M. M., The arterial blood gases in pulmonary heart failure, *Clin. Sc.* **12**, 63 (1953).   [29

PORGES, O., A. LEIMDÖRFER, and E. MARKOVICI, Ueber die Kohlensäurespannung des Blutes in pathologischen Zuständen. II. Ueber die Kohlensäurespannung des Blutes in der kardialen und pulmonalen Dyspnoe, *Ztschr. f. klin. Med.* **77**, 446 (1913).   [29

RICHARDS, D. W., JR., and A. L. BARACH, Prolonged residence in high oxygen atmospheres. Effects on normal individuals and on patients with chronic cardiac and pulmonary insufficiency, *Quart. J. Med.* **3**, 437 (1934).   [29, 30, 31

RIGONI, M., Il ricambio respiratorio, la portata circolatoria e la gittata sistolica nelle cardiopatie compensate e nello scompenso di circolo. I. Metabolismo basale, ventilazione polmonare e tensione dei gas alveolari, *Cuore e circolaz.* **21**, 157 (1937).   [28

RINGER, M., and M. D. ALTSCHULE, Studies on the circulation. II. Cardiac output in diseases of the heart, and under the influence of digitalis therapy, *Am. Heart J.* **5**, 305 (1930).   [28

SCHMITZ, H. W., and M. PRESTON, Changes in CO_2 combining capacity of blood following exercise in individuals with organic heart disease, *Proc. Soc. Exper. Biol. & Med.* **24**, 766 (1927).   [32

SCOTT, R. W., The total carbonate content of the arterial and venous plasma in patients with chronic heart disease, *Proc. Soc. Exper. Biol. & Med.* **17**, 19 (1919).   [29, 30

SHISKIN, C., The pH of human blood plasma in respiratory and cardiac disease, *Lancet* 2, 1191 (1937). [31

SONNE, C., Über die Bestimmung des Unterschiedes zwischen arterieller und venöser Kohlensäurespannung unter normalen und pathologischen Verhältnissen sowie über die Anwendung dieses Unterschiedes zur Messung von Veränderungen in der Grösse des Minutenvolumens, *Deutsches Arch. f. klin. Med.* 124, 358 (1918). [28, 29, 30

SONNE, C., and E. JARLÖV, Untersuchungen über die Wasserstoffionenkonzentration des Blutes bei verschiedenen Krankheiten, insbesondere solchen, die mit Dyspnoe oder anderen Zeichen cardialer oder renaler Insufficienz verbunden sind, *Deutsches Arch. f. klin. Med.* 124, 379 (1918). [32

WILSON, R. H., C. W. BORDEN, R. V. EBERT, and H. S. WELLS, A comparison of the effect of voluntary hyperventilation in normal persons, patients with pulmonary emphysema, and patients with cardiac disease, *J. Lab. & Clin. Med.* 36, 119 (1950). [31

WINKLER, A. W., and O. F. CRANKSHAW, Chloride depletion in conditions other than Addison's disease, *J. Clin. Investigation* 17, 1 (1938).

14. *Tissue Gas Tensions*

Techniques for measuring the tissue gas tensions directly are difficult, laborious and of doubtful accuracy; methods for measuring carbon dioxide tension appear to be considerably less inaccurate than those for oxygen. Only a few data obtained by these methods in patients with chronic cardiac decompensation are available. Del Baere (1939) and Meyer (1935, 1936) found abnormally low oxygen tensions and normal or high carbon dioxide tensions. It must be borne in mind that cutaneous vasoconstriction may lower cutaneous oxygen tension (Montgomery and Horwitz, 1950) and so the finding of cutaneous anoxia need not indicate stagnation owing to circulatory insufficiency. Sibree (1941) studied four patients and concluded that the oxygen tension was in the normal range, while the carbon dioxide tension was high. Much more work will have to be done before data of this sort can be considered conclusive.

Data derived from studies of venous blood gases are pertinent. The oxygen tension of tissue fluid cannot be higher than that found in the venous blood; it may be lower, since the opening of the widely distributed arteriovenous anastomoses may arterialize the venous blood to a greater or lesser degree, so that gas concentrations in the latter may not always accurately reflect conditions in the capillaries. Accordingly, since low venous oxygen contents are the rule (page 102), it must be concluded that tissue anoxia exists in chronic congestive failure. Similarly, the tissue carbon dioxide tensions must be at least as high as those which are found in the venous blood; that is, they are normal (page 110).

Bibliography

Chapter I — Section 14

DEL BAERE, L. J., Die Sauerstoffversorgung des Körpers, *Ztschr. f. klin. Med.* **136,** 43 (1939).

MEYER, F., Ueber die Messung des Sauerstoffdruckes im Gewebe und die relative Anoxie der Kreislaufkranken, *Klin. Wchnschr.* **14,** 627 (1935).

MEYER, F., Untersuchungen über die Ursachen der Sauerstoffarmut im Gewebe von Kreislaufkranken (mit einer Nomographischen Darstellung zur Erorterung der capillaren und Diffusionsanoxie), *Klin. Wchnschr.* **15,** 48 (1936).

MONTGOMERY, H., and O. HORWITZ, Oxygen tension of tissues by the polarigraphic method. I. Introduction: Oxygen tension and blood flow of the skin of human extremities, *J. Clin. Investigation* **29,** 1120 (1950).

SIBREE, E. W., Gas tensions in the tissues in pathological conditions, *M. J. Australia* **1,** 201 (1941).

15. *Blood Lactate and Pyruvate*

In 1913 Lewis *et al.* reported the finding of an increase in the blood lactic acid level in some patients with congestive failure. Clausen (1922) later noted a parallelism between blood lactic acid level and clinical condition in a patient with cardiac decompensation. Many additional observations have been recorded since that time. Some authors report levels within the normal range in their patients with myocardial insufficiency at rest (Weiss and Ellis, 1935; **33**), while others describe somewhat elevated levels in some or most of their patients (Jervell, 1928; **34**). Although a significant increase in blood lactate concentration is found infrequently in decompensated patients at rest, exercise almost always results in abnormally high levels which fall to normal slowly after the patient returns to the resting state (Meakins and Long, 1927; Jervell, 1928; **35**). Groag and Schwartz (1927) and Harris, Jones and Aldred (1935) noted a simultaneous fall in blood alkali reserve and pH. These authors and also Jervell (1928) found in addition a marked increase in lactic acid output in the urine of such patients. A number of authors (Bielschowsky and Thaddea, 1932; **36**) found an abnormally high level of blood lactate and a prolonged curve of disappearance after the injection of lactate in decompensated cases, with a good correlation between these conditions and the degree of failure. In a general way the resting blood lactate content and the level to which it rises after exercise or injection of lactate are related to the severity of congestive failure, although numerous exceptions are to be found. Hallock (1939) found a good correlation between the blood lactate level and severity of dyspnea. However, Dennig et al. (1931) reported that the accumulation of 10 milliequivalents of lactate completely prevents work by precipitating early exhaustion; lesser concentrations have a corresponding effect. Accordingly, excessive rises in lactate may possibly prevent the development of maximal dyspnea by limiting muscular effort.

Administration of glucose is followed by increases in blood lactate level that appear to be somewhat greater than normal (Tinelli, 1936).

The fact that the abnormal lactate metabolism which occurs in congestive failure resembles that seen in liver disease (Schumacher, 1928; Adler and Lange, 1927; Beckmann, 1929; Dresel and Himmelweit, 1930; Valentin, 1925) has led some authors to conclude that both originate in liver damage. However, Dresel and Himmelweit (1929, 1930) observed that although the blood lactate levels, both at rest and after exercise on a staircase, might be similar in patients with cardiac and with hepatic diseases, yet the metabolism of lactate in the peripheral tissues, as studied by means of dynamometer experiments, is impaired in congestive failure but not in liver disease. It appears, therefore, that the hepatic damage of congestive failure plays only a contributory role in the lactic acidosis seen in that condition. Tissue anoxia seems to be the most important factor in this regard. Weiss and Ellis (1935) correlated the rise in blood lactate with the fall in venous blood oxygen during exercise in some patients. Inhalation of oxygen may lower elevated blood lactate in patients with cardiac decompensation (Barach, 1931; Barach and Richards, 1931; Hick et al., 1937; Jervell, 1928); this phenomenon may be associated with "storage" of oxygen (Jervell, 1928; Hick et al., 1937). Conversely, anoxia induced in normal subjects by the breathing of air containing low concentrations of oxygen may give rise to an increase in blood lactic acid content at rest (Jervell, 1928; Bock et al., 1932; Friedemann et al., 1945) or during work (Asmussen et al., 1948; Asmussen and Chiodi, 1941; Dill et al., 1931; Lundin and Ström, 1947; Tepperman and Tepperman, 1948). The blood lactate curve found in normal subjects or decompensated cardiac patients after intravenous injection of lactate is lowered in both groups by the simultaneous breathing of air enriched with oxygen (Bielschowsky and Thaddea, 1932); Hewlett, Barnett, and Lewis (1926), Asmussen and Nielsen (1946), Asmussen et al. (1948), Lundin and Ström (1947), and Miller (1952) found a lowered blood lactate level and urine excretion when normal subjects exercised while breathing air enriched with oxygen.

Although the evidence strongly favors tissue anoxia as the cause of lactic acidosis in congestive failure, it is not possible to rule out thiamin deficiency as an additional factor in some instances. Studies of pyruvate metabolism in cardiac decompensation are fragmentary. Bueding, Wortis and Stern (1942) found it normal in patients at rest, while Taylor, Weiss and Wilkins (1937) and Yanoff (1942) found the blood level elevated commonly. Goldsmith (1947, 1948) also found it elevated in patients in cardiac failure and noted that the lactate-pyruvate ratio in these cases was similar to that in instances of beriberi; the ratio returned to normal when thiamin was given. Exercise in congestive failure causes an abnormally great and prolonged increase in blood pyruvate (Yanoff, 1943). The observation of Wilkins, Weiss, and Taylor (1939) that the curve of blood pyruvate after intravenous injection of that material is normal in congestive failure may be due to their use of too small a dose. Elevation of the blood pyruvate levels occurs less readily than does increase in lactate in normal subjects made anoxic (Friedemann et al., 1945). Elevation of the blood pyruvate level not only contributes to acidosis but also may possibly impair muscular function (page 224).

Bibliography

Chapter I — Section 15

ADLER, A., and H. LANGE, Der Milchsauregehalt des Blutes bei Leberkrankheiten, *Deutsches Arch. f. klin. Med.* **157**, 129 (1927).   [34

ASMUSSEN, E., and H. CHIODI, The effect of hypoxemia on ventilation and circulation in man, *Am. J. Physiol.* **132**, 426 (1941).

ASMUSSEN, E., and M. NIELSEN, Studies on the regulation of respiration in heavy work, *Acta Physiol. Scandinav.* **12**, 171 (1946).

ASMUSSEN, E., W. VON DÖBELN, and M. NIELSEN, Blood lactate and oxygen debt after exhaustive work at different oxygen tensions, *Acta physiol. Skandinav.* **15**, 57 (1948).

BARACH, A. L., The therapeutic use of oxygen in heart disease, *Ann. Int. Med.* **5**, 428 (1931).   [34

BARACH, A. L., and D. W. RICHARDS, JR., Effects of treatment with oxygen in cardiac failure, *Arch. Int. Med.* **48**, 325 (1931).   [34

BECKMANN, K., Klinische Erfahrungen mit der Leberfunktionsprüfung durch Milchsäurebelastung, *Ztschr. f. klin. Med.* **110**, 163 (1929).   [34, 36

BIELSCHOWSKY, P., and S. THADDEA, Ueber die Stoffwechselwirkung reiner Sauerstoffatmung, *Ztschr. f. klin. Med.* **120**, 330 (1932).   [34, 36

BOCK, A. V., D. B. DILL, and H. T. EDWARDS, Lactic acid in the blood of resting man, *J. Clin. Investigation* **11**, 775 (1932).

BUEDING, E., H. WORTIS, and M. STERN, Pathological variations in blood and spinal fluid pyruvic acid, *J. Clin. Investigation* **21**, 85 (1942).

BUFANO, M., and G. SANTUCCI, Le variazioni della lattacidemia dopo iniezione intravenosa di lattato di sodio nei vizi di cuore, *Cuore e circolaz.* **15**, 65 (1931).   [36

CALABRESI, M., and W. SCHWARZ, Sul contenuto in acido lattico del sangue in condizioni normali e patologiche, *Clin. med. ital.* **64**, 423 (1933).   [34, 35

CLAUSEN, S. W., A method for the determination of small amounts of lactic acid, *J. Biol. Chem.* **52**, 263 (1922).   [34

DENNIG, H., and S. H. PRODGER, Herzkranke bei Arbeit, *Deutsches Arch. f. klin. Med.* **175**, 170 (1933).   [35

DENNIG, H., J. H. TALBOTT, H. T. EDWARDS, and D. B. DILL, Effect of acidosis and alkalosis upon capacity for work, *J. Clin. Investigation* **9**, 601 (1930–31).

DILL, D. B., H. T. EDWARDS, A. FÖLLING, S. A. OBERG, A. M. PAPPENHEIMER, JR., and J. H. TALBOT, Adaptation of the organism to changes in oxygen pressure, *J. Physiol.* **71**, 47 (1931).

DRESEL, K., and F. HIMMELWEIT, Kreislaufinsufficienz und Muskelstoff-wechsel, *Klin. Wchnschr.* **8,** 294 (1929).   [34, 35

DRESEL, K., and F. HIMMELWEIT, Milchsäurestudien bei Gesunden, Kreis-lauf-, Leber-, und Basedowkranken in der Ruhe und nach Muskelar-beit, *Ztschr. f. klin. Med.* **112,** 528 (1930).   [34, 35

ELLIS, L. B., and S. WEISS, Studies in complete heart block. I. The cardiac output and the peripheral circulatory mechanism, *Am. J. M. Sc.* **182,** 195 (1931).

FRIEDEMANN, T. E., G. E. HAUGEN, and T. C. KMIECIAK, Pyruvic acids. III. The level of pyruvic and lactic acids, and the lactic-pyruvic ratio, in the blood of human subjects. The effect of food, light, muscular activity, and anoxia at high altitude, *J. Biol. Chem.* **157,** 673 (1945).

GAMBIGLIANI-ZOCCOLI, A., R. GIACCHERO, E. ZAMBELLI, and C. RESCHIA, Milchsäure und Kreislaufinsuffizienz, *Ztschr. f. klin. Med.* **135,** 457 (1939).   [34

GOLDSMITH, G. A., The blood lactate-pyruvate relationship in various physiologic and pathologic states, *Federation Proc.* **6,** 408 (1947).

GOLDSMITH, G. A., The blood lactate-pyruvate relationship in various physiologic and pathologic states, *Am. J. M. Sc.* **215,** 182 (1948).

GROAG, B., and H. SCHWARTZ, Der Einfluss der Muskelarbeit auf die Blutmilchsäure, Alkalireserve, Azidität des Harns, usw. bei Kreislauf-kranken, *Arch. f. exper. Path. u. Pharmakol.* **121,** 23 (1927).   [33, 35

HALLOCK, P., Lactic acid production during rest and after exercise in sub-jects with various types of heart disease with special reference to congenital heart disease, *J. Clin. Investigation* **18,** 385 (1939).
                    [33, 35

HARRIS, I., E. W. JONES, and C. N. ALDRED, Blood pH and lactic acid in different types of heart disease, *Quart. J. Med.* **28,** 407 (1935).   [34

HEFTER, A. J., and D. F. OKUNEW, Ueber Veranderungen des peripheren Stoffwechsels im Zusammenhang mit den Blutkreislaufstorungen bei der Muskelarbeit, *Ztschr. f. d. ges. exper. Med.* **79,** 806 (1931).
                    [34, 35

HERLITZKA, L., and C. ANGELERI, Richerche sull' importanza delle cure di carico con lattato di sodio come prova della funzionalita cardiaca, *Arch. per le sc. med.* **62,** 97 (1936).   [33, 36

HEWLETT, A. W., G. D. BARNETT, and J. K. LEWIS, The effect of breath-ing oxygen-enriched air during exercise upon pulmonary ventilation and upon the lactic acid content of blood and urine, *J. Clin. Investiga-tion* **3,** 317 (1926–27).

HICK, F. K., A. W. CHRISTIAN, and P. W. SMITH, Criteria of oxygen want, with especial reference to neurocirculatory asthenia, *Am. J. M. Sc.* **194,** 800 (1937).   [33

JAHN, D., Zur Störung des Milchsäurehaushaltes Kreislaufkranker, *Verhandl. d. deutsch. Gesellsch. f. inn. Med.* **41**, 346 (1929). [34

JERVELL, O., Investigation of the concentration of lactic acid in blood and urine under physiologic and pathologic conditions, *Acta med. Scandinav., Supp. No. 24*, 5 (1928). [34, 35

LAUTER, S., and H. BAUMANN, Zur Theorie der Herzinsufficienz und der Digitaliswirkung, *Klin. Wchnschr.* **8**, 263 (1929). [33

LEWIS, T., J. H. RYFFEL, C. G. L. WOLF, T. COTTON, and J. BARCROFT, Observations relating to dyspnea in cardiac and renal patients, *Heart* **5**, 45 (1913). [34

LUNDIN, G., and G. STRÖM, The concentration of blood lactic acid in man during muscular work in relation to the partial pressure of oxygen of the inspired air, *Acta Physiol. Scandinav.* **13**, 253 (1947).

MEAKINS, J., and C. N. H. LONG, Oxygen consumption, oxygen debt and lactic acid in circulatory failure, *J. Clin. Investigation* **4**, 273 (1927). [34, 35

MILLER, A. T., JR., Influence of oxygen administration on cardiovascular function during exercise and recovery, *J. Appl. Physiol.* **5**, 165 (1952).

PERGER, H., Ueber die Resynthese der Milchsäure bei Kreislaufkranken, *Klin. Wchnschr.* **6**, 1324 (1927). [36

RICHARDS, D. W., JR., and A. L. BARACH, Prolonged residence in high oxygen atmospheres. Effects on normal individuals and on patients with chronic cardiac and pulmonary insufficiency, *Quart. J. Med.* **3**, 437 (1934). [34

SCHUMACHER, H., Das Verhalten der Blutmilchsäure bei Leberkranken, *Klin. Wchnschr.* **7**, 1733 (1928). [34, 36

TAYLOR, F. H. L., S. WEISS, and R. W. WILKINS, The bisulphite binding power of the blood in health and in disease, with special reference to vitamin B_1 deficiency, *J. Clin. Investigation* **16**, 833 (1937).

TEPPERMAN, J. and H. M. TEPPERMAN, On the blood lactic acid response to measured exercise in hypoxic human subjects, *J. Clin. Investigation* **27**, 176 (1948).

TINELLI, G., La lattacidemia nei cardiopatici sottoposti a carico di glucosio, *Gior. di clin. med.* **17**, 1315 (1936). [34

VALENTIN, F., Ueber den Milchsäuregehalt des Blutes, *München. med. Wchnschr.* **72**, 86 (1925). [34

WEISS, S., and L. B. ELLIS, Oxygen utilization and lactic acid production in the extremities during rest and exercise, in subjects with normal and in those with diseased cardiovascular systems, *Arch. Int. Med.* **55**, 665 (1935). [33, 35

WILKINS, R. W., S. WEISS, and F. H. L. TAYLOR, The effect and rate of removal of pyruvic acid administered to normal persons and to patients with and without "vitamin B deficiency," *Ann. Int. Med.* **12,** 938 (1939).

WORTIS, S. B., and F. MARSH, Lactic acid content of the blood and of the cerebrospinal fluid, *Arch. Neurol. & Psychiat.* **35,** 715 (1936).

[33

YANOFF, Z. A., Blood pyruvic acid in heart disease, *Arch. Int. Med.* **69,** 1005 (1942).

YANOFF, Z. A., Effect of exercise on blood pyruvic acid. Observations on trained and untrained normal subjects and on patients with heart disease and with hypertension, *Arch. Int. Med.* **72,** 239 (1943).

16. *Oxygen Debt. Cost of Work*

The relation of accumulation of lactic acid in the blood during work to oxygen debt after work is well established. It is to be expected, therefore, that the oxygen debt in cardiac patients after performance of a given task would be abnormally large and prolonged; this has been shown in patients with various degrees of failure (Nylin, 1933, 1937, 1938, 1939; Eppinger *et al.*, 1925; **37**). Compensated cardiac patients take up normal amounts of oxygen during the performance of work (Alt *et al.*, 1930; Bowen and Carmer, 1926; Herbst, 1928*b*; Zaeper *et al.*, 1939), whereas with patients in failure the intake of oxygen during exertion is low, depending on the severity of the condition (Herbst, 1928*b*; Harrison and Pilcher, 1930; **38**). Carbon dioxide output may be low also (Campbell, 1934; Campbell and Sale, 1927). The size and duration of the oxygen debt after work is to some extent consequent to the deficit in oxygen intake during work. This is related to failure of the cardiac output to increase normally during exertion in cardiac patients (page 10) and also to impaired pulmonary function. It is to be noted in regard to the latter that in normal subjects the application of a suitable chest binder lowers vital capacity (Altschule *et al.*, 1943; Herbst, 1928*a*; Jacobaeus *et al.*, 1935; Ornstein *et al.*, 1946), may decrease tidal air volume (Sturgis *et al.*, 1922), increases respiratory rate and minute volume at rest and in exertion (Altschule *et al.*, 1943; Herbst, 1928; Sturgis *et al.*, 1922), and also results in a decreased intake of oxygen during work (Herbst, 1928*a*) and an abnormally large debt afterwards (Jacobaeus *et al.*, 1935).

Impaired pulmonary function is not the sole cause of the abnormal oxygen intake in congestive failure. In some instances the oxygen intake in work may be increased by inhalation of oxygen (Bolt et al., 1950); this resembles the condition that obtains in primary pulmonary disease. In other instances of congestive failure, however, oxygen inhalation during work has no significant effect on oxygen intake during the exertion (de Carrasco and Vorwerk, 1936; Herrmansen, 1938); this indicates that the primary difficulty is circulatory. The importance of anoxia in relation to the size of the oxygen debt is illustrated by the observation that normal individuals breathing air containing low concentrations of oxygen have increased debts after work (Clark-Kennedy and Owen, 1926; Asmussen et al., 1948; Bruce et al., 1952); contrariwise, inhalation of oxygen during work may reduce the debt below normal (Asmussen et al., 1948). The oxygen intake during the work is reduced (Bruce et al., 1952).

Another factor favoring increased oxygen debt after exercise is the increased cost of work, that is, lowered efficiency, in cardiac decompensation. The cost of work in terms of total oxygen consumption required for a given task has been found to be high (Eppinger et al., 1925; Harris and Lipkin, 1931; Herbst, 1928b; 39) except in mildly decompensated patients doing light work, where it is normal (Alt et al., 1930; Simonson et al., 1930; Zaeper et al., 1939). It is of interest that anaerobic work is inefficient in normal subjects (Asmussen, 1946).

That some patients are in oxygen debt even while at rest is suggested by the findings of Jervell (1928), Uhlenbruck (1930), Knipping et al. (1932), Jansen et al. (1932), Hick et al. (1937), and Malinow et al. (1950), who found that patients with cardiac decompensation took up abnormally large amounts of oxygen when exposed to high concentrations; in some instances this effect is masked by a simultaneous decrease in oxygen consumption associated with relief of dyspnea and hyperventilation. Although this "storage" is in part consequent to the retention of oxygen in saturating the undersaturated arterial blood often found in decompensated cardiac patients, another factor may be the discharge of accumulated oxygen debt. Thus, in cardiac patients with high blood lactate levels during rest, the blood lactate falls after these patients breathe air enriched with oxygen (page 122). In addition, the fact that the process of "storage" lasts for approximately forty minutes (Uhlenbruck, 1930) in cardiac patients also suggests an effect other than the raising to normal of the level of arterial blood oxygen saturation, for the latter requires only five or ten minutes.

The high cost of work and the smallness of the maximal oxygen debts that cardiac patients are capable of developing (Harrison and Pilcher, 1930; Meakins and Long, 1927) seriously impair ability to do work in congestive failure. Factors limiting the maximal oxygen debt include muscular weakness and the early development of dyspnea. The latter is at least in part related to lactic acidosis, which also has the effect of limiting work *per se*; according to Dennig *et al.* (1931), the presence of 10 milliequivalents of lactate in the blood completely prevents exertion because of exhaustion.

Bibliography

Chapter I — Section 16

ALT, H. L., G. L. WALKER, and W. C. SMITH, The cardiac output in heart disease. II. Effect of exercise on the circulation in patients with chronic rheumatic valvular disease, subacute rheumatic fever and complete heart block, *Arch. Int. Med.* **45,** 958 (1930).

ALTSCHULE, M. D., N. ZAMCHECK, and A. IGLAUER, The lung volume and its subdivisions in the upright and recumbent positions in patients with congestive failure. Pulmonary factors in the genesis of orthopnea, *J. Clin. Investigation* **22,** 805 (1943).

ASMUSSEN, E., Aerobic recovery after anaerobiosis in rest and work, *Acta Physiol. Scandinav.* **11,** 197 (1946).

ASMUSSEN, E., W. VON DÖBELN, and M. NIELSEN, Blood lactate and oxygen debt after exhaustive work at different oxygen tensions, *Acta physiol. Skandinav.* **15,** 57 (1948).

BANSI, H. W., and G. GROSCURTH, Die Kreislaufleistung während und nach der Arbeit beim gesunden und kranken Menschen, *Ztschr. f. Kreislauf.* **22,** 657 (1930).   [39

BANSI, H. W., and G. GROSCURTH, Funktionsprüfung des Kreislaufs durch Messung der Herzarbeit, *Klin Wchnschr.* **9,** 1902 (1930).   [37, 39

BOGARD, W., Beitrag zur Funktionsprüfung von Herz und Kreislauf, *Klin. Wchnschr.* **17,** 73 (1938).   [38

BOLT, W., H. VALENTIN, and H. NEURATH, Herzleistungsbreite der kardialen Linksinsuffizienz, *Ztschr. f. Kreislaufforsch.* **39,** 718 (1950).
                                                                    [38, 39

BOWEN, B. D., and M. E. CARMER, The effect of a standard exercise upon the oxygen consumption of normal, overweight, and chronically ill individuals, *J. Clin. Investigation* **2**, 299 (1925–26).   [37

BRUCE, R. A., F. W. LOVEJOY, JR., P. N. G. YU, and M. E. McDOWELL, Observations of cardiorespiratory performance in normal subjects under unusual stress during exercise, *Arch. Indust. Hyg. & Occupat. Med.* **6**, 105 (1952).

CAMPBELL, M., The respiratory exchange during exercise in heart disease. III, *Quart. J. Med.* **27**, 369 (1934).   [37, 38, 39

CAMPBELL, J. M. H., and F. J. SALE, Effect of exercise on respiratory exchange in heart disease. II, *Arch. Int. Med.* **40**, 237 (1927).   [37, 39

CLARK-KENNEDY, A. E., and T. OWEN, The limitation of muscular effort and its relation to cardiac failure, *Quart. J. Med.* **20**, 383 (1926).

DE CARRASCO, H. O., and W. VORWERK, Beitrag zur Lungen- und Herzfunktionsprüfung, *Arch. f. exper. Path. u. Pharmakol.* **184**, 156 (1936).   [38

DENNIG, H., J. H. TALBOTT, H. T. EDWARDS, and D. B. DILL, Effect of acidosis and alkalosis upon capacity for work, *J. Clin. Investigation* **9**, 601 (1930–31).

EPPINGER, H., and K. HINSBERG, Ueber die Möglichkeit einer peripheren Behandlung der Herzkranken, *Klin. Wchnschr.* **7**, 2284 (1928).   [37, 39

EPPINGER, H., F. KISCH, and H. SCHWARZ, Arbeit und Kreislauf, *Klin. Wchnschr.* **4**, 1101 (1925).   [37, 39

EPPINGER, H., F. KISCH, and H. SCHWARZ, *Das Versagen des Kreislaufes; dynamische und energetische Ursachen* (Berlin, 1927).   [37

HARRIS, I., and I. J. LIPKIN, Cardiac output and oxygen utilization in some types of heart disease, *Edinburgh M. J.* **38**, 501 (1931).   [37, 39

HARRISON, T. R., and C. PILCHER, Studies in congestive failure. II. The respiratory exchange during and after exercise, *J. Clin. Investigation* **8**, 291 (1929–30).   [37, 39

HERBST, R., Der Gasstoffwechsel als Mass der körperlichen Leistungsfähigkeit. II. Untersuchungen bei Emphysem, chronischer Bronchitis und Asthma bronchiale, *Deutsches Arch. f. klin. Med.* **162**, 129 (1928a).

HERBST, R., Der Gasstoffwechsel als Mass der körperlichen Leistungsfähigkeit. III. Untersuchungen am Herzkranken, *Deutsches Arch. f. klin. Med.* **162**, 257 (1928b).   [37, 38

HERRMANSEN, J., Die ergometrische Methode als Funktionsprüfung für Herz und Lunge, *Beitr. z. Klin. d. Tuberk.* **92**, 395 (1938).   [38

HICK, F. K., A. W. CHRISTIAN, and P. W. SMITH, Criteria of oxygen want, with especial reference to neurocirculatory asthenia, *Am. J. M. Sc.* **194**, 800 (1937).

JACOBAEUS, H. C., G. NYLIN, and B. ALMBERG, Recherches sur l'influence d'une diminution expérimentale de la mobilité du thorax sur la dette d'oxygène après travail gradué, *Acta med. Scandinav.* **86,** 455 (1935).

JANSEN, K., H. W. KNIPPING, and K. STROMBERGER, Klinische Untersuchungen über Atmung und Blutgase, *Beitr. z. Klin. d. Tuberk.* **80,** 304 (1932).

JERVELL, O., Investigation of the concentration of lactic acid in blood and urine under physiologic and pathologic conditions, *Acta med. Scandinav., Supp. No. 24,* 5 (1928).

KATZ, L. N., S. SOSKIN, W. J. SCHUTZ, W. ACKERMAN, and J. L. PLAUT, A "metabolic exercise tolerance test" for patients with cardiac disease. A feasible method for using the excess oxygen consumption and the recovery time of exercise as criteria of the cardiac status, *Arch. Int. Med.* **53,** 710 (1934).   [37, 39

KNIPPING, H. W., W. LEWIS, and A. MONCRIEFF, Ueber die Dyspnoe, *Beitr. z. Klin. d. Tuberk.* **79,** 1 (1932).

MALINOW, M. R., B. MOIA, and M. MANGUEL, Efficacité de l'oxygenotherapie determinée par la mesure de la consommation d'oxygène, *Acta cardiol.* **5,** 457 (1950).

MEAKINS, J., and C. N. H. LONG, Oxygen consumption, oxygen debt and lactic acid in circulatory failure, *J. Clin. Investigation* **4,** 273 (1927).   [37, 38, 39

NIELSEN, H. E., Clinical investigations into the cardiac output of patients with compensated heart disease during rest and during muscular work, *Acta med. Scandinav.* **91,** 223 (1937).   [39

NYLIN, G., Clinical tests of the function of the heart, *Acta med. Scandinav., Supp. No. 52,* 1 (1933).   [37

NYLIN, G., More recent developments of heart function tests, *J. A. M. A.* **109,** 1333 (1937).   [37

NYLIN, G., The practical applicability of the cardiopulmonary function test, *Acta med. Scandinav., Supp. No. 93,* 1 (1938).   [37

NYLIN, G., L'influence de la digitale sur la dette relative d'oxygène dans l'insuffisance cardiaque latente à rhythme cardiaque normal, *Arch. d. mal du cœur* **32,** 1010 (1939).   [37

ORNSTEIN, G. G., M. HERMAN, M. W. FRIEDMAN, and E. FRIEDLANDER, Pulmonary function tests. A discussion of ventilatory tests. A description of a method for measuring the diffusion of oxygen and carbon dioxide in the lungs, *Am. Rev. Tuberc.* **53,** 306 (1946).

SCHLOMOVITZ, B. H., A. B. THOMPSON, and L. G. GLICKMAN, A functional test in chronic pulmonary disease, *Am. Rev. Tuberc.* **37,** 369 (1938).   [37

SIMONSON, E., and K. GOLLWITZER-MEIER, Beiträge zur pathologischen Physiologie des respiratorischen Stoffwechsels. I. Mitt. Über den

Arbeitumsatz bei Herzinsuffizienz, *Ztschr. f. d. ges. exper. Med.* **71,** 329 (1930).   [37

STURGIS, C. C., F. W. PEABODY, F. C. HALL, and F. FREMONT-SMITH, Clinical studies on the respiration. VIII. The relation of dyspnea to the maximum minute-volume of pulmonary ventilation, *Arch. Int. Med.* **29,** 236 (1922).

SUTTON, F. C., J. A. BRITTON, and J. G. CARR, Estimation of cardiopulmonary functional capacity by means of oxygen debt studies, *Am. Heart J.* **20,** 423 (1940).   [37

THOMAS, D., Das sogennante erregbare Soldatenherz, *Deutsche. med. Wchnschr.* **66,** 989 (1940).   [37

UHLENBRUCK, P., Ueber die Wirksamkeit der Sauerstoffatmung, *Ztschr. f. d. ges. exper. Med.* **74,** 1 (1930).

VON PEIN, H., Die Messung des Gasstoffwechsels bei Belastungen also Herzfunktionsprüfung, *Ztschr. f. klin. Med.* **132,** 227 (1937).   [37

ZAEPER, G., Ueber Bedeutung und Verwertung arbeitsphysiologischer Erkenntnisse in der Klinik der Lungen- und Kreislauferkrankungen, *Deutsches Arch. f. klin. Med.* **186,** 1 (1940).

ZAEPER, G., H. HAEBISCH, A. CRANEFOD, and W. WOLF. Zur Charakterisierung bestimmter Formen von cardialer Arbeitsinsufficienz durch Arbeitsatmung, *Klin. Wchnschr.* **18,** 270 (1939).

17. *Plasma Protein and Oncotic Pressure*

Lowering of the plasma protein level in patients with cardiac decompensation has been recognized for over a half a century (**40;** Payne and Peters, 1932; Ellis, 1933). On the other hand, a few authors have reported normal values for plasma protein in their patients (Moore and Stewart, 1930; Kylin, 1931; Hand, 1934; Eichna *et al.*, 1951). Stewart (1941) and Moore and Stewart (1930) described the plasma specific gravity as normal also; Di Palma and Kendall (1944) and Layne *et al.* (1950), however, found the specific gravity low. Kylin (1931), who found the plasma protein level normal, reported low values for colloid oncotic pressure, which suggests some error in his techniques. It must be concluded that lowering of plasma protein level is of common occurrence in chronic cardiac decompensation.

As pointed out by Payne and Peters (1932), Thomson (1934), Luetscher (1941), Herrmann (1946), Nonnebruch (1943), Schwalm and Bröder (1943), Colcher *et al.* (1946), Dyer *et al.* (1949), Felder *et al.* (1950), Evans *et al.* (1952), and Sterling (1951), the plasma albumin is more likely to be so affected than the globulin. The globulin levels are more variable and may often be elevated, according to these authors and also to Rowe (1917) and Sherlock (1951). As is to be expected, the plasma colloid oncotic pressure is often low (**41**; Smirk, 1936); marked differences between arterial and venous bloods reported by some authors (Barath and Elias, 1930; Kylin, 1931) are difficult to accept. In a general way, low plasma protein levels or diminished plasma oncotic pressures are associated with the presence of edema, but in large series of patients (Cope, 1928; Payne and Peters, 1932; Ellis, 1933) a high degree of correlation between the presence of edema and a decrease in plasma protein level does not exist. Smirk (1936) showed that edema does not occur in non-cardiac patients in whom are found plasma protein levels as low as those that occur in edematous cardiac patients.

Ellis (1933) has contributed an excellent analysis of the pathogenesis of the changes in plasma protein, from which the present discussion deviates only slightly. Payne and Peters (1932), Ellis (1933) and Thomson (1934) stressed malnutrition as the principal cause of the observed diminution in plasma total protein and albumin levels, and the data of Proger and Magendantz (1936) show a fall of 50 per cent in plasma albumin in a cardiac patient in whom there was restriction of intake of food over a sixty-day period; the globulin rose in these experiments. Conversely, Ellis (1933) demonstrated the beneficial effects of a high protein intake. On the other hand, Felder *et al.* (1950) found that simple malnutrition played a secondary role. Several authors (Iversen and Nakazawa, 1927; Ellis, 1933; Ehrström, 1936) regard the marked albuminuria frequently seen in severe cardiac decompensation as an important contributory cause. Loss of protein as a consequence of repeated paracentesis may also be a factor (Ellis, 1933), for large amounts of protein are found in thoracic and abdominal fluids in congestive failure (page 141). The development of edema itself lowers the plasma protein level, either as a consequence of dilution of the blood or because protein is lost into edema fluids, or both. Thus salt retention causes lowering of plasma protein levels (Iversen and Nakazawa, 1927; Lyons *et al.*, 1944, 1945) in both normal subjects and cardiac patients. That some protein does pass into tissue fluid when the venous pressure is elevated has been shown by Senator (1888) and Landis *et al.* (1932). Increased protein catabolism caused by acidosis may also be a factor in patients receiving large amounts of ammonium chloride (page 273). Even in the absence of such medication, the rate of protein turnover seems to be accelerated in cardiac decompensation (Sterling, 1951).

The presence of severe hepatic damage is to be expected when the plasma globulin level is elevated in cardiac decompensation. Increase in globulin concentration of the plasma leads to a slight increase in the viscosity of the latter (Schwalm and Bröder, 1943); this finding is probably of no clinical significance. The observation of Glass (1950) that the serum of most patients with congestive failure has an abnormally high coagulation point probably reflects changes in composition of the plasma protein.

Loss of edema is commonly associated with a rise in plasma protein concentration, specific gravity, or oncotic pressure (**42**; Calvin *et al.*, 1940; Payne and Peters, 1932), although this finding is far from constant. Calvin, Decherd, and Herrmann (1940) and Seymour *et al.* (1942) stressed the fact that although plasma protein concentration rises, the total circulating plasma protein decreases in recovery from failure; this phenomenon suggests storage of protein.

Bibliography

Chapter I — Section 17

ALTSCHULE, M. D., and E. BUDNITZ, Rheumatic disease of the tricuspid valve, *Arch. Path.* **30**, 7 (1940).   [40

ALTSCHULE, M. D., and M. C. VOLK, Bilirubin in edema fluids in cardiac decompensation, *Proc. Soc. Exper. Biol. & Med.* **37**, 184 (1937).   [40

ATCHLEY, D. W., and E. M. BENEDICT, Serum electrolyte studies in normal and pathological conditions, pneumonia, renal edema, cardiac edema, uremia and diabetic acidosis, *J. Clin. Investigation* **9**, 265 (1930).   [40, 42

ATCHLEY, D. W., R. F. LOEB, E. M. BENEDICT, and W. W. PALMER. Physical and chemical studies of human blood serum. III. A study of miscellaneous disease conditions, *Arch. Int. Med.* **31**, 616 (1923).   [42

134 CHRONIC CARDIAC DECOMPENSATION

BARATH, E., and H. ELIAS, Klinische Beiträge zum Verhalten des on-kotischen (kolloidosmotischen) Druckes. II. Der onkotische Druck im Serum des arteriellen und venösen Blutes bei Kreislaufstörungen, *Ztschr. f. klin. Med.* **114,** 708 (1930). [41

BARNES, A. R., and J. KNUTSON, Evidence of hemodilution during diuresis produced by salyrgan in patients with congestive heart failure and a discussion on its possible clinical implications, *Tr. A. Am. Physicians* **62,** 169 (1949). [40

BARKER, M. H., Edema as influenced by a low ratio of sodium to potassium intake. Clinical observations, *J. A. M. A.* **98,** 2193 (1932). [40, 42

BECKMANN, K., Ödemstudien, *Deutsches Arch. f. klin. Med.* **135,** 39 (1921). [40, 42

BIÖRCK, G., S. HEDLUND, J. KARNELL, and H. KARNI, Serum proteiner vid hjartsjukdomar, *Nordisk Med.* **38,** 1179 (1948). [40, 42

BORST, J. G. G., The maintenance of an adequate cardiac output by the regulation of the urinary excretion of water and sodium chloride; an essential factor in the genesis of edema, *Acta med. Scandinav. Supp.*, 207 (1948). [40, 42

BRAMKAMP, R. G., The protein content of subcutaneous edema fluid in heart disease, *J. Clin. Investigation* **14,** 34 (1935). [40

BROD, J., and Z. FEJFAR, The origin of oedema in heart failure, *Quart. J. Med.* **19,** 187 (1950). [40

CALVIN, D. B., G. DECHERD, and G. HERRMANN, Plasma protein shifts during diuresis, *Proc. Soc. Exper. Biol. & Med.* **44,** 578 (1940). [42

CLAUSSEN, F., Ueber die Diurese der Herzkranken, *Ergebn. d. inn. Med. u. Kinderh.* **43,** 764 (1932). [42

COLCHER, H., A. J. PATEK, JR., and F. E. KENDALL, Galactose disappearance from the blood stream. Calculation of a galactose removal constant and its application to a test for liver function, *J. Clin. Investigation* **25,** 768 (1946).

COPE, C. L., The osmotic pressure of the blood proteins in nephritis, *Quart. J. Med.* **22,** 91 (1928). [40, 41

DI PALMA, J. R., and P. E. KENDALL, The relationship between blood volume and blood specific gravity in the recovery from cardiac decompensation, *J. Lab. & Clin. Med.* **29,** 390 (1944). [42

DRYER, R. L., J. H. BUDDE, W. D. PAUL, and J. I. ROUTH, Electrophoretic comparison of plasma and body fluid proteins in certain diseases, *Federation Proc.* **8,** 195 (1949).

EHRSTRÖM, M. C., Hypoproteinemi, stasalbuminurii och kardiala ödem, *Finska läk.-sällsk. handl.* **79,** 59 (1936). [40

EICHNA, L., S. J. FARBER, A. R. BERGER, D. P. EARLE, B. RADER, E. PELLE-GRINO, R E. ALBERT, J. D. ALEXANDER, H. TAUBE, and S. YOUNGWIRTH, The interrelationship of the cardiovascular, renal and electrolyte effects of intravenous digoxin in congestive heart failure, *J. Clin. Investigation* 30, 1250 (1951).   [40

EICHNA, L., S. J. FARBER, A. R. BERGER, D. P. EARLE, B. RADER, E. PELLE-GRINO, R. E. ALBERT, J. D. ALEXANDER, H. TAUBE, and S. YOUNGWIRTH, Cardiovascular dynamics, blood volumes, renal functions and electrolyte excretions in the same patients during congestive heart failure and after recovery of cardiac decompensation, *Circulation* 7, 674 (1953).

ELLIS, L. B., Plasma protein deficiency in patients with cardiac edema, *M. Clin. North America* 16, 943 (1933).   [40

EVANS, J. M., H. J. ZIMMERMAN, J. G. WILMER, L. J. THOMAS, and C. B. ETHRIDGE, Altered liver function of chronic congestive heart failure, *Am. J. Med.* 13, 705 (1952).

FELDER, L., A. MUND, and J. G. PARKER, Liver function tests in chronic congestive heart failure, *Circulation* 2, 286 (1950).   [40

FODOR, A., and G. H. FISCHER, Chemische und kolloidchemische Untersuchung des Blutserums und der Oedemflüssigkeit bei Oedematösen, *Ztschr. f. d. ges. exper. Med.* 29, 465 (1922).   [40, 42

GILLIGAN, D. R., M. C. VOLK, and M. D. ALTSCHULE, The diffusibility of plasma calcium following parathormone administration. Comparison of the calcium, phosphate and protein concentrations of serum and edema fluids, *J. Biol. Chem.* 103, 745 (1933).   [40

GILLIGAN, D. R., M. C. VOLK, and H. L. BLUMGART, Observations on the chemical and physical relation between blood serum and body fluids. I. The nature of edema fluids and evidence regarding the mechanism of edema formation, *J. Clin. Investigation* 13, 365 (1934).   [40, 42

GLASS, G. B. J., The thermal coagulation point of blood serum. I. Method and clinical interpretation, *Am. J. Med.* 8, 745 (1950).

GOLLWITZER-MEIER, K., Zur Oedempathogenese, *Ztschr. f. d. ges. exper. Med.* 46, 15 (1925).   [40

HAND, H. H., Concentration of serum protein in different types of edema. Illustrative cases, *Arch. Int. Med.* 54, 215 (1934).

HERRMANN, G. R., Blood plasma proteins in patients with heart failure, *Ann. Int. Med.* 24, 893 (1946).   [40

HOFFMANN, F. A., Globulinbestimmungen in Ascitesflüssigkeiten, *Arch. f. exper. Path. u. Pharmakol.* 16, 133 (1882).   [40

HORNBOSTEL, H., Feuchte Kreislaufdekompensation und Eiweissmangel, *Ztschr. f. Kreislaufforsch.* 39, 271 (1950).   [40, 41

HORSTERS, H., Oedemstudien. II. Krankheitszustände mit Aenderung des kolloid osmotischen Druckes, *Arch. f. exper. Path. u. Pharmakol.* **155**, 248 (1930). [41

IVERSEN, P., and E. H. JOHANSEN, Pathogenese und Resorption von Trans- und Exsudaten in der Pleura (Salyrganwirkung), *Klin. Wchnschr.* **8**, 309 (1929). [40, 42

IVERSEN, P., and F. NAKAZAWA, Om Oedempatogenese, *Ugesk. f. Læger.* **89**, 640 (1927). [40, 42

JAMES, A. H., The mechanism of pleural and ascitic effusions with a suggestive method for the indirect estimation of portal venous pressure, *Clin. Sc.* **8**, 291 (1949). [40

KYLIN, E., Studien über den kolloidosmotischen (onkotischen) Druck. XIV. Ueber den intermediären Wasserstoffwechsel bei Oedemstehung und Oedemausschwemmung, *Ztschr. f. d. ges. exper. Med.* **77**, 289 (1931). [41

LANDIS, E. M., L. JONAS, M. ANGEVINE, and W. ERB. The passage of fluid and protein through the human capillary wall during venous congestion, *J. Clin. Investigation* **11**, 717 (1932).

LAYNE, J. A., F. R. SCHEMM, and W. W. HURST, Further comparative studies on ascites in liver and heart disease, *Gastroenterol.* **16**, 91 (1950). [40, 42

LOEB, R. F., D. W. ATCHLEY, and W. W. PALMER, On the equilibrium condition between blood serum and serous cavity fluids, *J. Gen. Physiol.* **4**, 591 (1922). [40

LUETSCHER, J. A., JR., Electrophoretic analysis of the proteins of plasma and serous effusions, *J. Clin. Investigation* **20**, 99 (1941). [40

LYONS, R. H., S. D. JACOBSON, and N. L. AVERY, Increases in the plasma volume following the administration of sodium salts, *Am. J. M. Sc.* **208**, 148 (1944).

LYONS, R. H., S. D. JACOBSON, and J. L. NEERKIN, The relationship between changes in serum protein concentration and the plasma volume in normal subjects, *J. Lab. & Clin. Med.* **30**, 404 (1945).

MAYRS, E. B., The functional pathology of nephritis, *Quart. J. Med.* **19**, 273 (1926). [40, 41

MENEELY, G. R., and N. L. KALTREIDER, A study of the volume of the blood in congestive heart failure. Relation to other measurements in fifteen patients, *J. Clin. Investigation* **22**, 521 (1943). [40

MOORE, N. S., and H. J. STEWART, The variations of the specific gravity of the plasma of the blood and the means available for altering it, *J. Clin. Investigation* **9**, 423 (1930–31).

MUNTWYLER, E., C. T. WAY, D. BINNS, and V. C. MYERS, Plasma protein and plasma colloid osmotic pressure in pathological conditions with special reference to the occurrence of edema, *J. Clin. Investigation* **12**, 495 (1933).   [40

NIGGLI, S., Bluteiweissveränderungen bei Herzmuskelinsuffizienz, *Cardiologia* **17**, 29 (1950).

NONNENBRUCH, W., Klinische Odembeobachtungen (Die sog. Myodegeneratio cordis usw), *Deutsches Arch. f. klin. Med.* **191**, 113 (1943).   [40, 42

OELKERS, H. A., Untersuchungen über den kolloidosmotischen Druck des Serums, *Ztschr. f. klin. Med.* **115**, 854 (1931).   [41

PAYNE, S. A., and J. P. PETERS, The plasma proteins in relation to blood hydration. VIII. Serum proteins in heart disease, *J. Clin. Investigation* **11**, 103 (1932).   [40, 42

PROGER, S. H., and H. MAGENDANTZ, Effect of prolonged dietary restriction on patients with cardiac failure, *Arch. Int. Med.* **58**, 703 (1936).

RICHARDS, D. W., JR., and A. L. BARACH, Prolonged residence in high oxygen atmospheres. Effects on normal individuals and on patients with chronic cardiac and pulmonary insufficiency, *Quart. J. Med.* **3**, 437 (1934).   [40, 42

ROWE, A. H., Refractometric studies of serum proteins in nephritis, cardiac decompensation, diabetes, anemia, and other chronic diseases, *Arch. Int. Med.* **19**, 354 (1917).   [40

SALVESEN, H. A., and G. C. LINDER, Observations on the inorganic bases and phosphates in relation to the protein of blood and other body fluids in Bright's disease and in heart failure, *J. Biol. Chem.* **58**, 617 (1923).   [40

SCHWALM, H., and M. BRÖDER, Die Blutviskosimetrie in der Untersuchung des Wasserhaushaltes, *Deutsches Arch. f. klin. Med.* **191**, 455 (1943).   [40

SENATOR, H., Ueber Transsudation und über den Einfluss des Blutdrucks auf die Beschaffenheit der Transsudate, *Virchows Arch. f. path. Anat.* **111**, 219 (1888).

SEYMOUR, W. B., W. H. PRITCHARD, L. P. LONGLEY, and J. M. HAYMAN, JR., Cardiac output, blood, and interstitial fluid volumes, total circulating serum protein, and kidney function during cardiac failure and after improvement, *J. Clin. Investigation* **21**, 229 (1942).   [40, 42

SHANE, S. J., The plasma proteins in heart failure, *Canad. M. A. J.* **58**, 274 (1948).   [40

SHERLOCK, S., The liver in heart failure. Relation of anatomical, functional, and circulatory changes, *Brit. Heart J.* **13**, 273 (1951).

SMIRK, F. H., Observations on the causes of oedema in congestive heart failure, *Clin. Sc.* **2**, 317 (1936).   [41

STEAD, E. A., J. V. WARREN, and E. S. BRANNON, Cardiac output in congestive heart failure. An analysis of the reasons for the lack of close correlation between the symptoms of heart failure and the resting cardiac output, *Am. Heart J.* **35,** 529 (1948).   [40

STERLING, K., Serum albumin turnover in Laennec's cirrhosis as measured by I-131-tagged albumin, *J. Clin. Investigation* **30,** 1238 (1951).

STEWART, H. J., Mechanism of diuresis: alterations in the specific gravity of the blood plasma with onset of diuresis in heart failure, *J. Clin. Investigation* **20,** 1 (1941).

THOMSON, W. A. R., The plasma proteins and cardiac oedema, *Quart. J. Med.* **3,** 587 (1934).   [40, 41

WHITE, A. G., and B. A. SACHS, Studies in edema: cholesterol and its relation to protein nitrogen in edema fluid, *Science* **112,** 18 (1950).   [40

WOOD, W. B., and C. A. JANEWAY, Changes in plasma volume during recovery from congestive failure, *Arch. Int. Med.* **62,** 151 (1938).   [40

18. *Extracellular Fluid Volume. Edema Fluid*

Extracellular fluid volume. — Cardiac patients with edema have increased volume of fluid in the extracellular tissue spaces and in many cases in the serous cavities as well. This abnormally increased volume of fluid may be enormous; the loss of fifty pounds — a third or a quarter of the body weight — during a diuresis is not uncommon in severely edematous patients. Measurements of extracellular fluid volume by means of radioactive sodium (Kaltreider *et al.*, 1941; Prentice *et al.*, 1951; Warner *et al.*, 1952; Aikawa, 1952), chloride ion (Dunning *et al.*, 1951), bromide ion (Ferraro *et al.*, 1949; Brodie *et al.*, 1939) or thiocyanate (Gilligan and Altschule, 1939; Molenaar and Roller, 1939; Kaltreider *et al.*, 1941; Seymour *et al.*, 1942; Fowell *et al.*, 1948; Aikawa, 1952; Cardozo and Edelman, 1952; Miller, 1951; Briggs *et al.*, 1948) have been made in patients with heart disease; extracellular fluid volume may equal one-half to two-thirds of the body weight, as compared to the normal of a fifth or a quarter. Gilligan and Altschule (1939) found that such measurements were subject to error in the presence of marked generalized edema or single large accumulations of fluid in a body cavity, unless sufficient time were allowed for equilibration of injected thiocyanate. The same is true for inulin and mannitol (Last *et al.*, 1952).

The colloid content of the transudate apparently influences the distribution of thiocyanate, so that the presence of transudates of relatively high protein content, such as peritoneal and pleural effusions, makes the precise measurement of extracellular fluid volume impossible. The most recent work (Kaltreider *et al.*, 1941) suggests that thiocyanate combines with blood lipids. These measurements are, however, accurate when such large effusions are absent.

Molenaar and Roller (1939) found the extracellular fluid increased in some cardiac patients even in the absence of overt signs of failure; after recovery from severe congestive failure with edema the volume of extracellular fluid is still increased, often by half its normal volume (Altschule, 1937; Seymour *et al.*, 1942; Ferraro *et al.*, 1949). The body may actually harbor six or seven liters of edema fluid when the patient is considered to be free of edema or is even declared to be "cured of right heart failure."

The extracellular fluid volume increases after exercise in normal subjects (Collumbine and Koch, 1949). Even greater changes probably occur in patients with congestive heart failure.

Total body water. — Measurements, by means of the antipyrine method, of total body water in patients with cardiac edema reveal surprisingly low values, that is, in or only a little above the normal range (Soberman *et al.*, 1949; Steele *et al.*, 1950; Prentice *et al.*, 1952; Hurst *et al.*, 1952). Values obtained with deuterium or tritium are somewhat higher (Prentice *et al.*, 1952; Hurst *et al.*, 1952). The possibility must be considered that accumulation of greatly excessive amounts of extracellular fluid is associated with an electrolytic disturbance that causes depletion of intracellular water (and electrolytes).

Ionic constitution of edema fluid. — That cardiac edema is an ultrafiltrate derived from plasma appears to be established (Loeb *et al.*, 1922; Hastings *et al.*, 1925; Gilligan *et al.*, 1934*a,b*; Folk *et al.*, 1948). Data on the ionic constitution of edema fluid have also been published by Kylin (1927), Soloff *et al.* (1952), and Schroeder (1950, 1951). The fact that the ionic constitutions of plasma and of edema fluid are not identical is related to the differences in colloid content and is explicable on the basis of the Donnan equilibrium; edema fluid contains significantly more chloride than plasma, and changes in other electrolyte ratios have also been found. There seems to be no need to invoke vitalistic phenomena to explain edema formation in chronic congestive failure. Changing the ionic constitution of blood plasma by giving bicarbonate or ammonium chloride or by diuresis causes corresponding changes in edema fluid (Gilligan *et al.* 1943*a*; Schroeder, 1951).

Protein content. — Many authors have studied the protein content of subcutaneous edema fluid by the use of a variety of methods (**43**; Bramkamp, 1935). The reported values obtained by acceptable methods have usually been less than 0.6 Gm. per hundred cubic centimeters, although occasional levels of 1.0 Gm. per cent or more have been described. Bramkamp (1935) found little or no globulin in subcutaneous edema fluid drawn from patients with chronic cardiac decompensation. The fact that cardiac subcutaneous edema fluid contains more protein than the edema fluid of patients with renal disease (Beckmann, 1921; Falta and Quittner, 1917; Fodor and Fischer, 1922; Hoffman, 1889; Kerkhof, 1937; Vancura, 1931) or malnutrition (Falta and Quittner, 1917) has been recorded and suggests an increase in capillary permeability in congestive failure. However, Vancura (1931) found the ratio between plasma and edema fluid protein the same in cardiac and renal disease. On the other hand, Bramkamp (1935) found no relation between plasma and edema fluid protein in cardiacs. Stead and Warren (1944) obtained fluids from the subcutaneous tissues of the edematous extremities of cardiac patients and found their protein content to lie between 0.1 and 0.5 Gm. per hundred cubic centimeters. After these patients lost their edema, these authors placed tourniquets at a pressure of 40 cm-of-water about their limbs and obtained fluids containing 0.4 to 0.9 Gm.; they concluded that the fact that edema fluid from sick cardiac patients contained no more protein than that obtained from such patients after recovery indicated that no increase in capillary permeability occurred in cardiac decompensation. However, tourniquets at that pressure slow the blood flow (Friedland, Hunt and Wilkins, 1941), and there is no way of estimating the direction or the amount of difference in flow in the extremities of their cardiac patients when sick without tourniquets and when "recovered" with them in place; studies of venous blood oxygen would have been helpful. Senator (1888) recorded the interesting observation that putting a tourniquet about the limb of a cardiac patient with edema may raise the protein content of the edema fluid by as much as 40 per cent. More recently, Landis *et al.* (1932) published data in support of this finding in normal subjects, estimating an edema fluid protein level of 0.3 at tourniquet pressures up to 60 mm-of-mercury and of 1.5 at 80 mm-of-mercury. It is not possible, therefore, to evaluate the significance of the findings of Stead and Warren (1944) or to accept their conclusions.

Pleural fluids (**44**; Luetscher, 1941) and ascitic fluids (**45**; Luetscher, 1941) in cardiac patients contain appreciably larger amounts of protein than are to be found in subcutaneous edema fluids. Pleural fluids usually contain 1.0 to 3.0 Gm. per hundred cubic centimeters and abdominal fluids from 1.0 to as much as 5.0 Gm. The reason for these variations in protein content in fluids derived from various parts of the body is not apparent. Luetscher (1941) made a systematic study of the protein in pleural and abdominal fluids and found that such fluids taken from cardiac patients contained more protein than those removed from patients with renal disease or cirrhosis of the liver. Fluids obtained from cardiac patients also contained relatively more albumin and less globulin than either the plasma of the same patients or the fluids of patients with renal disease or cirrhosis, according to Luetscher (1941). On the other hand, Dryer *et al.* (1949) found that the electrophoretic composition of transudates resembled that of the plasmas from which they were derived. The significance of these differences is not clear, but it is to be noted that the deviations in the ratio of albumin to globulin in transudates in congestive failure resemble those seen in toxic edema due to increased capillary permeability (Chanutin *et al.*, 1947).

Lepehne (1951) showed that the positive cephalin flocculation and thymol turbidity tests may be obtained upon ascitic fluids of patients with congestive failure in whom hepatic damage caused these tests to become positive in the serum.

The joints in edematous extremities of cardiac patients contain much more fluid than normal (Coggeshall *et al.*, 1941; Gillanders, 1951), but the mucin, protein, and total solid concentrations are all lower.

All types of edema fluids frequently show elevation of protein concentration during and after diuresis (Beckmann, 1921; Claussen, 1932; Gilligan *et al.*, 1933, 1934*a*; Iversen and Johansen, 1929); the finding of Stead and Warren (1944) that the edema fluid protein does not change under these circumstances is discordant. The occurrence of such changes makes the use of data on tissue fluid content difficult to interpret in relation to variations in capillary permeability.

A finding of unknown significance is that the cholinesterase content of edema fluid varies with that of the plasma and also with the amount of protein in the blood (Grob *et al.*, 1947).

Lipid contents. — The cholesterol, total lipid and fatty acid concentrations of transudates vary with the protein content of these fluids and not with the plasma concentrations of any of them (Man and Peters, 1933). The cholesterol content of edema fluids is low (Chauffard, 1911). The cholesterol-ester content of edema fluid is relatively low (White and Sachs, 1950).

Bibliography

Chapter I — Section 18

AIKAWA, J., Comparison of the thiocyanate and radiosodium spaces in disease states, *Am. J. M. Sc.* **224,** 632 (1952).

ALTSCHULE, M. D., Latent edema following treatment for chronic congestive failure, *Unpublished data* (1938).

ALTSCHULE, M. D., and M. C. VOLK, Bilirubin in edema fluids in cardiac decompensation, *Proc. Soc. Exper. Biol. & Med.* **37,** 184 (1937).
[43, 44, 45

BECKMANN, K., Ödemstudien, *Deutsches Arch. f. klin. Med.* **135,** 39 (1921).   ⌈43

BRAMKAMP, R. G., The protein content of subcutaneous edema fluid in heart disease, *J. Clin. Investigation* **14,** 34 (1935).   [43

BRIGGS, A. P., D. M. FOWELL, W. F. HAMILTON, J. W. REMINGTON, N. C. WHEELER, and J. A. WINSLOW, Renal and circulatory factors in the edema formation of congestive heart failure, *J. Clin. Investigation* **27,** 810 (1948).

BRODIE, B. D., E. BRAND, and S. LESHIN, The use of bromide as a measure of extracellular fluid, *J. Biol. Chem.* **130,** 555 (1939).

CARDOZO, R. H., and I. S. EDELMAN, The volume of distribution of sodium thiosulfate as a measure of the extracellular fluid space, *J. Clin. Investigation* **31,** 280 (1952).

CHANUTIN, A., E. C. GJESSING, and S. LUDWIG, Alpha naphthylthiourea (Antu) in dogs: electrophoretic and cholesterol studies on blood plasma and pleural effusion, *Proc. Soc. Exper. Biol. & Med.* **64,** 174 (1947).

CHAUFFARD, A., Dosage comparé de la cholesterine dans le sérum et dans les oedèmes, *Compt. rend. Soc. biol.* **70**, 317 (1911).

CLAUSSEN, F., Ueber die Diurese der Herzkranken, *Ergebn. d. inn. Med. u. Kinderh.* **43**, 764 (1932). [**44, 45**

COGGESHALL, H. C., G. A. BENNETT, C. F. WARREN, and W. BAUER, Synovial fluid and synovial membrane abnormalities resulting from varying grades of systemic infection and edema, *Am. J. M. Sc.* **202**, 486 (1941).

COLLUMBINE, H., and A. C. E. KOCH, The changes in plasma and tissue fluid volume following exercise, *Quart. J. Exper. Physiol.* **35**, 39 (1949).

DRYER, R. L., J. H. BUDDE, W. D. PAUL, and J. I. ROUTH, Electrophoretic comparison of plasma and body fluid proteins in certain diseases, *Federation Proc.* **8**, 195 (1949). [**44, 45**

DUNNING, M. F., J. M. STEELE, and E. Y. BERGER, Measurement of total body chloride, *Proc. Soc. Exper. Biol. & Med.* **77**, 854 (1951).

FALTA, W., and M. QUITTNER, Ueber den Chemismus verschiedener Oedemformen, *Wien. klin. Wchnschr.* **30**, 1189 (1917). [**43**

FERRARO, L. R., M. M. FRIEDMAN, and H. E. MORELLI, Extracellular fluid in cardiac edema and ascites, *Arch. Int. Med.* **83**, 292 (1949).

FODOR, A., and G. H. FISCHER, Chemische und kolloidchemische Untersuchung des Blutserums und der Oedemflüssigkeit bei Oedematösen, *Ztschr. f. d. ges. exper. Med.* **29**, 465 (1922). [**43**

FOLK, B. P., K. L. ZIERLER, and J. L. LILIENTHAL, JR., Distribution of potassium and sodium between serum and certain extracellular fluids in man, *Am. J. Physiol.* **153**, 381 (1948).

FOWELL, D. M., A. P. BRIGGS, N. C. WHEELER, J. A. WINSLOW, JR., J. W. REMINGTON, and W. F. HAMILTON, Renal and circulatory factors in congestive failure of the circulation, *Federation Proc.* **7**, 35 (1948).

FRIEDLAND, C. K., J. S. HUNT, and R. W. WILKINS, Effects of changes in venous pressure upon blood flow in the limbs, *Am. Heart J.* **25**, 631 (1941).

GILLANDERS, A. D., Nutritional heart disease, *Brit. Heart J.* **13**, 177 (1951). [**43, 44, 45**

GILLIGAN, D. R., and M. D. ALTSCHULE, The rate of attainment of diffusion equilibrium for thiocyanate between plasma and transudates following the intravenous injection of sodium thiocyanate in patients with edema, *J. Clin. Investigation* **18**, 501 (1939). [**43, 44, 45**

GILLIGAN, D. R., M. C. VOLK, and M. D. ALTSCHULE, The diffusibility of plasma calcium following parathromone administration. Comparison of the calcium, phosphate and protein concentrations of serum and edema fluids, *J. Biol. Chem.* **103**, 745 (1933). [**43, 44, 45**

GILLIGAN, D. R., M. C. VOLK, and H. L. BLUMGART, Observations on the chemical and physical relation between blood serum and body fluids. I. The nature of edema fluids and evidence regarding the mechanism of edema formation, *J. Clin. Investigation* **13**, 365 (1934a). [**43, 44, 45**

GILLIGAN, D. R., M. C. VOLK, and H. L. BLUMGART, Observations on the chemical and physical relation between blood serum and body fluids. II. The chemical relation between serum and edema fluids as compared with that between serum and cerebrospinal fluid, *New England J. Med.* **210**, 896 (1934b). [**43, 44, 45**

GOLLWITZER-MEIER, K., Zur Oedempathogenese, *Ztschr. f. d. ges. exper. Med.* **46**, 15 (1925). [**43**

GROB, D., J. L. LILIENTHAL, JR., A. M. HARVEY, and B. F. JONES, The administration of di-isopropyl fluorophosphate (DFP) to man I. Effect on plasma and erythrocyte cholinesterase; general systemic effects; use in study of hepatic function and erythropoiesis; and some properties of plasma cholinesterase, *Bull. Johns Hopkins Hosp.* **81**, 217 (1947).

HAAS, G., Fragen zur Pathologie des menschlichen Oedems, *Ztschr. f. exper. Path. u. Therap.* **22**, 375 (1921). [**43**

HASTINGS, A. B., H. A. SALVESEN, J. SENDROY, JR., and D. D. VAN SLYKE, Studies of gas and electrolyte equilibria in the blood. IX. The distribution of electrolytes between transudates and serum, *J. Gen. Physiol.* **8**, 701 (1925). [**43, 45**

HOFFMANN, F. A., Globulinbestimmungen in Ascitesflüssigkeiten, *Arch. f. exper. Path. u. Pharmakol.* **16**, 133 (1882). [**45**

HOFFMANN, F. A., Der Eiweissgehalt der Oedemflüssigkeiten, *Deutsches Arch. f. klin. Med.* **44**, 313 (1889). [**43**

HURST, W. W., F. R. SCHEMM, and W. C. VOGEL, Simultaneous determination of total body water by antipyrine and deuterium oxide; evaluation of the methods on edematous subjects, *J. Lab. & Clin. Med.* **39**, 36 (1952).

IVERSEN, P., and E. H. JOHANSEN, Pathogenese und Resorption von Trans- und Exsudaten in der Pleura (Salyrganwirkung), *Klin. Wchnschr,* **8**, 309 (1929). [**44**

JAMES, A. H., The mechanism of pleural and ascitic effusions, with a suggested method for the indirect estimation of portal venous pressure, *Clin. Sc.* **8**, 291 (1949). [**44, 45**

KALTREIDER, N. L., G. R. MENEELY, J. R. ALLEN, and W. F. BALE, Determination of the volume of the extracellular fluid of the body with radioactive sodium, *J. Exper. Med.* **74**, 569 (1941). [**44, 45**

KERKHOF, A. C., Plasma colloid osmotic pressure as a factor in edema formation and edema absorption, *Ann. Int. Med.* **11**, 867 (1937). [**43**

KYLIN, E., Der Gehalt des Blutes an Calzium und Kalium, *Acta med. Scandinav. Supp.* **19**, 1 (1927).

LANDIS, E. M., L. JONAS, M. ANGEVINE, and W. ERB, The passage of fluid and protein through the human capillary wall during venous congestion, *J. Clin. Investigation* **11**, 717 (1932).

LAST, J. H., G. O. McDONALD, R. A. JONES, and E. E. BOND, Rates of equilibration of inulin and mannitol between plasma and interstitial water in edematous states, *J. Lab. & Clin. Med.* **39**, 62 (1952).

LAYNE, J. A., F. R. SCHEMM, and W. W. HURST, Further comparative studies on ascites in liver and heart disease, *Gastroenterol.* **16**, 91 (1950). [43, 44, 45]

LEPEHNE, G. M., Studies on ascitic fluid in patients with hepatic cirrhosis, heart failure and cancer: results of cephalin cholesterol flocculation, thymol turbidity, methylene blue, qualitative and quantitative bilirubin and other tests, *Am. J. Digest. Dis.* **18**, 86 (1951).

LOEB, R. F., D. W. ATCHLEY, and W. W. PALMER, On the equilibrium condition between blood serum and serous cavity fluids, *J. Gen. Physiol.* **4**, 591 (1922). [45

LUETSCHER, J. A., JR., Electrophoretic analysis of the proteins of plasma and serous effusions, *J. Clin. Investigation* **20**, 99 (1941). [44, 45

MAN, E. B., and J. P. PETERS, Permeability of capillaries to plasma lipids, *J. Clin. Investigation* **12**, 1031 (1933).

MEAKINS, J., Distribution of jaundice in circulatory failure, *J. Clin. Investigation* **4**, 135 (1927). [43, 44, 45

MEYER, P., and I. FRIEDHEIM, Untersuchungen über den kolloidosmotischen Druck biologische Flüssigkeiten. VI. Exsudate und Transudate, *Ztschr. f. klin. Med.* **119**, 236 (1931). [43, 44

MILLER, G. E., Water and electrolyte metabolism in congestive heart failure, *Circulation* **4**, 270 (1951).

MOLENAAR, H., and D. ROLLER, Die Bestimmung der extracellulären Wassers beim Gesunden und Kranken, *Ztschr f. klin. Med.* **136**, 1 (1939).

PRENTICE, T. C., N. I. BERLIN, G. M. HYDE, R. J. PARSONS, J. H. LAWRENCE, and S. PORT, Total red cell volume, plasma volume, and sodium space in congestive heart failure, *J. Clin. Investigation* **30**, 1471 (1951).

PRENTICE, T. C., W. SIRI, N. I. BERLIN, G. M. HYDE, R. J. PARSONS, E. E. JOINER, and J. H. LAWRENCE, Studies of total body water with tritium, *J. Clin. Investigation* **31**, 412 (1952).

REUSS, A., Beiträge zur klinischen Beurtheilung von Exsudaten und Transudaten, *Deutsches Arch. f. klin. Med.* **24**, 583 (1879). [43, 45

SALVESEN, H. A., and G. C. LINDER, Observations on the inorganic bases and phosphates in relation to the protein of blood and other body fluids in Bright's disease and in heart failure, *J. Biol. Chem.* **58**, 617 (1923).   **[43, 44, 45**

SCHALES, O., R. V. EBERT, and E. A. STEAD, JR., Capillary tube Kjeldahl method for determining protein content of 5 to 20 milligrams of tissue fluid, *Proc. Soc. Exper. Biol. & Med.* **49**, 1 (1942).   **[43**

SCHROEDER, H. A., Studies on congestive circulatory failure. III. The relation of edema to urinary chlorides, *Circulation* **1**, 481 (1950).
                                                                                              [44, 45

SCHROEDER, H. A., Studies on congestive circulatory failure. IV. The effect of various diuretics on the excretion of water and chlorides, *Circulation* **4**, 87 (1951).

SENATOR, H., Ueber Transsudation und über den Einfluss des Blutdrucks auf die Beschaffenheit der Transsudate. *Virchows Arch. f. path. Anat.* **111**, 219 (1888).   **[43, 45**

SEYMOUR, W. B., W. H. PRITCHARD, L. P. LONGLEY, and J. M. HAYMAN, JR., Cardiac output, blood and interstitial fluid volumes, total circulating serum protein, and kidney function during cardiac failure and after improvement, *J. Clin. Investigation* **21**, 229 (1942).   **[43, 45**

SOBERMAN, R., B. B. BRODIE, B. B. LEVY, J. AXELROD, V. HOLLANDER, and J. M. STEELE, The use of antipyrine in the measurement of total body water in man, *J. Biol. Chem.* **179**, 31 (1949).

STEAD, E. A., JR., and J. V. WARREN, The protein content of the extracellular fluid in normal subjects after venous congestion and in patients with cardiac failure, anoxemia and fever, *J. Clin. Investigation* **23**, 283 (1944)   **[43**

STEELE, J. M., E. Y. BERGER, M. F. DUNNING, and B. B. BRODIE, Total body water in man, *Am. J. Physiol.* **162**, 313 (1950).

SOLOFF, L. A., J. ZATUCHNI, and J. H. BOUTWELL, The relationship of some electrolytes of the serum, edema fluid, and urine in a case of intractable heart failure, *Am. Heart J.* **44**, 766 (1952).

VANCURA, A., Altérations de la perméabilité des parois capillaires dans les maladies du coeur et des reins. I. Étude du liquide des épanchements des séreuses et des oedèmes, *Arch. d. mal. d. reins* **6**, 147 (1931).   **[43, 44**

WARNER, G. F., E. L. DOBSON, C. E. ROGERS, M. E. JOHNSTON, and N. PACE, The measurement of total "sodium space" and total body sodium in normal individuals and in patients with cardiac edema, *Circulation* **5**, 915 (1952).

WHITE, A. G., and B. A. SACHS, Studies in edema: cholesterol and its relation to protein nitrogen in edema fluid, *Science* **112**, 18 (1950).
                                                                                              [43

19. *Blood Volume and Viscosity. Hemoglobin and Erythrocyte Count. Clotting*

Most authors report an increased blood volume in patients with congestive failure (**46**; Gibson and Evans, 1937; Meneely and Kaltreider, 1943; Seymour *et al.*, 1942). Plasma, red cell and total volumes are all increased to approximately the same degree; this is contradistinction to chronic pulmonary disease, where the plasma volume remains normal, only the red blood cell mass and total volume increasing (Richards, 1945). Bock (1921) described normal values in his one case, while others found it to be increased only inconstantly (**47**); these authors used methods of low accuracy. Wollheim (1931) and his followers, Goldbloom *et al.* (1935, 1939), concluded that either increased or decreased blood volumes might occur in cardiac failure and evolved the theory of two forms of failure, "plus" and "minus." However, their data actually show increased values in most instances of chronic congestive failure. Moreover, the methods used by the authors whose results are discordant have been criticized by Gibson and Evans (1927). Recently Ross *et al.* (1952) found normal values in patients with congestive failure studied by means of the radioactive phosphorus method. These authors criticized the blue dye method on the basis of loss of dye into the tissues. The loss of dye is well known but a correction, consisting in extrapolation of the disappearance curve back to the point of injection, presumably obviates errors caused by dye leaving the blood stream. Moreover, the radioactive phosphorus method has been criticized on technical grounds (Nickerson *et al.*, 1950). The final answer must await further study; nevertheless, the large amount of blood regularly found at autopsy in patients dying of congestive failure favors the conclusion that the blood volume is increased in that disorder.

After recovery from congestive failure, following digitalis or other forms of therapy, a decrease in blood volume occurs according to most authors (**48**; Gibson and Evans, 1937; Meneely and Kaltreider, 1943; Seymour *et al.*, 1942), while others (**49**) report variable changes. The latter results were largely obtained by the use of inaccurate methods. Gibson and Evans (1937) studied a large group of patients and found a high degree of correlation between the severity of the signs and symptoms of congestive failure and the increase in blood volume. In recovery from congestive failure, the blood volume decreases toward but only rarely attains normal values. Gibson and Evans (1937), Brandt (1931), Perera (1945) and Wollheim (1931) found a parallelism between changes in blood volume and venous pressure in individual cases; the increased blood volume was not responsible, however, for more than a small part of the venous pressure ruse, since diuresis caused marked decreases in blood volume and only small changes in venous pressure. In addition, Meneely and Kaltreider (1943) failed to find this parallelism in all stages of failure.

The question whether or not exercise in cardiac decompensation might force blood from the circulation into the hypothetical blood depots, or the other way, has been studied by a number of authors (Ewig and Hinsberg, 1931; Kaltreider and Meneely, 1940; Levin, 1935; Wollheim, 1931; Gilbert and Lewis, 1950; Berson et al., 1952). Kaltreider and Meneely (1940) found a slight decrease in blood volume in decompensated patients during exercise, much as in normal subjects, in contradiction to the results of Ewig and Hinsberg (1931). Gilbert and Lewis (1950) found a greater than normal decrease in plasma volume after exercise in patients with failure.

Changes in blood volume in various positions have been studied by a number of authors in normal subjects. Normal individuals show hemoconcentration and decreased plasma volume after standing still for some minutes (Asmussen et al., 1940; Youmans et al., 1934; Waterfield, 1931; Thompson et al., 1928). Changes in cardiac patients described in an unsatisfactory manner by de Flora and Ciravegna in 1931, have been studied thoroughly by Berson et al. (1952); standing decreases and lying flat increases the plasma volume in congestive failure.

The reason for the increases in blood volume in chronic cardiac decompensation is not known. Judging by the reported changes in plasma protein level (page 133), some dilution of the blood plasma may occur in patients with edema consequent to heart disease, but the cause of the phenomenon is also unknown. Salt retention is a possible factor, for increasing salt intake in normal subjects or in cardiac patients dilutes the blood (Iversen and Nakazawa, 1927; Lyons et al., 1945b) and increases the blood volume (Krauel, 1941;

Lyons *et al.*, 1944, 1945*a*, *b*; Warren and Stead, 1944; Grant and Reischman, 1946). However, dilution, if it occurs, would not explain the increase in circulating red cell mass which also has been noted. Anoxia may also be responsible for the increased blood volume, much as in dwellers at high altitudes (Douglas, 1910; Hurtado, 1932; Hurtado *et al.*, 1945; Laquer, 1924; Lippman, 1926; Smith *et al.*, 1925) or patients with severe pulmonary disease (page 461). However, these persons usually exhibit a considerable increase in hematocrit and circulating red cell mass which accounts for most or all of their increased blood volumes. It is to be noted that the bone marrow at high altitudes shows myeloid hyperplasia (Merino and Reynafarje, 1949) similar to that seen in congestive failure (page 150). The report of Bonsdorff and Jalavisto (1948) that blood plasma from patients with congestive failure causes elevation of the erythrocyte count when injected into rabbits is mystifying.

It is possible also that the increased blood volume of cardiac decompensation represents in part an attempt to compensate for a low cardiac output. It is obvious that if the flow of blood through a unit volume of tissue is low, anoxia will result. This can, to some extent, be obviated if a larger volume of blood is kept in contact with the unit volume of tissue for a longer period of time. It is interesting in this connection that the manifestations of surgical shock may occasionally be observed to develop in patients who enter the hospital with severe congestive failure, if they are treated by means of too enthusiastic diuretic therapy.

Still another factor has been emphasized by Landis *et al.* (1946) in a most convincing way. These authors showed in animals that the normal decrease in plasma volume which occurs during exertion is exceeded greatly if unusually high and prolonged elevations of venous pressure occur in exercise when the heart is incompetent. An increase in blood volume, participated in both by plasma and by erythrocytes, is a compensatory change that protects the body against the effects of a fall in blood volume to very low levels.

The increase in cardiac residual blood claimed by Nylin is discussed elsewhere (page 28). The data of Bing bearing on this point have also been mentioned (page 63). The increased pulmonary blood volume found in cardiac decompensation has likewise been discussed (page 79).

The red blood cell count and hemoglobin percentage show no consistent change in cardiac decompensation; in most instances normal values are observed. The individual cell size is also within the normal range (Price-Jones, 1921). Patients in severe congestive failure with marked cyanosis, especially those with severe pulmonary disease (Richards, 1945), may show an elevation of the red blood cell count and hemoglobin percentage. However, as pointed out above, the total circulating red cell mass is always increased in cardiac decompensation, even in the absence of abnormally high erythrocyte counts and hemoglobin levels. During recovery a transitory rise in hematocrit may be noted (50; Gibson and Evans, 1937) since the plasma volume decreases more rapidly than the red cell volume.

Ott (1939) and Groen and Gottfried (1948) examined the sternal marrow in patients with congestive failure and found hyperplasia of the red cell forming elements, with a return to normal after recovery. The red marrow mass is increased in cardiac decompensation (Shillingford, 1950). The reported measurements of oxygen saturation of the bone marrow show no striking abnormalities (Schwartz and Staats, 1949). The peripheral blood may contain immature erythrocytes (Frank and Hartmann, 1931; González Guzman, 1949; Groen and Gottfried, 1948); an odd type of erythrocyte, designated "burr cell," has also been observed (Schwartz and Motto, 1949). Ehrström (1936) and Waller et al. (1940) studied the changes in the blood during the various stages of congestive failure and found reticulocytosis with decompensation, and the expected evidences of blood destruction during recovery. The latter consisted in the finding of increased urobilinogen excretion in the stool, an observation recorded by others as well (Adler and Sachs, 1923; Francescon, 1936; Weiss, 1930). Eppinger and Walzel (1926) found an increase in bile pigment in the duodenum. The increase in urine urobilinogen discussed elsewhere (page 193) may also be due in part to increased blood destruction. However, Localio et al. (1941) and Watson (1937) found no increase in bile pigment excretion such as might indicate blood destruction; their patients may have been studied when in a steady state.

The fragility of the erythrocytes to hypotonic saline solution is increased in cyanotic or decompensated cardiac patients (Francescon,

1936; Greenthal and O'Donnell, 1921; Waller et al., 1940), but why this increased tendency toward hemolysis does not become markedly active until recovery begins is not clear. The cause of the increased fragility is likewise not established, although it is well known that venous blood is more fragile than arterial (Creed, 1938; Whitby and Hynes, 1935) and in cardiac decompensation the blood is more venous than normal in one respect, namely, its oxygen content. Exposure to high oxygen tensions in vitro decreases erythrocyte fragility (Butler, 1912; Creed, 1938; Dacie and Vaughan, 1938), and Booth (1941) demonstrated in dogs that the breathing of air low in oxygen content increased erythrocyte fragility. However, Whitby and Hynes (1935) concluded that the increased fragility of normal venous blood was related to its increased carbon dioxide content. Other observers showed that locally induced stasis in animals (Ham and Castle, 1940; Tsai et al., 1940) or in man (Waller, 1939) resulted in an increase in erythrocyte fragility; oxygen lack or carbon dioxide excess appear to have been ruled out, however, as causes of this phenomenon (Waller, 1939; Tsai et al., 1940). Blood stagnant in veins does not show any change in fragility (Erb and Tiefensee, 1931; Mettier et al., 1949). The observation of Francescon (1936) that cells which show increased resistance to hemolysis in dilute salt solution are also present in the blood in congestive failure is of interest in relation to the reported occurrence of target cells in this disorder (Valentine and Neel, 1944).

Changes in blood viscosity might be expected to occur when the number of red blood cells per cubic millimeter is increased. Bence (1905) thought that retention of carbon dioxide caused the changes in viscosity but showed that inhalation of oxygen by cyanotic patients lowered the viscosity of the blood. Extensive studies on the blood viscosity in congestive failure have been made by Albers (1937), Markson (1936), Rogen (1940), and Schwalm and Bröder (1943). The results of Albers (1937) are probably inaccurate, for he described an increase in viscosity but also found the plasma protein level elevated in congestive failure. The data of Markson (1936) and of Rogen (1940) are not presented in sufficient detail for analysis, but it appears that both observed normal or low values in edematous patients, while patients with marked cyanosis, especially with severe pulmonary disease and polycythemia, usually showed increased viscosity of the blood. Oxygen in such instances might very well reduce the viscosity, as Bence (1905) found. Schwalm and Bröder (1943) found the blood viscosity decreased in congestive failure but their patients were anemic.

Altana and Pulino (1947) have discussed the blood leucocytes in congestive failure.

Blood clotting mechanisms are of interest in congestive failure in view of the high incidence of intravascular thrombosis in this condition. However, clotting times are normal (Cathcart and Blood, 1950; Fowler, 1949; Massie *et al.*, 1944; Marvel and Shullenberger, 1951; Pere, 1950; Sokoloff and Ferrer, 1945; Sutton, 1950). In addition, prothrombin times commonly are prolonged (page 193). Beaumont and Lenègre (1951) found the heparin tolerance decreased. On the other hand, Sternberger (1952) reported that the thrombin recovery test yielded increased values in cardiac decompensation. Available data on clotting throw no light on the mechanism of the common occurrence of phlebitis in congestive failure.

Bibliography

Chapter I — Section 19

ADLER, A., and M. SACHS, Ueber Urobilin. IIIa. Die Urobilinausscheidung durch die Faeces nebst vergleichenden Untersuchungen über das Verhältnis der Urobilinmengen des Harnes und Stuhles, und dessen Verwertbarkeit als Leberfunktionsprüfung, *Ztschr. f. d. ges. exper. Med.* **31,** 370 (1923).

AIKAWA, J., Comparison of the thiocyanate and radiosodium spaces in disease states, *Am. J. M. Sc.* **224,** 632 (1952).   [46

ALBERS, D., Die Viskosität des Blutes in der kardialen Herzinsufficienz, *Ztschr. f. Kreislaufforsch* **29,** 914 (1937).

ALTANA G., and C. PULINO, Il quadro leucocitario nello scompenso cardiaco, *Folia Cardiol.* **6,** 193 (1947).

ASMUSSEN, E., E. H. CHRISTENSEN, and M. NIELSEN, The regulation of circulation in different postures, *Surgery* **8,** 604 (1940).

BEAUMONT, J.-L., and J. LENÈGRE, La coagulabilité du sang dans l'insuffisance cardiaque avant et après le traitement, *Semaine d. hôp. de Paris* **27,** 2128 (1951).

BENCE, J., Klinische Untersuchungen über die Viskosität des Blutes bei Störungen der Kohlensäureausscheidung, *Deutsche med. Wchnschr.* **31,** 590 (1905).

BERSON, S. A., R. S. YALOW, A. AZULAY, S. SCHREIBER, and B. ROSWIT, The biological decay curve of P³² tagged erythrocytes. Application to the study of acute changes in blood volume, *J. Clin. Investigation* **31,** 581 (1952).

BOCK, A. V., The constancy of the volume of the blood plasma, *Arch. Int. Med.* **27,** 83 (1921).

BONSDORFF, E., and E. JALAVISTO, A humoral mechanism in anoxic erythrocytosis, *Acta physiol. Skandinav.* **16,** 150 (1948).

BOOTH, M., Fragility of erythrocytes as affected by anoxia, CO_2 inhalation and insulin hypoglycemia, *Proc. Soc. Exper. Biol. & Med.* **46,** 640 (1941).

BRANDT, F., Die Abhängigkeit des Venendruckes von der Grösse der zirkulierenden Blutmenge, zugleich ein Beitrag zur Frage seiner klinischen Bedeutung, *Ztschr. f. klin. Med.* **116,** 398 (1931). [47, 48

BRIGGS, A. P., D. M. FOWELL, W. F. HAMILTON, J. W. REMINGTON, N. C. WHEELER, and J. A. WINSLOW, Renal and circulatory factors in the edema formation of congestive heart failure, *J. Clin. Investigation* **27,** 810 (1948). [47

BROD, J., and Z. FEJFAR, The origin of oedema in heart failure, *Quart. J. Med.* **19,** 187 (1950). [47, 50

BROWN, G. E., and L. G. ROWNTREE, The volume and composition of the blood and the changes incident to diuresis in cases of edema, *Arch. Int. Med.* **35,** 129 (1925). [47, 49

BURWELL, C. S., and L. DEXTER, Beri-beri heart disease, *Tr. A. Am. Physicians* **60,** 59 (1947). [46

BUTLER, G. G., The fragility of the red blood corpuscles, *Quart. J. Med.* **6,** 145 (1912).

CALVIN, D. B., G. DECHERD, and G. HERRMANN, Response of plasma volume to diuretics, *Proc. Soc. Exper. Biol. & Med.* **44,** 529 (1940). [48

CARDOZO, E. L., Bepaling van het bloedvolume met het blauw T 1824. *Nederl. tijdschr. v. geneesk.* **83,** 5357 (1939). [46

CARDOZO, E. L., Invloed van salyrgan op het bloedvolume, *Nederl. tijdschr. v. geneesk.* **83,** 5528 (1939). [46, 48

CATHCART, R. T., and D. W. BLOOD, Effect of digitalis on the clotting of the blood in normal subjects and in patients with heart failure, *Circulation* **1,** 1176 (1950).

COURNAND, A., A discussion of the concept of cardiac failure in the light of recent physiologic studies in man, *Ann. Int. Med.* **37,** 649 (1952). [46

COURNAND, A., H. D. LAUSON, R. A. BLOOMFIELD, E. S. BREED, and E. DE F. BALDWIN, Recording of right heart pressures in man, *Proc. Soc. Exper. Biol. & Med.* **55,** 34 (1944). [46

CREED, E., The estimation of the fragility of red blood corpuscles, *J. Path. & Bact.* **46**, 331 (1938).

DACIE, J. V., and J. M. VAUGHAN, The fragility of the red blood cells: its measurement and significance, *J. Path. & Bact.* **46**, 341 (1938).

DE FLORA, G., and M. CIRAVEGNA, Le variazione della massa sanguigna dei cardiopatici nei cambiamenti di decubito, *Cuore e circolaz.* **21**, 396 (1931).

DI PALMA, J. R., and P. E. KENDALL, The relationship between blood volume and blood specific gravity in the recovery from cardiac decompensation, *J. Lab. & Clin. Med.* **29**, 390 (1944).   [47, 49, 50

DOUGLAS, C. G., The determination of the total oxygen capacity and blood volume at different altitudes by the carbon monoxide method, *J. Physiol.* **40**, 472 (1910).

EHRSTRÖM, M. C., Blutstoffwechsel und Urobilinurie bei Herzinsufficienz, *Acta med. Scandinav.* **88**, 517 (1936).   [49

EPPINGER H., and P. WALZEL, *Die Krankheiten der Leber mit Einschluss der hepatolienalen Affektionen* (Berlin, 1926).

ERB, K. H., and K. TIEFENSEE, Untersuchungen über das Krampfaderblut, *Beitr. z. klin. Chir.* **152**, 400 (1931).

EWIG, W., and K. HINSBERG, Kreislaufstudien. II, *Ztschr. f. klin. Med.* **115**, 693 (1931).   [46, 48

FOWELL, D. M., A. P. BRIGGS, N. C. WHEELER, J. A. WINSLOW, JR., J. W. REMINGTON, and W. F. HAMILTON, Renal and circulatory factors in congestive failure of the circulation, *Federation Proc.* **7**, 35 (1948). [46, 48

FOWLER, N. O., A study of certain aspects of blood coagulation in the postoperative state in congestive failure and in thrombophlebitis, *J. Clin. Investigation* **28**, 671 (1949).

FRANCESCON, M., Comportamento della resistenza osmotica dei globuli rossi e del ricambio emoglobinico nei cardiopazienti in fase acuta discompenso e in fase compensatoria, *Minerva med.* **27**, (II), 255 (1936).

FRANK, E., and E. HARTMANN, Akute macrocytär-erythroblastische Blutbilder ohne Anemie bei hochgradige Schwäche der rechten Herzkammer, *Klin. Wchschr.* **10**, 15 (1931).

GIBSON, J. G., 2d, and W. A. EVANS, JR., Clinical studies of the blood volume. III. Changes in blood volume, venous pressure and blood velocity rate in chronic congestive heart failure, *J. Clin. Investigation* **16**, 851 (1937).   [46, 48, 50

GILBERT, R. P., and J. K. LEWIS, Effect of exercise on the plasma volume of patients with heart failure, *Circulation* **2**, 403 (1950).   [46

GOLDBLOOM, A. A., and I. LIBIN, Clinical studies in circulatory adjustments. I. Clinical evaluation of studies of circulating blood volume, *Arch. Int. Med.* **55,** 484 (1935). [49

GOLDBLOOM, A. A., and A. LIEBERSON, Clinical studies in circulatory adjustments. V. Clinical evaluation of cardio-dynamic studies, *Am. J. M. Sc.* **197,** 182 (1939).

GOLDHAMMER, S., G. LEINER, and D. SCHERF, Ueber die zirkulierende Blutmenge vor und nach der Quecksilberdiurese, *Klin. Wchnschr.* **14,** 1109 (1935). [48

GONZÁLEZ GUZMAN, I., Contribución para el estudio de la eritroblastemia de los cardiacos, *Arch. d. Inst. de cardiol. de Mexico* **19,** 420 (1949).

GRANT, H., and F. REICHSMAN, The effects of the ingestion of large amounts of sodium chloride on the arterial and venous pressures of normal subjects, *Am. Heart J.* **32,** 704 (1946).

GREENTHAL, R. M., and W. S. O'DONNELL, Studies on the fragility of the red blood cells, *Am. J. Physiol.* **58,** 271 (1921).

GROEN, J., and E. G. GODFRIED, The occurrence of normoblasts in the peripheral blood in congestive heart failure: an indication of unfavorable prognosis, *Blood* **3,** 1445 (1948).

HAM, T. H., and W. B. CASTLE, Relation of increased hypotemic fragility and of erythrostasis to the mechanism of hemolysis in certain anemias, *Tr. A. Am. Physicians* **55,** 127 (1940).

HARRIS, A. W., and J. G. GIBSON, II, Clinical studies of the blood volume. VII. Changes in blood volume in Bright's disease with or without edema, renal insufficiency or congestive heart failure, and in hypertension, *J. Clin. Investigation* **18,** 527 (1939). [46, 50

HARVEY, R. M., M. I. FERRER, R. T. CATHCART, D. W. RICHARDS, JR., and A. COURNAND, Some effects of digoxin upon the heart and circulation in man. Digoxin in left ventricular failure, *Am. J. Med.* **7,** 439 (1949). [46

HITZENBERGER, K., and F. TUCHFELD, Die zirkulierende Blutmenge bei Kreislaufserkrankungen im kompensierten und dekompensierten Zustand, *Wien. Arch. f. inn. Med.* **18,** 171 (1929). [46, 48

HURTADO, A., Studies at high altitude. Blood observations on the Indian natives of the Peruvian Andes, *Am. J. Physiol.* **100,** 487 (1932).

HURTADO, A., C. MERINO, and E. DELGADO, Influence of anoxemia on the hemopoietic activity, *Arch. Int. Med.* **75,** 284 (1945).

ISERI, L. T., A. J. BOYLE, and G. B. MYERS, Water and electrolyte balance during recovery from severe congestive failure on a 50 milligram sodium diet, *Am. Heart J.* **40,** 706 (1950). [46, 48

IVERSEN, P., and F. NAKAZAWA, Om Oedempatogenese, *Ugesk. f. læger* **89,** 640 (1927).

KALTREIDER, N. L., and G. R. MENEELY, The effect of exercise on the volume of the blood, *J. Clin. Investigation* **19**, 627 (1940).

KEITH, N. M., L. G. ROWNTREE, and J. T. GERAGHTY, A method for the determination of plasma and blood volume, *Arch. Int. Med.* **16**, 547 (1915).   [47

KINSMAN, J. M., and J. W. MOORE, The hemodynamics of the circulation in hypertension, *Ann. Int. Med.* **9**, 649 (1935).   [47

KOPELMAN, H., and G. DE J. LEE, The intrathoracic blood volume in mitral stenosis and left ventricular failure, *Clin. Sc.* **10**, 383 (1951).   [46

KRAUEL, G., Ueber den Einfluss der Ernährung auf die zirkulierende Blutmenge; kochsalzarme und kochsalzreiche Diät, *Ztschr. f. klin. Med.* **139**, 459 (1941).

LANDIS, E. M., E. BROWN, M. FAUTEUX, and C. WISE, Central venous pressure in relation to cardiac "competence," blood volume and exercise, *J. Clin. Investigation* **25**, 237 (1946).

LAQUER, F., Untersuchungen der Gesamtblutmenge im Hochgebirge mit der Greisbachschen Kongorotmethode, *Klin. Wchnschr.* **3**, 7 (1924).

LAYNE, J. A., F. R. SCHEMM, and W. W. HURST, Further comparative studies on ascites in liver and heart disease, *Gastroenterol.* **16**, 91 (1950).   [46, 49

LEVIN, E., Influencia del ejercicio muscular sobre el volumen de sangre circulante en estados normales y patologicos, *Rev. Soc. argent. de biol.* **11**, 83 (1935).

LIPPMAN, A., Blutzusammensetzung und Gesamtblutmenge bei Hochgebirgsbewohnern, *Klin. Wchnschr.* **5**, 1406 (1926).

LOCALIO, S. A., M. S. SCHWARTZ, and C. F. GANNON, The urinary/fecal coproporphyrin ratio in liver disease, *J. Clin. Investigation* **20**, 7 (1941).

LYONS, R. H., S. D. JACOBSON, and N. L. AVERY, Increases in the plasma volume following the administration of sodium salts, *Am. J. M. Sc.* **208**, 148 (1944).

LYONS, R. H., S. D. JACOBSON, and J. L. NEERKIN, The relationship between changes in serum protein concentration and the plasma volume in normal subjects, *J. Lab. & Clin. Med.* **30**, 404 (1945a).

LYONS, R. H., F. D. JOHNSON, and J. SANDERS, Studies on the changes in the circulation of normal subjects with small variations in the fluid content of the body, *J. Lab. & Clin. Med.* **30**, 376 (1945b).

MARKSON, A., Blood viscosity in congestive heart failure, *Glasgow M. J.* **7**, 201 (1936).

MARVEL, R. J., and W. A. SHULLENBERGER, Thromboembolic phenomena associated with rapid diuresis in the treatment of congestive heart failure, *Am. Heart J.* **42**, 194 (1951).

Massie, E., H. S. Stillerman, C.-S. Wright, and V. Minnich, Effect of administration of digitalis on coagulability of human blood, *Arch. Int. Med.* **74,** 172 (1944).

Meneely, G. R., and N. L. Kaltreider, A study of the volume of the blood in congestive heart failure. Relation to other measurements in fifteen patients, *J. Clin. Investigation* **22,** 521 (1943). [46, 48

Merino, C. F., and C. Reynafarje, Bone marrow studies in the polycythemia of high altitudes, *J. Lab. & Clin. Med.* **34,** 637 (1949).

Mettier, S. R., J. C. Weaver, and A. F. McBride, The effect of stasis of blood in varicose veins on erythrocyte fragility, with accompanying studies comparing red cells and other blood elements with cubital vein blood, *Blood* **4,** 1033 (1949).

Mies, H., Ueber die Wirkung des Strophanthin auf die zirkulierende Blutmenge, *Ztschr. f. Kreislaufforsch.* **23,** 460 (1931). [48

Myers, J. D., and J. B. Hickan, An estimation of the hepatic blood flow and splanchnic oxygen consumption in heart failure, *J. Clin. Investigation* **27,** 620 (1948). [46

Nickerson, J. L., M. I. Gregeren, W. S. Root, and L. M. Sharpe, Influence of blood incompatibilities on measurement of blood volume by cell-tagging methods, *Proc. Soc. Exper. Biol. & Med.* **75,** 61 (1950).

Nylin, G., Blood volume determinations with radioactive phosphorus, *Brit. Heart J.* **7,** 81 (1945). [46, 48

Nylin, G., and S. Hedlund, Weight of the red blood corpuscles in heart failure determined with labelled erythrocytes during and after decompensation, *Am. Heart J,* **33,** 770 (1947). [46

Ott, A., Ueber Blutmenge und Knochenmarksbefund bei Herzinsuffizienz, *Deutsches Arch. f. klin. Med.* **185,** 176 (1939). [46, 49

Pere, S. A. N., The effect of digitalis, strophanthin, and novurit on blood coagulation, *Acta med. Scandinav. Supp.* **215,** 1 (1950).

Perera, G. A., The increased plasma volume in cardiac insufficiency: its correlation with right-sided failure, *J. Clin. Investigation* **24,** 708 (1945). [46

Porter, R. B., and R. S. Downs, Some physiological observations on the circulation during recovery from vitamin B_1 deficiency, *Ann. Int. Med.* **17,** 645 (1942). [46

Price-Jones, C., The sizes of red blood cells in emphysema, *J. Path. & Bact.* **24,** 326 (1921).

Richards, D. W., Jr., Cardiac output by the catheterization technique in various clinical conditions, *Federation Proc.* **4,** 215 (1945). [46

Rogen, A. S., Blood viscosity in cardiac failure. Its modification by administration of calcium gluconate, *Lancet* **1,** 780 (1940).

Ross, J. F., R. B. Chodos, W. H. Baker, and E. D. Freis, The blood volume in congestive heart failure, *Tr. A. Am. Physicians* **65**, 75 (1952).

Rowntree, L. G., and G. E. Brown, *The volume of the blood and plasma in health and disease* (W. B. Saunders Co., Philadelphia and London, 1929). [47, 49

Schurmeyer, A., Ueber Blutmengengestimmungen bei Herzfehlern, *Verhandl. d. deutsch. Gesellsch. f. inn, Med.* **40**, 388 (1928). [46, 48

Schwalm, H., and M. Bröder, Die Blutviskosimetrie in der Untersuchung des Wasserhaushaltes, *Deutsches Arch. f. klin. Med.* **191**, 455 (1943).

Schwartz, B. A., and D. Stats, Oxygen saturation of sternal marrow blood in polycythemia vera, *J. Clin. Investigation* **28**, 736 (1949).

Schwartz, S. O., and S. A. Motto, The diagnostic significance of "burr" red blood cells, *Am. J. M. Sc.* **218**, 563 (1949).

Seymour, W. B., W. H. Pritchard, L. P. Longley, and J. M. Hayman, Jr., Cardiac output, blood and interstitial fluid volumes, total circulating serum protein, and kidney function during cardiac failure and after improvement, *J. Clin. Investigation* **21**, 229 (1942). [46, 48, 50

Shillingford, J. P., The red bone marrow in heart failure, *J. Clin. Path.* **3**, 24 (1950).

Smith, H. P., A. E. Belt, H. R. Arnold, and E. B. Carrier, Blood volume changes at high altitude, *Am. J. Physiol,* **71**, 395 (1925).

Sokoloff, L., and M. I. Ferrer, Effect of digitalization on the coagulation time in man, *Proc. Soc. Exper. Biol. & Med.* **59**, 309 (1945).

Spuhler, V. O., K. Wiesinger, and E. Meili, Diuretica und zirkulierende Plasmamenge, *Helvet Med. Acta* **15**, 95 (1948). [47, 49

Sternberger, L. A., Preliminary clinical evaluation of thrombin recovery test, *J. A. M. A.* **150**, 1591 (1952).

Sutton, G. C., Studies on blood coagulation and the effect of digitalis, *Circulation* **2**, 271 (1950).

Thompson, W. O., Studies in blood volume. I. The blood volume in myxedema, with a comparison of plasma volume changes in myxedema and cardiac edema, *J. Clin. Investigation* **2**, 477 (1925–26). [46, 48

Thompson, W. O., P. K. Thompson, and M. E. Dailey, The effect of posture upon the composition and volume of the blood in man, *J. Clin. Investigation* **5**, 573 (1927–28).

Tsai, C., J. S. Lee, and C. H. Wu, The role of splenic action in altering erythrocyte fragility, *Chinese J. Physiol.* **15**, 165 (1940).

Uhlenbruck, P., and R. Vogels, Zum Problem der zirkulierenden Plasmamenge (Blutmenge) bei Kreislaufstörungen, *Ztschr. f. klin. Med.* **118**, 172 (1931). [47

VALENTINE, W. N., and J. V. NEEL, Hematologic and genetic study of the transmission of thalassemia, *Arch. Int. Med.* **74**, 185 (1944).

WALLER, J. V., Cause of increased fragility of erythrocytes in congestive heart failure, *Proc. Soc. Exper. Biol. & Med.* **42**, 64 (1939).

WALLER, J. V., H. L. BLUMGART, and M. C. VOLK, Studies of the blood in congestive heart failure, with particular reference to reticulocytosis, erythrocyte fragility, bilirubinemia, urobilinogen excretion and changes in blood volume, *Arch. Int. Med.* **66**, 1230 (1940). [**46, 48, 50**

WARREN, J. V., and E. A. STEAD, JR., Fluid dynamics in chronic congestive heart failure. An interpretation of the mechanisms producing the edema, increased plasma volume and elevated venous pressure in certain patients with prolonged congestive failure, *Arch. Int. Med.* **73**, 138 (1944).

WATERFIELD, R. L., The effects of posture on the circulating blood volume, *J. Physiol.* **72**, 110, (1931).

WATSON, C. J., Studies of urobilinogen. III. The per diem excretion of urobilinogen in the common forms of jaundice and disease of the liver, *J. Physiol.* **59**, 206 (1937).

WEISS, M., Ueber Urobilin und seine diagnostische Verwertung, auf Grund quantitativer Bestimmungen in Harn, Stuhl und in der Galle, *Wien. Arch. f. inn. Med.* **20**, 39 (1930).

WHITBY, L. E. H., and M. HYNES, The quantitative estimation of the fragility of the red corpuscles, *J. Path. & Bact.* **40**, 219 (1935).

WOLLHEIM, E., Die zirkulierende Blutmenge und ihre Bedeutung für Kompensation und Dekompensation des Kreislaufs, *Ztschr. f. klin. Med.* **116**, 269 (1931). [**49**

WOOD, W. B., and C. A. JANEWAY, Changes in plasma volume during recovery from congestive failure, *Arch. Int. Med.* **62**, 151 (1938). [**50**

YOUMANS, J. B., H. S. WELLS, D. DONLEY, and D. G. MILLER, The effect of posture (standing) on the serum protein concentration and colloid osmotic pressure of blood from the foot in relation to the formation of edema, *J. Clin. Investigation* **13**, 447 (1934).

20. *Renal Function*

Striking changes in renal physiology are of frequent occurrence in congestive failure, although at postmortem examination not much more than congestion and edema of the kidney are to be found.

The renal blood flow, fist measured by means of various clearances, is decreased in congestive failure (Seymour *et al.*, 1944; Mokotoff, Ross and Leiter, 1948; **50A**); similar findings have recenlty been noted in measurements of arteriovenous oxygen difference estimated from samples of blood obtained by catheterization of the renal vein via the antecubital vein (Warren *et al.*, 1944; Merrill, 1946; Mokotoff *et al.*, 1949; Edelman *et al.*, 1950; Angelino and Actis-Dato, 1951; Davies and Kilpatrick, 1951). The arteriovenous oxygen difference may be normal in cor pulmonale (Davies and Kilpatrick, 1951). The renal blood flow is decreased to a far greater extent than the cardiac output in patients with congestive failure (Merrill, 1946); afferent vasoconstriction must also occur. However, efferent constriction is also present; the total peripheral renal vascular resistance increases (Eichna *et al.*, 1951, 1953; Mantero and Barlassina, 1951). The vasoconstriction is not relaxed by spinal anesthesia (Mokotoff and Ross, 1948). It is, therefore, not surprising that low values for urea clearance have been found in patients with congestive failure (Porge, 1939; Seymour *et al.*, 1944; Tiagi, 1946; Mathur, 1948; Aas and Blegen, 1949; Schneierson, 1949; Black and Litchfield, 1951); these values return to or toward normal with improvement, as shown by these authors and also by Stewart and McIntosh (1928). Borst (1948) found the urea clearance to be normal in his decompensated cardiac patients. The creatinine clearance is also low (Aas and Blegen, 1949; Lassen, 1932; Squires *et al.*, 1951). The decreases in urea clearance noted are not in themselves sufficiently marked to cause nitrogen retention, but they must play a contributory role. Glomerular filtration is decreased to a lesser degree than renal blood flow (Leiter *et al.*, 1950; **50B**); in some instances it may be within the normal range. It is evident, therefore, that efferent vasoconstriction must be present if the volume of glomerular filtrate relative to glomerular blood flow, that is, the filtration fraction, is increased. This mechanism prevents or minimizes nitrogen retention when the cardiac output is low. The renal venous pressure is elevated in congestive failure (Maxwell, Breed, and Schwartz, 1950; Angelino and Actis-Dato, 1951); this change constitutes only a small factor in the increase in renal vascular resistance. Renal tubular function, considered to be diminished in congestive failure by some (Earle *et al.*, 1949; Heller and Jacobson, 1950; Hilden, 1949) was found normal by others (Fishman *et al.*, 1951; Grossman *et al.*, 1950b, Leiter *et al.*, 1950; Mantera and Barlassina, 1951); it is possible that when impairment of tubular function is found it is not caused by the cardiac failure per se but is owing to associated vascular disease. In view of the fact that sodium clearance is markedly lowered in congestive failure (page 173), it is evident that tubular reabsorption, at least of sodium, must be increased relative to glomerular filtration; the absolute value for reabsorption is said to be in or above the normal range. However, skepticism concerning the validity of such calculations exists in some quarters (Barclay et al., 1952). The renal oxygen consumption may be somewhat low (Edelman et al., 1950).

During sleep, at which time the renal blood flow and glomerular filtration rate show no change or a slight fall in normal subjects, these functions, and also the creatinine clearance, rise in patients with congestive failure (Sirota et al., 1949; Baldwin et al., 1950; Brod and Fejfar, 1951); the mechanism and significance of these findings are not clear.

With still-standing there are decreases in normal subjects in the creatinine clearance (Ni and Rehberg, 1931; Netravisesh, 1953) and the renal blood flow and glomerular filtration rate (Brun et al., 1945a,b; Epstein et al., 1951; De Wardener and McSwiney, 1951; White and Rolf, 1948a); the glomerular filtration decreases less than the renal blood flow, indicating the development of efferent arteriolar constriction resulting in an increase in filtration fraction. Corresponding data are not available in congestive failure. Sitting has little effect on renal vascular dynamics (Kattus et al., 1949; Viar et al., 1951).

Exercise in normal subjects decreases renal blood flow and, to a lesser degree, the glomerular filtration rate (Aas and Blegen, 1949; Chapman et al., 1948; Kattus et al., 1949; Radigan and Robinson, 1949; White and Rolf, 1948a,b). Patients with congestive failure show similar changes (Aas and Blegen, 1949; Merrill and Cargill, 1947, 1948; Sinclair-Smith et al., 1949), although a short walk may not cause changes (Newman, 1949).

The decreased renal blood flow seen in untreated patients with congestive failure is owing only in part to diminished cardiac output. The vasoconstriction that accounts for the rest of the change has not been explained. Induced anoxia is not the mechanism, since it causes variable increases in renal blood flow in normal subjects (Aas and Blegen, 1949; Berger et al., 1949; Caldwell et al., 1949; Fishman *et al.*, 1951; Axelrod and Pitts, 1952) and in patients with congestive failure (Aas and Blegen, 1949; Fishman *et al.*, 1951); in anoxia the glomerular filtration rate does not change and the filtration fraction decreases, indicating efferent arteriolar dilatation.

Effects on renal blood flow similar to those seen in man in cardiac decompensation can be induced in animals by relatively high degrees of venous stasis (Blake *et al.*, 1949; Hall and Selkurt, 1951; Selkurt *et al.*, 1949; Davis and Howell, 1953; Frieden *et al.*, 1952; Jeanneret, 1951) or arterial constriction (Blake *et al.*, 1950). These observations throw little light on the mechanism of the changes seen in cardiac decompensation.

After treatment for congestive failure the renal vascular dynamics, although changed in the direction of normal, are still markedly abnormal (Heller and Jacobson, 1950; Earle *et al.*, 1950; Briggs *et al.*, 1948; Davies, 1951; Lewis *et al.*, 1952; Eichna *et al.*, 1953). It must be remembered that salt restriction causes a decrease in glomerular filtration rate (Black *et al.*, 1950), as does the application of tourniquets also (Chalmers *et al.*, 1951).

The nitrogen retention that occurs in severe congestive failure is well known. In addition to the above-noted lowered urea clearance, other causative factors must exist. One such factor is oliguria itself. Renal stasis, caused by venous obstruction, was shown by Rowntree, Fitz, and Geraghty (1913), by Winton (1931), and by Blake *et al.*, (1948*a,b*) to cause a decrease in the volume of urine formed.

Whatever the cause of the reduced urine volume in cardiac decompensation, it must, when marked, lead to nitrogen retention. Chesley (1937, 1938*a*, *b*) has shown that in normal individuals the urine is maximally concentrated with regard to total solids, urea, total nitrogen and creatinine when the volume reaches levels as low as 500 to 750 cc. per day; decreases in volume below that range result in no further increase in concentration. The importance of oliguria in the genesis of nitrogen retention is demonstrated by the effects of mercurial diuresis. The injection of mercurial diuretics causes no increase in renal blood flow (page 277), but does greatly increase urine volume; the diuresis usually results in the return to normal of previously elevated blood nonprotein nitrogen levels. The nitrogen retention in congestive failure may occasionally give rise to levels of 60 to 80 mg. per hundred cubic centimeters of nonprotein nitrogen in the blood; blood creatinine levels may also be elevated occasionally (Popper et al., 1937; Gavrila et al., 1929; Messina, 1936; Pescador and Perez López, 1941). The increased blood uric acid concentration that interested Williams (1929) is explained by the same mechanisms. It is important to note that these findings must not be considered contraindications to the use of mercurial diuretics; the elevated blood non-protein nitrogen levels of uncomplicated cardiac decompensation are only infrequently severe and are always transitory, disappearing with treatment.

Disturbances in water metabolism, discussed more fully elsewhere (page 177), may be related in part to normal renal function. There is no loss of concentrating ability, for the urinary specific gravity in congestive failure is high, as noted years ago by Rowntree and Fitz (1913); however, the capacity to form a dilute urine is impaired (Lassen, 1932) and water diuresis cannot be induced (page 177).

Impaired ability to excrete salt in congestive failure (page 173) is also probably related in some way to the abnormal renal vascular function found in this disease, for ligatures placed about renal veins (Rowntree, Fitz and Geraghty, 1913; Blake et al., 1949; Frieden et al., 1952; Davis and Howell, 1953; Jeanneret, 1951) or a renal artery (Blake et al., 1950) induce sodium retention. However neither oliguria (Rowntree, Fitz, and Geraghty, 1913) nor decreased renal flow or glomerular filtration (Blake et al., 1949; Hall and Selkurt, 1951; Frieden et al., 1952; Davis and Howell, 1953) need be present when sodium is retained excessively. These observations point to a disturbance of renal tubular function, as yet not characterized, as important in this regard. At any rate, renal blood flow does not seem to be a governing factor in most cases (Davies et al., 1952; Farber et al., 1951).

Another consequence of renal stasis is a reduction in phenolsulfonphthalein excretion. This occurs in patients with congestive failure (Agnew, 1914; Frothingham and Smillie, 1914; Rowntree et al., 1912, 1913, 1915) and can be induced in dogs by obstructing the renal veins (Rowntree, Fitz and Geraghty, 1913).

Albuminuria is almost a constant finding in moderate or severe cardiac failure. Nearly three-quarters of a century ago a number of authors, including Posner (1880), showed that albuminuria could be produced by obstructing renal blood flow. Posner (1880) and Tele-mann (1910) were among the early workers who showed that such albuminuria was caused by the escape of albumin into the glomerular capsules. Less complete stasis, such as that caused by constricting the renal vein so as to raise the venous pressure, has also been shown to cause albuminuria (Rowntree, Fitz and Geraghty, 1913; Winton, 1931). Clinically, however, albuminuria occurs in many decom-pensated cardiac patients in whom the venous pressure is within normal limits; the blood flow may be greatly decreased in such in-stances (Merrill, 1946). The albuminuria of congestive failure is usually of moderate degree, although at times it may approach in quantity that observed in renal disease. Brummer (1946) claimed that proteinuria increased with effort in cardiac patients but not in normal subjects; his conclusion is not supported with regularity by his data or by what is known of the physiology of exercise. Dryer *et al.* (1949) found small amounts of globulin in the urine in addition to albumin in cardiac decompensation.

Stewart and Moore (1930) investigated the formed elements in the urine in congestive failure and observed a rough parallelism between the number of casts and leucocytes and the clinical condition in a group of patients; erythrocytes tended to persist in abnormal num-bers even after recovery from severe cardiac failure. Rowntree, Fitz, and Geraghty (1913) in their experiments on obstruction of the renal vein in animals showed that the number of formed elements in the urine corresponded fairly well with the degree of renal congestion.

The urine contains normal amounts of acid, ammonia, and phos-phate (Friedberg *et al.*, 1952). Sodium, chloride, and often potassium excretions are abnormal (page 173).

Bibliography

Chapter I — Section 20

AAS, K., and E. BLEGEN, The renal blood flow and the glomerular filtra-tion rate in congestive heart failure and some other clinical conditions. The effect of exercise and hypoxemia. A preliminary report, *Scandinav. J. Clin. & Lab. Investigation* 1, 22 (1949).   [50A, 50B

AGNEW, J. H., Comparative study of phenolsulphonephthalein elimination and the incoagulable nitrogen of the blood in cardiorenal diseases, *Arch. Int. Med.* 13, 485 (1914).

ANGELINO, P. F., and A. ACTIS-DATO, La gasometria del sangue venoso renale e le pressioni venose renale studiate mediante cateterismo in soggetti normali, cardiopatici e in altre forme morbose, *Cuore e circolaz.* **35**, 283 (1951).

AXELROD, D. R., and R. F. PITTS, Effects on hypoxia on renal tubular function, *J. Appl. Physiol.* **4**, 593 (1952).

BALDWIN, D. S., J. H. SIROTA, and H. VILLARREAL, Diurnal variations in renal function in congestive heart failure, *Proc. Soc. Exper. Biol. & Med.* **74**, 578 (1950). [50A, 50B

BARCLAY, J. A., C. T. G. FLEAR, and M. IBRAHIM, Renal tubular reabsorption, *Acta med. Scandinav.* **143**, 361 (1952).

BERGER, E. Y., M. GALDSTON, and S. A. HORWITZ, The effect of anoxic anoxia on the human kidney, *J. Clin. Investigation* **28**, 648 (1949).

BLACK, A. B., and J. A. LITCHFIELD, Uraemia complicating low salt treatment of heart failure, *Quart. J. Med.* **20**, 149 (1951). [50A, 50B

BLACK, D. A. K., R. PLATT, and S. W. STANBURY, Regulation of sodium excretion in normal and salt-depleted subjects, *Clin. Sc.* **9**, 205 (1950).

BLAKE, W. D., R. WÉGRIA, R. P. KEATING, and H. P. WARD, Effect of increased renal venous pressure on renal function, *Am. J. Physiol.* **157**, 1 (1949).

BLAKE, W. B., R. WÉGRIA, H. P. WARD, and C. W. FRANK, Effect of renal arterial constriction on excretion of salt and water, *Am. J. Physiol.* **163**, 422 (1950).

BLEGEN, E., and K. AAS, Renal blood flow and glomerular filtration rate in patients with valvular heart disease, *Acta med. Scandinav.* **138**, 391 (1950). [50A, 50B

BORST, J. G. G., The maintenance of an adequate cardiac output by the regulation of the urinary excretion of water and sodium chloride; an essential factor in the genesis of edema, *Acta med. Scandinav. Supp. No. 207* (1948).

BRIGGS, A. P., D. M. FOWELL, W. P. HAMILTON, J. W. REMINGTON, N. C. WHEELER, and J. A. WINSLOW, Renal and circulatory factors in the edema formation of congestive heart failure, *J. Clin. Investigation* **27**, 810 (1948). [50A, 50B

BROD, J., and Z. FEJFAR, The origin of oedema in heart failure, *Quart. J. Med.* **19**, 187 (1950). [50A, 50B

BRUMMER, P., Proteinuria of effort and its significance in the diagnosis of congestive heart failure, *Acta med. Scandinav.* **124**, 252 (1946).

BRUN, C., E. O. E. KNUDSEN, and F. RAASCHOU, The influence of posture on the kidney function. I. The fall of the diuresis in the erect position, *Acta med. Scandinav.* **122**, 315 (1945).

BRUN, C., E. O. E. KNUDSEN, and F. RAASCHOU, The influence of posture on the kidney function. II. Glomerular dynamics in the passive erect posture, *Acta med. Scandinav.* **122,** 332 (1945).

BURCH, G. E., and P. REASER, Rates of turnover of radiosodium in the blood and urine of normal subjects and patients with congestive heart failure, *J. Clin. Investigation* **26,** 1176 (1947).

CALDWELL, F. T., D. ROLF, and H. L. WHITE, Effects of acute hypoxia on renal circulation in man, *J. Appl. Physiol.* **1,** 597 (1949).

CHAPMAN, C. B., A. HENSCHEL, J. MINCKLER, and A. KEYS, Effect of exercise on renal plasma flow, *Federation Proc.* **7,** 20 (1948).

CHESLEY, L. C., The validity of the calculation of standard urea clearances from low urine volumes, *J. Clin. Investigation* **16,** 653 (1937).

CHESLEY, L. C., Urea excretion at low urine volumes. The calculation of "minimal" urea clearances, *J. Clin. Investigation* **17,** 119 (1938*a*).

CHESLEY, L. C., Renal excretion at low urine volumes and the mechanism of oliguria, *J. Clin. Investigation* **17,** 591 (1938*b*).

DAVIES, C. E., The effect of treatment on the renal circulation in heart-failure, *Lancet* **2,** 1052 (1951).   [50A, 50B

DAVIES, C. E., and J. A. KILPATRICK, Renal circulation in low output and high output heart failure, *Clin. Sc.* **10,** 53 (1951).   [50A, 50B

DAVIES, C. E., J. MACKINNON, and M. M. PLATTS, Renal circulation and cardiac output in "low-output" heart failure and in myxoedema, *Brit. M. J.* **2,** 595 (1952).   [50A, 50B

DAVIS, J. O., and D. S. HOWELL, Mechanisms of fluid and electrolyte retention in experimental preparations in dogs. II. With thoracic inferior vena cava construction, *Circul. Res.* **1,** 171 (1953).

DAVIS, J. O., and N. W. SHOCK, The effect of theophylline ethylene diamine on renal function in control subjects and in patients with congestive heart failure, *J. Clin. Investigation* **28,** 1459 (1949).
                                                                     [50A, 50B

DAVISON, P. H., and R. GADDIE, The influence of intravenous digoxin on renal function in congestive cardiac failure, *Quart. J. Med.* **20,** 389 (1951).   [50A, 50B

DE WARDENER, H. E., and R. R. McSWINEY, Renal haemodynamics in vasovagal fainting due to hemorrhage, *Clin. Sc.* **10,** 209 (1951).

DRYER, R. L., J. H. BUDDE, W. D. PAUL, and J. I. ROUTH, Electrophoretic comparison of plasma and body fluid proteins in certain diseases, *Federation Proc.* **8,** 195 (1949).

EARLE, D. P., JR., S. J. FARBER, J. D. ALEXANDER, and L. W. EICHNA, Effects of treatment on renal functions and electrolyte excretion in congestive heart failure, *J. Clin. Investigation* **28,** 778 (1949).   [50A

EDELMAN, I. S., B. W. ZWEIFACH, D. J. W. ESCHER, J. GROSSMAN, R. MOKOTOFF, R. E. WESTON, L. LEITER, and E. SHORR, Studies on

VEM and VDM in blood in relation to renal hemodynamics and renal oxygen extraction in chronic congestive heart failure, *J. Clin. Investigation* **29,** 925 (1950).

EICHNA, L., S. J. FARBER, A. R. BERGER, D. P. EARLE, B. RADER, E. PELLEGRINO, R. E. ALBERT, J. D. ALEXANDER, H. TAUBE, and S. YOUNGWIRTH, The interrelationship of the cardiovascular, renal and electrolyte effects of intravenous digoxin in congestive heart failure, *J. Clin. Investigation* **30,** 1250 (1951).   [50A, 50B

EICHNA, L., S. J. FARBER, A. R. BERGER, D. P. EARLE, B. RADER, E. PELLEGRINO, R. E. ALBERT, J. D. ALEXANDER, H. TAUBE, and S. YOUNGWIRTH, Cardiovascular dynamics, blood volumes, renal functions and electrolyte excretions in the same patients during congestive heart failure and after recovery of cardiac decompensation, *Circulation* **7,** 674 (1953).   [50A, 50B

EPSTEIN, F. H., A. V. N. GOODYER, D. LAWRASON, and A. S. RELMAN, Studies of the antidiuresis of quiet standing: the importance of changes in plasma volume and glomerular filtration rate, *J. Clin. Investigation* **30,** 63 (1951).

FARBER, S. J., J. D. ALEXANDER, E. D. PELLEGRINO, and D. P. EARLE, The effect of intravenously administered digoxin on water and electrolyte excretion and on renal function, *Circulation* **4,** 378 (1951).   [50A, 50B

FARNSWORTH, E. B., and J. S. KRAKUSIN, Electrolyte partition in patients with edema of various origins. Qualitative and quantitative definition of cations and anions in cardiac decompensation, *J. Lab. & Clin. Med.* **33,** 1534 (1948).   [50A, 50B

FISHMAN, A. P., M. H. MAXWELL, C. H. CROWDER, and P. MORALES, Kidney function in cor pulmonale. Particular consideration of changes in renal hemodynamics and sodium excretion during variation in level of oxygenation, *Circulation* **3,** 703 (1951).   [50A, 50B

FOWELL, D. M., A. P. BRIGGS, N. C. WHEELER, J. A. WINSLOW, JR., J. W. REMINGTON, and W. F. HAMILTON, Renal and circulatory factors in congestive failure of the circulation, *Federation Proc.* **7,** 35 (1948).   [50A

FRIEDBERG, C. K., M. HALPERN, and R. TAYMOR, The effect of intravenously administered 6063, the carbonic anhydrase inhibitor, 2-acetylamino-1,3,4,-thiodiazole-5-sulfonamide, on fluid and electrolytes in normal subjects and patients with congestive heart failure, *J. Clin. Investigation* **31,** 1074 (1952).

FRIEDEN, J., L. RICE, E. I. ELISBERG, B. EISENSTEIN, and L. N. KATZ, Effects of chronic peripheral venous congestion on renal sodium excretion, *Am. J. Physiol.* **168,** 650 (1952).

FROTHINGHAM, C., JR., and W. G. SMILLIE, The relation between the phenolsulphonephthalein excretion in the urine and the nonprotein nitrogen content of the blood in human cases, *Arch. Int. Med.* **14,** 541 (1914).

GAVRILA, J., V. VIOR, and RAMNEANTZU, La créatininémie et la créatinémie dans quelques états pathologiques, *Compt. rend. Soc. de biol.* **100,** 381 (1929).

GROSSMAN, J., R. E. WESTON, I. S. EDELMAN, and L. LEITER, Studies on thiomerin — a subcutaneously administerable mercurial diuretic, *Circulation* **1,** 502 (1950).   [50A, 50B

GROSSMAN, J., R. E. WESTON, J. P. HALPERIN, and L. LEITER, The nature of the renal circulatory changes in chronic congestive failure as reflected by renal tubular maximal functions. *J. Clin. Investigation* **29,** 1320 (1950).   [50A, 50B

GROSSMAN, J., R. E. WESTON, and L. LEITER, A method for determining cardiac output by the direct Fick principle without gas analysis, *J. Clin. Investigation* **32,** 161 (1953).   [50A, 50B

HALL, P. W., III., and E. E. SELKURT, Effects of partial graded venous obstruction on electrolyte clearance by the dog's kidney, *Am. J. Physiol.* **164,** 143 (1951).

HELLER, B. I., and W. E. JACOBSON, Renal hemodynamics in heart disease, *Am. Heart J.* **39,** 188 (1950).   [50A, 50B

HILDEN, T., Glomerular filtration rate and maximal tubular excretory capacity in congestive heart failure, *Scandinav. J. Clin. & Lab. Investigation* **1,** 305 (1949).   [50B

JEANNERET, P., A modified procedure for assessing separate kidney function in chronic dog preparations with observations on the effect of chronic unilateral venous congestion, *J. Lab. & Clin. Med.* **38,** 604 (1951).

KATTUS, A. A., B. SINCLAIR-SMITH, J. GENEST, and E. V. NEWMAN, Effect of exercise on the renal mechanism of electrolyte excretion in normal subjects, *Bull. Johns Hopkins Hosp.* **84,** 344 (1949).

LASSEN, H. C. A., Some investigations on the kidney function in heart lesions, *Acta med. Scandinav. Supp.* **50,** 413 (1932).

LEITER, L., J. GROSSMAN, J. P. HALPERIN, and R. E. WESTON, Studies on renal tubular maximal functions in relation to the abnormal renal hemodynamics in chronic congestive failure, *Tr. A. Am. Physicians* **63,** 51 (1950).   [50A, 50B

LEWIS, C. S., A. J. SAMUELS, M. C. DAINES, and H. H. HECHT, Chronic lung disease, polycythemia and congestive heart failure. Cardiorespiratory, vascular and renal adjustments in cor pulmonale, *Circulation* **6,** 874 (1952).   [50A, 50B

MANTERO, O., and G. BARLASSINA, Contributo allo studio della emodinamica renale nei cardiopatici mediante le prove selettive di funzionalitá renale, *Minerva med.* **42,** 1049 (1951).   [50A, 50B

MATHUR, K. S., Hippuric acid synthesis test as an aid to prognosis in congestive heart failure, *Indian M. Gaz.* **83,** 262 (1948).

MAXWELL, M. H., E. S. BREED, and I. L. SCHWARTZ, Renal venous pressure in chronic congestive heart failure, *J. Clin. Investigation* **29,** 342 (1950).

MERRILL, A. J., Edema and decreased renal blood flow in patients with chronic congestive heart failure. Evidence of "forward failure" as the primary cause of edema, *J. Clin. Investigation* **25,** 389 (1946).
[50B

MERRILL, A. J., and W. H. CARGILL, "Forward failure": the mechanism of cardiac edema in subjects with normal or high cardiac outputs, *J. Clin. Investigation* **26,** 1190 (1947).

MERRILL, A. J., and W. H. CARGILL, The effect of exercise on the renal plasma flow and filtration rate of normal and cardiac subjects, *J. Clin. Investigation* **27,** 272 (1948). [50A, 50B

MESSINA, R., Richerche sulla creatininemia totale nei cardiopatici, *Clin. med. ital.* **67,** 324 (1936).

MOKOTOFF, R., D. J. W. ESCHER, I. S. EDELMAN, J. GROSSMAN, and L. LEITER, Studies on vasotropic principles of blood (VEM and VDM) and renal hemodynamics in chronic heart failure, *Federation Proc.* **8,** 112 (1949). [50A, 50B

MOKOTOFF, R., and G. ROSS, The effect of spinal anesthesia on the renal ischemia in congestive heart failure, *J. Clin. Investigation* **27,** 335 (1948).

MOKOTOFF, R., G. ROSS, and L. LEITER, Renal plasma flow and sodium reabsorption and excretion in congestive heart failure, *J. Clin. Investigation* **27,** 1 (1948). [50A, 50B

NEWMAN, E. V., Function of the kidney and metabolic changes in cardiac failure, *Am. J. Med.* **7,** 490 (1949). [50A, 50B

NETRAVISESH, V., Effects of posture and of neck compression on outputs of water, sodium and creatinine, *J. Appl. Physiol.* **5,** 544 (1953).

NI, T.-G., and P. B. REHBERG, On the influence of posture on kidney function, *J. Physiol.* **71,** 331 (1931).

PESCADOR, L., and J. PEREZ LÓPEZ, Sobre el comportamiento de la creatinina en los portadores de cardiopatias descompensadas, *Rev. clin. españ.* **2,** 262 (1941).

POPPER, H., E. MANDEL, and H. MAYER, Die diagnostische Bedeutung der plasma Kreatininebestimmung, *Ztschr. f. klin. Med.* **133,** 56 (1937).

PORGE, J. F., L'appréciation du facteur rénal chez les cardiaques par la mesure du coefficient de Van Slyke, *Arch. d. mal. du cœur* **32,** 469 (1939).

POSNER, C., Studien über pathologische exsudatbildungen, *Virchows Arch. f. path. Anat.* **79,** 311 (1880).

RADIGAN, L. R., and S. ROBINSON, Effects of environmental heat stress and exercise on renal blood flow and filtration rate, *J. Appl. Physiol.* **2**, 185 (1949).

REVELEY, H. P., G. R. HERRMANN, and J. A. ORTIZ, Studies of factors in congestive heart failure during effective therapy, *Texas State J. Med.* **47**, 617 (1951). [50A, 50B

ROWNTREE, L. G., and R. FITZ, Studies of renal function in renal, cardiorenal and cardiac diseases, *Arch. Int. Med.* **11**, 258 (1913).

ROWNTREE, L. G., R. FITZ, and J. T. GERAGHTY, The effects of experimental chronic passive congestion on renal function, *Arch. Int. Med.* **11**, 121 (1913).

ROWNTREE, L. G., and J. T. GERAGHTY, The phthalein test. An experimental and clinical study of phenolsulphonphthalein in relation to renal function in health and disease, *Arch. Int. Med.* **9**, 284 (1912).

ROWNTREE, L. G., E. K. MARSHALL, JR., and W. A. BAETJER, Further studies of renal function in renal, cardiorenal and cardiac diseases, *Arch. Int. Med.* **15**, 543 (1915).

SCHNEIERSON, S. J., Continuous peritoneal irrigation in the treatment of intractable edema of cardiac origin, *Am. J. M. Sc.* **218**, 76 (1949).

SELKURT, E. E., P. W. HALL, and M. P. SPENCER, Response of renal blood flow and clearance to graded partial obstruction of the renal vein, *Am. J. Physiol.* **157**, 40 (1949).

SEYMOUR, W. B., W. H. PRITCHARD, L. P. LONGLEY, and J. M. HAYMAN, JR., Cardiac output, blood and interstitial fluid volumes, total circulating serum protein, and kidney function during cardiac failure and after improvement, *J. Clin. Investigation* **21**, 229 (1949). [50A

SINCLAIR-SMITH, B., A. A. KATTUS, J. GENEST, and E. V. NEWMAN, The renal mechanism of electrolyte excretion and the metabolic balances of electrolytes and nitrogen in congestive cardiac failure; the effects of exercise, rest and aminophyllin, *Bull. Johns Hopkins Hosp.* **84**, 369 (1949). [50A, 50B

SINCLAIR-SMITH, H., J. SISSON, A. A. KATTUS, A. GENECIN, C. MONGE, W. MCKEEVER, and E. V. NEWMAN, The effects of posterior pituitary extract and smoking on water, sodium and chloride excretion in normal subjects and in patients with congestive cardiac failure, *Bull. Johns Hopkins Hosp.* **87**, 221 (1950). [50B

SIROTA, J. H., D. S. BALDWIN, and H. VILLARREAL, Diurnal variations in glomerular activity in normal man and in patients with congestive heart failure, *Federation Proc.* **8**, 147 (1949).

SQUIRES, R. D., A. P. CROSLEY, JR., and J. R. ELKINTON, The distribution of body fluids in congestive heart failure. III. Exchanges in patients during diuresis, *Circulation* **4**, 868 (1951). [50B

Stewart, H. J., and J. F. McIntosh, The function of the kidneys in patients suffering from chronic cardiac disease without signs of heart failure, *J. Clin. Investigation* **6**, 325 (1928–29).

Stewart, H. J., and N. S. Moore, The number of formed elements in the urinary sediment of patients suffering from heart disease, with particular reference to the state of heart failure, *J. Clin. Investigation* **9**, 409 (1930–31).

Telemann, W., Ueber den Ausscheidungsort des Eiweiss bei kurzdauernden Gefassligaturen der Niere, *Deutsches Arch. f. klin. Med.* **98**, 506 (1910).

Thompson, D. D., and R. F. Pitts, Effects of alterations of renal arterial pressure on sodium and water excretion, *Am. J. Physiol.* **168**, 490 (1952).

Tiagi, G. K., Van Slyke's urea clearance test in Indians in health and disease, *J. Indian M. A.*, **15**, 287, 1946.

Viar, W. N., B. B. Oliver, S. Eisenberg, T. A. Lombardo, K. Willis, and T. R. Harrison, The effect of posture and of compression of the neck on excretion of electrolytes and glomerular filtration: further studies, *Circulation* **3**, 105 (1951).

Warren, J. V., A. J. Merrill, and E. S. Brannon, Observations on renal venous blood in normal unanesthetized subjects and patients with severe congestive heart failure, *J. Clin. Investigation* **23**, 928 (1944).

Weston, R. E., D. J. W. Escher, J. Grossman, and L. Leiter, Mechanisms contributing to unresponsiveness to mercurial diuretics in congestive failure, *J. Clin. Investigation* **31**, 901 (1952).   [50B

White, H. L., and D. Rolf, Effects of exercise and of some other influences on the renal circulation in man, *Am. J. Physiol.* **152**, 505 (1948).

White, H. L., and D. Rolf, Effects of exercise on renal circulation, *Federation Proc.* **7**, 133 (1948).

Williams, J. L., The uric acid increase in the blood of patients with cardiac decompensation, *J. Lab. & Clin. Med.* **15**, 13 (1929).

Winton, F. R., The influence of venous pressure on the isolated mammalian kidney, *J. Physiol.* **72**, 49 (1931).

21. *Salt and Water Metabolism*

Clinicians have long believed that edema formation parallels salt intake in patients with congestive heart failure. Even normal individuals gain weight when given excessive amounts of sodium chloride (Krauel, 1941; Lyons, Jacobson and Avery, 1944); they lose weight when salt intake is restricted (Krauel, 1941). These changes in weight are consequent to corresponding changes in the volume of extracellular fluid (Grant and Reichsman, 1946; Chapman *et al.*, 1950; McCance, 1938; Murphy, 1949), although the plasma volume shows smaller parallel variations (Krauel, 1941; Lyons *et al.*, 1944, 1945; Warren and Stead, 1944; Grant and Reichsman, 1946; Currens *et al.*, 1949; Murphy, 1949; Weston *et al.*, 1950). Increased salt intake apparently causes hemodilution also (Lyons *et al.*, 1944, 1945; Warren and Stead, 1944). The venous pressure may rise slightly (Lyons *et al.*, 1945; Warren and Stead, 1944; Grant and Reichsman, 1946) but the cardiac output does not change, according to Lyons *et al.* (1945). The renal blood flow and the glomerular filtration rate also do not change (Murphy and Stead, 1951).

Achard and Loeper (1901) and Rowntree and Fitz (1913) many years ago showed that edematous cardiac patients retain salt, and McLean (1915) also recognized the fact that the excretion of salt in such patients might be low relative to their blood levels. These observations have been confirmed and extended by many (Futcher and Schroeder, 1942; Burch and Reaser, 1947; Threefoot *et al.*, 1947; Sinclair-Smith *et al.*, 1949, 1950; **50C**). The finding of decreased excretion of chlorides (Fejfar and Brod, 1950; Grossman *et al.*, 1950; Layne *et al.*, 1950; Schroeder, 1950, 1951) has the same significance. That retention of sodium depends to some extent on the associated negative ion and also on the state of potassium balance was shown by Fox, Friedberg, and White (1949). A curious finding is that while normal subjects show decreased sodium excretion during sleep, edematous cardiac patients may show a slight increase in this function (Baldwin, Sirota and Villarreal, 1950; Goldman, 1951; Goldman and Bassett, 1952). Still-standing diminishes sodium excretion (Epstein *et al.*, 1951) and exercise has the same effect in normal subjects and cardiac patients (Barclay *et al.*, 1947; Kattus *et al.*, 1949; Newman, 1949; Sinclair-Smith, 1949, 1950). In the sitting position the excretion of sodium chloride is somewhat lower than in recumbency in normal subjects (Lewis *et al.*, 1950; Viar *et al.*, 1951; Lombard *et al.*, 1951; Strauss *et al.*, 1952; Rosenbaum *et al.*, 1953; Netravisesh, 1953; Barbour *et al.*, 1953); tourniquets placed around the neck when the subject is upright eliminate this difference. Bandages on the legs have a similar effect (Lusk *et al.*, 1952). However, patients with congestive heart failure do not often show this postural difference in renal function (Lombardo, 1953; Borst and De Vries, 1950).

As a rule the renal excretion of soduim is much increased during treatment of cardiac decompensation (page 275); however, patients receiving cation exchange resins show a decrease in urinary excretion of sodium and potassium as edema recedes, owing to the removal of these ions via the gastrointestinal tract (page 287).

The plasma sodium concentration in untreated patients with uncomplicated congestive failure is usually normal or slightly decreased (Miller, 1951; **50D**). Several authors have reported elevated values (Iseri et al., 1950, 1952; Prentice et al., 1951; Squires et al., 1951). The combination of normal plasma level and greatly decreased output establishes the fact that the renal clearance of sodium is markedly decreased in cardiac decompensation.

Burch et al. (1947) have shown that the diffusion of sodium across the capillary walls is more rapid than normal in edema, the overall turnover in plasma being more rapid also while that in the greatly increased volume of interstitial fluid is slower (Burch et al., 1947; Ray et al., 1952). The sodium space is very large (Aikawa, 1952; Warner et al., 1952; Prentice et al., 1951).

Schroeder (1941), Proger et al. (1942), Schemm (1942, 1944), Warren and Stead (1944), Wolf et al. (1947), Elkinton et al. (1952), De Vries et al. (1950), Newman and Fishel (1950), and Fox et al. (1949) have shown how an increased salt intake alone gives rise to edema formation in cardiac patients; Warren and Stead (1944) also demonstrated an increase in plasma volume, and hemodilution is also known to occur (Iversen and Nakazawa, 1927). The extracellular fluid volume increases (Elkinton et al., 1952). The venous pressure rises (Warren and Stead, 1944; De Vries et al., 1950; Newman and Fishel, 1950; Lombardo, 1953). The vital capacity and circulation time also become more abnormal (Lombardo, 1953). However, Proger et al. (1942) also showed that the increase in respiratory minute volume and oxygen consumption, the elevation of venous and arterial pressures, the slowing of the circulation time and the reduction in vital capacity that result are prevented if the patient is digitalized. The conclusion of Warren and Stead (1944) that the observed rise in venous pressure was owing to an increase in plasma volume caused by salt retention is to be criticized because in the patients studied by these authors the regular injection of diuretics was stopped at the same time as the giving of large amounts of sodium chloride was begun. Moreover, a regular relation between change in weight and in venous pressure does not always exist in patients with congestive failure fed salt (De Vries *et al.*, 1950). The use of peritoneal dialysis to remove retained sodium and relieve edema has been reported (Schneierson, 1949). Patients previously depleted of salt fail to gain weight when first given sodium chloride in large amount (Lusk and Palmer, 1953); this finding suggests that such patients have lost intracellular sodium.

The reason for the abnormal retention of salt is not clear. One explanation for the salt retention is that "prerenal deviation" of water leads to salt retention also, that is, salt is retained because edema fluid is being formed. However, many authors have shown that the volume of water taken by the patient does not influence the accumulation of fluid (Barker, 1932; Proger *et al.*, 1942; Schroeder, 1941; Wolf *et al.*, 1947; Leevy *et al.*, 1946). This is sometimes seen very strikingly in the case of edematous cardiac patients given urea; they exhibit a marked diuresis in spite of increased intake, occasionally reaching ten liters a day, occasioned by the severe thirst that the ingestion of large amounts of urea may cause. Moreover, the fact that changing the renal function, by the injection of a mercurial diuretic, for instance, leads to the excretion of the retained sodium chloride, suggests that the kidney is at fault. More than thirty years ago, Rowntree, Fitz and Geraghty (1913) induced partial renal stasis by means of ties on the renal veins in dogs and demonstrated retention of sodium chloride and also sodium iodide. This observation has been amply confirmed (page 162). It seems reasonable to conclude that stasis so changes renal function as to impair the excretion of the sodium. Available evidence indicates that a reduction in renal blood flow is the rule in patients with congestive failure (page 159). However, the glomerular filtration rate is less affected and may even be within the normal range in edematous cardiac patients. Indeed, many authors have shown that there is no correspondence between glomerular filtration rate and sodium retention in man (Baldwin *et al.*, 1950; Davis and Shock, 1949; Earle *et al.*, 1950; Farnsworth and Krakusin, 1948; Grossman *et al.*, 1950; Kattus *et al.*, 1949; Newman, 1949; Sinclair-Smith *et al.*, 1949, 1950; Davies *et al.*,

1952) or in animals (Blake *et al.*, 1949, 1950; Selkurt and Hall, 1951; Davis and Howell, 1953; Jeanneret, 1951, Frieden *et al.*, 1952). Moreover, sodium retention may occur with superior caval obstruction alone (Rice *et al.*, 1952).

It is evident that some derangement involving tubular reabsorption of salt is present in congestive failure. Additional evidence in this direction is the observation of Brown, Tanner, and Hecht (1951) that at high levels of potassium intake slowed excretion of that ion becomes manifest; of interest in this respect is the observation of Selkurt *et al.* (1951) that high degrees of renal stasis impair potassium excretion in animals. However, these considerations become less clearly significant in the light of the observations of Elkinton *et al.* (1952) that giving excess potassium causes intracellular storage of that ion, a finding suggestive of potassium depletion (page 224). This depletion may be hidden behind the facade of a normal or slightly elevated blood potassium level (Iseri *et al.*, 1952; **50E**). Additional evidence of derangement of the function of the kidneys is afforded by the observation that when the plasma chloride levels fall in some cardiac patients, the excretion of chloride ion continues (Winkler and Crankshaw, 1938; Futcher and Schroeder, 1942) even though the blood level is one which in normal persons would be accompanied by the cessation of all urinary chloride output. For the most part, however, blood chloride levels are in or close to the normal range (Dochios and Dreyfus, 1951; Mokotoff *et al.*, 1952; Squires *et al.*, 1951; Dunning *et al.*, 1951; Farber *et al.*, 1951; Weston *et al.*, 1952).

The mechanisms underlying the renal derangements of cardiac decompensation are far from clear in many respects. Anoxia can be ruled out as the prime factor in the renal disorder of congestive failure since the effect of induction of severe anoxia on the kidney in man, at least in short experiments, is an increased loss of sodium, chloride, potassium and water in normal subjects (Burrill *et al.*, 1945; Berger *et al.*, 1949), and even to some extent some patients with congestive failure (Fishman *et al.*, 1951). However, anoxia inhibits mercurial diuresis (page 278). Although the kidney as a filter is fairly well understood, its workings as a gland are not; explanation of the above findings in congestive failure must wait upon extension of knowledge regarding tubular function.

An additional factor making for later salt retention is an initially low salt intake. It has been demonstrated that subjects maintained on a low salt intake retain sodium chloride when given it later in larger amounts (Rowntree and Fitz, 1913; Loeb *et al.*, 1932; McCance, 1936; White and Findley, 1939; Black *et al.*, 1950*a,b*; Daughaday and MacBryde, 1950). This is owing to increased reabsorption by the tubules (Black *et al.*, 1950*a,b*; Wiggins *et al.*, 1951), in spite of the fact that severe sodium restriction may apparently depress some tubular functions (Weston *et al.*, 1948; Currens *et al.*, 1949; Chasis *et al.*, 1949, 1950). As salt restriction is prolonged, the body retains what is given it with increasing tenacity. In extreme instances, oliguria, fall in urea clearance and glomerular filtration, and nitrogen retention may occur (Landis *et al.*, 1935; Wilkinson and McCance, 1940; Mokotoff, Ross and Leiter, 1948; Hellman *et al.*, 1948; Black *et al.*, 1950*a*; Chasis *et al.*, 1949, 1950; Currens *et al.*, 1949; McCance and Widdowson, 1938; Weston *et al.*, 1948, 1950; Wiggins *et al.*, 1951). Although cardiac patients on a low sodium intake lose remarkably little salt in the urine (Burch and Reaser, 1946; Threefoot *et al.*, 1947) the combination of marked sodium restriction and frequent diuresis with mercurials may lead to a lowering of plasma sodium level (Fox *et al.*, 1949; McGuire, 1948; Schroeder, 1949; Sinclair-Smith *et al.*, 1949; Stock *et al.*, 1951; Elkinton *et al.*, 1952; Schwartz and Wallace, 1951; Stapleton and Harvey, 1952) with various deleterious consequences (page 277) and with the persistence in some instances of edema. A recent study by Warming-Larsen (1953) describes the changes in salt excretion that occur during sodium restriction in normal subjects.

Sodium retention may be caused by adrenocortical hormones; substances having such actions have been found in the urine of edematous cardiac patients (Parrish, 1949; Deming and Leutscher, 1950; Lasché *et al.*, 1951; Goldman and Bassett, 1952; Singer and Wener, 1953). However, it is not yet proved that they are produced in excess. Bornstein and Trewhella (1950) reported increased amounts of adrenocorticotrophic hormone in the blood. The urinary 17-ketosteroid output is low (Dochios and Dreyfus, 1951; Lasché *et al.*, 1951), a finding consistent with malnutrition and liver disease. However, the sweat sodium concentration (Merrill, 1949; Steele and Berger, 1951) and the saliva sodium, chloride, and potassium concentrations (White, Gordon, and Leiter, 1950; Steele and Berger, 1951) show changes indicative of adrenocortical hyperactivity in cardiac decompensation. This effect may be owing to discomfort in general, to prolonged anoxia (Pennys, Thomas, and Lewis, 1950), or to restriction of sodium intake (McCance, 1938; Leaf and Couter, 1949; Leaf et al., 1949; Daughaday and MacBryde, 1950; White et al., 1950; Warming-Larsen, 1953; Harris et al., 1953). On the other hand, Reynolds (1952) found no decrease in the sweat sodium level in congestive failure. The blood eosinophil count may be low in failure (Leaf and Mamby, 1952) and rises after treatment (Eliakim and De Vries, 1952). The observation that excretion of adrenal corticoids varies with glomerular filtration rate (Marks and Leaf, 1953) introduces a factor that may confuse the results of all such studies.

Although Shapiro (1928) could find no pituitary hormone activity in the cerebrospinal fluid of cardiac patients, antidiuretic substances were found in the urine of edematous patients by Bercu (1950), Leaf and Mamby (1952), and Dochios and Dreyfus (1951). The normal serum levels found by Perry and Fyles (1953) await corroboration. In normal man excessive intake of salt causes the appearance of these substances in the urine (Hickey and Hare, 1944; Hollond and Stead, 1951); the fact that cardiac patients retain salt abnormally may possibly explain the finding of antidiuretic activity in their urines. In addition, treatment may have this effect also, for Taylor and Noble (1950) showed that restriction of intake of water in normal man causes the urine to exhibit antidiuretic properties. It is also pertinent that the liver inactivates antidiuretic substances normally (Heller and Urban, 1935; Birnie, 1953; Eversole, 1949); in the presence of hepatic damage this function might be impaired. However, White et al. (1951; 1953) dispute this concept. The recent work of Shorr and his co-workers (Shorr et al., 1950; Edelman et al., 1950; Mokotoff et al., 1949) that showed the occurrence of VDM, a substance derived from the liver, in the blood and body fluid of patients with congestive failure, is of interest in view of its antidiuretic properties; its role in edema formation in heart disease awaits clarification.

The occurrence in patients with cardiac decompensation of substances with antidiuretic actions is of interest in view of the fact that water diuresis is much reduced in patients with this disorder (Pratt,

1926; Fremont-Smith *et al.*, 1930; Elkinton *et al.*, 1952; Dochios and Dreyfus, 1951; Tarail *et al.*, 1951; Lassen, 1932; Crutchfield *et al.*, 1948). This may be owing to the disease itself, or the use of sodium restriction in its treatment (Black *et al.*, 1950; McCance, 1936; McCance and Widdowson, 1937). In addition, both restriction of water and severe exercise have been shown to have a similar effect in normal man (Barclay *et al.*, 1947). The matter is still not settled, however; White *et al.* (1953) showed that although cardiac patients exhibit decreased water diuresis, they respond normally to injected pitressin.

Wheals made with saline solution in the skin of edematous cardiac patients disappear abnormally rapidly (Elias and Goldstein, 1932; Kiss, 1931; Zak *et al.*, 1934; Zak, 1949; Johanson, 1948). The significance of this phenomenon in relation to water metabolism is not clear.

That severe restriction of water may be harmful is evident. The question whether it impairs renal function cannot be answered on the basis of available data (McCance and Young, 1944; Kenney, 1949). Contrariwise, the routine forcing of fluids in edematous patients, recommended in some quarters, cannot be shown to be beneficial in cardiac decompensation (Wolf *et al.*, 1947), not an unexpected finding in view of the loss of water diuresis in this condition. That excessive intake of water may depress salt excretion under some conditions is well known (McCance and Widdowson, 1944; Barclay and Nutt, 1944); in addition, in view of the fact that water may be retained without sodium, there is a danger of water intoxication (Schroeder, 1941).

Rigid restriction of salt intake may result in a lowering of plasma chloride and base levels (Loeb *et al.*, 1932; McCance, 1936; Peschel and Lohmann-Peschel, 1952). Since salt depletion and low plasma chloride concentrations inhibit the action of diuretics, and administration of sodium chloride enhances their action (page 277), it may at times be preferable to avoid unduly severe dietary salt restriction. The difficulties involved in preparing the low salt diet recommended by some authors, the extremely unpalatable character of the food it offers to anorectic cardiac patients, the facts that the low salt diet is also low in animal protein, that cardiac patients on a low salt regimen excrete less salt than is normal under the circumstances, that many of the effects of salt intake are obviated by digitalization (Proger *et al.*, 1942) and that too rigid restriction of sodium chloride intake inhibits the action of diuretics, all suggest that the avoidance of such severe restriction of salt intake over extended periods of time might be wise. In addition, when sodium depletion is present, the occurrence of renal failure, shock, and coma are additional hazards (page 176).

As has been pointed out above, severe restriction of water may be harmful. There is no evidence, however, that forcing of fluids is beneficial in congestive failure (Wolf *et al.*, 1947); in this condition the diuretic action of water is lost, for reasons which are not established (Fremont-Smith *et al.*, 1930; Crutchfield *et al.*, 1948) and indeed excessive intake of fluid may possibly depress sodium excretion in congestive failure.

In addition to the disturbances in over-all salt and water metabolism now recognized, there are changes in diurnal rhythm that are difficult to explain. The night volume of urine is greater than the day volume (Quincke, 1877; Wilson, 1889; Borst and De Vries, 1950; Goldman, 1951; Goldman and Bassett, 1952). Corresponding changes in the excretion of solids occur. The changes are probably not explained by variations in renal blood flow or glomerular filtration that occur at night (page 161). Cortisone causes similar changes in excretory function in normal persons (Rosenbaum *et al.*, 1952).

Lowe (1951) has attempted to resolve some of the difficulties that prevent a satisfactory understanding of water metabolism in congestive heart failure.

Bibliography

Chapter I — Section 21

ACHARD, C., and M. LOEPER, Sur la rétention des chlorures dans les tissues au cours de certains états morbides, *Compt. rend. Soc. de biol.* **53,** 346 (1901).

AIKAWA, J., Comparison of the thiocyanate and radiosodium spaces in disease states, *Am. J. M. Sc.* **224,** 632 (1952).

BALDWIN, D. S., J. H. SIROTA, and H. VILLARREAL, Diurnal variations in renal function in congestive heart failure, *Proc. Soc. Exper. Biol. & Med.* **74,** 578 (1950).   [50C

BARBOUR, A., G. M. BULL, B. M. EVANS, N. C. HUGHES JONES, and J. LOGOTHETOPOULOS, The effect of breathing 5 to 7% carbon dioxide on urine flow and mineral excretion, *Clin. Sc.* **12,** 1 (1953).

BARCLAY, J. A., W. T. COOKE, R. A. KENNEY, and M. E. NUTT, The effects of water diuresis and exercise on the volume and composition of the urine, *Am. J. Physiol.* **148,** 327 (1947).

BARCLAY, J. A., and M. E. NUTT, Urinary changes during water diuresis, *J. Physiol.* **103,** 20 P (1944).

BARKER, M. H., Edema as influenced by a low ratio of sodium to potassium intake. Clinical observations, *J. A. M. A.* **98,** 2193 (1932).

BERCU, B. A., S. N. ROKAW, and E. MASSIE, Antidiuretic action of the urine of patients in cardiac failure, *Circulation* **2,** 409 (1950).

BERGER, E. Y., M. GALDSTON, and S. A. HORWITZ, The effect of anoxic anoxia on the human kidney, *J. Clin. Investigation* **28,** 648 (1949).

BEST, M. M., W. F. HURT, J. E. SHAW, and J. D. WATHEN, Study of the mercurial diuretic, dicurin procaine (merethoxylline procaine) by subcutaneous injection, *Am. J. M. Sc.* **225,** 132 (1953).   [50C

BIRNIE, J. H., The inactivation of posterior pituitary anti-diuretic hormone by liver extracts, *Endocrinology* **52,** 33 (1953).

BLACK, D. A. K., R. PLATT, and S. W. STANBURY, Regulation of sodium excretion in normal and salt-depleted subjects, *Clin. Sc.* **9,** 205 (1950).

BLACK, D. A. K., R. PLATT, and S. W. STANBURY, Change in kidney tubule functions on a diet poor in sodium chloride, *Nature* **165,** 605 (1950).

BLAKE, W. D., R. WÉGRIA, R. P. KEATING, and H. P. WARD, Effect of increased renal venous pressure on renal function, *Am. J. Physiol.* **157,** 1 (1949).

BLAKE, W. D., R. WÉGRIA, H. P. WARD, and C. W. FRANK, Effect of renal arterial constriction on excretion of salt and water, *Am. J. Physiol.* **163,** 422 (1950).

BORNSTEIN, J., and P. TREWHELLA, Adrenocortico-tropic activity of blood plasma extracts, *Lancet* **2,** 678 (1950).

BORST, J. G. G., and L. A. DE VRIES, The three types of "natural" diuresis, *Lancet* **2,** 1 (1950).

BRIGGS, A. P., D. M. FOWELL, W. F. HAMILTON, J. W. REMINGTON, N. C. WHEELER, and J. A. WINSLOW, Renal and circulatory factors in the edema formation of congestive heart failure, *J. Clin. Investigation* **27,** 810 (1948).   [50D

BROWN, H., G. L. TANNER, and H. H. HECHT, The effects of potassium salts in subjects with heart disease, *J. Lab. & Clin. Med.* **37,** 506 (1951).

BURCH, G. E., and P. REASER, Rates of turnover of radiosodium in the blood and urine of normal subjects and patients with congestive heart faliure, *J. Clin. Investigation* **26**, 1176 (1947). [50C

BURCH, G., P. REASER, and J. CRONVICH, Rates of sodium turnover in normal subjects and in patients with congestive heart failure, *J. Lab. & Clin. Med.* **32**, 1169 (1947). [50C

BURRILL, M. W., S. FREEMAN, and A. C. IVY, Sodium, potassium and chloride excretion of human subjects exposed to a simulated altitude of 18,000 feet, *J. Biol. Chem.* **157**, 297 (1945).

CALLAHAN, E. J., III, N. R. FRANK, H. KRAUS, and L. B. ELLIS, Clinical use of cation exchange resins in the treatment of congestive heart failure, *Am. J. M. Sc.* **223**, 117 (1952). [50D, 50E

CHAPMAN, C. B., T. GIBBONS, and A. HENSCHEL, The effect of the rice-fruit diet on the composition of the body, *New England J. Med.* **243**, 899 (1950).

CHASIS, H., W. GOLDRING, E. BREED, A. BOLOMEY, and H. W. SMITH, Effect of salt and protein restriction on blood pressure and renal hemodynamics in hypertensive patients, *J. Clin. Investigation* **28**, 775 (1949).

CHASIS, H., W. GOLDRING, E. S. BREED, G. E. SCHREINER, and A. A. BOLOMEY, Salt and protein restriction. Effects on blood pressure and renal hemodynamics in hypertensive patients, *J. A. M. A.* **142**, 711 (1950).

CRUTCHFIELD, A. J., JR., and J. E. WOOD, JR., Urine volume and total renal sodium excretion during water diuresis., *Ann. Int. Med.* **28**, 28 (1948).

CURRENS, J. H., E. A. S. REID, E. A. MacLACHLAN, M. L. TERRY, A. M. BUTLER, and P. D. WHITE, Physiologic, metabolic, and electrolytic balance studies of hypertensive patients while on the rice diet, *J Clin. Investigation* **28**, 776 (1949).

DAUGHADAY, W. H., and C. M. MACBRIDE, Renal and adrenal mechanisms of salt conservation: The excretion of urinary formaldehydogenic steroids and 17-ketosteroids during salt deprivation and desoxycorticosterone administration, *J. Clin. Investigation* **29**, 591 (1950).

DAVIES, C. E., and J. A. KILPATRICK, Renal circulation in low output and high output heart failure, *Clin. Sc.* **10**, 53 (1951). [50C

DAVIS, J. O., and D. S. HOWELL, Mechanisms of fluid and electrolyte retention in experimental preparations in dogs. II. With thoracic inferior vena cava construction, *Circul. Res.* **1**, 171 (1953).

DAVIS, J. O., and N. W. SHOCK, The effect of theophylline ethylene diamine on renal function in control subjects and in patients with congestive heart failure, *J. Clin. Investigation* **28**, 1459 (1949). [50C

DEMING, Q. B., and J. A. LUETSCHER, JR., Bioassay of desoxycorticos-terone-like material in urine, *Proc. Soc. Exper. Biol. & Med.* **73,** 171 (1950).

DE VRIES, A., C. H. FRYD, and S. GITELSON, Observations on heart failure. The effect of withdrawal and administration of salt on body weight and venous pressure in heart failure, *Cardiologia* **15,** 368 (1950).

DOCHIOS, M., and L. S. DREIFUS, Antidiuretic hormone studies in patients presenting edema, *Am. J. M. Sc.* **222,** 539 (1951).   [50D

DUNNING, M. F., J. M. STEELE, and E. Y. BERGER, Measurement of total body chloride, *Proc. Soc. Exper. Biol. & Med.* **77,** 854 (1951).

EARLE, D. P., JR., S. J. FARBER, J. D. ALEXANDER, and L. W. EICHNA, Effects of treatment on renal functions and electrolyte excretion in congestive heart failure, *J. Clin. Investigation* **28,** 778 (1949).   [50C

EICHNA, L., S. J. FARBER, A. R. BERGER, D. P. EARLE, B. RADER, E. PELLE-. GRINO, R. E. ALBERT, J. D. ALEXANDER, H. TAUBE, and S. YOUNG-WIRTH, The interrelationship of the cardiovascular, renal and electro-lyte effects of intravenous digoxin in congestive heart failure, *J. Clin. Investigation* **30,** 1250 (1951).   [50C

EICHNA, L., S. J. FARBER, A. R. BERGER, D. P. EARLE, B. RADER, E. PELLE-GRINO, R. E. ALBERT, J. D. ALEXANDER, H. TAUBE, and S. YOUNG-WIRTH, Cardiovascular dynamics, blood volumes, renal functions and electrolyte excretions in the same patients during congestive heart failure and after recovery of cardiac decompensation, *Circulation* **7,** 674 (1953).

ELIAKIM, M., and A. DE VRIES, Observations on the eosinophil count in congestive heart failure, *Cardiologia* **21,** 44 (1952).

ELIAS, H., and J. GOLDSTEIN, Beiträge zum Studium der Stauungstypen. IV Mitt. Experimentelle Untersuchungen über den Einstrom von Gewebsfüssigkeit in die Gefassbahn bei Herzfehlerkranken, *Ztschr. f. klin. Med.* **121,** 88 (1932).   [50C

ELKINTON, J. R., R. D. SQUIRES, and L. W. BLUEMLE, JR., The distribu-tion of body fluids in congestive heart failure. IV. Exchanges in patients, refractory to mercurial diuretics, treated with sodium and potassium, *Circulation* **5,** 58 (1952).   [50D, 50E

EPSTEIN, F. H., A. V. N. GOODYER, D. LAWRASON, and A. S. RELMAN, Studies of the antidiuresis of quiet standing: the importance of changes in plasma volume and glomerular filtration rate, *J. Clin. Investiga-tion* **30,** 63 (1951).

EVERSOLE, W. J., J. H. BIRNIE, and R. GAUNT, Inactivation of posterior pituitary anti-diuretic hormone by the liver, *Endocrinology* **45,** 378 (1949).

FARBER, S. J., J. D. ALEXANDER, E. D. PELLEGRINO, and D. P. EARLE, The effect of intravenously administered digoxin on water and electrolyte excretion and on renal function, *Circulation* **4**, 378 (1951).
[50C, 50D

FARNSWORTH, E. B., Electrolyte partition in patients with edema of various origins. Sodium and chloride, *Am. J. Med.* **4**, 338 (1948). [50D

FARNSWORTH, E. B., and J. S. KRAKUSIN, Electrolyte partition in patients with edema of various origins. Qualitative and quantitative definition of cations and anions in cardiac decompensation, *J. Lab. & Clin. Med.* **33**, 1534 (1948). [50D, 50E

FEJFAR, Z., and J. BROD, The excretion of chlorides in patients with heart failure, *Quart. J. Med.* **19**, 221 (1950).

FISHMAN, A. P., M. H. MAXWELL C. H. CROWDER, and P. MORALES, Kidney function in cor pulmonale. Particular consideration of changes in renal hemodynamics and sodium excretion during variation in level of oxygenation, *Circulation* **3**, 703 (1951). [50C

FOWELL, D. M., A. P. BRIGGS, N. C. WHEELER, J. A. WINSLOW, JR., J. W. REMINGTON, and W. F. HAMILTON, Renal and circulatory factors in congestive failure of the circulation, *Federation Proc.* **7**, 35 (1948).

FOX, C. L., JR., C. K. FRIEDBURG, and A. G. WHITE, Electrolyte abnormalities in chronic congestive heart failure; effects of administration of potassium and sodium salt, *J. Clin. Investigation* **28**, 781 (1949).
[50C, 50D

FRIEDEN, J., L. RICE, E. I. ELISBERG, B. EISENSTEIN, and L. N. KATZ, Effects of chronic peripheral venous congestion on renal sodium excretion, *Am. J. Physiol.* **168**, 650 (1952).

FREMONT-SMITH, F., M. FREMONT-SMITH, M. E. DAILEY, P. SOLOMON, DEW. STETTEN, JR., and M. P. CARROLL, Studies in edema. I. The mechanism of water diuresis in man, *J. Clin. Investigation* **9**, 7 (1930).

FUTCHER, P. H., and H. A. SCHROEDER, Studies on congestive failure. II. Impaired renal excretion of sodium chloride, *Am. J. M. Sc.* **204**, 52 (1942). [50C, 50D

GOLDMAN, R., Studies in diurnal variation of water and electrolyte excretion: nocturnal diuresis of water and sodium in congestive cardiac failure and cirrhosis of the liver, *J. Clin. Investigation* **30**, 1191 (1951).

GOLDMAN, R., and S. H. BASSETT, Diurnal variation in the urinary excretion of neutral lipid-soluble reducing steroids in congestive cardiac failure and cirrhosis of the liver with ascites, *J. Clin. Investigation* **31**, 253 (1952).

GRANT, H., and F. REICHSMAN, The effects of the ingestion of large amounts of sodium chloride on the arterial and venous pressures of normal subjects, *Am. Heart J.* **32**, 704 (1946).

GREEN, D. M., W. C. BRIDGES, A. D. JOHNSON, J. H. LEHMAN, F. GRAY, and L. FIELD, Relation of glomerular filtration rate and sodium tubular rejection fraction to renal sodium excretion, *Am. J. Physiol.* **160,** 306 (1950).

GROSSMAN, J., R. E. WESTON, I. S. EDELMAN, and L. LEITER, Studies on thiomerin — a subcutaneously administerable mercurial diuretic, *Circulation* **1,** 502 (1950). [50C

HALL, P. W., III, and E. E. SELKURT, Effects of partial graded venous obstruction on electrolyte clearance by the dog's kidney, *Am. J. Physiol.* **164,** 143 (1951).

HARRIS, J. F., C. W. LLOYD, and J. LOBOTSKY, Some studies of posterior pituitary and adrenal interrelationships in patients with and without cirrhosis of the liver, *J. Clin. Investigation* **32,** 885 (1953).

HAY, S. H., and J. E. WOOD, JR., Cation exchange resins in the treatment of congestive heart failure, *Ann. Int. Med.* **33,** 1139 (1950).

HELLER, H., and F. F. URBAN, The fate of the antidiuretic principle of postpituitary extracts in vivo and in vitro, *J. Physiol.* **85,** 502 (1935).

HICKEY, R. C., and K. HARE, The renal excretion of chloride and water in diabetes insipidus, *J. Clin. Investigation* **23,** 768 (1944).

HOLLAND, B. C., and E. A. STEAD, JR., Effect of vasopressin (pitressin)-induced water retention on sodium excretion, *Arch. Int. Med.* **88,** 571 (1951).

ISERI, L. T., A. J. BOYLE, and G. B. MYERS, Water and electrolyte balance during recovery from severe congestive failure on a 50 milligram sodium diet, *Am. Heart J.* **40,** 706 (1950).

ISERI, L. T., R. S. MCCAUGHEY, L. ALEXANDER, A. J. BOYLE, and G. B. MYERS, Plasma sodium and potassium concentrations in congestive heart failure. Relationship to pathogenesis of failure, *Am. J. M. Sc.* **224,** 135 (1952). [50D, 50E

IVERSEN, P., and F. NAKAZAWA, Om Oedempatogenese, *Ugesk. f. læger* **89,** 640 (1927).

JEANNERET, P., A modified procedure for assessing separate kidney function in chronic dog preparations with observations on the effect of chronic unilateral venous congestion, *J. Lab. & Clin. Med.* **38,** 604 (1951).

JOHANSON, C., On the intradermal salt solution test in forming diagnostics of edema, *Acta med. Scandinav.* **130,** 156 (1948).

KATTUS, A., T. M. ARRINGTON, and E. V. NEWMAN, Clinical observations on a new oral diuretic 1-propyl-3-ethyl-6-aminouracil and preliminary studies on 1-allyl-3-ethyl-6-aminouracil, *Am. J. Med.* **12,** 319 (1952). [50C

KATTUS, A. A., B. SINCLAIR-SMITH, J. GENEST, and E. V. NEWMAN, Effect of exercise on the renal mechanism of electrolyte excretion in normal subjects, *Bull. Johns Hopkins Hosp.* **84,** 344 (1949).

KENNEY, R. A., Effects of water deprivation on the renal hemodynamics in man, *Acta med. Scandinav.* **135,** 172 (1949).

KISS, A., Ueber örtlich beschrankte Wirkung von Hormonen, Speziell des Pituitrins auf den Wasserwechsel, *Klin. Wchnschr.* **10,** 162 (1931).

KLINGENSMITH, W. C., JR., and J. R. ELKINTON, Cation exchange resin in the treatment of congestive heart failure. II. Clinical effectiveness and chemical complications during prolonged periods of use, *Circulation* **5,** 842 (1952). [50D, 50E

KRAUEL, G., Ueber den Einfluss der Ernährung auf die zirkulierende Blutmenge; kochsalzarme und kochsalzreiche Diät, *Ztschr. f. klin. Med.* **139,** 459 (1941).

LANDIS, E. M., K. A. ELSOM, P. A. BOTT, and E. SHIELS, Observations on sodium chloride restriction and urea clearance in renal insufficiency, *J. Clin. Investigation* **14,** 525 (1935).

LASCHÉ, E. M., W. H. PERLOFF, and T. M. DURANT, Some aspects of adrenocortical function in cardiac decompensation, *Am. J. M. Sc.* **222,** 459 (1951).

LASSEN, H. C. A., Some investigations on the kidney function in heart lesions, *Acta med. Scandinav., Supp.* **50,** 413 (1932).

LAYNE, J. A., F. R. SCHEMM, and W. W. HURST, Further comparative studies on ascites in liver and heart disease, *Gastroenterol.* **16,** 91 (1950).

LEAF, A., and W. T. COUTER, Evidence that renal sodium excretion by normal human subjects is regulated by adrenal cortical activity, *J. Clin. Investigation* **28,** 1067 (1949).

LEAF, A., W. T. COUTER, and L. H. NEWBURGH, Some effects of variation in sodium intake and of different sodium salts in normal subjects, *J. Clin. Investigation* **28,** 1082 (1949).

LEAF, A., and A. R. MAMBY, An antidiuretic mechanism not regulated by extracellular fluid tonicity, *J. Clin. Investigation* **31,** 60 (1952). [50D

LEEVY, C. M., J. A. STRAZZA, and A. E. JAFFIN, Fluids in congestive heart failure, *J. A. M. A.* **131,** 1120 (1946).

LEFKEN, E. B., D. K. HAWLEY, and A. IGLAUER, Ammonium and potassium cation exchange resin in treatment of congestive heart failure, *Postgrad. Med.* **12,** 537 (1952). [50C

LEVITT, M. F., L. B. TURNER, and A. Y. SWEET, The effect of experimental venous obstruction on salt and water distribution and excretion in man, *J. Clin. Investigation* **31,** 885 (1952). [50D, 50E

LEWIS, J. M., JR., R. M. BUIE, S. M. SEVIER, and T. R. HARRISON, The effect of posture and of congestion of the head on sodium excretion in normal subjects, *Circulation* 2, 822 (1950).

LOEB, R. F., D. W. ATCHLEY, D. W. RICHARDS, JR., E. M. BENEDICT, and M. E. DRISCOLL, On the mechanism of nephrotic edema, *J. Clin. Investigation* 11, 621 (1932).

LOMBARDO, T. A., The effect of posture on the excretion of water and sodium by patients with congestive heart failure, *Circulation* 7, 91 (1953).   [50C, 50D

LOMBARDO, T. A., S. EISENBERG, B. B. OLIVER, W. N. VIAR, E. E. EDDLEMAN, and T. R. HARRISON, Effects of bleeding on electrolyte excretion and on glomerular filtration, *Circulation* 3, 260 (1951).

LOMBARDO, T. A., and T. R. HARRISON, Effect of neck compression on sodium excretion in subjects with congestive heart failure, *Circulation* 7, 88 (1953).   [50C

LOWE, T. E., Fluid balance in congestive cardiac failure. Two mechanisms of diuresis, *Lancet* 2, 851 (1951).

LUSK, J. A., III, and S. D. PALMER, Long-range observations of sodium exchange in patients with congestive heart failure, *Circulation* 7, 282 (1953).

LUSK, J. A., W. N. VIAR, and T. R. HARRISON, Further studies on the effects of changes in the distribution of extracellular fluid on sodium excretion. Observations following compression of the legs, *Circulation* 6, 911 (1952).

LYONS, R. H., S. D. JACOBSON, and N. L. AVERY, JR., Increases in the plasma volume following the administration of sodium salts, *Am. J. M. Sc.* 208, 148 (1944).

LYONS, R. H., S. D. JACOBSON, and J. L. NEERKIN, The relationship between changes in serum protein concentration and the plasma volume in normal subjects, *J. Lab. & Clin. Med.* 30, 404 (1945).

LYONS, R. H., F. D. JOHNSON, and J. SANDERS, Studies on the changes in the circulation of normal subjects with small variations in the fluid content of the body, *J. Lab. & Clin. Med.* 30, 376 (1945).

MARKS, L. J., and A. LEAF, The relationship of the renal excretion of adrenal corticoids to variations in renal hemodynamics, *J. Clin. Investigation* 32, 813 (1953).

McCANCE, R. A., Medical problems in mineral metabolism. III. Experimental human salt deficiency, *Lancet* 1, 823 (1936).

McCANCE, R. A., The effect of salt deficiency in man on the volume of the extracellular fluids and on the composition of sweat, saliva, gastric juice and cerebrospinal fluid, *J. Physiol.* 92, 208 (1938).

McCANCE, R. A., and E. M. WIDDOWSON, The secretion of urine in man during experimental salt deficiency, *J. Physiol.* 91, 222 (1937).

McCance, R. A., and W. F. Young, The secretion of urine during dehydration and rehydration, *J. Physiol.* **102,** 415 (1944).

McGuire, W. B., Jr., Risk of uremia due to sodium depletion, *J. A. M. A.* **137,** 1377 (1948).

McLean, F., The numerical laws governing the rate of excretion of urea and chlorides in man. II. The influence of pathological conditions and of drugs on excretion, *J. Exper. Med.* **22,** 366 (1915).

Merrill, A. J., Edema and decreased renal blood flow in patients with chronic congestive heart failure. Evidence of "forward failure" as the primary cause of edema, *J. Clin. Investigation* **25,** 389 (1946).

Merrill, A. J., Mechanisms of salt and water retention in heart failure, *Am. J. Med.* **6,** 357 (1949).

Miller, G. E., Water and electrolyte metabolism in congestive heart failure, *Circulation* **4,** 270 (1951). [50D

Mokotoff, R., D. J. W. Escher, I. S. Edelman, J. Grossman, and L. Leiter, Studies on vasotropic principles of blood (VEM and VDM) and renal hemodynamics in chronic heart failure, *Federation Proc.* **8,** 112 (1949).

Mokotoff, R., G. Ross, and L. Leiter, Renal plasma flow and sodium reabsorption and excretion in congestive heart failure, *J. Clin. Investigation* **27,** 1 (1948). [50D

Mokotoff, R., G. Ross, and L. Leiter, The electrolyte content of skeletal muscle in congestive heart failure; a comparison of results with inulin and chloride as reference standards for extracellular water, *J. Clin. Investigation* **31,** 291 (1952). [50D, 50E

Murphy, R. J. F., Plasma volume, red cell volume and "extravascular thiocyanate space" changes in patients on a rice diet, *J. Clin. Investigation* **28,** 800 (1949).

Murphy, R. J. F., and E. A. Stead, Jr., Effects of exogenous and endogenous posterior pituitary hormone on water and electrolyte excretion, *J. Clin. Investigation* **30,** 1055 (1951).

Newman, E. V., Function of the kidney and metabolic changes in cardiac failure, *Am. J. Med.,* **7,** 490 (1949).

Newman, W., and L. Fishel, Observations on the daily changes in venous pressure and weight in a case of chronic congestive heart failure, *Circulation* **1,** 706 (1950).

Parrish, A. E., The bioassay of adrenal corticoids in the urine of patients with congestive heart failure, *J. Clin. Investigation* **28,** 45 (1949).

Penneys, R., C. B. Thomas, and R. A. Lewis, Reduction in the number of circulating eosinophils following induced anoxia, *Bull. Johns Hopkins Hosp.* **86,** 102 (1950).

PERRY, W. F., and T. W. FYLES, Antidiuretic activity of the serum of normal and diseased subjects, *J. Clin. Endocrinol. & Metab.* **13**, 64 (1953).

PESCHEL, E., and R. LOHMANN-PESCHEL, Electrolyte metabolism during rice diet. I. Serum electrolytes in hypertensive patients without evidence of advanced renal involvement, *Arch. Int. Med.* **89**, 234 (1952).

PRATT, J. H., The dilution and concentration tests of renal function, *Boston M. & S. J.* **195**, 203 (1926).

PRENTICE, T. C., N. I. BERLIN, G. M. HYDE, R. J. PARSONS, J. H. LAWRENCE, and S. PORT, Total red cell volume, plasma volume, and sodium space in congestive heart failure, *J. Clin. Investigation* **30**, 1471 (1951).   [50D

PROGER, S., E. GINSBURG, and H. MAGENDANTZ, The effects of the ingestion of excessive amounts of sodium chloride and water on patients with heart disease, *Am. Heart J.* **23**, 555 (1942).

QUINCKE, H., Ueber den Einfluss des Schlafes auf die Harnabsonderung, *Arch f. exper. Path. u. Pharm.* **7**, 115 (1877).

RAY, C. T., G. E. BURCH, and S. A. THREEFOOT, Biologic decay rates of chloride in normal and diseased man, determined with long-life radiochlorine Cl^{36}, *J. Lab. & Clin. Med.* **39**, 673 (1952).

REASER, P. R., and G. E. BURCH, Radiosodium tracer studies in congestive heart failure, *Proc. Soc. Exper. Biol. & Med.* **63**, 543 (1946).

REYNOLDS, T., Sweat sodium levels in congestive heart failure, *Proc. Soc. Exper. Biol. & Med.* **79**, 118 (1952).

RICE, L., J. FRIEDEN, L. N. KATZ, E. I. ELISBERG, and E. ROSENBERG, A case of spontaneous thrombosis of the superior vena cava with some observations on the mechanism of edema formation, *Am. Heart J.* **43**, 821 (1952).

ROSENBAUM, J. D., B. C. FERGUSON, R. K. DAVIS, and E. C. ROSSMEISL, The influence of cortisone upon the diurnal rhythm of renal excretory function, *J. Clin. Investigation* **31**, 507 (1952).

ROSENBAUM, J. D., W. P. NELSON, III, M. B. STRAUSS, R. K. DAVIS, and E. C. ROSSMEISL, Variation in the diuretic response to ingested water related to the renal excretion of solutes, *J. Clin. Investigation* **32**, 394 (1953).

ROWNTREE, L. G., and R. FITZ, Studies of renal function in renal, cardio-renal and cardiac diseases, *Arch. Int. Med.* **11**, 258 (1913).

ROWNTREE, L. G., R. FITZ, and J. T. GERAGHTY, The effects of experimental chronic passive congestion on renal function, *Arch. Int. Med.* **11**, 121 (1913).

SCHEMM, F. R., A high fluid intake in the management of edema, especially cardiac edema. I. The details and basis of the regime, *Ann. Int. Med.* **17**, 952 (1942).

SCHEMM, F. R., A high fluid intake in the management of edema, especially cardiac edema. II. Clinical observation and data, *Ann. Int. Med.* **21,** 937 (1944).

SCHNEIERSON, S. J., Continuous peritoneal irrigation in the treatment of intractable edema of cardiac origin, *Am. J. M. Sc.* **218,** 76 (1949).

SCHROEDER, H. A., Studies on congestive heart failure. I. The importance of restriction of salt as compared to water, *Am. Heart J.* **22,** 141 (1941).

SCHROEDER, H. A., Renal failure associated with low extracellular sodium chloride. The low salt syndrome, *J. A. M. A.* **141,** 117 (1949).

SCHROEDER, H. A., Studies on congestive circulatory failure. III. The relation of edema to urinary chlorides, *Circulation* **1,** 481 (1950).

SCHROEDER, H. A., Studies on congestive circulatory failure. IV. The effect of various diuretics on the excretion of water and chlorides, *Circulation* **4,** 87 (1951).

SCHWARTZ, W. B., and W. M. WALLACE, Electrolyte equilibrium during mercurial diuresis, *J. Clin. Investigation* **30,** 1089 (1951).

SELKURT, E. E., P. W. HALL, and M. P. SPENCER, Response of renal blood flow and clearance to graded partial obstruction of the renal vein, *Am. J. Physiol.* **157,** 40 (1949).

SHAPIRO, S., The presence of an oxytocic substance (posterior hypophysis extract) in cerebrospinal fluid, *Arch. Neurol. & Psychiat.* **15,** 331 (1928).

SHORR, E., S. BAEZ, B. W. ZWEIFACH, M. A. PAYNE, and A. MAZUR, The antidiuretic action of the hepatic vaso-depressor ferritin (VDM) and its occurrence in conditions associated with antidiuresis in man, *Tr. A. Am. Physicians* **63,** 39 (1950).

SINCLAIR-SMITH, B., A. A. KATTUS, J. GENEST, and E. V. NEWMAN, The renal mechanism of electrolyte excretion and the metabolic balances of electrolytes and nitrogen in congestive cardiac failure; the effects of exercise, rest and aminophyllin, *Bull. Johns Hopkins Hosp.* **84,** 369 (1949). [50C

SINCLAIR-SMITH, B., J. SISSON, A. A. KATTUS, A. GENECIN, C. MONGE, W. McKEEVER, and E. V. NEWMAN, The effects of posterior pituitary extract and smoking on water, sodium and chloride excretion in normal subjects and in patients with congestive cardiac failure, *Bull. Johns Hopkins Hosp.* **87,** 221 (1950). [50C

SINGER, B., and J. WENER, Excretion of sodium-retaining substances in patients with congestive heart failure, *Am. Heart J.* **45,** 795 (1953).

SOLOFF, L. A., J. ZATUCHNI, and J. H. BOUTWELL, The relationship of some electrolytes of the serum, edema fluid, and urine in a case of intractable heart failure, *Am. Heart J.* **44,** 766 (1952).

SQUIRES, R. D., R. B. SINGER, G. R. MOFFITT, JR., and J. R. ELKINTON, The distribution of body fluids in congestive heart failure. II. Abnormalities in serum electrolyte concentration and in acid-base equilibrium, *Circulation* 4, 697 (1951).   [50D, 50E

STAPLETON, J. F., and W. P. HARVEY, Hypochloremic alkalosis induced by mercurial diuretics in congestive heart failure, *Arch. Int. Med.* 90, 425 (1952).

STEELE, J. M., and E. Y. BERGER, Evidence for desoxycorticosterone-like activity in the accumulation of edema, *Tr. A. Am. Physicians* 64, 262 (1951).

STOCK, R. J., G. H. MUDGE, and M. J. NURNBERG, Congestive heart failure. Variations in electrolyte metabolism with salt restriction and mercurial diuretics, *Circulation* 4, 54 (1951).

STRAUSS, M. B., R. K. DAVIS, J. D. ROSENBAUM, and E. C. ROSSMEISL, Production of increased renal sodium excretion by the hypotonic expansion of extracellular fluid volume in recumbent subjects, *J. Clin. Investigation* 31, 80 (1952).

TARAIL, R., D. W. SELDIN, and A. V. N. GOODYEAR, Effects of injection of hypertonic glucose on metabolism of water and electrolytes in patients with edema, *J. Clin. Investigation* 30, 111 (1951).

TAYLOR, N. B. G., and R. L. NOBLE, Appearance of an antidiuretic substance in the urine of man after various procedures, *Proc. Soc. Exper. Biol. & Med.* 73, 207 (1950).

THREEFOOT, S., G. BURCH, and P. REASER, The biologic decay periods of sodium in normal man, in patients with congestive heart failure, and in patients with the nephrotic syndrome as determined by Na^{22} as the tracer, *J. Lab. & Clin. Med.* 34, 1 (1949).

THREEFOOT, S., T. GIBBONS, and G. BURCH, Relationship of weight, venous pressure and radiosodium (Na^{22}) excretion in chronic congestive heart failure, *Proc. Soc. Exper. Biol. & Med.* 66, 369 (1947).   [50C

VIAR, W. N., B. B. OLIVER, S. EISENBERG, J. A. LOMBARDO, K. WILLIS, and T. R. HARRISON, The effect of posture and of compression of the neck on excretion of electrolytes and glomerular filtration: further studies, *Circulation* 3, 105 (1951).

WARMING-LARSEN, A., Natriumudskillelsen gennem nyrer og svedkirtler på saltrig og saltfattig kost, *Ugeskr. f. Laeger.* 115, 49 (1953).

WARNER, G. F., E. L. DOBSON, C. E. RODGERS, M. E. JOHNSTON, and N. PACE, The measurement of total "sodium space" and total body sodium in normal individuals and in patients with cardiac edema, *Circulation* 5, 915 (1952).

WARREN, J. V., and E. A. STEAD, JR., Fluid dynamics in chronic congestive heart failure. An interpretation of the mechanisms producing the edema, increased plasma volume and elevated venous pressure in certain patients with prolonged congestive failure, *Arch. Int. Med.* **73**, 138 (1944).

WESTON, R. E., L. HELLMAN, D. J. W. ESCHER, I. S. EDELMAN, J. GROSSMAN, and L. LEITER, Studies on the influence of the low sodium cardiac diet and the regimen on renal hemodynamics and electrolyte excretion in hypertensive subjects, *J. Clin. Investigation* **29**, 639 (1950).

WESTON, R. E., L. HELLMAN, D. J. W. ESCHER, and L. LEITER, Effect of low sodium and Kempner diets on renal hemodynamics and electrolyte excretion in hypertension, *Federation Proc.* **7**, 132 (1948).

WHITE, A. G., H. GORDON, and L. LEITER, Studies in edema. II. The effect of congestive heart failure on saliva electrolyte concentrations, *J. Clin. Investigation* **29**, 1445 (1950).

WHITE, A. G., G. RUBIN, and L. LEITER, Studies in edema. III. The effect of pitressin on the renal excretion of water and electrolytes in patients with and without liver disease, *J. Clin. Investigation* **30**, 1287 (1951).

WHITE, A. G., G. RUBIN, and L. LEITER, Studies in edema. IV. Water retention and the anti-diuretic hormone in hepatic and cardiac disease, *J. Clin. Investigation* **32**, 931 (1953).

WHITE, H. L., and T. FINDLEY, JR., Responses of normal subjects and of patients with diabetes insipidus to water and salt ingestion, *J. Clin. Investigation* **18**, 377 (1939).

WIGGINS, W. S., C. H. MANRY, R. H. LYONS, and R. F. PITTS, The effect of salt loading and salt depletion on renal function and electrolyte excretion in man, *Circulation* **3**, 275 (1951).

WILKINSON, B. M., and R. A. McCANCE, Secretion of urine in rabbits during experimental salt deficiency, *Quart. J. Exper. Physiol.* **30**, 249 (1940).

WILSON, C., On the diurnal and nocturnal excretion of urine, *Lancet* **1**, 1299 (1889).

WINKLER, A. W., and O. F. CRANKSHAW, Chloride depletion in conditions other than Addison's disease, *J. Clin. Investigation* **17**, 1 (1938).

WOLF, A. V., D. E. LESTER, L. W. GORHAM, and H. H. SHULTZ, The relative importance of dietary sodium chloride and water in cardiac edema, *Federation Proc.* **6**, 229 (1947).

ZAK, E. R., Liver function in cardiac failure, *Acta med. Scandinav.* **134**, 428 (1949).

ZAK, E., S. FEHÉR, and A. RABL, Geänderte Haut- und Gefassreaktionen bei Kreislaufkranken mit Stauungsleber, *Ztschr. f. klin. Med.* **127**, 323 (1934).

22. *Hepatic Function. Porphyrinuria*

Hepatic enlargement is one of the commonest and often one of the earliest signs of cardiac decompensation. Although exertional dyspnea usually precedes enlargement of the liver, the latter may be noted weeks or months before edema or râles can be detected. This phenomenon is readily understandable in the light of Brunton's (1908) observations on the enormous distensibility of the liver. In very severe failure jaundice may become manifest, with bile in the urine, but this is not the rule. In spite of the absence of frank jaundice, however, some increase in the serum bilirubin level is common in cardiac decompensation (**51**; Jolliffe, 1930; Chavez *et al.*, 1943); the ratio of direct-reacting to indirect-reacting bilirubin is normal (Cantarow *et al.*, 1942). In general the degree of elevation of the plasma bilirubin corresponds with the severity of the cardiac failure, but values much above 2.0 mg. are not common. The degree of bilirubinemia is not necessarily related to the increase in size of the liver. The bilirubin tolerance test shows retarded excretion (Eilbott, 1927).

Dye retention may occur (**52**; Bernstein *et al.*, 1942), although Epstein *et al.* (1927) found none, and Piersol and Rothman (1928) found it only infrequently and in mild degree in patients in failure. Dye retention is related to slow hepatic blood flow, according to Ingelfinger (1947) and Myers (1949, 1950); however, Sherlock (1951) disagrees. The colloidal red test is positive in some instances (Strade *et al.*, 1949*a,b*). The cephalin flocculation test may be abnormal in some patients in failure (Colcher *et al.*, 1946; Felder *et al.*, 1950; Kissane *et al.*, 1950*a,b*; Strade *et al.*, 1949; White *et al.*, 1951; Evans *et al.*, 1952; Marvel and Shullenberger, 1951). The thymol turbidity test is more likely to be abnormal (Carter and Maclaglan, 1946; Denninger and Goedtler, 1950; Ernst and Dotti, 1950; Lepehne, 1951; Stillerman, 1948; Strade *et al.*, 1949*a,b*; van Dommelen and Francke, 1950; White *et al.*, 1951; Evans *et al.*, 1952; Marvel and Shullenberger, 1951). Ascitic fluid taken from patients whose sera show positive tests may also give positive tests (Lepehne, 1951). The Takata-Ara test may also give an abnormal result, according to Chavez *et al.* (1943*a,b*). The levulose tolerance is occasionally impaired in congestive failure (Jolliffe, 1930; King,

1927); the result of the galactose tolerance test is often abnormal (Adler and Lange, 1927; Chavez *et al.*, 1943*a,b*; Robertson *et al.*, 1932; Routier *et al.*, 1935; Colcher *et al.*, 1946; Wagner, 1914), but may also be abnormal in the absence of frank decompensation (Chavez *et al.*, 1943*a,b*). The serum alkaline phosphatase level is often elevated in cardiac decompensation (Gutman *et al.*, 1940; Sherlock, 1951; Strade *et al.*, 1949; Felder *et al.*, 1950; White *et al.*, 1951). Routier *et al.* (1935) detected bile salts in the blood in patients with failure of recent onset. D'Ardois (1942) found the blood citrate level to be elevated in chronic but not acute failure, and Loeper *et al.* (1934) and Scaglioni (1935) described increased amounts of oxalate in the blood in cardiac decompensation; the significance of these observations is obscure, but they probably indicate a disturbance of carbohydrate metabolism. The abnormal result of the hippuric acid test noted in congestive failure (Aldersberg and Minibeck, 1936; Lindboom, 1939; Wahi, 1946; Mathur, 1948) may be consequent to faulty absorption of the test material, according to the first authors. Blood diastase is abnormally low in cardiac decompensation (Grey *et al.*, 1941). The cholesterol-ester concentration may be diminished in some patients (White *et al.*, 1951).

Measurements of prothrombin time have yielded diverse results (Cathcart and Blood, 1950; Colcher *et al.*, 1946; Cotlove and Vorzimer, 1946; Harvey and Finch, 1950; Pere, 1950; Sutton, 1950; White *et al.*, 1951; Beaumont and Lenègre, 1951; Griffith *et al.*, 1952; Jurgens, 1952; Marvel and Shullenberger, 1951). Although abnormalities are small and found in a minority of instances, a significant number of patients with congestive failure are unusually sensitive to dicoumerol (Reisner *et al.*, 1949; Stats and Davidson, 1949).

The abnormal porphyrinuria that may occur in congestive failure (Thiel and Kämmerer, 1933; Dobriner, 1936; Dobriner and Rhoads, 1940; Kaunitz, 1938) is probably also a manifestation of impaired liver function; its occurrence is not universally reported in congestive failure, however (Localio *et al.*, 1941).

Disturbances of urobilinogen excretion have also been noted. Increased urobilinogen content in the urine is described either as such (**53**; Chavez *et al.*, 1943*a,b*; Waller *et al.*, 1940) or by implication in the form of an elevated urine to stool ratio (Adler and Sachs, 1923;

Localio *et al.*, 1941). Robertson *et al.* (1932) found it normal, however. Although this phenomenon may be influenced by the abnormal blood destruction observed in some stages of congestive failure (page 148), the chief cause must be hepatic dysfunction.

Meakins (1927) found that jaundice, when it occurred, was most marked over the upper chest and face. He also stated that bile pigment is not found in edema fluids, although his data show otherwise. Andrews (1924) detected appreciable amounts of bilirubin in ascitic fluid taken from a cardiac patient and Altschule and Volk (1937) also found it in this as well as other edema fluids in cardiac patients with normal or elevated serum bilirubin levels. The quantity of bilirubin present in edema fluids roughly parallels but is always less than that found in the serum at the time; the protein content of the edema fluid also appears to influence to some degree the bilirubin content (Altschule and Volk, 1937).

The abnormal liver function observed in cardiac decompensation is reflected in the typical histologic changes found in the liver, but the extent of the two is not always parallel. Many authors have related the degree of hepatic engorgement and central necrosis to the increased venous pressure of cardiac decompensation. Mallory (1911), however, pointed out that if back pressure were the cause of necrosis, it should involve the entire liver lobule, since the increased pressure must be distributed everywhere. Indeed, the pressure must actually be higher in the periphery of the liver lobule if the gradient of pressure necessary for flow of blood is to be maintained. Mallory felt that a toxin of some sort was responsible.

Diminution in hepatic blood flow, with the development of abnormal venous blood unsaturation, occurs in congestive failure (Myers and Hickam, 1948; Evans *et al.*, 1952; Myers, 1949, 1950; Edelman *et al.*, 1950). The splanchnic oxygen consumption is elevated in proportion to the metabolic rate (Myers, 1950). Delivery of glucose from the liver appears to be retarded (Myers, 1950). It is probable that anoxia is the important factor in the genesis of the altered histology and physiology of the liver in cardiac decompensation. Neubauer (1913) and Mattson (1929) showed that anoxia causes a striking increase in the size of the liver in animals; the opposite findings of Griffith and Emery (1930) are discordant. Rich (1930) found the typical histological changes of congestive failure in the livers of patients with anoxemia due to severe anemia and in animals exposed to low oxygen tensions. McMichael (1937) found central necrosis in the livers of cats when the inflow of blood into the liver was diminished. Resnik and Keefer (1926), Barron (1931) and Rich (1930) observed a low liver function as measured by the bilirubin excretion test in anoxic animals. The outflow of bile from the liver has also been shown to be depressed by anoxia in animals (Schnedorf and Orr, 1941); men at high altitudes often show elevation of plasma bilirubin (Hurtado et al., 1945), as do anoxic animals also (Giannini, 1919).

On the other hand, available evidence indicates that the hyperbilirubinemia of cardiac decompensation is not due solely to faulty excretion of bile pigment, for several observers (page 150) have found increased amounts of bile pigment in the stool or urine, or both, in certain stages of failure, and increased fragility of the red blood cells has also been reported in patients with cardiac decompensation (page 150). It is of interest that the breakdown of hemoglobin causes greater elevation of blood bilirubin level in patients with cardiac decompensation than in normal subjects (Gilligan, Altschule and Katersky, 1941). Ernstene (1932) pointed out that the jaundice of heart disease is due to a combination of increased production and diminished excretion of bile pigment.

The diminished liver function in heart failure is in itself rarely severe enough to be clinically important. It is of significance because it indicates the presence of liver damage which may lead to cirrhosis. That so few patients with congestive failure develop clinically important cirrhosis of the liver is unquestionably due to the fact that few of them live long enough (Katzin, Waller and Blumgart, 1939). Many authors have reproduced in animals the central scarring which is said to be typical of cardiac cirrhosis, but Bolton (1914) observed portal infiltration and fibrosis. The latter observation is significant in view of the fact that not infrequently patients in whom a clinical diagnosis of "cardiac" or central cirrhosis of the liver is made, are found, on autopsy, to show unmistakable evidences of portal cirrhosis (Altschule, 1938; Katzin et al., 1939).

The role of hepatic damage in causing nutritional changes is discussed elsewhere (pages 132 and 207). In addition, the possible effects of hepatic dysfunction in relation to antidiuretic phenomena must also be borne in mind (page 177).

Bibliography

Chapter I — Section 22

ADLER, A., and H. LANGE, Der Milchsäuregehalt des Blutes bei Leberkrankheiten, *Deutsches Arch. f. klin. Med.* **157,** 129 (1927). [51

ADLER, A., and M. SACHS, Ueber Urobilin. IIIa. Die Urobilinausscheidung durch die Faeces nebst vergleichenden Untersuchungen über das Verhältnis der Urobilinmengen des Harnes und Stuhles, und dessen Verwertbarkeit als Leberfunktionsprüfung, *Ztschr. f. d. ges. exper. Med.* **31,** 370 (1923).

ADLERSBERG, D., and J. MINIBECK, Ist die Hippursäureausscheidung nach Belastung mit Benzoesäure eine brauchbare Lebersfunktionsprüfung?, *Ztschr, f. klin. Med.* **129,** 392 (1936).

ALTSCHULE, M. D., The pathological physiology of chronic cardiac decompensation, *Medicine* **17,** 75 (1938).

ALTSCHULE, M. D., and M. C. VOLK, Bilirubin in edema fluids in cardiac decompensation, *Proc. Soc. Exper. Biol. & Med.* **37,** 184 (1937). [51

ANDREWS, C. H., A clinical study of van den Bergh's test in jaundice, *Quart. J. Med.* **18,** 19 (1924). [51

BARRON, E. S. G., Bilirubinemia, *Medicine* **10,** 77 (1931).

BARROW, J. V., E. L. ARMSTRONG, and W. H. OLDS, A clinical, pathological and operative study of the icterus index, *Am. J. M. Sc.* **169,** 583 (1925). [51

BEAUMONT, J.-L., and J. LENÈGRE, La coagulabilité du sang dans l'insuffisance cardiaque avant et après le traitement, *Semaine d. hôp. de Paris* **27,** 2128 (1951).

BERNHEIM, A. R., The icterus index (a quantitative estimation of bilirubinemia). An aid in diagnosis and prognosis, *J. A. M. A.* **82,** 291 (1924). [51

BERNSTEIN, M., E. B. LE WINN, and S. SIMKINS, Heart disease and liver function, *J. Lab. & Clin. Med.* **28,** 1, (1942). [52

BLUMBERG, N., and E. M. SCHLOSS, The effect of circulatory factors on the bromsulphalein test in liver disease, *Am. J. M. Sc.* **213,** 470 (1947). [52

BOLTON, C., The pathological changes in the liver resulting from passive venous congestion experimentally produced, *J. Path. & Bact.* **19,** 258 (1914).

BRANWOOD, A. W., Some observations on liver function in heart failure, *Edinburgh M. J.* **57,** 129 (1950). [51, 53

BRUNTON, T. L., *Therapeutics of the circulation* (P. Blakiston's Son & Co., Philadelphia, 1908), p. 17.

CANTAROW, A., Studies of hepatic function. II. In portal cirrhosis and congestive heart failure, *Arch. Int. Med.* **56**, 521 (1935).   [51, 52

CANTAROW, A., C. W. WIRTS, JR., and G. HOLLANDER, Quantitative studies of direct-reacting serum bilirubin, *Arch. Int. Med.* **69**, 986 (1942).   [51

CARTER, A. B., and N. F. MACLAGLAN, Some observations on liver function tests in diseases not primarily hepatic, *Brit. M. J.* **2**, 80 (1946).   [53

CATHCART, R. T., and D. W. BLOOD, Effect of digitalis on the clotting of the blood in normal subjects and in patients with heart failure, *Circulation* **1**, 1176 (1950).

CHAVEZ, I., B. SEPULVEDA, and A. ORTEGA, La exploración funcional del hígado en la insuficiencia cardiaca, *Arch. latino am. de cardiol. y hemat.* **13**, 51 (1943*a*).   [51, 52, 53

CHAVEZ, I., B. SEPULVEDA, and A. ORTEGA, The functional value of the liver in heart disease. An experimental study, *J. A. M. A.* **121**, 1276 (1943*b*).   [51, 52, 53

COLCHER, H., A. J. PATEK, JR., and F. E. KENDALL, Galactose disappearance from the blood stream. Calculation of a galactose removal constant and its application as a test for liver function, *J. Clin. Investigation* **25**, 768 (1946).

COTLOVE, E., and J. J. VORZIMER, Serial prothrombin estimations in cardiac patients: diagnostic and therapeutic implications; use of dicumarol, *Ann. Int. Med.* **24**, 648 (1946).

D'ARDOIS, G. S., Acido citrico en el suero sanguineo como exponente del estado del parénquima hepático en los enfermos de cardiopatia, *Arch. latino am. de cardiol. y hemat.* **12**, 53 (1942).

DENNINGER, K., and GOEDTLER, Verhalten der Thymoltrübungsprobe bei verschiedenen Erkrankungen, *Deutsche med. Wchnschr.* **75**, 169 (1950).

DIAMOND, J. S., The value of routine estimations of blood bilirubin, with a report of 567 cases including a group of unrecognized toxic hepatitis, *Am. J. M. Sc.* **176**, 321 (1928).   [51

DOBRINER, K., Urinary porphyrins in disease, *J. Biol. Chem.* **113**, 1 (1936).

DOBRINER, K., and C. P. RHOADS, The porphyrins in health and disease, *Physiol. Rev.* **20**, 416 (1940).

EDELMAN, I. S., B. W. ZWEIFACH, D. J. W. ESCHER, J. GROSSMAN, R. MOKOTOFF, R. E. WESTON, L. LEITER, and E. SHORR, Studies on VEM and VDM in blood in relation to renal hemodynamics and renal oxygen extraction in chronic congestive heart failure, *J. Clin. Investigation* **29**, 925 (1950).

EHRSTRÖM, M. C. Blutstoffwechsel und Urobilinurie bei Herzinsuffizienz, *Acta med. Scandinav.* **88,** 517 (1936).   [53

EILBOTT, W., Funktionsprüfung der Leber mittels Bilirubinbelastung, *Ztschr. f. klin. Med.* **106,** 529 (1927).

EPSTEIN, N. N., G. D. DELPRAT, and W. J. KERR, The rose bengal test for liver function. Further studies, *J. A. M. A.* **88,** 1619 (1927).

ERNST, R. G., and L. B. DOTTI, An evaluation of the thymol turbidity test, *Am. J. M. Sc.* **216,** 316 (1948).

ERNSTENE, A. C., Jaundice in heart disease, *M. Clin. North America* **15,** 1005 (1932).

EVANS, J. M., H. J. ZIMMERMAN, J. G. WILMER, L. J. THOMAS, and C .B. ETHRIDGE, Altered liver function of chronic congestive heart failure, *Am. J. Med.* **13,** 705 (1952).   [51, 52

FEIGL, J., and E. QUERNER, Bilirubinämie, *Ztschr. f. d. ges. exper. Med.* **9,** 153 (1919).   [51

FELDER, L., A. MUND, and J. G. PARKER, Liver function tests in chronic congestive heart failure, *Circulation* **2,** 286 (1950).   [51, 52

FISHBERG, A. M., Jaundice in myocardial insufficiency, *J. A. M. A.* **80,** 1516 (1923).   [51, 53

FOLEY, E. F., The clinical value of tests of liver function, *Arch. Int. Med.* **45,** 302 (1930).   [51, 52

FRANCESCON, M., Comportamento della resistenza osmotica dei globuli rossi e del ricambio emoglobinico nei cardiopazienti in fase acuta di scompenso e in fase compensatoria, *Minerva med.* **27,** [II], 255 (1936).   [53

GIANNINI, G., Ueber die Wirkung starker Luftverdünnung auf Erythrocytenzahl und Hämoglobingehalt des Blutes bei normalen und milzlosen Tieren, *Ztschr. f. d. ges. exper. Med.* **64,** 431 (1919).

GILBERT, A., and M. HERSCHER, Sur la teneur en bilirubine du sérum sanguin dans la congestion hépatique liée à l'asystolie, *Compt. rend. Soc. de biol.* **60,** 515 (1906).   [51

GILLIGAN, D. R., M. D. ALTSCHULE, and E. M. KATERSKY, Studies of hemoglobinemia and hemoglobinuria produced in man by intravenous injection of hemoglobin solutions, *J. Clin. Investigation* **20,** 177 (1941).

GIORDANO, B. P., Sul comportamento e sul significato della reazione di Hijmans van den Bergh nei cardiopazienti, *Arch. per le sc. med.* **62,** 81 (1936).   [51

GRAY, S. H., J. G. PROBSTEIN, and C. J. HEIFETZ, Clinical studies on blood diastase. I. Low blood diastase as an index of impaired hepatic function, *Arch. Int. Med.* **67,** 805 (1941).

GRIFFITH, F. R., JR., and F. E. EMERY, The vasomotor control of the liver circulation, *Am. J. Physiol.* **95,** 20 (1930).

GRIFFITH, G. C., R. STRAGNELL, D. C. LEVINSON, F. J. MOORE, and A. G. WARE, A study of the beneficial effects of anticoagulant therapy in congestive heart failure, *Ann. Int. Med.* **37**, 867 (1952).

GUTMAN, A. B., K. B. OLSON, E. B. GUTMAN, and C. A. FLOOD, Effect of disease of the liver and biliary tract upon the phosphatase activity of the serum, *J. Clin. Investigation* **19**, 129 (1940).

HARVEY, W. P., and C. A. FINCH, Dicumarol prophylaxis of thromboembolic disease in congestive heart failure, *New England J. Med.* **242**, 208 (1950).

HURTADO, A., C. MERINO, and E. DELGADO, Influence of anoxemia on the hemopoietic activity, *Arch. Int. Med.* **75**, 284 (1945).

INGELFINGER, F. I., Hepatic function with respect to bromsulphalein removal, *Bull. New England M. Center* **9**, 25 (1947).   [52

JOLLIFFE, N., Liver function in congestive heart failure, *J. Clin. Investigation* **8**, 419 (1929–30).   [51, 52, 53

JÜRGENS, J., Kreislaufdynamik, Gerinnungspotential und Thrombose, *Klin. Wchnschr.* **30**, 483 (1952).

KATZIN, H. M., J. V. WALLER, and H. L. BLUMGART, "Cardiac cirrhosis" of the liver. A clinical and pathologic study, *Arch. Int. Med.* **64**, 457 (1939).

KAUNITZ, H., Ueber Porphyrinurie nach Haemoglobinbelastung, *Ztschr. f. klin. Med.* **133**, 552 (1938).

KING, G., A study of the laevulose tolerance test for hepatic efficiency, *Lancet* **1**, 385 (1927).   [51

KISCH, F., Über das Verhalten des Blutjodspiegels Kreislaufkranker, *Wien. klin. Wchnschr.* **47**, 1317 (1934).   [51

KISSANE, R. W., R. S. FIDLER, T. E. CLARK, and J. J. CONN, Cephalin-cholesterol flocculation reaction in rheumatic heart disease. I, *Am. J. M. Sc.* **219**, 48 (1950).

KISSANE, R. W., R. S. FIDLER, T. E. CLARK, and J. J. CONN, Cephalin-cholesterol flocculation reaction in heart disease. Part 2, *Am. J. M. Sc.* **219**, 52 (1950).

KUGEL, M. A., and S. S. LICHTMAN, Factors causing clinical jaundice in heart disease, *Arch. Int. Med.* **52**, 16 (1933).   [51

LAYNE, J. A., F. R. SCHEMM, and W. W. HURST, Further comparative studies on ascites in liver and heart disease, *Gastroenterology* **16**, 91 (1950).   [51, 52

LEPEHNE, G., Wertere Untersuchungen über Gallenfarbstoff im Blutserum des Menschen, *Deutsches Arch. f. klin. Med.* **135**, 79 (1921)   [51

LEPEHNE, G. M., Studies on ascitic fluid in patients with hepatic cirrhosis, heart failure and cancer: results of cephalin cholesterol flocculation, thymol turbidity, methylene blue, qualitative and quantitative bilirubin and other tests, *Am. J. Digest Dis.* **18**, 86 (1951).

LINDBOOM, G. A., Die Hippursäuresynthese als Leberfunktionsprobe, *Acta med. Scandinav.* **99**, 147 (1939).

LOCALIO, S. A., M. D. SCHWARTZ, and C. F. GANNON, The urinary/fecal coproporphyrin ratio in liver disease, *J. Clin. Investigation* **20**, 7 (1941).

LOEPER, M., D. MAHOUDEAU, and J. TONNET, L'oxalémie des cardiaques, *Bull. et mem. Soc. med. d. hôp. de Paris* **50**, 88 (1934).

MALLORY, F. B., Chronic passive congestion of the liver, *J. M. Research* **24**, 455 (1911).

MARVEL, R. J., and W. A. SHULLENBERGER, Thromboembolic phenomena associated with rapid diuresis in the treatment of congestive heart failure, *Am. Heart J.* **42**, 194 (1951). [52

MATHUR, K. S., Hippuric acid synthesis test as an aid to prognosis in congestive heart failure, *Indian M. Gaz.* **83**, 262 (1948).

MATTSON, H., A plethysmographic study of changes in the volume of the liver in the intact animal, *Am. J. Physiol.* **90**, 146 (1929).

MCMICHAEL, J., The oxygen supply of the liver, *Quart. J. Exper. Physiol.* **27**, 73 (1937).

MEAKINS, J., Distribution of jaundice in circulatory failure, *J. Clin. Investigation* **4**, 135 (1927). [51

MEULENGRACHT, E., Die klinische Bedeutung der Untersuchung auf Gallenfarbstoff im Blutserum, *Deutsches Arch. f. klin. Med.* **132**, 285 (1920). [51

MILANOVIC, J. B., and L. STANAJÉVIC, Ueber den Gallenfarbstoff im Blute beim dekompensierten Herz, *Ztschr. f. klin. Med.* **128**, 163 (1935). [51

MYERS, J. D., Observations on the excretion of bromsulphalein, *J. Clin. Investigation* **28**, 800 (1949). [52

MYERS, J. D., Net splanchnic glucose production in normal man and in various disease states, *J. Clin. Investigation* **29**, 1421 (1950). [52

MYERS, J. D., and J. B. HICKAM, An estimation of the hepatic blood flow and splanchnic oxygen consumption in heart failure, *J. Clin. Investigation* **27**, 620 (1948).

NEUBAUER, E., Ueber die Wirkung antiglucosurischer Mittel und über Leberglucosurie. III. Die Durchblutung der Leber unter dem Einfluss verschiedener Agenzien, *Biochem. Ztschr.* **52**, 118 (1913).

OTTENBERG, R., S. ROSENFELD, and L. GOLDSMITH, The clinical value of the serum-tetrachlorphenolphthalein test for liver function, *Arch. Int. Med.* **34**, 206 (1924). [51, 52

PERE, S. A. N., The effect of digitalis, strophanthim, and novurit on blood coagulation, *Acta. med. Scandinav. Supp.* **251**, 1 (1950).

PIERSOL, G. M., and M. M. ROTHMAN, Practical value of liver function tests. A comparative study, *J. A. M. A.* **91**, 1768 (1928). [51, 53

RAVDIN, E. G., An estimation of the clinical value of the van den Bergh test, *Am. J. M. Sc.* **169**, 850 (1925). [51

REISNER, E. H., JR., J. NORMAN, W. W. FIELD, and R. BROWN, The effect of liver dysfunction on the response to dicumarol, *Am. J. M. Sc.* **217**, 445 (1949).

RESNIK, W. H., and C. S. KEEFER, Jaundice following pulmonary infarction in patients with myocardial insufficiency. II. An experimental study, *J. Clin. Investigation* **2**, 389 (1925–26).

RICH, A. R., The pathogenesis of the forms of jaundice, *Bull. Johns Hopkins Hosp.* **47**, 338 (1930).

ROBERTSON, W. E., W. A. SWALM, and F. W. KONZELMANN, Functional capacity of the liver. Comparative merits of the five most popular tests, *J. A. M. A.* **99**, 2071 (1932). [51, 52

ROUTIER, D., J. COTTET, and P. MOLINGHEN, Contribution à l'étude des fonctions hépatiques au cours de l'asystolie, *Arch. d. mal. de l'app. digestif* **25**, 801 (1935). [51

SCAGLIONI, C., Ossalemia e ossaluria nelle affezioni cardio-vascolari, *Riforma med.* **51**, 164 (1935).

SCHALM, L., and W. A. H. HOOGENBOOM, Blood bilirubin in congestive heart failure, *Am. Heart J.* **44**, 571 (1952). [51, 52, 53

SCHEEL, O., Ueber den Nachweis von Gallenfarbstoff im Blutserum und dessen klinische Bedeutung, *Ztschr. f. klin. Med.* **74**, 13 (1912). [51

SCHIFF, L., Serum bilirubin in health and in disease, *Arch. Int. Med.* **40**, 800 (1927). [51

SCHNEDORF, J. G., and T. G. ORR, The effect of anoxemia and oxygen therapy upon the flow of bile and urine in the nembutalized dog. II. Its possible relationship to the hepatorenal syndrome, *Am. J. Digest, Dis. & Nutrition* **8**, 356 (1941).

SERBY, A. M., and L. BLOCH, Liver function as determined by bromsulphalein in seventy-six cases, *Am. J. M. Sc.* **176**, 367 (1928). [52

SHERLOCK, S., The liver in heart failure. Relation of anatomical, functional, and circulatory changes, *Brit. Heart J.* **13**, 273 (1951). [51, 52

STATS, D., and S. DAVISON, The increased hypoprothrombinemic effect of a small dose of dicumarol in congestive heart failure, *Am. J. M. Sc.* **218**, 318 (1949).

STILLERMAN, H. B., The thymol turbidity test in various disease, *J. Lab. & Clin. Med.* **33**, 565 (1948).

STRADE, H. A., and L. B. DOTTI, A clinical evaluation of a new liver function test, the colloidal red test, in comparison with the thymol turbidity test, *Am. J. M. Sc.* **217**, 448 (1949).

STRADE, H. A., L. B. DOTTI, and S. J. ILKA, A comparative study of the colloidal red test in liver disease, with special reference to the zinc turbidity, thymol turbidity and bromsulphalein tests, *Gastroenterol.* **12,** 934 (1949).　　　　　　　　　　　　　　　　　　　　　[51, 52

SUTTON, G. C., Studies on blood coagulation and the effect of digitalis, *Circulation* **2,** 271 (1950).　　　　　　　　　　　　　　　　　[52

THIEL, W., and H. KÄMMERER, Quantitative Porphyrinmessungen bei verschiedenen Krankheiten, insbesondere bei Leberfällen, *Verhandl. d. deutsch. Gesellsch. f. inn. Med.* **45,** 81 (1933).

VAN DEN BERGH, A. A. H., and J. SNAPPER, Die Farbstoffe des Blutserums, *Deutsches Arch. f. klin. Med.* **110,** 540 (1913).　　　　　　　　[51

VAN DOMMELEN, C. K. V., and C. FRANCKE, Thymol and dilution turbidity tests, their relation to the gamma-globulin content of the serum and the morphology of the liver parenchyma, *Acta med. Scandinav.* **136,** 177 (1950).

VOLGIN, O., and L. STANOJÉVIC, Vergleichende Untersuchungen der Bilirubinämie und Kreislaufzeit bei Dekompensation des Herzens, *Klin. Wchnschr.* **17,** 569 (1938).　　　　　　　　　　　　　　　　　　[51

WAGNER, F., Klinische Untersuchungen über die Bedeutung der verscheidenen Zuckerproben für die Beurteilung der Leberfunktion, *Ztschr. f. klin. Med.* **80,** 174 (1914).

WAHI, P. N., Observations on the interpretation of the hippuric acid synthesis test of liver function, *Indian M. Gaz.* **81,** 521 (1946).

WALLACE, G. B., and J. S. DIAMOND, The significance of urobilinogen in the urine as a test for liver function; with a description of a simple quantitative method for its estimation, *Arch. Int. Med.* **35,** 698 (1925).　　　　　　　　　　　　　　　　　　　　　　　　　[51, 53

WALLER, J. V., H. L. BLUMGART, and M. C. VOLK, Studies of the blood in congestive heart failure, with particular reference to reticulocytosis, erythrocyte fragility, bilirubinemia, urobilinogen excretion and changes in blood volume, *Arch. Int. Med.* **66,** 1230 (1940).　　　　[51, 53

WATSON, C. J., Studies of urobilinogen. III. The per diem excretion of urobilinogen in the common forms of jaundice and disease of the liver, *Arch. Int. Med.* **59,** 206 (1937).　　　　　　　　　　　[51, 53

WHITE, T. J., R. B. WALLACE, A. M. GNASSI, N. F. KEMP, H. P. PRICE, and C. M. LEEVY, Hepatic abnormalities in congestive heart failure, *Circulation* **3,** 501 (1951).　　　　　　　　　　　　　　　[51, 52

23. *Gastro-intestinal Function*

Anorexia, nausea, distention, gaseous eructations, constipation and flatulence are frequent complaints in moderate or severe congestive failure. Data on gastro-intestinal function in patients with chronic congestive failure, are, however, fragmentary. Costadoni (1938), Bologna and Costadoni (1938), Furbetta *et al.* (1951), Deinstfertig (1922), Fliederbaum and Pianko (1929), Frandsen (1949) and Levitan and Alexeief-Berkman (1935) found greatly lowered gastric acid values, even after histamine, although Fliederbaum and Pianko (1929) found the latter normal. The last authors also reported no disturbance in proteolytic function, but they did find retarded gastric emptying. Costadoni (1938) and Bologna and Costadoni (1938) found an abnormal amount of nitrogen in the stool, while Levitan and Alixeief-Berkman (1935) reported partly digested food. This finding was regarded by these authors as evidence of hyper-motility of the intestines, but this cannot be related definitely to congestive failure, since three-quarters of their patients had worms or protozoa in their stools. An excellent study by Hardy and Schultz (1952) demonstrated retarded absorption of amino acids from the jejunum in edematous cardiac patients.

Thirst in congestive heart failure appears to be related to decreased salivary flow (Holmes and Montgomery, 1953). Gross (1950) has shown how dyspnea may impair swallowing.

The stool sodium output is decreased in chronic cardiac decompensation (Berger and Steele, 1952).

Studies of the effects of anoxia on gastro-intestinal function are pertinent, but are difficult to evaluate since the conditions under which they were performed gave rise to the loss of considerable amounts of carbon dioxide from the blood; this loss causes a depression of secretion of gastric acidity (Delhougne, 1927; Browne and Vineberg, 1932; Delrue, 1934; Hartiala and Karoonen, 1946). The consequences of experimental anoxia are also difficult to relate to the tissue anoxia of congestive failure, because in the former the arterial blood oxygen saturation falls far below that commonly encountered in congestive failure, but this change is compensated for by an increase in cardiac output (page 101), so that the state of the tissues cannot be determined from the data reported. At any rate, the effects of experimentally induced anoxia on gastro-intestinal motility have been reviewed by Van Liere (1942) and include depressed gastric motility, lessened force of gastric contractions, decreased gastric tone, slowed gastric emptying time associated with pyloric spasm, no change in small intestinal motility and slowed colonic function. Anoxia does not influence intestinal secretion, but does lower the volume of gastric secretion and secretion of acid and chloride (Van Liere, 1942). Van Liere further showed that absorption from the small intestine is also affected by anoxia, that of saline solution and of glycine being depressed, while that of glucose and of water is increased; absorption of fat is unchanged (Machlachlan and Thacker, 1945) except when anoxia is extreme.

More direct experimental evidence bearing on gastro-intestinal function is afforded by studies of the effects of stasis induced by ties placed about the portal vein. The rise in gastro-intestinal venous pressure so induced slows absorption (McMichael and Smirk, 1933; Wells, 1940; Stickney, et al., 1947) and results in a type of gastritis (Gülzow and Afendulis, 1938). In addition, edema of the stomach and intestines has been shown to delay emptying (Barden et al., 1938; Mecray, et al., 1937).

Any of the physiologic changes just mentioned could explain the gastro-intestinal symptoms associated with cardiac decompensation and thereby throw some light on the mechanism of malnutrition which commonly develops in cardiac patients.

The distention that occurs in severe congestive failure can be quite severe. Distention of the small intestine in itself results in a derangement of the circulation whereby blood is shunted through arteriovenous anastomoses and away from the capillaries (Lawson and Ambrose, 1942; Oppenheimer and Mann, 1943), thereby further depressing absorption and possibly digestion also.

Bibliography

Chapter I — Section 23

BARDEN, R. P., W. D. THOMPSON, I. S. RAVDIN, and I. L. FRANK, The influence of serum protein on the motility of the small intestine, Surg., Gynec. & Obst. 66, 819 (1938).

BERGER, E. Y., and J. M. STEELE, Suppression of sodium excretion by the colon in congestive heart failure and cirrhosis of the liver demonstrated by the use of cation exchange resins, J. Clin. Investigation 31, 451 (1952).

BOLOGNA, A., and A. COSTADONI, Osservazioni sulla funzione gastropancreatica nei cardiopazienti, Arch. ital. d. mal. d. app. diger. 7, 215 (1938).

BROWNE J. S. L., and A. M. VINEBERG, The interdependence of gastric secretion and the CO_2 content of the blood, *J. Physiol.* **75**, 345 (1932).

COSTADONI, A., Osservazioni sulla funzione gastro-pancreatica nei cardiopazienti, *Arch. ital. d. mal. d. app. diger.* **7**, 215 (1938).

DEINSTFERTIG, A., Die Säureverhaltnisse bei den Magenbeschwerden Zirkulationskranker, *Arch. f. Verdauungskr.* **29**, 346 (1922).

DELHOUGNE, F., Hyperventilation der Lungen und Magensaftsekretion, *Klin. Wchnschr.* **6**, 804 (1927).

DELRUE, G., Étude de la sécrétion acide de l'estomac. III. Sécrétion durant le séjour à haute altitude, *Arch. internat. de physiol.* **38**, 126 (1934).

FLIEDERBAUM, J., and N. PIANKO, Untersuchungen über die Funktionen des Magens bei Herz- und Nierenkrankheiten, *Klin. Wchnschr.* **8**, 1076 (1929).

FRANDSEN, E., Gastric achylia and so-called B-hypovitaminotic symptoms in cardiac disease, *Acta med. Scandinav.* **135**, 381 (1949).

FURBETTA, D., V. GIUNTI, and P. SOLINAS, Il comportamento della secrezione cloridrica nei cardiopatici, *Gior. di clin. med.* **32**, 277 (1951).

GROSS, D., La capacidad de beber agua y la función cardiaca, *Prensa méd. argent.* **37**, 984 (1950).

GÜLZOW, M., and T. C. AFENDULIS, Ueber die Stauungsgastritis. Tiereexperimentelle Untersuchungen, *Ztschr. f. d. ges. exper. Med.* **104**, 465 (1938).

HARDY, J. D., and J. SCHULTZ, Jejunal absorption of an amino acid mixture in normal and in hypoproteinemic subjects, *J. Appl. Physiol.* **4**, 789 (1952).

HARTIALA, K., and M. KAROONEN, The influence of anoxia on the gastric HCl-secretion, *Acta Physiol.* **11**, 85 (1946).

HOLMES, J. H., and A. V. MONTGOMERY, Thirst as a symptom, *Am. J. M. Sc.* **225**, 281 (1953).

LAWSON, H., and A. M. AMBROSE, The utilization of blood oxygen by the distended intestine, *Am. J. Physiol.* **135**, 650 (1942).

LEVITAN and ALEXEIEF-BERKMAN, Digestion chez les malades porteurs de lésions cardiaques, selon les régimes alimentaires, *Arch. d. mal. de l'app. digestif.* **25**, 162 (1935).

MACHLACHLAN, P. L., and C. W. THACKER, The effect of anoxia on fat absorption in rats, *Am. J. Physiol.* **143**, 391 (1945).

McMICHAEL, J., and F. H. SMIRK, The effect of experimental portal congestion on the absorption and excretion of water, *J. Path. & Bact.* **37**, 81 (1933).

MECRAY, P. M., R. P. BARDEN, and I. S. RAVDIN, Nutritional edema: its effect on the gastric emptying time before and after gastric operations, *Surgery* **1**, 53 (1937).

OPPENHEIMER, M. J., and F. C. MANN, Intestinal capillary circulation during distension, *Surgery* **13**, 548 (1943).

STICKNEY, J. C., D. W. NORTHRUP, and E. J. VAN LIERE, Systemic blood pressure as a factor in the absorption of saline from the small intestine, *Am. J. Physiol.* **150**, 466 (1947).

VAN LIERE, E. J., Anoxia. Its effect on the body (University of Chicago Press, Chicago, 1942).

WELLS, H. S., The balance of physical forces which determine the rate and direction of flow of fluid through the intestinal mucosa, *Am. J. Physiol.* **130**, 410 (1940).

24. Nutrition. Blood Enzymes. Intermediary Metabolism

Nutritional studies on congestive failure are few in number. The previously discussed fall in plasma protein level (page 131) has been ascribed in part to malnutrition, but data that show a negative nitrogen balance are scanty (Payne and Peters, 1932). Several authors also referred to the finding of a marked positive balance during recovery from failure (Payne and Peters, 1932; Newman, 1949; Sinclair-Smith *et al.*, 1949). It must be borne in mind that the elaboration or resorption of large amounts of edema fluid containing appreciable amounts of nitrogen make such studies difficult. The reported excessive loss of potassium in failure and the marked retention of this substance in recovery (Iseri *et al.*, 1950; Fox *et al.*, 1949; Newman, 1949) may have the same significance although the changes in sodium metabolism that occur at this time undoubtedly play a role. Harrison (1945) has shown that the measured intake of protein and also of vitamins often is low in sick cardiac patients. Robinson, Melnick, and Field (1940) also found the ingestion of thiamine to be low in decompensated cardiacs. These authors showed in addition that the urinary excretion of thiamine is low after the administration of a test dose by mouth. A study by Pollack *et al.* (1940) in patients with congestive failure gave similar results after the injection of thiamine intramuscularly, but the methods used by these authors are not specific and the period during which they collected urine may have been too short. The fact that diuresis may remove thiamine from the body has been reported (Williams and

Bissell, 1944). The statement of Goldsmith (1948) that abnormal lactate-pyruvate ratios, indicative of thiamine deficiency, occur often in congestive failure is difficult to evaluate. Also pertinent is the finding of Grieg and Govier (1943), who showed that simple anoxia disturbs the utilization of thiamine and leads to a depletion of tissue cocarboxylase (thiamine diphosphate). The plasma tocopherol level is normal (Lemley et al., 1949), as is the plasma vitamin A concentration also (Tomaszewski and Dzialoszyński, 1945).

Studies of enzyme systems in patients with congestive failure are fragmentary. In addition to the above-described changes in thiamine metabolism, with their consequent disturbances in cocarboxylase activity and carbohydrate utilization, other scattered observations must be borne in mind. Although the diastatic activity of blood is normal (page 193), disturbances in citrate and oxalate metabolism (page 193) constitute further evidence of abnormal intermediary carbohydrate metabolism. Perhaps the observations of Galeone, Levi, and Segre (1951) on lowering of blood DPN in anoxic cardiac patients are pertinent in this general direction.

The blood amino nitrogen content is normal (Greene et al., 1924; Witts, 1929) and deamination of administered glycine proceeds at a normal rate (Witts, 1929).

The blood total glutathione level is normal or increased in congestive failure (Platt, 1931; Tschiloff, 1942) with a relative but not absolute decrease in reduced glutathione (Tschiloff, 1942). Copper, an important co-enzyme, is described as elevated in cardiac decompensation (Heilmeyer et al., 1941). Cholinesterase activity of blood is normal (McGeorge, 1937; Grob et al., 1947) in cardiac decompensation. Alkaline phosphatase activity is increased owing to hepatic damage in some instances (page 193).

It is evident that the entire field of nutrition, enzymology, and intermediary metabolism in congestive failure requires investigation.

The fact that decompensated cardiac patients develop low plasma protein levels and lose their normal tissue tension because of loss of flesh is obviously of importance in the genesis of edema. Thiamine depletion, which probably occurs in almost all patients with congestive failure of some duration, must not be overlooked as a factor making for increased severity of the signs and symptoms. Occasionally patients are seen in whom the usual therapeutic measures for cardiac decompensation are partly or entirely without benefit and who, because of overt clinical evidence of vitamin B deficiency, are given vitamin B complex parenterally, after which a remarkable improvement in the symptoms of cardiac decompensation occurs.

Bibliography

Chapter I — Section 24

Fox, C. L., Jr., C. K. Friedburg, and A. G. White, Electrolyte abnormalities in chronic congestive heart failure; effects of administration of potassium and sodium salt, *J. Clin. Investigation* **28,** 781 (1949).

Galeone, A., E. Levi, and G. Segre, Blood levels of reduced and oxidized cozymase in cardio-patients, *Acta med. Scandinav.* **139,** 308 (1951).

Goldsmith, G. A., The blood lactate-pyruvate relationship in various physiologic and pathologic states, *Am. J. M. Sc.* **215,** 182 (1948).

Greene, C. H., K. Sandiford, and H. Ross, The amino-acid content of the blood in normal and pathologic conditions, *J. Biol. Chem.* **58,** 845 (1924).

Greig, M. E., and W. M. Govier, Studies on the shock induced by hemorrhage. IV. The dephosphorylation of cocarboxylase in tissues during shock and anoxia, *J. Pharmacol. & Exper. Therap.* **79,** 169 (1943).

Grob, D., J. L. Lilienthal, Jr., A. M. Harvey, and B. F. Jones, The administration of di-isopropyl fluorophosphate (DFP) to man. I. Effect on plasma and erythrocyte cholinesterase; general systemic effects; use in study of hepatic function and erythropoiesis; and some properties of plasma cholinesterase, *Bull. Johns Hopkins Hosp.* **81,** 217 (1947).

Harrison, J. V., Diet therapy in congestive heart failure, *J. Am. Dietet. A.* **21,** 86 (1945).

Heilmeyer, L., W. Keiderling, and G. Stüwe, *Kupfer und Eisen als körpereigene Wirkstoffe und ihre Bedeutung beim Krankheitsgeschehen* (G. Fischer, Jena, 1941).

Iseri, L. T., A. J. Boyle, and G. B. Meyers, Water and electrolyte balance during recovery from severe congestive failure on a 50 milligram sodium diet, *Am. Heart J.* **40,** 706 (1950).

Lemley, J. M., R. G. Gale, R. H. Furman, M. E. Cherrington, W. J. Darby, and G. R. Meneely, Plasma tocopherols in cardiac patients, *Am. Heart J.* **37,** 1029 (1949).

McGeorge, M., Choline esterase activity in disease. With special reference to myasthenia gravia, *Lancet* **1,** 69 (1937).

Newman, E. V., Function of the kidney and metabolic changes in cardiac failure, *Am. J. Med.* **7,** 490 (1949).

PAYNE, S. A., and J. P. PETERS, The plasma proteins in relation to blood hydration. VIII. Serum proteins in heart disease, *J. Clin. Investigation* **11**, 103 (1932).

PLATT, R., The blood glutathione in disease, *Brit. J. Exper. Path.* **12**, 139 (1931).

POLLACK, H., H. DOLGER, M. ELLENBERG, and S. COHEN, A test proposed to measure vitamin B_1 saturation in humans, *Proc. Soc. Exper. Biol. & Med.* **44**, 98 (1940).

ROBINSON, W. D., D. MELNICK, and H. FIELD, JR., Urinary excretion of thiamin in clinical cases and the value of such analyses in the diagnosis of thiamin deficiency, *J. Clin. Investigation* **19**, 399 (1940).

SINCLAIR-SMITH, B., A. A. KATTUS, J. GENEST, and E. V. NEWMAN, The renal mechanism of electrolyte excretion and the metabolic balances of electrolytes and nitrogen in congestive cardiac failure; the effects of exercise, rest and aminophyllin, *Bull. Johns Hopkins Hosp.* **84**, 369 (1949).

TOMASZEWSKI, W., and L. DZIALOSZÝNSKI, The value of vitamin A estimation in the blood, *Edinburgh M. J.* **53**, 379 (1945).

TSCHILOFF, K., Il contenuto in glutatione del sangue nei cardiaci in rapporto alla funzione epatica, *Minerva med.* **1**, 14 (1942).

WILLIAMS, R. H., and G. W. BISSELL, Thiamine metabolism with particular reference to the role of liver and kidneys, *Arch. Int. Med.* **73**, 203 (1944).

WITTS, L., Observations on the metabolism of amino-acids in health and disease, *Quart. J. Med.* **22**, 477 (1929).

25. *Abdominal Distention*

The distention that results from accumulation of very large amounts of ascites or of intra-intestinal gas in patients with cardiac decompensation gives rise to changes in circulation and respiration which aggravate the symptoms of congestive failure.

Studies of the lung volume and its subdivisions are fragmentary but in good agreement. Distention of the abdomen decreases the residual air volume only slightly and, although the functional residual air is appreciably diminished (Altschule, 1943; Bittorf and Forschbach, 1910; Wright *et al.*, 1949), it is doubtful whether this lessening of the space available for respiration is in itself harmful. The reserve air, however, decreases almost to zero (Altschule, 1943; Bittorf and Forschbach, 1910; Knipping *et al.*, 1932; Rubow, 1908; Wright *et al.*, 1949), which indicates that the intrapleural pressure is much more positive than normal and approaches atmospheric pressure (Prinzmetal and Kountz, 1935). The latter change has actually been measured in the dog (Frey, 1923). Loss of the normal negative intrapleural pressure impairs respiratory efficiency. The complemental air volume is also greatly diminished (Altschule, 1943; Bittorf and Forschbach, 1910; Knipping *et al.*, 1932), indicating a corresponding degree of decrease in the expansibility of the lungs. This loss of normal ability of the lungs to expand may give rise to a compensatory increase in respiratory minute volume relative to oxygen consumption at rest (Knipping *et al.*, 1932) with aggravation of dyspnea; there is an abnormally large oxygen debt after exercise (Nylin, 1937, 1938), owing to a marked decrease in maximal possible ventilation (Wright *et al.*, 1949). Since the reserve and complemental air volumes are much smaller than normal, the vital capacity is also decreased (Altschule, 1943; Knipping *et al.*, 1932; Peabody and Wentworth, 1917; McClure and Peabody, 1917; Rubow, 1908; Wright *et al.*, 1949). A few studies in cardiac patients show that the relief of abdominal distention which follows paracentesis for ascites relieves dyspnea, lowers the oxygen consumption and diminishes the respiratory minute volume (Resnik *et al.*, 1935a,b). In dogs, excessive distention may ultimately cause respiratory failure (Coombs, 1922). It must be understood that small amounts of ascites have no effect upon respiration (Mills, 1949).

The rise in intra-abdominal pressure which distention may cause (Davidson *et al.*, 1950) is reflected in the corresponding rise in femoral or iliac venous pressures noted in human subjects or in dogs (**54**; Burwell, 1938). James (1949) has also studied ascitic fluid pressure. The increased pressure in the veins of the leg must aggravate the tendency toward edema. If distention is severe enough to elevate intrapleural pressure, an increase in venous pressure is also found in the tributaries of the superior cava (Brams *et al.*, 1933; Burwell, 1938; Ferris and Wilkins, 1937; Frey, 1923; Griffith *et al.*, 1934; Davidson *et al.*, 1950); abdominal paracentesis may result in a fall in the venous pressure (Burwell, 1938; Ferris and Wilkins, 1937; Griffith *et al.*, 1934; Olmer, 1938; Davidson *et al.*, 1950). It is apparent, therefore, that a considerable degree of impairment of venous return from the extremities may develop consequent to the increased intra-abdominal and intrathoracic pressures resulting from distention (Emerson, 1911; Booker *et al.*, 1947). A similar disturbance in flow through the abdominal viscera is suggested by the observation of Bradley and Bradley (1944; Bradley *et al.*, 1949) that the inferior caval pressure is high in man and the renal blood flow decreased when the intra-abdominal pressure is elevated. Glomerular filtration is also diminished and tubular reabsorption increases. Although the impairment of venous return consequent to the distention that may develop in congestive failure may not result in a fall in cardiac output (Bielschowsky, 1932; Resnik *et al.*, 1935*b*) or increase in circulation time (Wall, 1939) at rest, it probably prevents or limits the rise in output of the heart which should occur during exercise, thereby contributing to dyspnea and weakness, and favoring an abnormally increased oxygen debt. It has been shown that increased abdominal pressure increases peripheral venous pressure more in patients with congestive failure than in normal subjects (Zeus, 1941).

Additional consequences of increased intra-abdominal pressure are oliguria, albuminuria, and salt retention (Bradley and Bradley, 1944; Thorington and Schmidt, 1923), the results apparently of decreased renal blood flow; hepatic blood flow is also diminished (Bradley, 1946).

It is clear from the foregoing discussion that the symptoms of congestive failure may be greatly reduced when intestinal distention is relieved or ascites removed. Patients with edema may occasionally exhibit a spontaneous diuresis or may become responsive to mercurial diuretics after abdominal paracentesis. The manifestations of impaired respiration and circulation appear to vary with the intraabdominal pressure rather than with the changes in the volume of the abdomen and its contents; the loss of extensibility of the abdominal wall which occurs with distention (Sodeman and Burch, 1937) is therefore important.

Bibliography

Chapter I — Section 25

ALTSCHULE, M. D., The significance of changes in the lung volume and its subdivisions during and after abdominal operations, *Anesthesiology* **4**, 384 (1943).

ALTSCHULE, M. D., Elevation of femoral venous pressure in abdominal distention, *Unpublished data* (1938).   [54

BELLIS, C. J., and O. H. WANGENSTEEN, Venous circulatory changes in the abdomen and lower extremities attending intestinal distention, *Proc. Soc. Exper. Biol. & Med.* **41,** 490 (1939).   [54

BIELSCHOWSKY, P., Ueber den Einfluss des Lagewechsels, insbesondere der Beinhochlagerung auf das Minutenvolumen des Herzens bei gesunden und kranken Menschen, *Klin. Wchnschr.* **11,** 1252 (1932).

BITTORF, A., and J. FORSCHBACH, Untersuchungen über Lungenfüllung bei Krankheiten, *Ztschr, f. klin. Med.* **70,** 474 (1910).

BOOKER, W. M., D. M. FRENCH, and P. A. MOLANO, Further studies on the acute effects of intra-abdominal pressure, *Am. J. Physiol.* **149,** 292 (1947).

BRADLEY, S. E., Studies of hepatic blood flow in man, *J. Clin. Investigation* **25,** 918 (1946).

BRADLEY, S. E., and G. P. BRADLEY, The effect of increased intra-abdominal pressure upon renal function in normal human subjects, *J. Clin. Investigation* **23,** 939 (1944).   [54

BRADLEY, S. E., G. H. MUDGE, W. D. BLAKE, and P. ALPHONSE, The effect of increased intra-abdominal pressure upon renal excretion of water, sodium and potassium in normal human subjects and in patients with diabetes insipidus, *J. Clin. Investigation* **28,** 772 (1949).

BRAMS, W. A., L. N. KATZ, and L. KOHN, The effect of abdominal distention and release on the blood pressures in the arteries and veins *Am. J. Physiol.* **104,** 120 (1933).   [54

BURWELL, C. S., A comparison of the pressures in arm veins and femoral veins with special reference to changes during pregnancy, *Ann. Int. Med.* **11,** 1305 (1938).   [54

COOMBS, H. C., The mechanism of the regulation of intra-abdominal pressure, *Am. J. Physiol.* **61,** 159 (1922).

DAVIDSON, C. S., T. B. GIBBONS, and W. W. FALOON, Systemic and portal venous pressures in cirrhosis of the liver, *J. Lab. & Clin. Med.* **35,** 181 (1950).   [54

EMERSON, H., Intra-abdominal pressures, *Arch. Int. Med.* **7,** 754 (1911).

FERRIS, E. B., JR., and R. W. WILKINS, The clinical value of comparative measurements of the pressure in the femoral and cubital veins, *Am. Heart J.* **13,** 431 (1937).   [54

FREY, W., Das Verhalten des arteriellen und venösen Blutzirkulation bei experimenteller Steigerung des intraabdominellen Drucks, *Ztschr. f. d. ges. exper. Med.* **31,** 49 (1923).

GRIFFITH, G. C., C. T. CHAMBERLAIN, and J. R. KITCHELL, Observation on the practical significance of venous pressure in health and disease, with a review of the literature, *Am. J. M. Sc.* **187,** 642 (1934).

JAMES, A. H., The mechanism of pleural and ascitic effusions, with a suggested method for the indirect estimation of portal venous pressure, *Clin. Sc.* **8**, 291 (1949).

KNIPPING, H. W., W. LEWIS, and A. MONCRIEFF, Ueber die Dyspnoe, *Beitr. z. Klin. d. Tuberk.* **79**, 1 (1932).

LEVY, L. K., and G. E. BURCH, Studies on venous pressure in hepatic cirrhosis, *Ann. Int. Med.* **29**, 274 (1948).   [54

McCLURE, C. W., and F. W. PEABODY, Relation of vital capacity of lungs to clinical condition of patients with heart disease, *J. A. M. A.* **69**, 1954 (1917).

MILLS, J. N., The influence of abdominal distension upon the vital capacity, *J. Physiol.* **110**, 83 (1949).

NYLIN, G., More recent developments of heart function tests, *J. A. M. A.* **109**, 1333 (1937).

NYLIN, G., The practical applicability of the cardio-pulmonary function test, *Acta med. Scandinav., Supp. No. 93*, 1 (1938).

OLMER, D., A.-X. JOUVE, and J. VAGUE, Une épreuve fonctionelle de la circulation de retour, *Presse méd.* **46**, 1233 (1938).

PEABODY, F. W., and J. S. WENTWORTH, Clinical studies of the respiration. IV. The vital capacity of the lungs and its relation to dyspnea, *Arch. Int. Med.* **20**, 443 (1917).

PLUMIER, L., Étude expérimentale des variations de la pression veineuse, *Arch. Internat. de physiol.* **8**, 1 (1909).   [54

PRINZMETAL, M., and W. B. KOUNTZ, Intrapleural pressure in health and disease and its influence on body function, *Medicine* **14**, 457 (1935).

RESNIK, H. JR., and B. FRIEDMAN, Studies on the mechanism of the increased oxygen consumption in patients with cardiac disease, *J. Clin. Investigation* **14**, 551 (1935a).

RESNIK, H., JR., B. FRIEDMAN, and T. R. HARRISON, The effect of certain therapeutic measures on the cardiac output of patients with congestive heart failure, *Arch. Int. Med.* **56**, 891 (1935b).

RUBOW, V., Untersuchungen über die Atmung bei Herzkrankheiten. Ein Beitrag zum Studium der Pathologie des kleinen Kreislaufes, *Deutsches Arch. f. klin. Med.* **92**, 255 (1908).

SODEMAN, W. A., and G. E. BURCH, The tissue pressure in subcutaneous edema, *Am. J. M. Sc.* **194**, 846 (1937).

THORINGTON, J. M., and C. F. SCHMIDT, A study of urinary output and blood-pressure changes resulting in experimental ascites, *Am. J. M. Sc.* **165**, 880 (1923).   [54

VILLARET, M., and F. ST. GIRONS, La tension veineuse périphérique au cours des cirrhoses veineuses, *Paris méd.* **51**, 471 (1924).

WALL, H. C., Measurement of circulation time with calcium gluconate in patients receiving digitalis, with electrocardiographic studies, *Am. Heart J.* **18** 228 (1939).

WRIGHT, G. W., R. PLACE, and F. PRINCI, The physiological effects of pneumoperitoneum upon the respiratory apparatus, *Am. Rev. Tuberc.* **60**, 706 (1949).

ZEUS, L., Beeinflussbarkeit des Venendruckes durch intraabdominelle Drucksteigerung, *Arch. f. Kreislaufforsch.* **8**, 330 (1941).

26. *Basal Metabolic Rate. Iodine Metabolism*

Elevation of the basal metabolic rate in congestive failure has been noted by many authors (**55**; Peabody *et. al.*, 1916, 1917, 1922). Peabody, Wentworth and Barker (1917) and Resnik and Friedman (1935) found a close correlation between the degree of dyspnea and the rise in metabolism; the latter authors also correlated the rise in metabolic rate with the ratio of respiratory minute volume to vital capacity. Resnik and Friedman (1935) felt that the increased muscular effort associated with dyspnea was the cause of the change in metabolism. However, the slight rise in rectal temperature found in severely decompensated patients (page 39) may also be a factor. Both elevation of rectal temperature and severe dyspnea occur in the most severely decompensated patients, and the increased metabolism could well be related to both at the same time. The fact that hepatic oxygen consumption increases parallel with the metabolic rate (Myers, 1950) indicates that increased respiratory activity is not the sole cause for the rise in the latter.

The apparent degree of elevation of the basal metabolic rate found in some instances may be misleading because the values obtained may be too high. This is owing largely to the fact that it is frequently impossible for the anxious or sick cardiac patient to assume a truly basal state. Another factor leading to error in measuring basal metabolism in severely decompensated patients is the fact that such patients, when exposed to the high concentration of oxygen in the ordinary type of basal metabolism apparatus, take up excessive amounts of oxygen (page 127) in saturating their abnormally unsaturated arterial blood or in discharging their oxygen debts.

Blood iodine. — The common finding of elevated basal metabolic rates in patients with congestive failure has stimulated interest in the blood iodine level in such cases. Most authors agree that the blood iodine level is normal in patients in failure, including those with elevated metabolic rates not due to thyrotoxicosis (Kisch 1934; Löhr, 1936; Turner *et al.*, 1940; Freedberg *et al.*, 1950; Silver *et al.*, 1950; Myers and Man, 1951). The findings of Veil and Sturm (1925), who reported elevated levels in patients in failure with rapid heart rates, and a fall in blood iodine to or toward normal after the administration of digitalis, are discordant. Roversi (1949) found the protein-bound iodine in the normal range in his patients but the inorganic iodine elevated; this finding requires corroboration. The same is true of the findings of Matiseck and Siedek (1939), who observed normal values at rest but excessively high levels after exercise. The uptake of radioactive iodine in cardiac decompensation is described variously. The accumulation of the test substance in edema fluid (Birkhill *et al.*, 1952) may introduce errors in calculation. Perhaps technical factors account for the differences reported (Birkhill *et al.*, 1952; Freedberg *et al.*, 1950, 1951*a,b*; Skanse, 1949; Silver *et al.*, 1950).

Bibliography

Chapter I — Section 26

Ascarelli, E., Rapporti tra velocità di corrente e metabolismo basale nei cardiopazienti, *Cuore e circolaz.* **22**, 44 (1938). [55

Birkhill, R., K. E. Corrigan, and H. S. Hayden, The metabolism of radioactive iodine (I^{131}) in patients with cardiac disease, *Am. J. Roentgenol.* **76**, 42 (1952).

Boothby, W. M., and F. A. Willius, The basal metabolic rate in cases of primary cardiac disease, *M. Clin. North America* **8**, 1171 (1925). [55

Eppinger, H., L. von Papp, and H. Schwarz, Ueber das Asthma cardiale. *Versuch zu einer peripheren Kreislaufpathologie* (Berlin, 1924). [55

Espersen, T., Congestive heart failure, oxygen consumption and lung ventilation, *Acta med. Scandinav.* **108**, 183 (1941). [55

Freedberg, A. S., H. L. Blumgart, G. S. Kurland, and D. L. Chamovitz, The treatment of euthyroid cardiac patients with intractable angina pectoris and congestive failure with radioactive iodine, *J. Clin. Endocrinol.* **10**, 1270 (1950).

Freedberg, A. S., D. L. Chamovitz, and G. S. Kurland, Thyroid function in normal and pathological states as revealed by radioactive iodine studies. I. Thyroid I¹³¹ uptake and turnover in euthyroid, hyperthyroid and hypothyroid subjects, *Metabolism* **1**, 26 (1951).

FREEDBERG, A. S., D. L. CHAMOVITZ, and G. S. KURLAND, Thyroid function in normal and pathological states as revealed by radioactive iodine studies. II. Factors influencing the uptake and turnover of I¹³¹ by the thyroid gland, *Metabolism* **1**, 36 (1951).

HAMBURGER, W. W., and M. W. LEV, Basal metabolism in organic heart disease with decompensation. Preliminary report, *J. A. M. A.* **84**, 587 (1925).   [55

HARRISON, T. R., B. FRIEDMAN, G. CLARK, and H. RESNIK, The cardiac output in relation to cardiac failure, *Arch. Int. Med.* **54**, 239 (1934).   [55

HARROP, G. A., JR., The oxygen and carbon dioxide content of arterial and of venous blood in normal individuals and in patients with anemia and heart disease, *J. Exper. Med.* **30**, 241 (1919).   [55

HERBST, R., Der Gasstoffwechsel als Mass der körperlichen Leistungsfähigkeit. III. Untersuchungen am Herzkranken, *Deutsches Arch. f. klin. Med.* **162**, 257 (1928).   [55

JAHN, D., Zur Störung des Milchsäurehaushaltes Kreislaufkranker, *Verhandl. d. deutsch. Gesellsch. f. inn. Med.* **41**, 346 (1929).   [55

KISCH, F., Ueber das Verhalten des Blutjodspiegels Kreislaufkranker, *Wien. klin. Wchnschr.* **47**, 1317 (1934).

KNIPPING, H. W., Ueber die respiratorische Insufficienz, *Klin. Wchnschr.* **14**, 406 (1935).   [55

LAGERLÖF, H., and L. WERKÖ, Studies on the circulation in man. V. The effect of cedilanid (lanatoside C) on cardiac output and blood pressure in the pulmonary circulation in patients with compensated and decompensated heart disease, *Acta cardiol.* **4**, 1 (1949).   [55

LEQUIME, J., Le débit cardiaque. Études expérimentales et cliniques, *Acta med. Scandinav., Supp. No. 107* (1940).   [55

LÖHR, H., Beitrag zur Kenntnis des Jodstoffwechsels. I. Mitt. Blutjodstudien unter physiologischen Verhältnissen, *Arch. f. exper. Path. u. Pharmakol.* **180**, 332 (1936).

MATISECK, H., and H. SIEDEK, Kardiale Dekompensation, Schilddruse und Blutjod, *Ztschr. f. klin. Med.* **137**, 350 (1939).

McGUIRE, J., R. SHORE, V. HAUENSTEIN, and F. GOLDMAN, The cardiac output in compensation and decompensation in the same individual, *Am. Heart J.* **16**, 449 (1938).   [55

McGUIRE, J., R. SHORE, V. HAUENSTEIN, and F. GOLDMAN, Relation of cardiac output to congestive heart failure, *Arch. Int. Med.* **63**, 290 (1939).   [55

MEAKINS, J., L. DAUTREBANDE, and W. J. FETTER, The influence of circulatory disturbances on the gaseous exchange of the blood. IV. The blood gases and circulation rate in cases of mitral stenosis, *Heart* **10**, 153 (1923). [55

MEYERS, J. H., and E. B. MAN, Artifactual values of serum precipitable iodine after clinical intramuscular injections of mercuhydrin, *J. Lab. & Clin. Med.* **37**, 867 (1951).

MYERS, J. D., Net splanchnic glucose production in normal man and in various disease states, *J. Clin. Investigation* **29**, 1421 (1950). [55

NYLIN, G., Clinical tests of the function of the heart, *Acta med. Scandinav., Supp. No. 52*, 1, (1933). [55

PEABODY, F. W., A. L. MEYER, and E. F. DuBois, Clinical calorimetry. XVI. The basal metabolism of patients with cardiac and renal disease, *Arch. Int. Med.* **17**, 980 (1916). [55

PEABODY, F. W., and C. C. STURGIS, Clinical studies on respiration. IX. The effect of exercise on the metabolism, heart rate and pulmonary ventilation of normal subjects and patients with heart disease, *Arch. Int. Med.* **29**, 277 (1922). [55

PEABODY, F. W., J. A. WENTWORTH, and B. I. BARKER, Clinical studies on the respiration. V. The basal metabolism and the minute-volume of the respiration of patients with cardiac disease, *Arch. Int. Med.* **20**, 468 (1917). [55

RESNIK, H. JR., and B. FRIEDMAN, Studies in the mechanism of the increased oxygen consumption in patients with cardiac disease, *J. Clin. Investigation* **14**, 551 (1935). [55

RIGONI, M., Il ricambio respiratorio, la portata circolatoria e la gittata sistolica nelle cardiopatie compensate e nello scompenso di circolo. I. Metabolismo basale, ventilazione pulmonare e tensione dei gas alveolari, *Cuore e circolaz.* **21**, 157 (1937). [55

RINGER, M., and M. ALTSCHULE, Studies on the circulation. II. Cardiac output in diseases of the heart, and under the influence of digitalis therapy, *Am. Heart J.* **5**, 305 (1930). [55

ROVERSI, L., Studi sulla iodemia nei cardiaci scompensati, *Policlinico (sez. med.)* **56**, 187 (1949).

SILVER, S., P. POROTO, and E. B. CROHM, Hypermetabolic states without hyperthyroidism (Nonthyrogenous hypermetabolism), *Arch. Int. Med.* **85**, 479 (1950). [55

SKANSE, B., Radioactive iodine in the diagnosis of thyroid disease, *Acta med. Scandinav. Supp.* **235** (1949).

STEWART, H. J., W. F. EVANS, H. BROWN, and J. R. GERJUOY, Peripheral blood flow, rectal and skin temperature in congestive heart failure. The effects of rapid digitalization in this state, *Arch. Int. Med.* **77**, 643 (1946). [55

TURNER, K. B., A. DeLAMATER, and W. D. PROVINCE, Observations on the blood iodine. I. The blood iodine in health, in thyroid and cardiorenal disease, and in leukemia. *J. Clin. Investigation* **19**, 515 (1940).

VEIL, W. H., and A. STURM, Beitrage zur Kenntnis des Jodstoffwechsels, *Deutsches Arch. f. klin. Med.* **147**, 166 (1925).

WERKÖ, L., and H. LAGERLÖF, Studies on the circulation in man. IV. Cardiac output and blood presure in the right auricle, right ventricle and pulmonary artery in patients with hypertensive cardiovascular disease, *Acta med. Scandinav.* **133**, 427 (1949).   [55

27. Insensible Perspiration

The insensible water loss is normal or, at times, abnormally low in congestive failure (**56**; Kesterman and Schleining, 1936) in spite of the fact that most patients in failure hyperventilate and should, therefore, vaporize more than a normal amount of water in the lungs (Christie and Loomis, 1932; Burch, 1946*a*); loss via the skin is low (Burch, 1946*b*). Impairment of cutaneous blood flow is probably responsible for this phenomenon. Di Macco (1921), who measured water loss directly, reported low values only over edematous skin, but his methods are of doubtful accuracy; the fact that overt sweating is diminished in the presence of severe stasis (Ichihashi and Ogata, 1935) may have introduced errors also.

The attempts of Conti (1932), Neurath (1939), and Zak *et al.* (1929, 1935*a*, *b*) to establish the theory that the body colloids of edematous patients actually absorb water from the air, since the measured insensible perspiration is negative, have been widely criticized on the ground of errors in technique (**56**; Newburgh and Johnston, 1942).

Bibliography

Chapter I — Section 27

BURCH, G. E., Rate of water and heat loss from the respiratory tract of patients with congestive heart failure who were from a subtropical climate and resting in a comfortable atmosphere, *Am. Heart J.* **32**, 88 (1946*a*).

BURCH, G. E., The influence of environmental temperature and relative humidity on the rate of water loss through the skin in congestive heart failure in a subtropical climate, *Am. J. M. Sc.* **211**, 181 (1946*b*).

CHRISTIE, R. V., and A. L. LOOMIS, The pressure of aqueous vapour in the alveolar air, *J. Physiol.* **77**, 35 (1932).

CONTI, F., La perspiratio insensibilis nei cardiopatici scompensati, *Minerva med.* **23** [2], 789 (1932).

D'ALTON, C. J., R. C. DARLING, and E. SHEA, The insensible loss of water in congestive failure, *Am. J. M. Sc.* **216**, 516 (1948).   [56

DI MACCO, G., La perspiratio insensibilis in diversi stati morbosi, *Ann. di clin. med.* **11**, 165 (1921).

GABRIEL, G., and H. KAHLER, Ueber den Einfluss des respiratorischen Quotienten auf die Höhe der Gewichtsabgabe. Zur Frage der perspiratio insensibilis bei Kreislaufkranken, *Wien. Arch. f. inn. Med.* **24**, 181 (1934).   [56

HELLER, H., Kritische Betrachtungen uber "Autochthone Wasserbildung" und "Negative Perspiratio insensibilis" Nebst Bemerkungen uber Theorie und Praxis der Indirekten Bestimmung der Extrarenalen Wasserausscheidung., *Zeitschr. f. klin. Med.* **114**, 315 (1930).   [56

ICHIHASHI, T., and K. OGATA, The effect of a local obstruction of the blood flow on the sweat secretion in man, *J. Orient. Med.* **23**, 1 (1935).

KAHLER, H., and R. SCHMIDT, Ueber die Teilfaktoren der unmerklichen Gewichtsabgabe und ihre Änderungen unter verschiedenen Bedingungen. Zugleich ein Beitrag zur Frage der "negativen perspiratio insensibilis," *Wien. Arch. f. inn. Med.* **28**, 67 (1936).   [56

KESTERMAN, E., and T. SCHLEINING, Das Verhalten des unmerklichen Gewichtsverlustes bei hydropischen Erkrankungen, *Deutsches Arch. f. klin. Med.* **179**, 609 (1936).   [56

MAGENDANTZ, H., and F. STRATMAN, Ueber die extrarenale Wasserausscheidung bei Herzinsufficienz, *Deutsches Arch. f. klin. Med.* **174**, 1 (1933).   [56

NEURATH, O., Paradoxes Verhalten des Körpergewichtes bei Herzkranken und Fettsuchtigen, hervorgerufen durch "perspiratio insensibilis negativa," *Cardiologia* **3**, 353 (1939).

NEWBURGH, L. H., and M. W. JOHNSTON, The insensible loss of water, *Physiol. Rev.* **22**, 1 (1942).

SODERSTROM, G. F., and E. F. DuBOIS, Clinical calorimetry XXV. The water elimination through the skin and respiratory passages in health and disease, *Arch. Int. Med.* **19**, 931 (1917).   [56

ZAK, E., Ueber das Verhalten der Perspiratio insensibilis und das Körpergewichtes bei dekompensierten Kreislauf, *Ztschr. f. klin. Med.* **110**, 44 (1929).

ZAK, E., G. FEHER, and O. NEURATH, Paradoxes Verhalten des Körpergewichtes gewisser Herzkranker durch negative Perspiratio insensibilis, *Ztschr. f. klin. Med.* **127**, 201 (1935a).

ZAK, E., G. FEHER, and A. RABL, Geänderte Haut- und Gefässreaktionen bei Kreislaufkranken mit Stauungsleber. (Fernwirkungen der Stauungsleber), *Ztschr. f. klin. Med.* **127**, 323 (1935*b*).

28. *Lymphatics*

The studies of McMaster (1937) on the lymphatics of the skin in patients with congestive failure are important in relation to the mechanism of formation of cardiac edema. McMaster found dilatation and valvular incompetence of the lymphatic channels and complete absence of lymph flow in the skin of edematous legs of patients. Administration of diuretics caused no apparent change in the function of the lymphatic vessels. Elevating the edematous limb, however, caused small increases in lymphatic flow. McMaster's inability to reproduce the typical lymphatic stasis of congestive failure by means of tourniquets in normal subjects led him to rule out increased venous pressure as the cause of the lymphatic stasis observed by him in cardiac decompensation; anoxia may be the factor responsible. It is probable, however, that the elevated venous pressure found in many patients with congestive failure is also a factor preventing normal lymphatic function, for increases in venous pressure must be transmitted to the lymphatic vessels.

Bibliography

Chapter I — Section 28

MCMASTER, P. D., The lymphatics and lymph flow in the edematous skin of human beings with cardiac and renal disease, *J. Exper. Med.* **65**, 373 (1937).

29. *Central Nervous System Function*

Patients with moderate or severe congestive failure not infrequently show evidence of psychic disturbances ranging from inability to concentrate or mild changes in personality to coma or psychosis.

Gross (1940) studied intellectual function by means of a number of tests of intelligence and attempted to correlate changes so revealed with variations in circulation time in cardiac patients. Although cerebral function improved with amelioration of cardiac decompensation, the changes were usually not parallel to those in circulation time.

Neither gross motor change, such as paralysis or impairment of reflexes, nor measurable impairment of sensation occur. Moderate anoxia does not depress sensory acuity (Stokes, Chapman, and Smith, 1948). However, studies made by Simonson and Enzer (1941) and Enzer *et al.* (1942) on the fusion frequency of flicker and the maximal frequency of motor impulses do show impairment of that function in congestive failure. It is of interest that similar changes occur in anoxia also (Enzer *et al.*, 1942; Simonson and Winchell, 1951). It is not unlikely that the limited ability to do physical work commonly seen in congestive failure is related in part to this phenomenon.

The circulation through the central nervous system has not been studied extensively in congestive failure. Calhoun *et al.* (1931) studied the jugular venous blood and found no evidence of slow flow, while McMichael (1939) and Himwich and Fazekas (1944) found the cerebral arteriovenous oxygen difference to be increased as a rule. Moyer *et al.* (1952) and Scheinberg (1950) found the cerebral flow to be diminished in proportion to the fall in cardiac output; the vascular resistance was doubled and no definite fall in oxygen consumption was found; Novack *et al.* (1953) studied patients who had received some treatment and concluded that the cerebral flow was normal, although the arteriovenous difference was high in three-quarters of their cases. Edema of the brain occurs in congestive heart failure; Alexander and Looney (1938) found the white matter of the brain to be more edematous than the gray. White *et al.* (1942) studied the effect of anoxia on the brain in dogs and concluded that lack of oxygen caused cerebral edema. In addition, elevation of spinal fluid pressure occurs in cardiac decompensation as a result of elevation of the venous pressure (page 73). All these mechanisms are probably responsible for the central nervous system symptoms found in patients with chronic cardiac decompensation.

The occurrence of Cheyne-Stokes respiration is probably also a consequence of impaired cerebral function in congestive failure. In animals, periodic breathing has been induced either by elevation of the cerebrospinal fluid pressure or by slowing of the blood flow through the brain (Greeley and Greeley, 1930).

Bibliography

Chapter I — Section 29

ALEXANDER, L., and J. M. LOONEY, Physicochemical properties of brain, especially in senile dementia and cerebral edema. Differential ratio of skull capacity to volume, specific weight, water content, water-binding capacity and pH of the brain, *Arch. Neurol. & Psychiat.* **40,** 877 (1938).

CALHOUN, J., G. E. CULLEN, T. R. HARRISON, W. L. WILKINS, and M. M. TIMS, Studies in congestive heart failure. XIV. Orthopnea: its relation to ventilation, vital capacity, oxygen saturation and acid-base condition of arterial and jugular blood, *J. Clin. Investigation* **10,** 833 (1931).

ENZER, N., E. SIMONSON, and S. S. BLANKSTEIN, Fatigue of patients with circulatory insufficiency investigated by means of the fusion frequency of flicker, *Ann. Int. Med.* **16,** 701 (1942).

GREELEY, C. E., and P. O. GREELEY, Circulatory changes during periodic ventilation with apneas produced by marked curtailment of blood flow to the brain, *Am. J. Physiol.* **95,** 382 (1930).

GROSS, D., Estudio psicofisico de los cardiacos, *Rev. méd. de Chile* **68,** 258 (1940).

HIMWICH, H. E., and J. E. FAZEKAS, The oxygen content of cerebral blood in patients with acute symptomatic psychoses and acute destructive brain lesions, *Am. J. Psychiat.* **100,** 648 (1944).

MCMICHAEL, J., Hyperpnoea in heart failure, *Clin. Sc.* **4,** 19 (1939).

MOYER, J. H., S. I. MILLER, A. B. TASHNEK, and R. BOWMAN, The effect of theophylline with ethylenediamine (aminophylline) on cerebral hemodynamics in the presence of cardiac failure with and without Cheyne-Stokes respiration, *J. Clin. Investigation* **31,** 267 (1952).

NOVACK, P., B. GOLUBOFF, L. BORTIN, A. SOFFE, and H. A. SHENKIN, Studies of the cerebral circulation and metabolism in congestive heart failure, *Circulation* **7,** 724 (1953).

SCHEINBERG, P., Cerebral circulation in heart failure, *Am. J. Med.* **8,** 148 (1950).

SIMONSON, E., and N. ENZER, State of motor centers in circulatory insufficiency, *Arch. Int. Med.* **68,** 498 (1941).

SIMONSON, E., and P. WINCHELL, Effect of high carbon dioxide and of low oxygen concentration on fusion frequency of flicker, *J. Appl. Physiol.* **3,** 637 (1951).

STOKES, J., III, W. P. CHAPMAN, and L. H. SMITH, Effects of hypoxia and hypercapnia on perception of thermal cutaneous pain, *J. Clin. Investigation* **27,** 299 (1948).

WHITE, J. C., M. VERLOT, B. SELVERSTONE, and H. K. BEECHER, Changes in brain volume during anesthesia: the effects of anoxia and hypercapnia, *Arch. Surg.* **44**, 1 (1942).

30. *Skeletal Muscle Function*

It is well known that many patients with cardiac decompensation complain of generalized muscular weakness. Indeed, in some instances this complaint is a much more prominent symptom than dyspnea. Under the latter circumstances an interesting parallel may be drawn with the effects of exercise under anoxic conditions at high altitudes, as described by Edwards (1936); exhaustion occurred before the subjects could work long enough to develop a significant rise in blood lactate.

The muscular weakness of cardiac decompensation may be related to abnormal creatine metabolism, for Kindler (1936) and Pescador and Perez López (1941) studied the incidence of creatinuria in patients with cardiac decompensation and found it present in all patients with signs of severe failure; Herrmann (1935), without recording data, also described creatinuria as common in cardiac decompensation. Kindler (1936) and Pescador and Perez López (1941) reported regression of creatinuria with improvement and believed that the observed deviation from normal creatine metabolism was a result of the effect of anoxia on skeletal muscle. However, the phenomenon may possibly be one manifestation of a generalized metabolic disturbance due to severe illness; malnutrition and prolonged rest in bed probably play contributory roles. Other mechanisms which possibly may be involved in giving rise to muscular weakness and easy fatigability are disturbances in the enzyme systems that participate in muscular action. Data in this regard are lacking but studies have been made on the synthesis of acetylcholine which are of interest. Anoxia has been shown to retard the synthesis of acetylcholine in vitro (Quastel *et al.*, 1936; Mann *et al.*, 1938; Welsch and Hyde, 1944); Torda and Wolff (1945) found the synthesis of acetylcholine to be depressed by blood drawn from an arm exercised under conditions of ischemia. The observations of Nachmansohn and John (1944), who found depression in the synthesis of that substance in the presence of elevated pyruvate in concentrations that may be reached in man, may be related. Putnam and Merritt (1941) earlier recorded the fact that pyruvate depresses muscular action. The rise in blood pyruvate that occurs in cardiac decompensation is discussed elsewhere (page 122).

Harrison *et al.* (1930) described lowering of the potassium content of skeletal muscle in congestive failure. These authors regarded this finding as indicative of impairment of buffering power; it is possible that it has a more specific significance in muscle function. The findings of Harrison *et al.* (1930) were corroborated by Iseri *et al.* (1952) and Mokotoff *et al.* (1952); the last named also showed an increase in water, sodium, chloride, and magnesium in the muscle. The loss of potassium is not due solely to wasting, since it exceeds the loss of nitrogen. The total exchangeable potassium in the body as a whole is often decreased in chronic cardiac decompensation (Aikawa *et al.*, 1952). The negative potassium balance seen in congestive failure has been discussed elsewhere (page 175). Feeding potassium results in some retention (Elkinton *et al.*, 1952).

Animals made anoxic show loss of myoglobin in skeletal muscles (Bowen and Eads, 1949; Poel, 1949); this matter has not been studied in man.

Bibliography

Chapter I — Section 30

AIKAWA, J. K., J. H. FELTS, JR., M. P. TYOR, and G. T. HARRELL, The exchangeable potassium content in disease states, *J. Clin. Investigation* **31**, 743 (1952).

BOWEN, W. J., and H. J. EADS, Effects of 18,000 feet simulated altitude on the myoglobin content of dogs, *Am. J. Physiol.* **159**, 77 (1949).

EDWARDS, H. T., Lactic acid in rest and work at high altitude, *Am. J. Physiol.* **116**, 367 (1936).

ELKINTON, J. R., R. D. SQUIRES, and L. W. BLUEMLE, JR., The distribution of body fluids in congestive heart failure. IV. Exchanges in patients, refractory to mercurial diuretics, treated with sodium and potassium, *Circulation* **5**, 58 (1952).

HARRISON, T. R., C. PILCHER, and G. EWING, Studies in congestive heart failure. IV. The potassium content of skeletal and cardiac muscle, *J. Clin. Investigation* **8**, 325 (1930).

HERRMANN, G. R., Creatine metabolism with especial reference to heart disease, *J. Lab. & Clin. Med.* **20**, 890 (1934–35).

ISERI, L. T., L. C. ALEXANDER, R. S. McCAUGHEY, A. J. BOYLE, and G. B.

MYERS, Water and electrolyte content of cardiac and skeletal muscle in heart failure and myocardial infarction, *Am. Heart J.* **43**, 215 (1952).

KINDLER, E., Kreatinurie bei kardialer Dekompensation, *Klin. Wchnschr.* **15**, 267 (1936).

MANN, P. J. G., M. TENNENBAUM, and J. H. QUASTEL, On the mechanism of acetylcholine formation in the brain in vitro, *Biochem. J.* **32**, 243 (1938).

MOKOTOFF, R., G. ROSS, and L. LEITER, The electrolyte content of skeletal muscle in congestive heart failure; a comparison of results with inulin and chloride as reference standards for extracellular water, *J. Clin. Investigation* **31**, 291 (1952).

NACHMANSOHN, D., and H. M. JOHN, Inhibition of choline acetylene by a-keto acids, *Proc. Soc. Exper. Biol. & Med.* **57**, 361 (1944).

PESCADOR, L., and J. PEREZ LÓPEZ, Sobre el comportamiento de la creatinina en los portadores de cardiopatias descompensadas, *Rev. clin. españ.* **2**, 262 (1941).

POEL, W. E., Effect of anoxic anoxia on myoglobin concentration in striated muscle, *Am. J. Physiol.* **156**, 44 (1949).

PUTNAM, T. J., and H. H. MERRITT, Chemistry of anticonvulsant drugs, *Arch. Neurol. & Psychiat.* **45**, 505 (1941).

QUASTEL, J. H., M. TENNENBAUM, and A. H. M. WHEATLEY, Choline ester formation in, and choline esterase activities of, tissues in vitro, *Biochem. J.* **30**, 1668 (1936).

TORDA, C., and H. G. WOLFF, Depression of acetylcholine synthesis by serum from working muscle. Healthy subjects and myasthenia gravis patients, *Proc. Soc. Exper. Biol. & Med.* **59**, 13 (1945).

WELSCH, J. H., and J. E. HYDE, The effects of potassium on the synthesis of acetylcholine in brain, *Am. J. Physiol.* **142**, 512 (1944).

31. *Tissue Pressure. Cutaneous Pressure and Distensibility*

A number of authors (Krogh *et al.*, 1932; Landis and Gibbon, 1933; Youmans *et al.*, 1934) have in the past stressed the importance of changes in tissue pressure in edematous patients and their role in limiting the formation of edema. Burch and Sodeman (1937) and Sodeman and Burch (1937) measured the subcutaneous tissue pressure in edematous cardiac patients and found it greatly elevated, but never above the venous pressure; diuresis after the injection of salyrgan lowered it to or almost to normal. In general the tissue pressure varied with the amount of edema, but in the chronic state the relationship was not present, since the tissues had lost much of their elasticity (Sodeman and Burch, 1938); distensibility decreased as edema fluid increased and tissue pressure rose. As is to be expected, the intracutaneous pressure also is elevated in the presence of edema (McMaster, 1946); earlier work purporting to show the opposite (Hajen, 1927; Holland and Meyer, 1932) is inaccurate, according to McMaster (1946). All authors agree that as edema forms the increase in tissue pressure exerts more and more of an inhibiting effect on transudation, with stretching of the skin to the point of loss of distensibility playing a similar role. In the chronic state, however, this limiting effect is lessened, apparently because of repeated stretchings and also as a consequence of loss of flesh due to malnutrition.

Bibliography

Chapter I — Section 31

BURCH, G. E., and W. A. SODEMAN, The estimation of the subcutaneous tissue pressure by a direct method, *J. Clin. Investigation* **16**, 845 (1937).

HAJEN, H., Über die Beziehung des intracutanen Gewebsdruckes zur Inaddelbildung. Untersuchungen über den intracutanen Gewebsdruck, *Ztschr. f. d. ges. exper. Med.* **57**, 203 (1927).

HOLLAND, G., and F. MEYER, Der Gewebsdruck beim Ödem. II. Mitt. *Arch. f. exper. Path. u. Pharmakol.* **168**, 603 (1932).

KROGH, A., E. M. LANDIS, and A. H. TURNER, The movement of fluid through the human capillary wall in relation to venous pressure and to the colloid osmotic pressure of the blood, *J. Clin. Investigation* **11**, 63 (1932).

LANDIS, E. M., and J. H. GIBBON, JR., The effects of temperature and of tissue pressure on the movement of fluid through the human capillary wall, *J. Clin. Investigation* **12**, 105 (1933).

MCMASTER, P. D., The effects of venous obstruction upon interstitial pressure in animal and human skin, *J. Exper. Med.* **84**, 495 (1946).

SODEMAN, W. A., and G. E. BURCH, The tissue pressure in subcutaneous edema, *Am. J. M. Sc.* **194**, 846 (1937).

SODEMAN, W. A., and G. E. BURCH, A direct method for the estimation of skin distensibility with its application to the study of vascular states, *J. Clin. Investigation* **17**, 785 (1938).

Youmans, J. B., H. S. Wells, D. Donley, and D. G. Miller, The effect of posture (standing) on the serum protein concentration and colloid osmotic pressure of blood from the foot in relation to the formation of edema, *J. Clin. Investigation* **13**, 447 (1934).

32. *Edema*

Tissue anoxia. — The role of anoxia in the genesis of cardiac edema has been discussed for many years, but available data bearing on this matter are incomplete and in part discrepant. Careful work (Barach and Richards, 1931; Richards and Barach, 1934) has shown that some edematous cardiac patients respond to the administration of air enriched with oxygen by a profuse diuresis, only to regain their edema when removed from the oxygen tent. Anoxia was evidently of primary importance in these patients, for the administration of oxygen caused no change in cardiac output and the disappearance of edema was followed, rather than preceded, by a lowering of the venous pressure. Anoxia may well account also for the loss of abnormally large amounts of fluid from the blood to the tissues found by Dautrebande *et al.* (1923) after occlusion of the arterial flow in a limb. Smirk's (1936) experiments demonstrated a tendency in edematous cardiac patients toward the elaboration of abnormally large amounts of tissue fluid at given effective filtering pressures. He showed by means of plethysmographic studies that raising the venous pressure to the same level above the measured plasma oncotic pressure in normal subjects and in patients with cardiac decompensation resulted in the elaboration of larger amounts of this fluid in the latter than in the former. Smirk therefore concluded that capillary permeability is increased in chronic cardiac decompensation.

On the other hand, McMichael and Morris (1936) and Henry *et al.* (1946) reported plethysmographic studies of short duration from which they concluded that induced anoxia does not increase capillary permeability in normal man. These authors presented no data, so that analysis of their findings is impossible. Moreover, anoxia in such experiments may induce vasoconstriction (Henry *et al.*, 1947*a*) and so reduce filtering area, and increase in rate of blood flow may counteract to some extent the lowering of arterial oxygen saturation. When conditions of low venous oxygen saturation are induced, an increase in capillary permeability occurs (Henry *et al.*, 1947*b*). The fact that Fishman *et al.* (1951) found no increase in sodium retention when their patients with severe anoxia owing to chronic cor pulmonale were given low concentrations of oxygen to breath for periods of 19 to 40 minutes cannot be interpreted in view of the fact that the procedure of study required the forcing of fluids and the period of anoxia was short; however, it is evident that the effect of short periods of anoxia is not to cause primary salt retention.

Stead and Warren (1944) studied the edema-fluid protein in cardiac patients and compared it with the protein content obtained in normal subjects after the application of tourniquets; they found no increase in the former over the latter and, therefore, concluded that no increase in capillary permeability occurred in congestive failure. Stead and Warren (1944) further found that the application of tourniquets to the limbs of normal subjects and of cardiac patients resulted in elaboration of fluid of similar protein content in both groups. The validity of this comparison is not established and, in addition, many authors have shown (page 102) that cardiac subcutaneous edema fluid has a higher protein content than that obtained from patients with renal disease or cirrhosis.

Stead and Warren also presented data on two patients with arterial anoxemia consequent to chronic pulmonary disease and found that subcutaneous fluid that developed in these subjects after application of a tourniquet was not different in protein content from the normal. These authors presented no measurements of venous blood oxygen content, data which are important since the response to anoxia in patients with normal hearts is an increase in velocity and volume of blood flow (page 101); the tissues in the patients studied may have been less anoxic than the arterial blood oxygen level indicated. Indeed, there is no conclusive evidence that it is valid to use the protein content of a fluid as a measure of permeability.

In this connection it should be remembered that the protein content of edema fluid often rises during diuresis in cardiac patients and also that in the same patient pleural and ascitic fluids usually have protein contents many times that of the subcutaneous fluid (page 140). The situation becomes further confused when it is realized that even normal capillaries are believed to be freely permeable to water and salt; any increase in permeability must, therefore, refer to protein. However, variable amounts of protein do pass through the capillaries normally and if a small additional amount passed through, it would probably draw water with it and so make its presence undetectable. It is apparent that even if normal subjects and edematous cardiac patients have approximately equal tissue fluid protein contents, large amounts of protein must have entered the tissue spaces in the cardiac patients to maintain that protein concentration in the edema fluid. The fact that studies by means of dyes show no increase in capillary permeability in congestive failure (Lange, 1944) is not helpful, for studies with dyes are notoriously misleading in this respect.

If anoxia results in increased elaboration of fluid in cardiac patients, it may act by giving rise to vasodilatation which would exaggerate whatever tendency toward increased filtration existed as a consequence of other factors; Krogh (1929) and Landis (1928) showed that anoxia causes capillary dilatation. That this phenomenon accounts for part or all of the effect of anoxia in cardiac patients in whom other mechanisms for edema formation are already operative cannot be ruled out on the basis of available data, and it is clear that further studies are indicated. On the other hand, the fact that simple anoxia, induced by breathing air depleted of oxygen, has been demonstrated to cause increased water content (White et al., 1942) or a profuse flow of lymph from several organs (Gesell, 1928; Maurer, 1940; Warren and Drinker, 1942; Warren et al., 1942) strongly suggests that the effect of anoxia may be specific increase in capillary permeability. The work of Landis (1928), of Saslow (1938) and of Pappenheimer and Soto-Rivera (1948), which showed that extreme degrees of anoxia cause increased permeability of the capillaries, may or may not be applicable to the more moderate degrees of tissue anoxia which exist in cardiac decompensation.

Increased venous pressure. — Elevation of filtering pressure is an important factor favoring the elaboration of increased amounts of tissue fluid. The approximate observations of Mende (1919), Drury and Jones (1927) and McMichael and Morris (1936) on the relation of filtering pressure to edema formation in the extremities have been supplanted by the precise quantitative studies of Krogh et al. (1932) and of Landis et al. (1932, 1933), and the relationship is now established. Similar studies on the elaboration of tissue fluid in the lungs have been made by Warren and Drinker (1942). It is clear that extreme rises in venous pressure, to 30 or 40 cm-of-water, may by themselves cause the appearance of edema in the tissues. However, the relation of these findings to the moderate increases in venous pressure commonly observed in congestive failure is not established. Certainly the contention of Reichsman and Grant (1946), that the role of elevated venous pressure is paramount in the formation of edema, is much too far-reaching a conclusion to be derived from their observation, corroborated by Newman and Fishel (1950), that venous pressure rises before weight is gained when digitalis is omitted in congestive failure. Clinically, it has long been known that some patients with venous engorgement do not have edema and that, conversely, some patients with cardiac edema do not have venous engorgement. Measurements of venous pressure in heart disease (page 47) show much overlapping of values in edematous and nonedematous cardiac patients. A large series of patients, excluding those with thyroid diseases, nephritis, emphysema, pericarditis and tricuspid disease, has been analyzed from this point of view (Altschule, 1938). Eighty-three with no history or evidence of congestive failure had venous pressures ranging as high as 11.8 cm-of-water; of these only three had levels of 11 cm-of-water or more. Of thirty-three with congestive failure, but no history or evidence of edema, seven had venous pressure levels above 11.0 and ranging as high as 14.5 cm-of-water. Thirty-five patients admitted to the hospital with edema, but who became free of visible edema and remained so at rest in bed, had venous pressures ranging as high as 14.0 cm-of-water; in eleven the pressure was above 11.0 cm-of-water. Of fifteen patients who regained edema constantly although at rest in bed, eight had venous pressures above 11.0 and as high as 18.2 cm-of-water, while seven had pressures between 0.8 and 7.1 cm-of-water. These observations on the lack of correlation between increased venous pressure and edema formation in congestive failure have been corroborated by studies in congestive failure by other authors (Winsor and Burch, 1946; Merrill, 1946), in tricuspid disease (Altschule et al., 1937, 1940) and in patients with superior vena caval obstruction (Smirk, 1936; Altschule et al., 1945). A similar lack of correlation between right auricular pressure and edema formation was observed by Ellis et al. (1951).

It is therefore concluded that while extreme rises in venous pressure, to levels of 30 or 40 cm-of-water, may by themselves cause the appearance of edema, the moderate increases in venous pressure commonly found in congestive failure merely constitute an important contributory factor, but do not result in edema formation unless additional influences are operating at the same time. The rise in venous pressure seen in cardiac decompensation is itself the consequence of a number of factors. The occurrence of edema mostly in dependent parts is probably related to venous pressure levels but this does not explain the development of pleural effusion. It should also be borne in mind that venous pressures in the legs are higher while the patient stands still than when he is walking (Runge, 1924; Smirk, 1936; Beecher, 1937; Hickam *et al.*, 1948; Pollack and Wood, 1949; Pollack *et al.*, 1949; Walker and Longland, 1950; O'Keefe *et al.*, 1951; De Camp *et al.*, 1951) or even when he is sitting quietly; the average values in normal subjects were found by Pollack and Wood (1949) to be 12 cm-of-water lying, 56 sitting, 86 standing, and 23 walking. On the other hand, straining raises the femoral venous pressure (page 48), as would be expected from the observed changes in intra-abdominal pressure (Keith, 1923; Drye, 1948). Of interest in relation to the increase in edema in hot weather is the fact that heat causes the venous pressure to rise (Budelmann, 1935; Henry and Gauer, 1950; Threefoot, 1952), presumably as a consequence of opening of cutaneous arteriovenous shunts (Altschule and Freedberg, 1945); exposure to heat is said to cause a greater rise in venous pressure in cardiac patients than in normal subjects (Budelmann, 1935).

Low plasma protein level. — A pronounced lowering of the plasma protein level, namely, to less than 5.0 Gm./100 cc., with a corresponding or greater fall in plasma albumin concentration, may result in the appearance of edema, as in malnutrition or the nephrotic syndrome. Such marked lowering of the total protein and albumin levels is, however, rarely encountered in uncomplicated congestive failure and lesser decreases are common; the plasma total protein content usually lies between 5.5 and 6.5 Gm./100 cc. Decreases of this magnitude are, however, of importance in the genesis of edema when combined with abnormalities in other factors, since the rate of filtrations from the capillaries at a given pressure varies inversely as the plasma protein level (Krogh *et al.*, 1932).

Abnormal lymphatic function. — Clinical and experimental observations have conclusively proved the occurrence of edema following injury to lymphatics. It remained for McMaster (page 148) to demonstrate the absence of normal lymphatic flow in patients with cardiac edema in contrast to the striking lymphatic hyperactivity which he observed in patients with nephritic edema. The mechanisms underlying the change found in chronic cardiac decompensation are obscure; it is possible that both a rise in venous pressure and anoxia may be implicated. Whatever the causes of this phenomenon, however, it is apparent that this factor is of great importance in the genesis of cardiac edema.

Diminished tissue pressure. — The elaboration of tissue fluid depends not only on intravascular conditions favoring transudation, but also on extravascular factors which resist the escape of fluid into the tissues. Landis and his co-workers (Krogh *et al.*, 1932; Landis *et al.*, 1932, 1933) have studied this relationship in normal man, and Sodeman and Burch (page 153) have made clinical studies bearing on it in patients with congestive failure. The ease with which edema develops in cachectic patients with lax subcutaneous tissues exemplifies the importance of lowered tissue pressure in accelerating the formation of edema. Loss of flesh consequent to malnutrition is recognized as frequently present in chronic congestive failure. Prolonged bed rest results in laxity of the muscles, which probably causes similar changes. It has been demonstrated (page 226) that repeated bouts of edema followed by loss of edema as a result of diuresis results in a more or less permanent impairment of tissue elasticity. Additional pertinent evidence is the fact that patients who have had repeated bouts of cardiac decompensation harbor several times as much invisible edema fluid as do those recovered from their first attack of congestive failure (page 139).

The foregoing considerations point to the conclusion that low tissue tension and loss of tissue elasticity contribute to the ease with which edema develops in cardiac patients.

Sodium chloride retention. — Clinicians have long been aware of the relation of sodium chloride intake to the formation of edema in congestive failure; recent physiologic studies have emphasized the importance of abnormal sodium chloride retention in this regard and also suggest that the latter is associated with abnormal renal tubule function (page 161), although other factors brought out by changes in posture (page 161) and intraabdominal pressure (page 211) must be borne in mind. In some cases the intake of relatively small amounts of sodium chloride seems to play a decisive role in the occurrence of edema; in most other instances it plays an important part also. A discussion of the problem by Peters (1948) is of interest.

Water retention. — Edema may be present in spite of a lowering of blood sodium concentration, suggesting that more water than salt may be retained (page 176). Indeed, edema may accumulate while the blood sodium level is being lowered by hypotonic infusions (Lombardo, 1953). When edema is lost during induced diuresis (pages 275 and 285) or as a consequence of bed rest (Miller, 1951), more water than salt usually is lost, again suggesting that more water than salt may be retained. However, the extensive derangements in electrolytic composition of the body present in failure and during diuresis require that caution be exhibited in the interpretation of the above phenomena. On the other hand, the role of antidiuretic substances in congestive failure may be important (page 177).

Capillary dilatation. — The widespread capillary dilatation found in decompensated cardiac patients increases the filtering surface area and enhances whatever tendency toward edema formation exists as a consequence of the action of other factors.

Alkalosis. — Alkalosis clinically is often associated with edema formation but it is extremely unlikely that the slight degree of alkalosis of the arterial blood that may occur in markedly dyspneic patients is important in the genesis of cardiac edema, particularly since the venous blood (and presumably, therefore, the tissues also) usually shows no such change in the direction of alkalinity.

Blood histamine. — Because the injection of histamine is known to cause edema, the possible role of that substance in edema formation in cardiac patients was studied by Barsoum and Smirk (1936). Although an increase in blood histamine was demonstrated in chronic cardiac decompensation by these authors, the fact that the increase is limited to the erythrocytes and not the plasma appears to rule it out as a factor in the elaboration of excessive amounts of tissue fluid in heart disease, in spite of the fact that stasis, anoxia, and exercise increase the blood histamine (Anrep *et al.*, 1944; Barsoum and Gaddum, 1935).

Conclusions. — A general conclusion based on all the foregoing considerations is that the edema of congestive failure is usually not due to the operation of any one factor. It is impossible to correlate with absolute agreement the presence of edema with changes in any one of the factors discussed. Extreme changes in a single factor, such as the venous pressure or plasma protein level, may in themselves result in the appearance of edema, but such extreme changes occur only uncommonly in uncomplicated congestive failure. It appears that the formation of cardiac edema in most patients is the result of the combination of submaximal or even minimal changes in many factors. The relative importance of each of the above-discussed factors unquestionably varies from patient to patient.

Bibliography

Chapter I — Section 32

ALTSCHULE, M. D., The pathological physiology of chronic cardiac decompensation, *Medicine* **17,** 75 (1938).

ALTSCHULE, M. D., and H. L. BLUMGART, The circulatory dynamics in tricuspid stenosis. Their significance in the pathogenesis of edema and orthopnea, *Am. Heart J.* **13,** 589 (1937).

ALTSCHULE, M. D., and E. BUDNITZ, Rheumatic disease of the tricuspid valve, *Arch. Path.* **30,** 7 (1940).

ALTSCHULE, M. D., and A. S. FREEDBERG, Circulation and respiration in fever, *Medicine* **24,** 403 (1945).

ALTSCHULE, M. D., A. IGLAUER, and N. ZAMCHECK, Respiration and circulation in patients with obstruction of the superior vena cava. Cerebral factors in dyspnea and orthopnea, *Arch. Int. Med.* **75,** 24 (1945).

ANREP, G. V., G. S. BARSOUM, S. SALAMA, and Z. SOUIDAN, Liberation of histamine during reactive hyperaemia and muscle contraction in man, *J. Physiol.* **103,** 297 (1944).

BARACH, A. L., and D. W. RICHARDS, JR., Effects of treatment with oxygen in cardiac failure, *Arch. Int. Med.* **48,** 325 (1931).

BARSOUM, G. S., and J. H. GADDUM, The liberation of histamine during reactive hyperemia, *J. Physiol.* **85,** 13 P (1935).

BARSOUM, G. S., and F. H. SMIRK, Observations on the histamine yielding substance in the plasma and red cells of normal human subjects and of patients with congestive heart failure, *Clin. Sc.* **2,** 337 (1936).

BEECHER, H. K., Adjustment of the flow of tissue fluid in the presence of localized, sustained high venous pressure as found with varices of the great saphenous system during walking, *J. Clin. Investigation* **16**, 733 (1937).

BUDELMANN, G., Untersuchungen über den Venendruck, die Vitalkapazität der Lunge und das Herzminutenvolumen bei Gesunden und Herzkranken in Ruhe und bei Kreislaufbelastung, *Ztschr. f. klin. Med.* **127**, 15 (1935).

DAUTREBANDE, L., H. W. DAVIES, and J. MEAKINS, The influence of circulatory changes on the gaseous exchanges of the blood. III. An experimental study of circulatory stasis, *Heart* **10**, 133 (1923).

DECAMP, P. T., J. A. WARD, and A. OCHSNER, Ambulatory venous pressure studies in postphlebitic and other disease states, *Surgery* **29**, 365 (1951).

DRURY, A. N., and N. W. JONES, Observations upon the rate at which edema forms when the veins of the human limb are congested, *Heart* **14**, 55 (1927).

DRYE, J. C., Intraperitoneal pressure in the human, *Surg., Gynec. & Obst.* **87**, 472 (1948).

ELLIS, L. B., R. A. BLOOMFIELD, G. K. GRAHAM, D. J. GREENBERG, H. N. HULTGREN, H. KRAUS, G. MARESH, J. G. MEBANE, P. H. PFIFFER, L. A. SELVERSTONE, and J. A. TAYLOR, Studies in mitral stenosis. I. The correlation of physiologic and clinical findings, *Arch. Int. Med.* **88**, 515 (1951).

FISHMAN, A. P., M. H. MAXWELL, C. H. CROWDER, and P. MORALES, Kidney function in cor pulmonale. Particular consideration of changes in renal hemodynamics and sodium excretion during variation in level of oxygenation, *Circulation* **3**, 703 (1951).

GESELL, R., Further observations on respiratory control, *Am. J. Physiol.* **85**, 373 (1928).

HENRY, J. P., and O. H. GAUER, The influence of temperature upon venous pressure in the foot, *J. Clin. Investigation* **29**, 855 (1950).

HENRY, J. P., J. GOODMAN, and J. P. MEEHAN, Effects of acute anoxia on the capillary permeability of the human arm, *Am. J. Med.* **2**, 657 (1947a).

HENRY, J., J. GOODMAN, and J. MEEHAN, Capillary permeability in relation to acute anoxia and to venous oxygen saturation, *J. Clin. Investigation* **26**, 1119 (1947b).

HENRY, J. P., I. KLAIN, E. MOVITT, and J. P. MEEHAN, The effects of anoxia on the capillary permeability of the human arm, *Federation Proc.* **5**, 44 (1946).

HICKAM, J. B., R. P. McCULLOCH, and R. J. REEVES, Normal and impaired function of the leg veins, *Am. Heart J.* **37**, 1017 (1948).

KEITH, A., Man's posture: its evolution and disorders, *Brit. M. J.* **1**, 624 (1923).

KROGH, A., *The Anatomy and Physiology of Capillaries* (Yale Univ. Press, New Haven, 1929), pp. 230, 332.

KROGH, A., E. M. LANDIS, and A. H. TURNER, The movement of fluid through the human capillary wall in relation to venous pressure and to the colloid osmotic pressure of the blood, *J. Clin. Investigation* **11**, 63 (1932).

LANDIS, E. M., Micro-injection studies of capillary permeability. III. The effect of lack of oxygen on the permeability of the capillary wall to fluid and to the plasma proteins, *Am. J. Physiol.* **83**, 528 (1928).

LANDIS, E. M., and J. H. GIBBON, JR., The effects of temperature and of tissue pressure on the movement of fluid through the human capillary wall, *J. Clin. Investigation* **12**, 105 (1933).

LANDIS, E. M., L. JONAS, M. ANGEVINE, and W. ERB, The passage of fluid and protein through the human capillary wall during venous congestion, *J. Clin. Investigation* **11**, 717 (1932).

LANGE, K., Capillary permeability in myxedema, *Am. J. M. Sc.* **208**, 5 (1944).

LOMBARDO, T. A., The effect of posture on the excretion of water and sodium by patients with congestive heart failure, *Circulation* **7**, 91 (1953).

MAURER, F. W., The effects of decreased blood oxygen and increased blood carbon dioxide on the flow and composition of cervical and cardiac lymph, *Am. J. Physiol.* **131**, 331 (1940).

McMICHAEL, J., and K. M. MORRIS, Acute oxygen lack and capillary permeability in man, *J. Physiol.* **87**, 74P (1936).

MENDE, Ueber Hyperämie und Oedem bei der Hemmung des Rückflusses des venösen Blutes durch die Staubinde, *Deutsche Ztschr. f. Chir.* **150**, 379 (1919).

MERRILL, A. J., Edema and decreased renal blood flow in patients with chronic congestive heart failure: evidence of "forward failure" as the primary cause of edema, *J. Clin. Investigation* **25**, 389 (1946).

MILLER, G. E., Water and electrolyte metabolism in congestive heart failure, *Circulation* **4**, 270 (1951).

NEWMAN, W., and L. FISHEL, Observations on the daily changes in venous pressure and weight in a case of chronic congestive heart failure, *Circulation* **1**, 706 (1950).

O'KEEFE, A. F., R. WARREN, and G. A. DONALDSON, Venous circulation in lower extremities following vein interruption, *Surgery* **29**, 267 (1951).

PAPPENHEIMER, J. R., and A. SOTO-RIVERA, Effective osmotic pressure of the plasma proteins and other quantities associated with the capillary circulation in the hind limbs of cats and dogs, *Am. J. Physiol.* **152**, 471 (1948).

PETERS, J. P., The role of sodium in the production of edema, *New England J. Med.* **239**, 353 (1948).

POLLACK, A. A., and E. H. WOOD, Venous pressure in the saphenous vein at the ankle in man during exercise and changes in posture, *J. Appl. Physiol.* **1**, 649 (1949).

POLLACK, A. A., B. E. TAYLOR, T. T. MYERS, and E. H. WOOD, The effect of exercise and body position on the venous pressure at the ankle in patients having venous valvular defects, *J. Clin. Investigation* **28**, 559 (1949).

REICHSMAN, F., and H. GRANT, Some observations on the pathogenesis of edema in cardiac failure, *Am. Heart J.* **32**, 438 (1946).

RICHARDS, D. W., JR., and A. L. BARACH, Prolonged residence in high oxygen atmospheres. Effects on normal individuals and on patients with chronic cardiac and pulmonary insufficiency, *Quart. J. Med.* **3**, 437 (1934).

RUNGE, H., Ueber den Venendruck in Schwangerschaft, Geburt und Wochenbett, *Arch. f. Gynäk.* **122**, 142 (1924).

SASLOW, G., The relation between the oxygenation of fluids and the occurrence of edema in the perfused frog web, *Am. J. Physiol.* **124**, 360 (1938).

SMIRK, F. H., Observations on the causes of œdema in congestive heart failure, *Clin. Sc.* **2**, 317 (1936).

STEAD, E. A., JR., and J. V. WARREN, The protein content of the extracellular fluid in normal subjects after venous congestion and in patients with cardiac failure, anoxemia and fever, *J. Clin. Investigation* **23**, 283 (1944).

THREEFOOT, H. K., The response of the venous pressure of man to a hot and humid environment, *Am. J. M. Sc.* **224**, 643 (1952).

WALKER, A. J., and C. J. LONGLAND, Venous pressure measurement in the foot in exercise as an aid to investigation of venous disease of the leg, *Clin. Sc.* **9**, 101 (1950).

WARREN, M. F., and C. K. DRINKER, The flow of lymph from the lungs of the dog, *Am. J. Physiol.* **136**, 207 (1942).

WARREN, M. F., D. K. PETERSON, and C. K. DRINKER, The effects of heightened negative pressure in the chest, together with further experiments upon anoxia in increasing the flow of lung lymph, *Am. J. Physiol.* **137**, 641 (1942).

WHITE, J. C., M. VERLOT, B. SELVERSTONE, and H. K. BEECHER, Changes in brain volume during anesthesia: the effects of anoxia and hypercapnia, *Arch. Surg.* **44**, 1 (1942).

WINSOR, T., and G. E. BURCH, Use of the phlebomanometer: normal venous pressure values and a study of certain clinical aspects of venous hypertension in man, *Am. Heart J.* **31**, 387 (1946).

33. *Cyanosis*

Some degree of cyanosis is commonly observed in chronic cardiac decompensation. Its onset frequently precedes that of edema and orthopnea, but only uncommonly that of dyspnea, except in the cases of some patients with congenital heart disease. Cyanosis may also appear relatively early in patients with marked prominence of the veins due to tricuspid valvular disease or concretio cordis. Its earliest manifestations consist of slight blueness in areas where the skin is thinnest, such as the nailbeds and the lips. When generalized, it is usually most marked over the extremities of the body, namely, fingers, toes, nose, earlobes and lips.

Lundsgaard and Van Slyke (1923) have defined the conditions under which cyanosis may occur. The factors of greatest importance in uncomplicated congestive failure are (i) abnormal deoxygenation of the blood present in the skin and (ii) the abnormal amount of blood in the skin. It has been demonstrated by these authors that the presence of unsaturated hemoglobin in a concentration of at least 5 Gm./100 cc. of blood is necessary for the occurrence of cyanosis. They also pointed out that the low blood hemoglobin concentration of severe anemia may prevent the appearance of cyanosis; conversely, the presence of polycythemia facilitates the development of cyanosis.

A high concentration of reduced hemoglobin can result from (i) lowering of the oxygen saturation before the blood reaches the tissues or (ii) extraction of abnormally large amounts of oxygen from the blood in the tissues.

Decreased arterial blood oxygen saturation. — Decreased arterial blood oxygen saturation consequent to inadequate aeration of the blood in the lungs is frequently found in congestive failure (page 100). Its importance in the genesis of cyanosis is shown by the lessening of cyanosis that follows the administration of air enriched with oxygen; accompanying this improvement is a return to or toward normal of the arterial blood oxygen saturation. In patients with chronic cardiac decompensation, however, relief of cyanosis resulting from oxygen therapy is frequently only partial; in addition the degree of cyanosis cannot be correlated exactly with the arterial oxygen saturation.

Increased deoxygenation of capillary blood. — Calculations of capillary unsaturation demonstrate that abnormally great deoxygenation of the capillary blood occurs in congestive failure as a result of a lowered cardiac output and consequent slowing of the peripheral blood flow (Meneely and Kaltreider, 1943). Studies on the venous blood show that concentrations of reduced hemoglobin well above 5 Gm./100 cc. of blood may occur (page 102), with the resultant appearance of cyanosis.

Capillary and venous dilatation. — The widespread capillary dilitation and increased prominence of the subpapillary venous plexus exhibited by patients with chronic cardiac decompensation exaggerate the degree of blueness present. Indeed, Goldschmidt and Light (1925) have shown that these phenomena when induced in normal individuals may in themselves cause cyanosis, even in the absence of abnormal blood gas values.

It is evident, therefore, that the cyanosis of congestive failure is due to a combination of factors. All factors operate in greater or lesser degrees in different patients, although the relative importance of each factor varies from patient to patient.

Bibliography

Chapter I — Section 33

GOLDSCHMIDT, S., and A. B. LIGHT, A cyanosis, unrelated to oxygen unsaturation, produced by increased peripheral venous pressure, *Am. J. Physiol.* **73**, 173 (1925).

LUNDSGAARD, C., and D. D. VAN SLYKE, Cyanosis, *Medicine* **2**, 1 (1923).

MENEELY, G. R., and N. L. KALTREIDER, A study of the volume of the blood in congestive heart failure. Relation to other measurements in fifteen patients, *J. Clin. Investigation* **22**, 521 (1943).

34. *Dyspnea*

In discussing dyspnea it is well to bear in mind certain general considerations as to the nature of this symptom. It cannot be emphasized too often that dyspnea is a sensation and as such is not amenable to objective measurement. There is, however, a general correlation between the symptom dyspnea and the sign hyperpnea, and the latter can be measured. On the other hand, marked differences in the degree of dyspnea which are consequent to changes in subjective sensitivity can occur in different patients in whom all physiological measurements are the same, or even at times in the same patient with relative constancy of the physical status. These facts necessarily make it difficult to evaluate accurately the significance of the physiological and chemical changes that lead to dyspnea. It must be borne in mind also that hyperpnea is a response to certain abnormalities in the physiologic or chemical status of the patient and that hyperpnea itself may cause compensatory changes in the opposite direction, so that deviations from the normal, observed, for instance, in the blood, may be negligible. In addition, hyperpnea may occur as a consequence of immeasurably small changes in the blood.

For the purposes of this discussion no attempt will be made to distinguish dyspnea at rest from dyspnea on exertion. The assumption will be made that similar factors are responsible for both, with the reservation, however, that the various mechanisms may be relatively more or less important in each type of dyspnea.

Tissue anoxia. — Much has been written in recent years regarding the greater responsiveness to anoxia of the peripheral chemoreceptors than of the medullary centers. This material is difficult to evaluate for a number of reasons. The precise localization and role of the centers that influence respiration is far from established, although the impulses that actually give rise to changes in respiratory rate and volume must obviously arise in the medullary centers. The latter may be influenced directly by changes in the composition of the blood, or by nervous impulses arising elsewhere. The sources of the latter impulses have not been completely studied. Although most of the work reported has involved the carotid and aortic bodies, there is evidence that other similar structures lie along the course of the pulmonary artery (Schmidt and Comroe, 1940) or other parts of the lung (Heymans and Heymans, 1927); on the other hand, Aviado *et al.* (1951) found no evidence of the functioning of such receptors. If all such bodies respond to changes in oxygen tension in the blood, it is apparent that the range of change for those bathed in arterial blood must be different from that which stimulates those bathed in venous blood. Thus the fact that significant arterial anoxia may be absent in many patients with congestive failure does not rule out stimulation of the respiratory center by means of impulses originating in bodies which may possibly lie along the pulmonary arterial tree, for blood traversing this portion of the circulatory system is almost uniformly abnormally deoxygenated in patients with cardiac decompensation.

Another difficulty regarding evaluation of the role of the peripheral chemoreceptors in man is that published conclusions are based on experiments done not on man but on another species, usually the dog, under anesthesia, which ordinarily depresses the sensitivity of medullary centers, thereby enhancing the relative importance of the peripheral receptors. These experiments on dogs involve extremely complicated and shocking preparations. Some of these difficulties have been emphasized by Schmidt and Comroe (1940) as follows:

Furthermore, as the reviewers know from personal experience, there is a psychological hazard in experiments like this which can easily lead to exaggeration of the value of an unusually favorable result, in the following manner: the preparation involves extensive dissection, ligation of vessels, artificial circulation, and numerous other factors, all operating in the direction of diminished effectiveness of the reflexes. The experimenter must be prepared to find that a certain proportion of such preparations will have inactive reflexes, and this he will (quite properly) ascribe to artifacts. In another (and larger) group, reflexes will be present, though of variable activity and in a third (perhaps quite small) group, they will be extremely active. It is natural to regard the most striking results as those to be expected in the absence of artifacts and to publish them as the closest approach to the normal state. Actually, however, the investigator can never know that to be the case; perhaps he was dealing with responses that are wholly exceptional, and, for all that he can tell, the less impressive results may really be closer to those to be expected in the average animal. Furthermore, as the experimenter's experience and skill increase, he incorporates in his technique various items and procedures which he has found helpful to bring out the desired result in maximum intensity; in so doing, he may remove the experimental conditions further and further from the normal state, but it is not easy to allow for this in drawing conclusions from experiments that represent a real masterpiece of technical proficiency.

These remarks are pertinent, for even the experiments by Bouckaert, Heymans and Samaan (1938), designed to show the primacy of the peripheral receptors in the respiratory response to anoxia, show that this response may occur when these receptors are denervated. It is not the purpose of this discussion to prove that the role of the peripheral receptors is negligible, or to derogate the work of Heymans and his co-workers who established its importance; the intent here is merely to indicate the invalidity of ascribing no role at all to the cranial centers. The experiments of Gemmill et al. (1934), Decharneux (1934), Gesell (1939), Moyer and Beecher (1942) and Davenport et al. (1943, 1947), performed largely on unanesthetized or only lightly anesthetized animals, suggest that denervation of all the known pathways from peripheral receptors does not eliminate hyperpnea consequent to anoxia; the medullary centers apparently are still important in this respect. Accordingly, because of all this uncertainty, it has been decided for the purposes of the present review to use the concept of anoxemia of the respiratory centers as including both the medullary centers and the peripheral receptors.

The role of anoxia in the causation of dyspnea has for many years been considered an important one. There is no need to review here the large amount of experimental work done in animals and normal man on which this conclusion is based. Even in normal man exercising at sea level the dyspnea and hyperventilation of exertion are considerably abated by breathing oxygen (Briggs, 1920; Hewlett et al., 1926; Asmussen and Nielsen, 1946; Nielsen and Hansen, 1937; Nielsen, 1936); a similar observation has been made in cardiac patients (page 91). It is, however, necessary to review the data bearing on the role of anoxia in the genesis of cardiac dyspnea because of attempts which have been made to negate their importance.

That anoxia of the tissues exists in congestive failure is shown by a large number of observations. These include evidence that the venous blood oxygen tension is low and that, therefore, the tissue oxygen tension must also be low. The few available measurements of tissue oxygen tension support this view. More specifically, the observations (page 221) that show a low concentration of oxygen in the jugular blood and a high jugular arteriovenous difference in most patients with cardiac dyspnea should be noted. It is pertinent to point out that slowing the cerebral circulation in animals leads to hyperpnea (Schmidt, 1928; Greeley and Greeley, 1930). Additional evidence is offered by the many observations proving the presence of increased blood lactate and pyruvate levels at rest, and more constantly and strikingly after exertion; similar significance is also to be attached to the impaired lactate tolerance and abnormally prolonged oxygen debt after exercise in patients with congestive failure. The fact that some decompensated patients store oxygen when exposed to air containing high concentrations of that gas is also pertinent. Finally, in some patients at least, a lowered arterial blood oxygen saturation points to tissue anoxia, particularly since cardiac patients do not exhibit the increase in circulation which is a normal compensatory mechanism for anoxic anoxia (page 101), indeed, decompensated cardiac patients are abnormally sensitive to oxygen lack (Graybiel et al., 1937; Landt and Benjamin, 1941). That degrees of anoxia such as commonly exist in patients with cardiac decompensation are of importance in the causation of dyspnea is shown by the response of such patients to the administration of air enriched with oxygen; in most instances there is an immediate and striking improvement in dyspnea. Clinical improvement under such circumstances is not consequent to an increase in cardiac output or a fall in venous pressure. The changes that occur in the venous blood oxygen tension after a variety of therapeutic measures are confirmatory evidence in that return toward normal of the venous blood oxygen tension is usually associated with improvement in dyspnea.

The objection has been raised that the hyperpnea of congestive failure could not be anoxic in origin, since anoxia in normal subjects or animals is not usually associated with shallow and very rapid respiration such as occurs in congestive failure. This objection is not valid for two reasons: (i) experimental anoxia is of short duration, and there are indications that more chronic anoxia, even in normal man, may give rise to rapid shallow breathing; (ii) the increased rigidity of the lungs in congestive failure prevents a normal increase in tidal air volume, so that the increased respiratory activity of anoxia in patients with this disorder is expressed largely as an increase in respiratory rate (Graybiel et al., 1937).

The many factors that act to cause tissue anoxia in chronic cardiac decompensation may be divided into two groups: (i) those that cause decreased delivery of blood to the tissues and (ii) those that result from pulmonary congestion. The latter act to cause a lowering of the arterial oxygen saturation by edema of the alveolar walls and by impairment of the bellows function of the lungs. Impairment of the mechanics of respiration is in turn an expression of various subsidiary factors (page 89). Shallow respiration consequent to increased pulmonary rigidity, together with poor mixing due to increased rigidity, impaired elasticity and inefficient respiration, lead to lessened arterialization of blood in the lungs. It appears reasonable to believe that the increased respiratory activity of congestive failure compensates to some extent for the effects of anoxia which otherwise might be more severe. However, this increased respiratory activity itself gives rise to dyspnea. Inability to increase the tidal air because of pulmonary rigidity may give rise to extreme tachypnea, which by itself may result in a lowering of arterial blood oxygen saturation. The high level of respiratory activity at rest, and the fact that increased pulmonary rigidity prevents normal increases in exertion, together limit respiratory reserve markedly.

Lactic acid metabolism. — One of the manifestations of tissue anoxia in cardiac patients is the occurrence of increased amounts of lactic acid in the blood at rest and, more consistently and markedly, after exertion. The accumulation of lactic acid in the blood, and presumably in tissues also, indicates a breakdown in the normal mechanisms involved in the oxidation of that substance. It is known that the brain itself produces lactic acid (McGinty, 1929), and there is evidence to indicate that interference with the normal rapid oxidative destruction of lactic acid produced in the respiratory center may be a fundamental cause of hyperpnea and dyspnea. Gesell (1925, 1928a, b) has elaborated this concept. In addition, the lactic acid formed in muscles that are exercised under anoxic conditions acts as a strong respiratory stimulant (Barman et al., 1942, 1943). Asmussen and Nielsen (1950) showed that blood trapped in the legs after work, if released as long as a quarter of an hour later, still causes hyperpnea, and that these effects are minimized by inhalation of oxygen. Even in normal subjects, lowering of blood lactate levels during exertion by means of inhalation of oxygen results in lessened hyperventilation (Hewlett et al., 1926; Asmussen and Nielsen, 1946). That lactic acid in the blood is a stronger respiratory stimulant than mineral acids is well known; a recent discussion of this matter by Rosenbaum (1942) emphasizes this difference and points out that lactic acid has a stronger action because it is rapidly diffusible across the cell membrane.

Changes in the lungs. — The increased pulmonary rigidity which decompensated patients show may by itself cause or aggravate dyspnea. The impaired expansibility which is consequent to increased rigidity makes inhalation more arduous, and the associated loss of pulmonary elasticity makes expiration more difficult. These effects cause dyspnea both in themselves and by giving rise to shallow and rapid respiration, which is inefficient. The impaired pulmonary expansibility becomes especially troublesome during exertion, where the normal response is a considerable increase in tidal air volume. The maximal possible respiration per minute is low in patients with cardiac decompensation and the elevated resting respiratory minute volume that results from inefficient respiration further encroaches on the respiratory reserve available for use during exertion.

Some authors refer all dyspnea in cardiac decompensation to the observable changes in pulmonary function. It is important to note, however, that some types of congestive heart failure are accompanied by little or no change in these functions, in spite of which dyspnea may be severe (Dresdale *et al.*, 1952).

Abnormal stimuli from the lungs. — It has been shown in experiments on animals that hyperpnea results from the activation of reflexes originating in the lungs. Intrapulmonary factors giving rise to stimuli that may activate these reflexes appear to be (i) abnormal rigidity of the lungs, which activates the Hering-Breuer reflex, and (ii) distention of pulmonary vessels, which activates the Churchill-Cope reflex (page 67). The nervous pathways involved in these reflexes are present in all individuals; in cardiac decompensation changes occur within the lungs, resulting in the transmission of afferent impulses to the brain which evoke a motor response, namely, hyperpnea. Perception by the patient of this increased respiratory activity may result in a sensation of dyspnea. There is no evidence to indicate that the congestive changes in the lungs result in dyspnea by giving rise to afferent impulses directly to the sensorium. Although reflex mechanisms have been demonstrated to be important in the manifestations of cardiac asthma (page 319), there are no data bearing on their significance in the dyspnea of chronic congestive failure. Although lowering of pulmonary vascular pressure was found by Fries *et al.* (1949) to be associated with relief of dyspnea in several patients in cardiac decompensation, no interpretation can be made of these results since a rise in cardiac output occurred at the same time.

Reflexes from the great veins. — The question of dyspnea, or at least hyperpnea, consequent to the stimulation of pressor receptors in the auricle or great vein, has been raised by Harrison *et al.* (1932*a, b*) and by Megibow *et al.* (1943). There is no conclusive evidence that the experiments described by these authors ruled out slowing of cerebral circulation when the right auricle or the great veins were distended. Moreover, in normal man, infusion intravenously of large amounts of fluid, so rapidly as to distend the veins and raise the venous pressure to levels found in congestive failure, does not cause dyspnea or hyperpnea (Altschule *et al.*, 1938, 1942; Warren *et al.*, 1948). It is not demonstrated that reflexes from this part of the circulatory system are implicated in the dyspnea and hyperpnea of cardiac decompensation.

Reflexes from other proprioceptors. — The question whether other proprioceptors, located in or near skeletal muscle, may be involved in the hyperventilation of exercise in normal conditions is still a matter of dispute (von Euler and Liljestrand, 1946). The contention of Harrison *et al.* (1932*a*) that these mechanisms are important in the genesis of cardiac dyspnea has little to support it; the fairly vigorous exercise that is required to bring out the phenomenon of hyperpnea precipitated by movement of a single extremity (Grandpierre *et al.*, 1951) is not often attainable in cardiac decompensation.

Tissue carbon dioxide. — Direct measurements of tissue carbon dioxide tension, though scanty, suggest that elevated levels occur (page 119). Although, in general, the venous blood carbon dioxide content is within normal limits in congestive failure, McMichael (1939) pointed out that many dyspneic cardiac patients have elevated jugular venous blood carbon dioxide tensions. A number of authors (page 76) have suggested that the low arterial blood carbon dioxide content and tension of cardiac decompensation constitute a compensatory mechanism to prevent accumulation of carbon dioxide in the tissues, particularly the brain, consequent to decreased flow. Lowering of arterial carbon dioxide content and tension is a conse-

quence of hyperventilation, which thereby masks the tendency toward accumulation of carbon dioxide in the tissues. It is possible,
therefore, that this tendency is a cause of hyperventilation and
dyspnea in congestive failure. It must be borne in mind that hypoxia
potentiates the effect of carbon dioxide on respiration (Nielsen and
Smith, 1952).

Impaired heat dispersal. — A cause of cardiac dyspnea that is
usually overlooked is alteration of the heat-dispersal mechanisms due
to a decreased blood flow through the skin. Observations on the occurrence of low skin temperatures in spite of high rectal temperatures
in cardiac decompensation strongly indicate the existence of this
factor (page 39). The hyperpnea that is a response to inability to
disperse normal amounts of heat via the skin in cardiac decompensation (page 40) must contribute to dyspnea. The fact that many

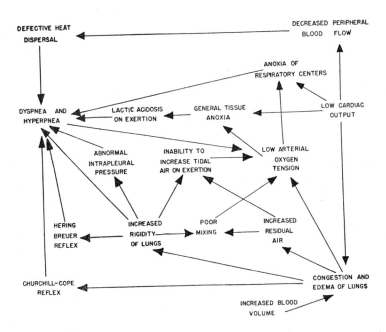

patients with severe decompensation claim to experience relief of
dyspnea as a result of removing bed clothes and being placed in front
of an open window is in harmony with this concept (Burch, 1946).

Increased blood volume. — The increase in blood volume that occurs in congestive failure results in an increase in the amount of blood in the lungs, thereby exaggerating the pulmonary congestion which is consequent to other factors. Diuresis, which decreases the blood volume and raises vital capacity (page 277), frequently results in a striking improvement in dyspnea. The possibility that at least part of the improvement following diuresis is due to dissipation of edema of the alveolar walls is also to be borne in mind.

Conclusions. — It is apparent that cardiac dyspnea, like the previously discussed cyanosis and edema, is a consequence of the operation of a multiplicity of factors. Figure 1 indicates how these factors are interrelated. The inability of various investigators to correlate in a convincing manner changes in a given physiological measurement with the degree of dyspnea is due not only to the fact that dyspnea is a sensation and, therefore, unmeasurable, but also to the fact that the importance of each factor in the production of dyspnea varies from patient to patient.

Bibliography

Chapter I — Section 34

ALTSCHULE, M. D., and D. R. GILLIGAN, The effects on the cardiovascular system of fluids administered intravenously in man. II. The dynamics of the circulation, *J. Clin. Investigation* **17,** 401 (1938).

ALTSCHULE, M. D., D. R. GILLIGAN, and N. ZAMCHECK, The effects on the cardiovascular system of fluids administered intravenously in man. IV. The lung volume and pulmonary dynamics, *J. Clin. Investigation* **21,** 365 (1942).

ASMUSSEN, E., and M. NIELSEN, Studies on the regulation of respiration in heavy work, *Acta physiol. Scandinav.* **12,** 171 (1946).

ASMUSSEN, E., and M. NIELSEN, The effect of auto-transfusion of "work-blood" on the pulmonary ventilation, *Acta physiol. Scandinav.* **20,** 79 (1950).

AVIADO, D. M., JR., T. H. LI, W. KALOW, C. F. SCHMIDT, G. L. TURNBULL, G. W. PESKIN, M. E. HESS, and A. J. WEISS, Respiratory and circulatory reflexes from the perfused heart and pulmonary circulation of the dog, *Am. J. Physiol.* **165,** 261 (1951).

BARMAN, J. M., M. F. MOREIRA, and F. CONSOLAZIO, Metabolic effects of local ischemia during muscular exercise, *Am. J. Physiol.* **138,** 20 (1942).

BARMAN, J. M., M. F. MOREIRA, and F. CONSOLAZIO, The effective stimulus for increased pulmonary ventilation during muscular exertion, *J. Clin. Investigation* **22,** 53 (1943).

BOUCKAERT, J. J., C. HEYMANS, and A. SAMAAN, The role of the carotid sinus and vagal chemoreceptors in the respiratory and vasomotor effects of hypoxaemia in anaesthetized and normal dogs, *J. Physiol.* **94,** 4P (1938).

BRIGGS, H., Physical exertion, fitness and breathing, *J. Physiol.* **54,** 292 (1920).

BURCH, G. E., Influence of variations in atmospheric temperature and humidity on the rates of water and heat loss from the respiratory tract of patients with congestive heart failure living in a subtropical climate, *Am. Heart J.* **32,** 191 (1946).

DAVENPORT, H. W., G. BREWER, A. H. CHAMBERS, and S. GOLDSCHMIDT, The respiratory reactions to hypoxia in dogs with deafferented carotid and aortic receptor areas, *Am. J. M. Sc.* **205,** 311 (1943).

DAVENPORT, H. W., G. BREWER, A. H. CHAMBERS, and S. GOLDSCHMIDT, The respiratory responses to anoxemia of unanesthetized dogs with chronically denervated aortic and carotid chemoreceptors and their causes, *Am. J. Physiol.* **148,** 406 (1947).

DECHARNEUX, G., L'influence de l'altitude sur la respiration de deux chiens privés de leurs sinus carotidiens, *Compt. rend. Soc. de biol.* **116,** 352 (1934).

DRESDALE, D. T., M. SCHULTZ, and R. J. MICHTOM, Primary pulmonary hypertension. I. Clinical and hemodynamic study, *Am. J. Med.* **11,** 686 (1951).

FRIES, E. D., J. R. STANTON, J. W. CULBERTSON, J. LITTER, M. H. HALPERIN, C. H. BURNETT, and R. W. WILKINS, The hemodynamic effects of hypotensive drugs in man. I. Veratrum viride, *J. Clin. Investigation* **28,** 353 (1949).

GEMMILL, C. L., E. M. K. GEILING, and D. L. REEVES, The respiratory effect of prolonged anoxemia in normal dogs before and after denervation of the carotid sinus, *Am. J. Physiol.* **109,** 709 (1934).

GESELL, R., The chemical regulation of respiration, *Physiol. Rev.* **5,** 551 (1925).

GESELL, R., Further observations on respiratory control. *Am. J. Physiol.* **85,** 373 (1928a).

GESELL, R., Regulation of pulmonary ventilation by acidity of blood, tissue fluids and tissue, *J. A. M. A.* **91,** 1256 (1928b).

GESELL, R., Respiration and its adjustments, *Annual Rev. Physiol.* **1,** 185 (1939).

GRANDPIERRE, R., C. FRANCK, and F. VIOLETTE, Hyperventilation provoquée par les mouvements passifs, *Compt. rend. Soc. de biol.* **145,** 1100 (1951).

GRAYBIEL, A., W. MISSIURO, D. B. DILL, and H. T. EDWARDS, Experimentally induced asphyxiation in cardiac patients, with especial reference to certain hazards in air travel and to the use of asphyxiation as a cardiac functional test, *J. Aviation Med.* **8,** 178 (1937).

GREELEY, C. E., and P. O. GREELEY, Circulatory changes during periodic ventilation with apneas produced by marked curtailment of blood flow to the brain, *Am. J. Physiol.* **95,** 382 (1930).

HARRISON, T. R., W. G. HARRISON, JR., J. A. CALHOUN, and J. P. MARSH, Congestive heart failure. XVII. The mechanism of dyspnea on exertion, *Arch. Int. Med.* **50,** 690 (1932a).

HARRISON, T. R., W. G. HARRISON, JR., and J. P. MARSH, Reflex stimulation of respiration from increase in venous pressure, *Am. J. Physiol.* **100,** 417 (1932b).

HEWLETT, A. W., G. D. BARNETT, and J. K. LEWIS, The effect of breathing oxygen-enriched air during exercise upon pulmonary ventilation and upon the lactic acid content of blood and urine, *J. Clin. Investigation* **3,** 317 (1926–27).

HEYMANS, J.-F., and C. HEYMANS, Stimulation et inhibition réflexes des mouvements respiratoires de la tête "isolée" du chien B dont le coeur-poumon "isolée" est perfusé par un chien C, *Compt. rend. Soc. de biol.* **95,** 1118 (1927).

LANDT, H., and J. E. BENJAMIN, Respiratory changes produced in the cardiac patient by rebreathing experiments as compared with those of the normal individual, *Am. Heart J.* **15,** 83 (1938).

LANDT, H., and J. E. BENJAMIN, Changes in the content of carbon dioxide in venous blood during rebreathing experiments. Comparison of change in persons with a normal heart and in patients with cardiac disease, *Arch. Int. Med.* **67,** 72 (1941).

McGINTY, D. A., The regulation of respiration. XXV. Variations in the lactic acid metabolism in the intact brain, *Am. J. Physiol.* **88,** 312 (1929).

MEGIBOW, R. S., L. N. KATZ, and M. FEINSTEIN, Kinetics of respiration in experimental pulmonary embolism, *Arch. Int. Med.* **71,** 536 (1943).

MOYER, C. A., and H. K. BEECHER, Central stimulation of respiration during hypoxia, *Am. J. Physiol.* **136,** 13 (1942).

NIELSEN, M., Untersuchungen über die Atemregulation beim Menschen, *Skandinav. Arch. f. Physiol.* **74,** *Supp.* 10, 85 (1936).

NIELSEN, M., and O. HANSEN, Maximale körperliche Arbeit bei Atmung O_2-reicher Luft, *Skandinav. Arch. f. Physiol.* **76,** 37 (1937).

NIELSEN, M., and H. SMITH, Studies on the regulation of respiration in

acute hypoxia. With an appendix on respiratory control during prolonged hypoxia, *Acta physiol. Scandinav.* **24,** 293 (1952).

ROSENBAUM, J. D., The influence of alterations in acid-base balance upon
transfers of carbon dioxide and bicarbonate in man. *J. Clin. Investigation* **21,** 735 (1942).

SCHMIDT, C. F., The influence of cerebral blood-flow on respiration. I.
The respiratory responses to changes in cerebral blood-flow, *Am. J.
Physiol.* **84,** 202 (1928).

SCHMIDT, C. F., and J. H. COMROE, JR., Functions of the carotid and
aortic bodies, *Physiol. Rev.* **20,** 115 (1940).

VON EULER, V. S., and G. LILJESTRAND, The regulation of respiration
during muscular work, *Acta physiol. Scandinav.* **12,** 268 (1946).

WARREN, J. V., E. S. BRANNON, H. S. WEENS, and E. A. STEAD, JR., Effect
of increasing the blood volume and right atrial pressure on the circulation of normal subjects by intravenous infusions, *Am. J. Med.* **4,**
193 (1948).

35. *Orthopnea*

Orthopnea, like dyspnea, is a symptom, and analysis of the pathogenesis of the former is subject to the same above-discussed limitations as the latter. Orthopnea has been classified clinically as "orthopnea of necessity" and "orthopnea of choice." These terms merely
distinguish degrees in the feeling of urgency to sit up experienced by
patients, that is, degrees of orthopnea itself. It is probable that a
better term than "orthopnea" is "dyspnea of recumbency." The
severity of orthopnea varies considerably from patient to patient,
although, in general, it parallels the severity of the degree of dyspnea.
The time of onset of the sensation of respiratory distress after lying
down varies a good deal; in some instances, the sensation appears
immediately and is unbearable from the start; in others, it appears
immediately but does not become unbearable for some minutes; in
still others, it may never become unbearable. The more severe degrees
of orthopnea are often associated with a rapid increase of cyanosis of
the face on lying down.

Changes in blood flow through the lungs. — Lindhard (1913) first
pointed out the decrease in minute volume blood flow through the
lungs of normal subjects when they pass from the lying to the sitting

or standing position. Many authors have since corroborated this observation (**57**). The apparently discrepant results of Grollman (1928) and of Schelling and Heinemeier (1933) are due to changes in oxygen consumption which mask the variations in arteriovenous oxygen difference, as Nylin (1934) pointed out. Wide variations in cardiac output with changes in position were noted in studies made with the ballistocardiograph (Starr, 1943; Starr and Rawson, 1941), but the accuracy of these results is questionable. All available data obtained by reliable methods show that in normal individuals the cardiac output relative to oxygen consumption is largest in recumbency, intermediate sitting, and smallest standing. A. V. Bock and his co-workers (Field and Bock, 1925; Lawrence, *et al.*, 1927) and Nielsen (1936) regarded the changes that occur in cardiac output when the patient moves from the sitting to the recumbent position as of importance in the genesis of orthopnea, since an increased flow through the lungs in recumbency might cause congestion. The earlier observations (Bielschowsky, 1932; Bock, 1934; Lawrence *et al.*, 1927; Mobitz, 1927; Nielsen, 1936) of the effects of changes in posture on the output of the heart in cardiac subjects are fragmentary and difficult to interpret, because many of the patients had only mild failure and some are not described in sufficient detail to permit analysis. However, the more recent experiments of Goldbloom *et al.* (1940) and McMichael (1938a, b) in patients with moderate or severe failure show that the normal changes do not occur, as is possibly to be expected from the known decreased responsiveness of the cardiac output of patients with congestive failure to other stimuli. Accordingly, it is concluded that the shift in position from sitting to lying does not cause increased blood flow through the lungs. *This conclusion has no bearing on the relief of dyspnea due to the changes that result from prolonged still-standing, or sitting with legs hanging.*

Redistribution of blood. — Although increase in the flow of blood through the lungs does not appear to be a factor in the genesis of orthopnea in cardiac patients, it is possible that the shift of blood into the trunk that occurs when a person changes from the sitting to the recumbent position may cause a brief sensation of discomfort; that such redistributions of blood do occur with changes in position seems to be established. Indeed, Lagerlöf *et al.* (1951) have shown that sitting on a tilt-table with legs dangling results in a fall in peripheral venous and pulmonary arterial and capillary pressures with a decrease also in pulmonary blood volume. Kjellberg et al. (1951) showed that still-standing makes the lungs more radiotranslucent in normal subjects. These changes have been suggested as the cause of dyspnea of recumbency. Mills (1944) has shown that the reëntry into the circulation of blood released from an occluded extremity causes brief hyperpnea in normal individuals, and Mackay (1943) reported a sense of suffocation under such circumstances. Mills (1944) concluded that this phenomenon was a consequence of stimulation of pressor receptors in the pulmonary arterial tree, but his experiments are far from conclusive in this regard.

That chemical factors rather than stimulation of pressor receptors account for the hyperpnea and dyspnea occurring after the release of occluded blood is suggested by several observations: large intravenous infusions do not cause dyspnea or hyperpnea (Altschule et al., 1938, 1942; Doyle et al., 1951); increased respiration following stimulation of pressor receptors should lower the carbon dioxide content of alveolar air, but the release of occluded blood from an extremity is followed by a significant rise in alveolar air carbon dioxide (Mackay, 1943). At any rate, the hyperpnea that may result from redistribution of blood with a shift in position is very brief in duration and wears off as soon as the relatively small excess volume of blood carried to the lungs at one time is redistributed among the thoracic viscera and muscles, the head and neck and the arms. It does not seem to be an important factor, for reproducing it by heavy pressure on the engorged liver of congestive failure does not cause dyspnea.

Increased pulmonary congestion. — The frequent association of orthopnea and pulmonary congestion has properly led many authors to regard congestion of the lungs as an important factor in the genesis of dyspnea in the recumbent position. There has, however, been no general agreement regarding the mechanism whereby pulmonary congestion induces or exaggerates dyspnea in recumbency. A number of authors have stated that dyspnea of recumbency results from increased pulmonary congestion in the recumbent position, consequent to a shift of blood from the lower part of the body (Hill, 1895), pressure on (Reid, 1940) or unfavorable hydrostatic relations within (Dock, 1935) the pulmonary veins, kinking of the pulmonary vessels (Rubow, 1909), or an increase in the volume flow of blood through the lungs in the recumbent position (Field and Bock, 1925; Lawrence *et al.*, 1927; Nielsen, 1936). The last-named cause appears to be ruled out (page 176).

The increase in pulmonary congestion by one or more of these factors is believed to induce the dyspnea of recumbency, either by influencing adversely the respiratory exchange (Dock, 1935), by activating reflexes initiated by changes in the parenchyma or blood vessels of the lungs (Dock, 1935; Christie, 1938; Field and Bock, 1925), or by causing increased rigidity of the lungs (Dock, 1935; Christie, 1938). Calhoun *et al.* (1931) and Christie and Beams (1923) found abnormally large decreases in vital capacity in orthopneic patients when the recumbent position was assumed; the findings of the latter are difficult to evaluate, since nonorthopneic patients with congestive failure showed little or no decrease in vital capacity under these circumstances. Harrison's (1933) data are not in agreement with the latter finding.

This point was recently reinvestigated (Altschule *et al.*, 1943) by studying the pattern of changes in the subdivisions of the lung volume in recumbent cardiac patients. Congestion of the lungs causes a characteristic change in the relations between various components of the lung volume (page 53): the vital and total capacities are greatly reduced because of corresponding changes in the complemental and reserve airs, and the residual air is somewhat increased. The residual and functional residual air volumes are greatly increased relative to the total lung volume. It was felt that a further change in this direction should be detectable if increasing pulmonary congestion occurred on lying down. On the other hand, if no increase in congestion of the lungs occurred in cardiac patients who changed from the sitting to the recumbent position, they would show only the changes associated with recumbency, that is, small decreases in vital and total capacity, diminution in reserve and functional residual airs, no change in residual air, and an increase in complemental air (58; McMichael and McGibbon, 1939). Both orthopneic and nonorthopneic patients with heart disease showed changes which, though smaller, were qualitatively the same as those that occur in normal subjects. Accordingly, it was concluded (Altschule *et al.*, 1943) that no measurable change in the degree of pulmonary congestion occurred when the orthopneic or nonorthopneic cardiac patient lay down.

It should be noted that Livingstone (1928) many years ago found the same changes with variation in posture in the lungs of orthopneic cardiacs as in normal subjects. McMichael (1938*b*) reported a marked decrease in lung volume in one orthopneic patient on lying down; this was associated with decreases in reserve air and vital capacity and an increase in complemental air, similar in magnitude to those observed by Altschule *et al.* (1943). McMichael's (1938*b*) finding of a decrease of 50 per cent in the residual air in recumbency suggests some gross error in its measurement, as does the fact that the ratio of functional residual air to total capacity in his patient, which was definitely abnormal in the sitting position, became quite normal in recumbency. Accordingly, his conclusion that an increase in pulmonary congestion occurred in recumbency in that patient cannot be accepted.

Kelley *et al.* (1953) found that orthopnea might disappear although the vital capacity remained unchanged. Wade *et al.* (1952) found no relation between orthopnea and pulmonary circulatory dynamics in some patients. Hamilton and Morgan (1932), Hamilton and Mayo (1944), Dow (1939), Mackay (1943), Mills (1949), and Campbell and Harvey (1948) felt that the changes in vital capacity that occur in recumbency in normal subjects are due to an increase in the amount of blood in the lungs. However, their conclusions, based on the fact that placing tourniquets on all the extremities resulted in increases in vital capacity of only 3 to 11 per cent, must be considered too sweeping, particularly since they present no analysis of the pattern of changes in the subdivisions of the lung volume in their studies. The fact that application of tourniquets changes the vital capacity slightly, or prevents some of the postural changes, surely does not prove that the changes in lung volume are due to shifts in the distribution of blood in the main. Moreover, the finding of Osler (1950) that 10 minutes after lying down about half of the change in vital capacity disappears with no change in reserve (supplemental) air, should direct attention toward phenomena other than redistribution of blood as responsible for the slight lowering of vital capacity in recumbency. Previous discussion (page 79) relative to the minor influence of pulmonary blood volume on vital capacity is also pertinent.

Changes in respiratory dynamics. — Although no increase in pulmonary congestion in recumbency has been demonstrated, it is not to be concluded that changes in pulmonary dynamics in that position are unrelated to the genesis of orthopnea. The decrease in reserve air and increase in complemental air in recumbency in normal subjects were shown by McMichael and McGibbon (1939) to be caused by a cephalad shift of the diaphragm, due presumably to the pressure of the abdominal viscera; this study confirmed the earlier work of Haldane *et al.* (1919) and of Livingstone (1928). The occurrence of similar changes in recumbency in congestive failure also appears to be due to a shift in the diaphragm. Thus, forcing the diaphragm upward by application of an upper abdominal binder in cardiac subjects in the sitting position caused approximately the same decrease in reserve air, without change in the residual air, as did assuming the recumbent position (Altschule *et al.*, 1943). The increase in complemental air that occurs on lying down could not always be reproduced in these experiments by the application of the upper abdominal binder, which, in contrast to the abdominal viscera, is inelastic and prevents full expansion of the lungs. It is worthy of note that the application of the abdominal binder made the patients, normally comfortable when sitting, dyspneic in that position and increased their respiratory minute volumes. It is to be concluded, therefore, that a cephalad shift of the diaphragm, which occurs in recumbency and is due to pressure of the abdominal viscera, is responsible in part for orthopnea.

Other authors have shown that the shift in the level of the diaphragm in recumbency results in a decrease in the volume of the functional residual air (Christie and McIntosh, 1934) and an associated lessening of the negativity of the intrapleural pressure in that position (Aron, 1891, 1900; Christie and McIntosh, 1934; Prinzmetal and Kountz, 1934, 1935). The intrapleural pressure in patients with congestive failure is, however, less negative than normal and may be positive during expiration, even in the sitting position (Christie and McIntosh, 1934); further changes in this direction cause increased respiratory embarrassment and inefficiency. The claim of Prinzmetal and Kountz (1934) that changes in intrapleural pressure in orthopneic patients are greater than in normal subjects with shifts in position is not supported by the data they presented.

Impaired respiratory function is probably the cause of the smaller tidal volumes in recumbency, as compared to the sitting position, in a majority of orthopneic cardiac patients noted by Calhoun *et al.* (1931) and also by others (Altschule *et al.*, 1943). A decrease in tidal air volume in recumbency favors less complete aeration of blood passing through the lungs. On the other hand, the relatively small decreases in lung volume and its subdivisions that occur when orthopneic patients lie down indicate that decrease of space available for breathing does not cause orthopnea, as Christie and Beams (1923) and Calhoun *et al.* (1931) believed.

When normal subjects change from the sitting to the lying position, respiration is often slowed and the tidal air increases. If this increase in tidal air cannot occur, even normal subjects may develop evidence of anoxemia (Haldane *et al.*, 1919). It is, therefore, not surprising that increased dyspnea occurs in many patients with congestive failure in recumbency, since the increased rigidity of their lungs (page 53) makes it difficult to augment the tidal air, and the aforementioned respiratory inefficiency in recumbency may actually result in a decrease in tidal volume. Lower levels of arterial blood oxygen saturation in the recumbent position, as compared to the sitting position, have been reported by Calhoun *et al.* (1931) in patients with congestive failure. These authors reported arterial blood oxygen saturations of 88.6 to 94.0 per cent in the recumbent position in seven orthopneic cardiac patients, without associated pulmonary disease; these levels increased to 93.5 to 98.6 per cent in the upright position in six of the seven cases, the increases ranging between 0.6 and 8.1 per cent. In some instances a considerable rise in respiratory rate may occur in recumbency, possibly as a consequence of anoxia, and this increase in respiratory activity may increase the severity of dyspnea. In addition to all these factors there appears to be a greater ease of movement in the upright position, which contributes to the genesis of orthopnea.

Recumbency causes qualitatively the same changes in the respiratory dynamics in normal subjects as it does in patients with congestive failure; indeed, the changes in normal subjects are considerably greater than in patients with congestive failure. Nevertheless, orthopnea does not occur in the former and is frequently observed in the latter. Neither the nature of the postural changes in pulmonary dynamics nor their magnitude appears to be responsible for orthopnea in patients with pulmonary congestion. Rather, it is the state of respiration and circulation at the time these changes occur which is important in the genesis of orthopnea.

Changes in cerebral blood flow. — Ernstene and Blumgart (1930) stressed the importance of changes in cerebral blood flow in the genesis of orthopnea. They correlated level of venous pressure with degree of orthopnea and concluded that venous engorgement in the brain might be relieved by sitting up; measurements of jugular pressure by Myerson and Loman (1932) and Scheinberg (1949) corroborate this conclusion. Of great importance in this connection are the observations (page 47) that have demonstrated that while the venous pressure remained unchanged in normal subjects who moved from the recumbent to the sitting position, the pressure in the veins fell in cardiac patients with this shift in posture. In addition, the data of other authors also show that, even in patients with low vital capacities, factors operating outside of the lungs are significant in the genesis of orthopnea. The data of Robb and Weiss (1934) show that, for a given ratio of vital capacity to body surface, patients with peripheral signs of congestive failure, including elevation of the venous pressure, generally exhibit more severe orthopnea than do patients with no peripheral signs of congestive failure and normal venous pressure. The data of Howard and Leathart (1951) also relate orthopnea to high venous pressures. Ernstene and Blumgart (1930) pointed out that when orthopneic cardiac patients who are recumbent merely flex the neck forward, orthopnea may be relieved; this maneuver does not change the vital capacity, but does raise the level of the medullary centers with respect to the auricle and facilitates venous drainage. These observations have been corroborated by Calhoun *et al.* (1931) and by Battro and Labourt (1943); the last named also showed that flexing the head forward lowered the respiratory minute volume and did not change the vital capacity.

Altschule and Blumgart (1937) studied a patient with marked engorgement of the face and scalp veins due to tricuspid stenosis. It was found that positions in which collapse of the engorged veins over the face and scalp occurred were associated with relief of orthopnea. whereas engorgement of these veins was always associated with the presence of that symptom. Many authors have reported the occurrence of orthopnea in patients with superior caval obstruction; a recent study (Altschule *et al.*, 1945) of this disorder again stresses the role of venous stasis in causing orthopnea. Calhoun *et al.* (1931) found increased respiration in normal and cardiac patients with tourniquets about their necks, but respiratory distress did not occur; it is possible that any dyspnea that occurred may have been subordinated to other discomforts brought on by this procedure.

An argument advanced against acceptance of the importance of changes in cerebral flow in the causation of dyspnea is the fact that normal subjects do not experience that symptom in the head-down position; actually, however, they do hyperventilate sufficiently to lower the alveolar carbon dioxide content (Donal *et al.*, 1934). The validity of this argument is further weakened by the fact that normal persons develop severe respiratory distress when even minimal exertion is attempted in the head-down position (Donal *et al.*, 1934). Relief of orthopnea often occurs after procedures that lower venous pressure, such as venesection (page 227) and administration of diuretics (page 196), are instituted; these phenomena cannot, however, be interpreted, since favorable changes also occur in the lungs and in spinal fluid pressure under these circumstances.

Cerebral venous engorgement appears to be a factor responsible for orthopnea. However, it does not cause orthopnea unless other factors are also operating. The need for additional data bearing on this matter is evident. The study of Scheinberg (1949) on changes in cerebral circulatory dynamics in the upright position and of Shenkin *et al.* (1948) on the effect of elevation of the head were made only on normal subjects and cannot be applied to patients with congestive failure without reservations.

Changes in cerebrospinal fluid pressure. — Increased cerebral venous pressure results in an elevation of cerebrospinal fluid pressure (page 49). Harrison (1933) has expressed the view that this increase in spinal fluid pressure is a primary factor in the genesis of orthopnea, since lumbar puncture relieves the symptom for a time. It is possible that the relief of dyspnea and orthopnea which occurs after removal of spinal fluid is a consequence of a temporary increase in local blood flow related to lowering of intracranial pressure; elevation of spinal fluid pressure is known to slow the cerebral circulation and cause other circulatory changes (page 74).

Mechanical factors. — It is more than likely that mechanical factors are of some importance as causes of orthopnea. The pressure of abdominal viscera, or ascites, or both, on the diaphragm when the patient is recumbent may interfere with its movement to some degree. The occurrence of orthopnea in patients with ascites due to other causes, such as cirrhosis or neoplasm, favors this view. The somewhat greater ease of thoracic movement in the upright position may be important, but is not by itself sufficient to explain orthopnea.

Peripheral blood flow. — The observations of Brigden and Sharpey-Schafer (1950) that orthopneic cardiac patients do not exhibit the vasoconstriction seen normally in the upright position is of interest but has no evident bearing on the problem of orthopnea.

Possible disadvantages of the upright position. — Several observations suggest that in some degree recumbency may be advantageous in patients with congestive failure. Deep breathing causes a much greater increase in venous return in the upright position (Armitage and Arnott, 1949), a factor that might possibly increase pulmonary congestion. The respiratory dead space is lower in recumbency (Fowler, 1950), a phenomenon that would tend to make respiration somewhat more efficient. It is probable that these phenomena cause effects that are small compared to those that result in relief of dyspnea when the patient sits up.

Conclusions. — It appears to be valid to regard orthopnea as a consequence of the combined action of a number of factors; additional factors may be present but still unrecognized. The occurrence of orthopnea, although influenced profoundly by the above-discussed factors, is conditioned by fundamental changes due to congestive failure. These are (i) increased venous and spinal fluid pressure and (ii) increased rigidity of the lungs and lessened negativity of the intrapleural pressure. It is apparent, therefore, that more marked myocardial insufficiency, or an exaggeration of (i) or (ii) not due to increased failure of the heart, must result in more severe orthopnea as long as the patient remains conscious. Conversely, the relief of orthopnea may be a consequence of improved cardiac function or it may occur as a result of lowered venous or spinal fluid pressures or lessened rigidity of the lungs, independent of changes in cardiac function.

Bibliography

Chapter I — Section 35

ALTSCHULE, M. D., and H. L. BLUMGART, The circulatory dynamics in tricuspid stenosis. Their significance in the pathogenesis of edema and orthopnea, *Am. Heart J.* **13,** 589 (1937).

ALTSCHULE, M. D., and D. R. GILLIGAN, The effects on the cardiovascular system of fluids administered intravenously in man. II. The dynamics of the circulation, *J. Clin. Investigation* **17,** 401 (1938).

ALTSCHULE, M. D., D. R. GILLIGAN, and N. ZAMCHECK, The effects on the cardiovascular system of fluids administered intravenously in man. IV. The lung volume and pulmonary dynamics, *J. Clin. Investigation* **21,** 365 (1942).

ALTSCHULE, M. D., A. IGLAUER, and N. ZAMCHECK, Respiration and circulation in patients with obstruction of the superior vena cava. Cerebral factors in dyspnea and orthopnea, *Arch. Int. Med.* **75,** 24 (1945).

ALTSCHULE, M. D., N. ZAMCHECK, and A. IGLAUER, The lung volume and its subdivisions in the upright and recumbent positions in patients with congestive failure. Pulmonary factors in the genesis of orthopnea. *J. Clin. Investigation* **22,** 805 (1943). [58

ANTHONY, A. J., Untersuchungen über Lungenvolumina und Lugenventilation, *Deutsches Arch. f. klin. Med.* **167,** 129 (1930). [58

ARMITAGE, G. H., and W. M. ARNOTT, Effect of voluntary hyperpnoea on pulmonary blood flow, *J. Physiol.* **109,** 65 (1949).

ARON, E., Ueber einen Versuch, den intrapleuralen Druck am lebenden Menschen zu messen, *Virchows Arch. f. path. Anat.* **126,** 517 (1891).

ARON, E., Der intrapleurale Druck beim lebenden gesunden Menschen, *Virchows Arch. f. path. Anat.* **160,** 226 (1900).

ASMUSSEN, E., E. H. CHRISTENSEN, and M. NIELSEN, The regulation of circulation in different postures, *Surgery* **8,** 604 (1940). [57

BATTRO, A., and F. E. LABOURT, Consideraciones sobre la determinacion de la ventilacion maxima, la reserva pulmonar y la hiperpnea de los cardiacos, *Rev. argent. de cardiol.* **10,** 83 (1943).

BAZETT, H. C., F. S. COTTON, L. B. LAPLACE, and J. C. SCOTT, The calculation of cardiac output and effective peripheral resistance from blood pressure measurements, with an appendix on the size of the aorta in man, *Am. J. Physiol.* **113,** 312 (1935). [57

BIELSCHOWSKY, P., Ueber den Einfluss des Lagewechsels, insbesondere der Beinhochlagerung auf das Minutenvolumen des Herzens bei gesunden und kranken Menschen, *Klin. Wchnschr.* **11,** 1252 (1932). [57

BOCK, H. E., Das Minutenvolumen des Herzens im Liegen und Stehen, *Ztschr. f. d. ges. exper. Med.* **92,** 782 (1934). [57

CHRONIC CARDIAC DECOMPENSATION

BÖHME, M., Untersuchungen über Kreislauf und Atmung bei verschiedenen Körperhaltungen, *Ztschr. f. Kreislaufforsch.* **29,** 657 (1937). [57

BOHR, C., Die funktionellen Änderungen in der Mittelage und Vitalkapazität der Lungen. Normales und pathologisches Emphysem, *Deutsches Arch. f. klin. Med.* **88,** 305 (1906–07). [58

BRIGDEN, W., and E. P. SHARPEY-SCHAFER, Postural changes in peripheral blood flow in cases with left heart failure, *Clin. Sc.* **9,** 93 (1950).

CALHOUN, J. A., G. E. CULLEN, T. R. HARRISON, W. L. WILKINS, and M. M. TIMS, Studies in congestive heart failure. XIV. Orthopnea: its relation to ventilation, vital capacity, oxygen saturation and acid-base condition of arterial and jugular blood. *J. Clin. Investigation* **10,** 833 (1931). [58

CAMPBELL, G. S., and R. B. HARVEY, Postural changes in vital capacity with differential cuff pressures at the bases of the extremities, *Am. J. Physiol.* **152** 671 (1948).

CHRISTIE, C. D., and A. J. BEAMS, The estimation of normal vital capacity, with especial reference to the effect of posture, *Arch. Int. Med.* **30,** 34 (1922). [58

CHRISTIE, C. D., and A. J. BEAMS, Orthopnea, *Arch. Int. Med.* **31,** 85 (1923). [58

CHRISTIE, R. V., Dyspnoea: a review, *Quart. J. Med.* **31,** 421 (1938).

CHRISTIE, R. V., and C. A. McINTOSH, The measurement of the intrapleural pressure in man and its significance, *J. Clin. Investigation* **13,** 279 (1934).

COLLET, M. E., and G. LILJESTRAND, Variations in the resting minute volume of the heart in man, *Skandinav. Arch. f. Physiol.* **45,** 17 (1924). [57

DAVIES, H. W., and A. R. GILCHRIST, Observations upon the circulation rate in man by the ethyl iodide method, *Quart. J. Med.* **20,** 245 (1927). [57

DOCK, W., The anatomical and hydrostatic basis of orthopnea and of right hydrothorax in cardiac failure, *Am. Heart J.* **10,** 1047 (1934–35).

DONAL, J. S. JR., C. J. GAMBLE, and R. SHAW, The cardiac output in man. An adaptation of the katharometer for the rapid determination of ethyl iodide in estimations of cardiac output by the ethyl iodide method. A study of the effect of posture upon cardiac output and other circulatory and respiratory measurements, *Am. J. Physiol.* **109,** 666 (1934). [57

DOW, P., The venous return as a factor affecting the vital capacity, *Am. J. Physiol.* **127,** 793 (1939).

DOYLE, J. T., J. S. WILSON, E. H. ESTES, and J. V. WARREN, The effect of intravenous infusions of physiologic saline solution on the pulmonary arterial and pulmonary capillary pressure in man, *J. Clin. Investigation* **30**, 345 (1951).

ERNSTENE, A. C., and H. L. BLUMGART, Orthopnea. Its relation to the increased venous pressure of myocardial failure, *Arch. Int. Med.* **45**, 593 (1930).

FIELD, H. JR., and A. V. BOCK, Orthopnea and the effect of posture upon the rate of blood flow, *J. Clin. Investigation* **2**, 67 (1925–26). [57

FISHER, I. L., Das Schlag- und Minutenvolumen des menschlichen Herzens bei verschiedenen Körperstellungen, *Arbeitsphysiol.* **6**, 111 (1933). [57

FOWLER, W. S., Lung function studies. IV. Postural changes in respiratory dead space and in functional residual capacity, *J. Clin. Investigation* **29**, 1437 (1950). [58

GLADSTONE, S. A., Effect of posture and prolonged rest on the cardiac output and related functions, *Am. J. Physiol.* **112**, 705 (1935). [57

GOLDBLOOM, A. A., M. L. KRAMER, and A. LIEBERSON, Clinical studies in circulatory adjustments. VI. Physiologic relation between posture and cardiac output, *Arch. Int. Med.* **65**, 178 (1940). [57

GROLLMAN, A., The effect of variation in posture on the output of the human heart, *Am. J. Physiol.* **86**, 285 (1928).

HALDANE, J. S., J. C. MEAKINS, and J. G. PRIESTLEY, The effects of shallow breathing, *J. Physiol.* **52**, 433 (1919).

HAMILTON, W. F., and J. P. MAYO, Changes in the vital capacity when the body is immersed in water, *Am. J. Physiol.* **141**, 51 (1944).

HAMILTON, W. F., and A. B. MORGAN, Mechanism of the postural reduction in vital capacity in relation to orthopnea and storage of blood in the lungs, *Am. J. Physiol.*, **99**, 526 (1932). [58

HARRISON, W. G., JR., The cisternal pressure in congestive heart failure and its bearing on orthopnea, *J. Clin. Investigation* **12**, 1075 (1933).

HASSELBALCH, K. A., Ueber die Totalkapazität der Lungen, *Deutsches Arch. f. klin. Med.* **93**, 64 (1908). [58

HILL, L., The influence of the force of gravity on the circulation of the blood, *J. Physiol.* **18**, 15 (1895).

HITCHCOCK, F. A., and J. K. W. FERGUSON, Respiratory and circulatory adjustments to the erect posture, *Am. J. Physiol.* **124**, 457 (1938). [58

HOWARD, P., and G. L. LEATHART, Changes of pulse pressure and heart rate induced by changes of posture in subjects with normal and failing hearts, *Clin. Sc.* **10**, 521 (1951).

HURTADO, A., and W. W. FRAY, Studies of total pulmonary capacity and its subdivisions. III. Changes with body posture, *J. Clin. Investigation* **12**, 825 (1933). [58

KELLEY, R. T., E. D. FRIES, and T. F. HIGGINS, The effects of hexamethonium on certain manifestations of congestive heart failure, *Circulation* **7**, 169 (1953).

KJELLBERG, S. R., J. RUDHE, and T. SJÖSTRAND, The relationship between the pulmonary blood content, the heart volume and the filling rate of the left ventricle, *Acta physiol. Scandinav.* **24**, 49 (1951).

KROETZ, C., Messung des Kreislaufminutenvolumens mit Acetylen als Fremdgas. Ihre bisherigen Ergebnisse bei arteriellen Hochdruck und bei Dekompensation des Kreislaufs, *Klin. Wchnschr.* **9**, 966 (1930). [57

LAGERLÖF, H., H. ELIASCH, L. WERKÖ, and E. BERGLUND, Orthostatic changes of the pulmonary and peripheral circulation in man. A preliminary report, *Scandinav. J. Clin. & Lab. Investigation* **3**, 85 (1951). [57

LAWRENCE, J. S., L. M. HURXTHAL, and A. V. BOCK, Variations in blood flow with changes in position in normal and pathologic subjects, *J. Clin. Investigation* **3**, 613 (1926–27). [57, 58

LINDHARD, J., Effect of posture on the output of the heart, *Skandinav. Arch. f. Physiol.* **30**, 395 (1913). [57

LIVINGSTONE, J. L., Variations in the volume of the chest with changes of posture, *Lancet* **1**, 754 (1928). [58

MACKAY, I. F. S., The influence of posture on the pulmonary blood volume and the alveolar gas tensions, *J. Physiol.* **102**, 228 (1943).

MCMICHAEL, J., Postural changes in cardiac output and respiration in man, *Quart. J. Exper. Physiol.* **27**, 55 (1937). [57

MCMICHAEL, J., The output of the heart in congestive failure, *Quart. J. Med.* **7**, 331 (1938a).

MCMICHAEL, J., The significance of cardiac venous congestion, *Tr. Med.-Chir. Soc. Edinburgh* (1938b), p. 161.

MCMICHAEL, J., and J. P. MCGIBBON, Postural changes in the lung volume, *Clin. Sc.* **4**, 175 (1939). [58

MCMICHAEL, J., and E. P. SHARPEY-SCHAFER, Cardiac output in man by a direct Fick method. Effects of posture, venous pressure change, atropine and adrenaline, *Brit. Heart J.* **6**, 33 (1944). [57

MILLS, J. N., Hyperpnoea in man produced by sudden release of occluded blood, *J. Physiol.* **103**, 244 (1944).

MILLS, J. N., The influence upon the vital capacity of procedures calculated to alter the volume of blood in the lungs, *J. Physiol.* **110**, 207 (1949). [58

MOBITZ, W., Die Ermittlung des Herzschlagvolumens des Menschen durch Einatmung von Aethyljodiddampf. III. Konstanz der Ergebnisse und Werte beim Gesunden, *Ztschr. f. Kreislaufarsch.* **19**, 480 (1927). [57

MYERSON, A., and J. LOMAN, Internal jugular venous pressure in man.

Its relationship to cerebrospinal fluid and carotid arterial pressures, *Arch. Neurol. & Psychiat.* **27**, 836 (1932).

NIELSEN, H. E., Der Einfluss der Körperstellung auf das Herzminuten-volumen, *Acta med. Scandinav.* **90**, 456 (1936).   [57

NYLIN, G., The relation between heart volume and stroke volume in re-cumbent and erect positions, *Skandinav. Arch. f. Physiol.* **69**, 237 (1934).   [57

OSLER, W. J., Change of vital capacity with the assumption of the supine position, *Am. J. Physiol.* **161**, 352 (1950).   [58

PRINZMETAL, M., and W. B. KOUNTZ, Intrapleural pressure in orthopnea, *Proc. Soc. Exper. Biol. & Med.* **31**, 610 (1934).

PRINZMETAL, M., and W. B. KOUNTZ, Intrapleural pressure in health and disease and its influence on body function, *Medicine* **14**, 457 (1935).

RABINOWITCH, I. M., The vital capacity in hyperthyroidism with a study of the influence of posture, *Arch. Int. Med.* **31**, 910 (1923).   [58

REID, W. D., Engorgement of the pulmonary veins by extension of cardiac enlargement posteriorly. Relation to postural dyspnea in cardiac patients, *New England J. Med.* **222**, 627 (1940).

ROBB, G. P., and S. WEISS, The velocity of pulmonary and peripheral venous blood flow and related aspects of the circulation in cardio-vascular disease. Their relation to clinical types of circulatory failure, *Am. Heart J.* **9**, 742 (1934).

ROSEN, I. T., and H. L. WHITE, The relation of pulse pressure to stroke volume, *Am. J. Physiol.* **78**, 168 (1926).   [57

RUBOW, V., Die kardiale Dyspnoe, *Ergebn. d. inn. Med. u Kinderh.* **3**, 73 (1909).

SCHEINBERG, P., The effects of postural changes, stellate ganglion block, and anemia on the cerebral circulation, *J. Clin. Investigation* **28**, 808 (1949).

SCHELLONG, F., and M. HEINEMEIER, Über die Kreislaufregulation in aufrechter Körperstellung und ihre Störungen. II. Gute Regulation und Übergang zum Kollaps, *Ztschr. f. d. ges. exper. Med.* **89**, 61 (1933).

SCHNEIDER, E. C., and C. B. CRAMPTON, The effect of posture on the minute volume of the heart, *Am. J. Physiol.* **110**, 14 (1934).   [57

SCOTT, J. C., The cardiac output in the standing position, *Am. J. Physiol.* **115**, 268 (1936).   [57

SHENKIN, H. A., S. S. KETY, F. C. GRANT, and C. F. SCHMIDT, Cerebral blood flow and metabolism in patients with increased intracranial pressure, *Am. J. M. Sc.* **212**, 755 (1946).

SHENKIN, H. A., W. G. SCHEVERMAN, E. B. SPITZ, and R. A. GROFF, The effect of change of position upon the cerebral circulation of man, *Am. J. M. Sc.* **216,** 714 (1948).

SJÖSTRAND, T., Determination of changes in the intrathoracic blood volume in man, *Acta physiol. Scandinav.* **22,** 114 (1951). [58

STARR, I., Clinical studies on incoördination of the circulation, as determined by the response to arising, *J. Clin. Investigation* **22,** 813 (1943).

STARR, I., and M. McMICHAEL, Oxygen transport, circulation and respiration in healthy subjects at simulated altitudes of 16,000–18,000 feet, *J. Appl. Physiol.* **1,** 430 (1948). [57

STARR, I., and A. J. RAWSON, The vertical ballistocardiograph. Experiments on the changes in the circulation on arising; with a further study of ballistic theory, *Am. J. Physiol.* **134,** 403 (1941).

STEAD, E. A., JR., J. V. WARREN, A. J. MERRILL, and E. S. BRANNON, The cardiac output in male subjects as measured by the technique of right atrial catheterization. Normal values with observations on the effect of anxiety and tilting, *J. Clin. Investigation* **24,** 326 (1945). [57

SWEENEY, H. M., and H. S. MAYERSON, Effect of posture on cardiac output, *Proc. Soc. Exper. Biol. & Med.* **36,** 272 (1937). [57

TURNER, A. H., The circulatory minute volumes of healthy young women in reclining, sitting and standing positions, *Am. J. Physiol.* **80,** 601 (1927). [57

WADE, O. L., and J. C. GILSON, The effect of posture on diaphragmatic movement and vital capacity in normal subjects with a note on spirometry as an aid in determining radiological chest volumes, *Thorax* **6,** 103 (1951). [58

WILSON, W. H., The influence of posture on the volume of the reserve air, *J. Physiol.* **64,** 54 (1927). [58

WINSOR, T., and G. E. BURCH, Use of the phlebometer: Normal venous pressure values and a study of certain clinical aspects of venous hypertension in man, *Am. Heart J.* **31,** 387 (1946).

36. *Effects of Therapy. Status of the "Adequately" Treated Patient*

Effects of digitalis. — Many studies have been made of the effect of digitalis on cardiac output or arteriovenous difference in patients with chronic cardiac decompensation, but the available data are difficult to evaluate clearly. In most instances, the procedure followed has been to study the cardiac output in patients shortly after admission, administer the drug, and then measure the output of the heart again. Many of the patients so studied also received the benefit of other therapeutic procedures, such as bed rest, sedation, limitation of salt and the administration of diuretics; any or all of these may in some of the patients studied have been more important than digitalization itself in securing clinical improvement. In order to control such experiments adequately, further studies of the cardiovascular dynamics should have been made after withdrawal of the drug. However, the recent introduction into widespread clinical use of digitalis preparations, which act rapidly, makes this precaution unnecessary.

The work of Bing et al. (1950) shows that the action of digitalis is to increase cardiac work without increasing its oxygen consumption, that is, cardiac efficiency increases. This in itself is not enough to relieve the peripheral manifestations of failure, which can be ameliorated only by the circulatory changes that result from increased myocardial efficiency.

Almost all authors record a rise in cardiac output or a fall in arteriovenous difference in many or most patients after the administration of digitalis (59; McMichael and Sharpey-Schafer, 1944; Bloomfield et al., 1948; Stead et al., 1948). The results of Friedman, et al. (1935a) are, however, discordant, for they found no change. Systematic studies after administration and again after withdrawal of the drug have been carried out by only a few investigators (Ringer and Altschule, 1930; Stewart and Cohn, 1932) and these too show a rise in cardiac output in most patients with cardiac decompensation as a consequence of the action of digitalis. In addition, a number of observers have reported an increase in cardiac output in recovery from decompensation (Kroetz, 1930; Seymour et al., 1942; Merrill, 1946), and it is probable that most or all of the patients described received digitalis as part of their treatment. It appears to be valid to conclude, therefore, that the favorable action of digitalis is associated with a rise in cardiac output. The output of the heart, however, is not always significantly increased and often is not restored entirely to normal; indeed, in some instances the increase is slight — less than 20 per cent. This finding should not be surprising, for it is in harmony with clinical experience. Most patients, especially those with auricular fibrillation, show clinical evidence of improvement following the administration of digitalis, but complete clinical recovery is uncommon.

Most patients with cardiac decompensation experience considerable limitation of activity in spite of digitalization, and many require in addition restriction of salt and repeated administration of diuretics if clinical improvement is to be maintained. The effect of digitalis may be especially disappointing in some cases of cor pulmonale (Mounsey et al., 1952).

It is necessary to have in mind clearly the significance of the effect of digitalis in increasing cardiac output. Many other factors, such as oxygen lack and anemia, increased venous return, elevation of metabolism with exercise, fever, thyrotoxicosis and utilization of food, acidosis, anxiety, the injection of adrenalin, also increase cardiac output. In patients with damaged myocardium these factors constitute an additional strain on the heart and are, therefore, harmful. Digitalis, on the other hand, increases the cardiac output and thereby benefits the entire body, but the heart is not put under any deleterious burden; increase in cardiac output is associated with or caused by an improvement in the metabolism of the cardiac muscle itself, that is, an increase in efficiency.

Data on the effect of digitalis on peripheral blood flow in patients with congestive failure are scanty. No change was found by Eichna and Taube (1943, 1944) in the flow through the hand or calf; data on possible changes in metabolic rate were not reported by these authors, however. Stewart et al. (1946) reported a considerable increase in the peripheral circulation as a whole after digitalization. All observers agree that digitalization shortens the circulation time (**60**; Stewart et al., 1938, 1946; Wood, 1940) and lowers the venous pressure (**61**; Stewart and Cohn, 1932; Kinsman and Moore, 1935); in the case of digitalis preparations that act rapidly, it is possible to demonstrate that the fall in venous pressure precedes diuresis (Eichna and Taube, 1944; Eichna et al., 1951). Tepper (1950) stands alone in his contention that digitalis causes a rise in venous pressure in patients with pulmonary congestion. The abnormal rise in venous pressure that occurs in exercising cardiac patients (page 48) is diminished when digitalis is given (Gilbert and Lewis, 1950). The right auricular pressure also falls (Howarth et al., 1947; Kelly and Bayliss, 1949; Lagerlöf and Werkö, 1949; Wood and Paulett, 1949; Eichna et al., 1951, 1953; van Lingen, 1951).

The right ventricular pressures also fall to a variable extent (Bayliss *et al.*, 1950; Ferrer *et al.*, 1950, 1951; Harvey *et al.*, 1949; Lagerlöf and Werkö, 1949; Zimmerman, 1951; Cournand, 1952; Eichna *et al.*, 1951, 1953; Frisk *et al.*, 1952). The lowering of diastolic right ventricular pressure is indicative of improvement in myocardial function, while the more variable changes in systolic right ventricular pressure are the resultant of a tendency toward increase, owing to increased cardiac output, and a tendency toward decrease, owing to relaxation of pulmonary vasoconstriction. Similar variability of pulmonary arterial pressures has been noted (Ferrer *et al.*, 1950, 1951; Harvey *et al.*, 1949; Lagerlöf and Werkö, 1949; Zimmerman, 1950; Cournand, 1952; Eichna *et al.*, 1951, 1953; Frisk, 1952). However, in view of the considerable rise in pulmonary blood flow and the decreases or negligible increases in pulmonary arterial pressures, it is evident that pulmonary vascular resistance must be lowered significantly, as the calculations of Ferrer *et al.* (1950) show. Small changes in peripheral arterial pressure also have been recorded (Bayliss *et al.*, 1950; Bing *et al.*, 1950; Harvey *et al.*, 1950; Lagerlöf and Werkö, 1949; Cournand, 1952; Eichna *et al.*, 1951, 1953; van Lingen *et al.*, 1951; Tepper, 1950); here too the total peripheral resistance must be lowered, as the calculations of Harvey *et al.* (1950), Eichna *et al.* (1951, 1953), and Lagerlöf and Werkö (1949) show. The pulmonary capillary pressure falls (Frisk *et al.*, 1952).

After digitalization the vital capacity becomes increased (**62**; Friedman *et al.*, 1935*a*). The respiratory minute volume decreases (**63**; Boyer and Bailey, 1943), and alveolar carbon dioxide content rises (Ringer and Altschule, 1930; Smith *et al.*, 1930). The effect on arterial oxygen saturation is variable (Eichna *et al.*, 1951, 1953). The basal metabolic rate also falls (Grassman and Herzog, 1932; Ringer and Altschule, 1930; Stewart *et al.*, 1946). After exercise the oxygen debt is lower in a patient who has been digitalized than in the same patient before administration of the drug (Nylin, 1939). The blood volume diminishes after administration of digitalis (Ewig and Hinsberg, 1931; Brandt, 1931; Mies, 1931; Wollheim, 1950; Gilbert and Lewis, 1950; Berson *et al.*, 1952) however, the effect is slow to appear and presumably is the consequence of diuresis (Eichna *et al.*, 1951, 1953). The claim of Mies (1931) that the blood is merely driven into hidden depots appears to be unfounded.

The abnormally great fall in plasma volume found by Gilbert and Lewis (1950) in patients with congestive failure who exercised was minimized by the administration of digitalis, according to those authors.

The concept that the clotting of blood is accelerated by therapeutic doses of digitalis is not borne out by available data (Cathcart and Blood, 1950; Massie et al., 1944; Pere, 1950; Sokoloff and Ferrer, 1945; Sutton, 1950).

Studies of renal blood flow and of glomerular filtration rate show surprisingly small increases, especially in the latter, after digitalis (Davies, 1951; Davison and Gaddie, 1951; Eichna et al., 1951, 1953; Farber et al., 1951).

An unexplained effect of digitalis is to elevate the blood eosinophil count (Eliakim and De Vries, 1952).

It appears, therefore, that the effect of digitalis or similar substances administered in full doses is primarily a restoration of cardiac output to or toward normal, with a corresponding partial or complete removal of abnormalities in other phases of cardiorespiratory dynamics. The diuretic action of the drug is not entirely understood (page 284).

Effects of oxygen. — The administration of oxygen often results in striking relief of dyspnea and may be followed by a diuresis (Barach, 1931; Barach and Richards, 1931; Richards and Barach, 1934). The cardiac output (Barach and Richards, 1931; Howarth et al., 1947; Mounsey et al., 1952) and vital capacity (Barach and Woodwell, 1921; Katz et al., 1932) are not altered by oxygen therapy, and the venous pressure shows no consistent change (Katz et al., 1932) unless diuresis occurs, so that it must be concluded that the effects of the latter are the result of changes which occur in the blood and tissues. The arterial (Schoen and Derra, 1930; Barach, 1931; Barach et al., 1921, 1931; Cohn et al., 1932; Richards and Barach, 1934) and venous (Barach and Woodwell, 1921) blood oxygen saturations rise to or toward normal when patients with cardiac decompensation breathe air enriched with oxygen. The respiratory minute volume usually decreases significantly (**64**; Richards and Barach, 1934), while the expired air carbon dioxide rises (Campbell and Poulton, 1927); according to the last-named authors, however, these changes do not occur in cardiac patients in whom cyanosis is the consequence of a congenital shunt and is not associated with pulmonary congestion. The effects of oxygen therapy on the tissues are diminished when vaso-constriction is present (Montgomery and Horwitz, 1950).

The decrease in ventilation, consequent to oxygen therapy, results in a rise in carbon dioxide content in the arterial blood (Barach, 1931; Barach *et al.*, 1921, 1931; Cohn *et al.*, 1932; Richards and Barach, 1934), but the blood pH is not changed markedly (Barach and Richards, 1931). Decreases in blood lactate occur as a consequence of relief of anoxia (Barach, 1931; Barach and Richards, 1931; Jervell, 1928). Related to this phenomenon is the observation that carbon dioxide output during exercise is increased in patients with cardiac decompensation breathing air containing high concentrations of oxygen (Campbell and Poulton, 1927). If diuresis occurs as a consequence of the administration of oxygen, it is accompanied by the changes usually associated with it (page 195), namely, increased urinary excretion of chloride, fall in plasma chloride, rise in plasma protein and fall in venous pressure.

Emphasis must be laid upon the fact that the small degrees of arterial blood deoxygenation that commonly obtain in patients with cardiac decompensation give no accurate indication of the possible beneficial effects to be derived from oxygen therapy. The biological action of oxygen depends not on saturation directly but on the oxygen tension. Thus, while in normal subjects the arterial blood oxygen tension is in the neighborhood of 100 mm-of-mercury and the blood is over 95 per cent saturated, when 100 per cent oxygen is breathed, the percentage saturation increases only slightly but the tension rises to approximately 700 mm-of-mercury. This phenomenon is explainable by the fact that additional oxygen is carried in physical solution in the plasma, the amount of dissolved oxygen being determined by the percentage of that gas in the alveolar air. It is apparent that although the arterial blood oxygen tension in patients with congestive failure is usually somewhat below the normal, exposure to high oxygen tensions in the air breathed charges the blood with large amounts of dissolved oxygen. Further, even in those patients in whom no deficit of arterial blood oxygen exists, the addition of dissolved oxygen makes more of that gas available to the tissues, so that the capillary blood becomes less markedly deoxygenated than it would otherwise be.

On the other hand, prolonged exposure to very high oxygen concentrations, that is, in the neighborhood of 100 per cent, in the inspired air, has certain deleterious effects. Since the nitrogen in the lungs is washed out, atelectasis is favored; moreover, the gas in high concentrations is irritating to the lungs (Watt *et al.*, 1943; Bean, 1945; Alveryd and Brody, 1948). In high concentrations oxygen has a vasoconstricting effect on the cerebral vessels and the flow through the brain falls (Behnke *et al.*, 1935; Kety and Schmidt, 1946). The cardiac output is also somewhat diminished (Otis *et al.*, 1946; Whitehorn *et al.*, 1946). These deleterious effects can be avoided without sacrificing too much of the beneficial action of high oxygen tensions by the use of mixtures containing 60 or 70 per cent of oxygen.

Effects of diuretics. — (1) *Ammonium chloride diuresis.* Ammonium chloride is commonly regarded as a diuretic drug, which it is when given in fairly large doses, that is, more than 5 Gm. per day. In smaller doses it has no significant diuretic action, nor does it ordinarily enhance the action of mercurial diuretics (Goldring, 1929; Berglund and Sundh, 1935; Ethridge, 1936); giving ammonium chloride to patients in a state of chloride depletion does not cause a diuresis, since the chloride is retained (Schwartz, 1950). When given in appreciable dosage, it raises the plasma chloride level somewhat (**65**; Dennig *et al.*, 1929) and the changes that occur in the plasma are reflected in edema fluid (Gilligan *et al.*, 1934) but not in the spinal fluid (de Thurzo and Katzenelbogen, 1935). The total body chloride increases (Dunning *et al.*, 1951). There also occurs a marked increase in urinary chloride (**66**; Dennig *et al.*, 1929) and an increase in urinary acid (Keith and Whelan, 1926; Dennig *et al.*, 1929). Considerable, though lesser, amounts of body base are excreted with chloride (**67**; Gamble *et al.*, 1925), most of the base consisting of sodium, with smaller amounts of potassium and calcium; the blood sodium and potassium concentrations may fall slightly (Harris *et al.*, 1934; Sartorius *et al.*, 1949). The electrolyte pattern of the urine during the administration of ammonium chloride indicates that appreciable amounts of extracellular and small amounts of intracellular fluids are being excreted (Gamble *et al.*, 1925; Keith and Whelan, 1926; Dennig *et al.*, 1929). When given in large doses, ammonium chloride causes a decrease in plasma volume with evidences of hemoconcentration, that is, a rise in plasma protein level, in normal individuals (Lyons *et al.*, 1944*b*). It is important also that the changes in electrolyte balance (Dennig *et al.*, 1929; Ethridge *et al.*, 1936; Farnsworth and Krakusin, 1948; Sartorius *et al.*, 1949) and in plasma volume (Lyons *et al.*, 1944*b*) induced by continuous administration of ammonium chloride reach a maximum in three or four days and then become less marked. Renal vascular dynamics are not changed (Sartorius *et al.*, 1949).

When used in moderate or large doses, ammonium chloride lowers the blood bicarbonate level (**68**; Barach *et al.*, 1946) and in doses of 8 Gm. or more a day, it may lower the blood pH (**69**; Barron *et al.*, 1937); smaller doses do not affect the pH (Dennig *et al.*, 1931). Lowered blood pH is accompanied by an increased respiratory minute volume (**70**; Følling, 1929) and lowering of the alveolar (**71**; Haldane, 1921) and arterial (**72**; Keith and Whelan, 1926) carbon dioxide contents; the arterial blood oxygen saturation may fall slightly (Cullen *et al.*, 1931) or remain unchanged (Barach *et al.*, 1946).* The increased respiratory activity that the drug causes when given in large doses may make patients with congestive failure more uncomfortable. Indeed, it has been shown that as little as 7.5 Gm. per day appreciably reduces the potential oxygen debt, that is, the ability to do work, in normal individuals (Dennig *et al.*, 1931). Smaller doses may have a similar effect in cardiac patients.

Another deleterious effect of the use of ammonium chloride in large doses is the increase in cardiac output that it causes. This increase is due mainly to decreased carrying capacity for carbon dioxide and also to some extent to increased oxygen consumption, associated with hyperventilation (Norlin, 1933). The large doses of the drug required to make its diuretic action significant may often result in nausea or other signs of gastro-intestinal irritation although secretion of gastric acid is not changed (Maclaglan, 1935; Hartiala and Karoonen, 1946). Impairment of utilization of vitamin C may occur (Hawthorne and Storvick, 1948). In addition, continued acidosis may possibly increase catabolism of body proteins (Mackay *et al.*, 1941) by stimulating the adrenal cortex; it is interesting in this respect

---

* These changes refer to conditions at sea level and have no bearing on the disputed effectiveness of ammonium chloride in relieving altitude sickness (Barach *et al.*, 1946; Barron *et al.*, 1937).

that exhilaration or other mental change may result (Haldane, 1921; Hoff, 1935) and sugar tolerance may become impaired somewhat (Mackler et al., 1952; Thomson et al., 1933).

Cerebral blood flow diminishes when acidosis is induced (Schieve and Wilson, 1953).

There appears to be little justification for the use of ammonium chloride in large daily doses as a diuretic in the treatment of edema of congestive failure; these doses impair respiratory mechanisms, increase cardiac work, and may cause gastro-intestinal upsets and protein wastage. The use of small doses — 1 to 3 Gm. a day — is also not recommended. These small doses do not have a significant diuretic effect. The action of ammonium chloride as a diuretic, when given in small doses, depends largely upon its making available chloride for the purpose of carrying off sodium from the body. Since only a portion of the ingested ammonium chloride is so utilized, it is to be expected that a dose of 3 Gm., for instance, would result in the excretion of the sodium contained in only 200 cc. of edema fluid.

Ammonium chloride is nevertheless useful in the treatment of edema when used together with more potent diuretics. Since the volume of a diuretic response depends to a large extent on the plasma chloride level (page 277), it is apparent that ammonium chloride may sometimes enhance the action of more potent diuretic drugs by raising the plasma chloride level in patients who exhibit a diminished response to mercurial or xanthine diuretics as a consequence of low plasma chloride level. This low level may be the result of the combined effects of prolonged rigid salt deprivation and of frequently induced diuresis. This hypochloremia is particularly likely to occur in patients who repeatedly receive mercurial diuretics (page 276). Blumgart, Gilligan and Volk (1936) have shown that the administration of 7 to 10 Gm. of ammonium chloride prevents the fall in plasma chloride level that otherwise occurs as a consequence of the action of mercurial diuretics; Stock, Mudge, and Nurnberg (1951) have made similar observations. A reasonable plan, therefore, for the use of ammonium chloride in the treatment of cardiac edema is to give 1 to 2 Gm. five times a day for two days, beginning the day before a mercurial diuretic is to be injected.

(2) *Mercurial diuretics.* Although the chemical methods used in studying diuresis are far more accurate than the physiologic methods

used in studies on circulation and respiration, there is much more disagreement concerning the mode of action of diuretics than in any other branch of cardiovascular physiology. The literature on the action of mercurial diuretics is large and confusing.

(a) *Consequences of diuresis.* (i) *Urine chloride and base excretion.* Almost the only point agreed upon by all workers is that the injection of a mercurial diuretic in normal or edematous animals or men is followed by the formation of an increased volume of urine, which, though of a lower specific gravity than control specimens, has the same or a higher concentration of chloride, so that a very large output of chloride results (**73**; Blumgart *et al.*, 1934, 1936). There is a smaller increase in the output of base (**74**; Herrmann and Decherd, 1937), chiefly sodium, with considerably smaller amounts of potassium and calcium excreted; in some instances, however, loss of potassium may be excessive (Fox *et al.*, 1949; Schwartz, 1950, 1951; Lesser *et al.*, 1951) owing, in part at least, to previous depletion of body sodium. There is a variable relation between the outputs of sodium and of chloride (Blumgart *et al.*, 1934; Schwartz, 1950). The loss of chloride may be greater than can be accounted for by loss of extracellular fluid (Schwartz, 1950; Schwartz and Wallace, 1951; Squires *et al.*, 1951*b*). The ratio of water to salt loss is also variable (Blumgart *et al.*, 1934; Grossman *et al.*, 1950). Grossman *et al.* (1950) found that salt excretion exceeded and then fell behind that of water. Over all, the loss of water is greater than the loss of salt (Miller, 1951; Schroeder, 1950). Since the plasma sodium concentration remains unchanged or falls somewhat, it is evident that sodium must enter the cells, or cells must give up water, or both. A large loss of nitrogen (Stock *et al.*, 1951; Schwartz and Wallace, 1951) and of thiamin (page 206) may occur. Mercurial diuretics cause the loss of larger amounts of chloride than do any of the other diuretic substances. Following the diuresis a period of retention of chloride and base is observed.

(ii) *Late changes in plasma electrolytes.* The marked excretion of chloride leads to a lowering of plasma chloride late in and following the period of diuresis (**75**; Herrmann *et al.*, 1932*a, b*). The decrease in plasma chloride level is most marked in edematous subjects since it varies with the diuresis. It is prevented by the simultaneous administration of 7 to 10 Gm. per day of ammonium chloride (Blumgart *et al.*, 1936; Stock *et al.*, 1951). Simultaneously with the fall in plasma chloride, there usually occurs a corresponding rise in plasma bicarbonate (Bergner *et al.*, 1951; Bricker and Wesson, 1953; Platts, 1953; Schwartz and Wallace, 1951; Squires *et al.*, 1951*a,b*; Stapleton and Harvey, 1952). The plasma sodium level is usually unchanged, although variable decreases may occur in patients whose intake of sodium has been restricted (Keith and Whelan, 1926; Blumgart *et al.*, 1936; Herrman and Decherd, 1937; Harris *et al.*, 1934; Miller, 1951, Bricker and Wesson, 1953; Schwartz, 1950, Schwartz and Wallace, 1951; Squires *et al.*, 1951*a,b*; Stapleton and Harvey, 1952). Nothman (1933) and Squires *et al.* (1951*a,b*) reported slight rises in plasma potassium level in some cases; the work of Schwartz (1950) and Schwartz and Wallace (1951) indicates the occurence of a fall in some circumstances. The washing out of large amounts of calcium with resulting tetany described by Nothmann (1932) has not been found by any other observer. Stock *et al.* (1951) found a rise, usually small, in pH.

(iii) *Late changes in plasma protein.* The plasma protein level at the end of the diuresis (**76**; Calvin *et al.*, 1940*a, b*) in normal or edematous animals or men is often found to be elevated above the control value. The finding of de Vries (1946) that mercurial diuresis causes a rise in plasma protein level only in the absence of edema is discordant. The plasma specific gravity (Blumgart *et al.*, 1936) and colloid osmotic pressure (Bryan *et al.*, 1935; Claussen, 1932; Meyer, 1931) show changes parallel with those in plasma protein level. A slight rise in the ratio of albumin to globulin has also been reported (Claussen, 1932; Calvin *et al.*, 1940*a,b*). There is no early change in plasma specific gravity (Reveley *et al.*, 1951).

(iv) *Late changes in the tissues.* The edema fluid shows changes in electrolytes corresponding to those that occur in the blood (Crawford and McIntosh, 1925; Gilligan *et al.*, 1934; Schroeder, 1951). The protein content of the edema fluid rises (page 141). The tissue pressure falls (Burch and Sodeman, 1937) as diuresis proceeds. A change in the ratio of plasma and edema fluid sodium concentrations may occur (Soloff *et al.*, 1952).

(v) *Late changes in blood volume.* The plasma and blood volumes are decreased considerably at the end of diuresis in normal or edematous animals or men (**77**; Lyons *et al.*, 1944*a*, 1946). The more variable results recorded by Swigert and Fitz (1940) and by Spühler et al. (1948) are discordant. Plasma and total red cell volume decrease approximately in proportion, the hematocrit varying a little in either direction (Cardozo, 1939; Goldhammer et al., 1935) although small rises are perhaps more common (Crawford and McIntosh, 1925; Keith and Whelan, 1926; Lyons et al., 1944a, 1946; de Vries, 1946; Berson et al., 1952; Marvel and Shullenberger, 1951).

(vi) *Late changes in circulation.* Although a brief initial rise in cardiac output may have been found by Pugh and Wyndham (1949), who reported no arteriovenous oxygen differences, the more extensive studies of Frisk et al. (1952) revealed no change; no consistent change in circulation time occurs (Swigert and Fitz, 1940). There are no late changes in cardiac output (Friedman et al., 1935b; Pugh and Wyndham, 1949). The right auricular (Scébat et al., 1949; Pugh and Wyndham, 1949) and venous pressure fall after a time (Lyons et al., 1944a; Volini and Levitt, 1939, 1940; Kartun, 1950), owing apparently to a lowering of right ventricular pressure. The cerebrospinal fluid pressure falls with the venous pressure (Volini and Levitt, 1940). These changes are all late and no immediate, consistent fall in venous pressure (Swigert and Fitz, 1940; Reveley et al., 1951) and in pulmonary capillary, pulmonary arterial, right ventricular, and right auricular pressures occurs (Frisk et al., 1952). It is evident that the late fall in venous pressure that occurs is a consequence of diuresis caused by extracardiac factors; it is a beneficial change in that it retards the reaccumulation of edema fluid. Congestion in the lungs appears to be somewhat ameliorated, for the vital capacity increases by a few hundred cubic centimeters (Alsever and Levine, 1938; Swigert and Fitz, 1940).

(vii) *Variations in the volume of diuresis; role of salt.* A low plasma chloride level (Bouyoucos, 1934; Evans, 1936; Goldring, 1929; Keith and Whelan, 1926; Schwartz, 1950; Schroeder, 1949, 1951; Schwartz and Wallace, 1951; Stapleton and Harvey, 1952; Elkinton et al., 1952a) or the previous depletion of body chloride (Berglund and Sundh, 1935; Evans, 1936; Reaser and Burch, 1946; Schroeder, 1949) minimizes or altogether prevents diuresis following the injection of mercurial diuretics. In such instances restoration of chloride levels by means of ammonium chloride (page 193) restores the effectiveness of such diuretics. An interesting experiment was performed by Goldring (1929) in two patients no longer responsive to mercurial diuretics because of low plasma chloride levels. He gave 5 Gm. of sodium chloride daily for three days, during which time the patients gained several pounds of edema fluid; plasma chloride levels rose. When, however, another injection of salyrgan was given, the resultant diuresis carried off all the fluid gained and in addition very much more. A similar result was reported by Berglund and Sundh (1935), Squires et al. (1952), and Schroeder (1949). The marked chloride losses associated with diuresis by mercurials may lead to lowering of plasma chloride and refractoriness to diuretics if combined with rigid restriction of sodium chloride intake; it is obviated by avoidance of too rigid restriction of salt in the diet or by the use of ammonium chloride (page 274). Similarly, depletion of body sodium leads to unresponsiveness to subsequent injections of mercurial diuretics (Weston and Escher, 1948; Schroeder, 1949; Squires et al., 1952).

Other factors also operate to limit or prevent diuresis. An extremely low glomerular filtration rate may be associated with refractoriness to mercurial diuretics (Weston et al., 1952). Axelrod and Pitts (1952) showed that anoxia inhibits the action of these drugs, as does adrenocorticotrophic hormone also.

It must be borne in mind that factors that make for refractoriness to mercurial diuretics do not always operate, and the action of these drugs is unpredictable to some degree. One example is afforded by persistent diuresis in spite of marked bodily electrolyte depletion; in some instances inhibition of diuresis does not occur and the patient may develop serious or even fatal salt depletion (Schwartz, 1950). Of interest in this connection is the observation made in normal man by Pitts and Duggan (1949) that forcing water before and during a mercurial diuresis might result in collapse.

(b) *Mechanism of diuresis.* (i) *Early changes in plasma electrolytes.* Changes in plasma electrolytes during the first few hours after the injection of mercurial diuretics, that is, before the onset of the diuresis, have been studied in an attempt to ascertain whether chloride or water is mobilized from the tissues. The results are widely discrepant. Early rises in plasma chloride in animals and human subjects have been found by some (78; Stockton, 1936) and have led to the conclusion that mercurials act by mobilizing chloride from tissue fluid into blood. On the other hand, an early fall in plasma chloride (Nonnebruch, 1921; Crawford and McIntosh, 1925; Herrmann *et al.*, 1932*a, b*) observed by others has led to the conclusion that water is mobilized from the tissues. Still others have found the early changes in plasma chloride to be variable and inconstant (Claussen, 1932; Bouyoucous, 1934), while excellent work has been done that shows no early change at all (**79**; Blumgart *et al.*, 1934, 1936; Fulton *et al.*, 1934). It is concluded that no early changes in plasma electrolytes occur before the onset of the diuresis due to mercurials.

(ii) *Early changes in plasma protein and erythrocyte mass.* A fall in plasma protein within a few hours after injection of mercurials and before or with the onset of diuresis has been reported by some observers (**80**; Claussen, 1932) and has been taken to indicate hemodilution by mobilization of water from the tissues. Similar changes in plasma colloid osmotic pressure (Kylin, 1932; Meyer, 1931*a*) and red cell count (Bohn, 1923) or hematocrit (Simmert, 1935) have been interpreted in a similar fashion. However, some authors describe early elevation of plasma protein (Schally, 1935) or colloid osmotic pressure (Oelkers, 1931) with a rise in the ratio of albumin to globulin (Schally, 1935), which is interpreted as indicating transfer of albumin from the tissues into the blood together with a lesser amount of water. The hematocrit is also said to be variable (Feher, 1929; Petersen, 1940). The best work indicates that no dilution occurs (Bleyer, 1922; Bryan *et al.*, 1935; Schmitz, 1933; Reveley *et al.*, 1951; Stock *et al.*, 1951).

(iii) *Early changes in plasma volume.* Feher (1929) reported an early increase in plasma volume, but Levin (1941), Reveley *et al.* (1951), and Evans and Gibson (1937) found it unchanged.

(iv) *Studies of renal function. Conclusions.* The urea clearance is unchanged during mercury diuresis (Fulton *et al.*, 1934; Page, 1933; Brun *et al.*, 1947) or slightly decreased (Herrmann *et al.*, 1933); studies of inulin or creatinine clearance have shown no change in glomerular filtration (**81**; Farnsworth, 1946, Grossman *et al.*, 1950; Reveley *et al.*, 1951; Weston *et al.*, 1952). Renal blood flow similarly is unchanged (Brun *et al.*, 1947; Farnsworth and Krakusin, 1948; Grossman *et al.*, 1950; Pitts and Duggan, 1950; Reveley *et al.*,

1951; Weston et al., 1952). Calculations made from the enormous increase in sodium and chloride output and the usually small changes in their levels in the plasma show that sodium and chloride clearances are greatly increased. In the absence of any change in glomerular filtration rate, it is evident that a marked depression of tubular reabsorption of salt must occur; the fact that some fall in plasma electrolytes may occur might suggest that slightly less water than salt is excreted, although the opposite is the case (page 275). The work of Reaser and Burch (1946) and Grossman et al. (1950) shows that early in the course of diuresis the output of salt is proportionately even greater. Somewhat more chloride than sodium is excreted in some cases, whereas sodium excretion may be low in patients depleted of that ion, in which case potassium is the base chiefly excreted, indicating loss of intracellular electrolyte. For the most part, the excess urine excreted during mercurial diuresis is similar to extracellular fluid with respect to sodium and chloride content (Schwartz and Wallace, 1951). Depression of proximal renal tubular function, as revealed by studies of phosphate, ammonia, and titrable acidity in the urine, is evident (Weston et al., 1951). This phenomenon appears to be the mechanism of mercurial diuresis. Available studies suggest that other tubular functions may be depressed also (Berliner et al., 1948; Handley et al., 1949; Brun et al., 1947; Weston et al., 1949). Attempts also have been made to show that an increase in insensible water loss contributes to the disappearance of edema, but the observed results are variable (Gabriel and Kahler, 1934; Magendantz and Stratman, 1933; Squires et al., 1951a). Bartram (1932) found that the injection of small amounts of mercurial diuretics directly into a renal artery caused an immediate increase in the flow of a dilute urine from that side, with a later smaller increase in urine volume from the other kidney. Melville and Stehle (1927) performed similar experiments, but did not observe this response, probably because of the injection of too large a dose, for Bartram (1932) also showed that the injection of larger amounts into a renal artery results in oliguria. The cross-circulation experiments of Govaerts (1928), using one animal given a mercurial diuretic into the renal artery and another not so treated, afford convincing evidence of the renal site of action of mercurial diuretics. Kupfer et al. (1951) showed that these drugs do not influence blood flow or glomerular filtration in the isolated kidney; tubular function is depressed. The observation of Møller (1937) that mercurial diuretics cause renal vasoconstriction in animals is difficult to interpret. Mercurial diuresis is inhibited by BAL (Farah and Maresh, 1948; Berliner *et al.*, 1948; Duggan and Pitts, 1949, Pitts and Duggan, 1950) and also by morphine (Ferrer and Sokoloff, 1947) but not by pituitrin (Hoff and Werner, 1926). The mercurial diuretics cause no consistent change in blood clotting mechanisms (Pere, 1950; Marvel and Shullenberger, 1951); it must be borne in mind that some degree of hemoconcentration occurs following their successful use.

It appears that the action of the mercury in mercurial diuretics slightly impairs tubular function without otherwise damaging the kidney, so that the reabsorption of chloride is diminished and a large loss of chloride, water, and base is initiated. This phenomenon may result in stimulation of the posterior lobe of the pituitary gland and the consequent outpouring of pituitrin (Hoff and Werner, 1928); excretion of water may therefore be retarded somewhat while salt excretion is not affected. The action of pitressin is not influenced by mercurial diuretics (Capps *et al.*, 1952; Farah *et al.*, 1953). The possible effect of mercurial diuresis on adrenal cortical function is not clear. The blood eosinophil count rises (Eliakim and De Vries, 1952) but the sweat sodium concentration does not change (Reynolds, 1952).

Mercurial diuretics cause an artifactitious lowering of plasma protein-bound iodine (Meyers and Man, 1951).

(3) *Xanthine diuretics.* A large number of substances fall into the group of xanthine diuretics. There is no conclusive evidence that the action of all of them is similar, but for the purposes of discussion they have been grouped together.

(*a*) *Consequences of diuresis.* (i) *Urinary chloride excretion.* The occurrence of diuresis following the injection of xanthine diuretics of various types is associated with an increase in urine chloride content and total output (**83**; Blumgart *et al.*, 1934; Fulton *et al.*, 1934); the changes are not as striking as those that occur with mercurial diuresis. The excretion of base is increased also (Blumgart *et al.*, 1934; Herrmann *et al.*, 1932*a*, 1937; Keith and Whelan, 1926; Threefoot *et al.*, 1947; Fowell *et al.*, 1948; Davis and Shock, 1949;

Sinclair-Smith *et al.*, 1949; Truitt, 1950; Reveley *et al.*, 1951). There is a parallel excretion of base, chloride and water (Blumgart *et al.*, 1934).

(ii) *Late changes in plasma chloride.* Some decrease in plasma chloride level late during or after the period of diuresis has been reported (Möller, 1927; Fulton *et al.*, 1934) although Stockton (1936) reported a slight rise, Herrmann *et al.* (1932a) observed fluctuations and Blumgart *et al.* (1934, 1936) no change in normal subjects or edematous cardiacs. The blood sodium level is described by all authors as unchanged (Blumgart *et al.*, 1934, 1936; Herrmann and Decherd, 1937).

(iii) *Late changes in plasma protein and hemoglobin.* Increased plasma protein levels were found at the end of diuresis by Calvin *et al.* (1940b) and Atchley and Benedict (1930), but lowered levels for plasma protein and plasma colloid osmotic pressure were described by Meyer (1931b). On the other hand, the hemoglobin level (Möller, 1927) and plasma specific gravity (Stewart, 1941) have been reported as increased after the diuresis. It is probable that, after a diuresis due to the xanthines, some hemoconcentration occurs.

(iv) *Late changes in plasma and blood volumes.* The plasma and blood volumes are decreased after xanthine diuresis, according to Calvin *et al.* (1940a) and Fowell *et al.* (1948).

(v) *Changes in circulation.* Friedman *et al.* (1935b), Berseus (1945), and Werkö and Lagerlöf (1949) found no lasting change in cardiac output after administration of xanthine diuretics, but Stewart and Cohn (1932) reported a significant persistent rise. Hoen (1936), Starr *et al.* (1937), Howarth *et al.* (1947), Escher *et al.*, (1948), Fowell *et al.* (1948), Frisk *et al.* (1952), and Werkö and Lagerlöf (1949) observed increases in cardiac output shortly after the injection of theophylline, and Stewart and Jack (1940) also found a considerable increase in peripheral blood flow in similar experiments. This change was, however, of short duration in the study of Stewart and Jack (1940) and probably explains the untoward reactions to that drug more than it does anything else; additional discussion along these lines is given elsewhere (page 319). However, it must be borne in mind that, owing possibly to changes induced by these substances in the pulmonary circulation, the pulmonary arterial and right ventricular pressures fall (Frisk *et al.*, 1952); this phenomenon ultimately is followed by a fall in venous pressure, a change unfavorable to recurrence of edema.

(vi) *Role of chloride in diuresis.* As in the case of mercurial diuretics, little or no diuresis will occur with xanthine when the plasma chloride is low (Curtis, 1927, 1929). Similarly, the administration of chloride enhances xanthine diuresis; Frandsen and Møller (1928) gave saline solution to rabbits before the injection of a xanthine diuretic and noted a diuresis that contained the volume of saline solution given and a good deal more in addition.

(b) *Mechanism of diuresis.* (i) *Early changes in plasma chloride.* A rise of plasma chloride level after the injection of a xanthine diuretic, but before the onset of diuresis, has been described in rabbits (Curtis, 1925, 1929; Möller, 1927); this was taken to indicate mobilization of chloride from the tissues. However, an early fall was found in man (Stockton, 1936) and no consistent change in other experiments on rabbits (Möller, 1927), dogs (Hansen *et al.*, 1931), and human subjects (Blumgart *et al.*, 1934; Fulton *et al.*, 1934; Herrmann *et al.*, 1932a; Kirstein, 1947).

(ii) *Early changes in plasma protein and hemoglobin.* Decreased plasma protein levels were found by Calvin *et al.* (1940b) shortly after the injection of xanthines; however, Meyer (1931b) found increased plasma protein and oncotic pressure at this time. Meyer (1931b) considered that the latter indicated transfer of protein to the blood stream from the tissues. An early lowering of colloid osmotic pressure is, however, described (Kylin, 1932) in rabbits. Early decreases in hemoglobin (Möller, 1927) and in plasma specific gravity (Stewart, 1941) have also been noted. Kirstein (1947) found no consistent change in hematocrit value.

(iii) *Early changes in plasma volume.* A rise in plasma volume was noted by Calvin *et al.* (1940a) early in the course of xanthine diuresis.

(iv) *Studies of renal function. Conclusion.* The urea clearance is described as unchanged (Fulton *et al.*, 1934; Page, 1933) or increased (Herrmann *et al.*, 1933). Glomerular filtration is described as increased in man by Herrmann *et al.* (1932a, b, 1933, 1937), Chasis *et al.* (1938), Escher *et al.* (1948), Fowell *et al.* (1948), Reveley *et al.* (1951), Weston *et al.* (1952), Sinclair-Smith *et al.* (1949), and Davis and Shock (1949), and in dogs by Schmitz (1932); Blumgart *et al.* (1934) and Earle *et al.* (1949) found it unchanged in normal man, and Berglund and Sundh (1935) found the changes equivocal. No change was found in rabbits (Forster, 1947). Reabsorption is described as unchanged (Schmitz, 1932) or variably diminished (Blumgart *et al.*, 1934; Herrmann *et al.*, 1932a,b; Forster, 1947; Davis and Shock, 1949; Sinclair-Smith *et al.*, 1949). The injection of xanthines into a renal artery in dogs yielded diverse responses (Bartram, 1932); theobromine sodium acetate acted much like mercurials in that an immediate increase in urine flow from the injected kidney resulted, but theobromine sodium salicylate, theobromine calcium salicylate and aminophylline caused no such response but rather a delayed bilateral diuresis. In the experiments of Kupfer *et al.* (1951) aminophylline increased flow in the isolated kidney without affecting glomerular filtration rate; reabsorption was depressed. It is apparent that the available data are too contradictory to permit of any conclusion as to the mechanism of action of the xanthines. However, as with all substances that have diuretic effects, their action is associated with an outpouring of chloride and lesser amounts of base. The changes are less marked than those induced by mercurials.

Aminophylline given intravenously causes an unexplained increase in gastric acidity (Krausnow and Grossman, 1949). The cerebral blood flow is decreased (Wechsler, Kleiss, and Kety, 1950; Moyer *et al.*, 1952). Nothing is known about possible relations between decreased cerebral blood flow and inhibition of pitressin effects (Bricker and Woods, 1951) after aminophylline. At any rate, it is possible that inhibition of posterior pituitary hormone represents an important component of the action of xanthine diuretic drugs.

(4) *Digitalis as a diuretic.* — The diuresis that follows the administration of full doses of digitalis in a patient with congestive failure is apparently related to the improvement in circulation that results (page 189); an increase in renal blood flow (Herrmann *et al.*, 1932a; Merrill, 1946; Earle *et al.*, 1949; Sinclair-Smith *et al.*, 1950; Davison and Gaddie, 1951; Eichna *et al.*, 1951, 1953; Farber *et al.*, 1951) has also been noted. Urea clearance (Herrmann *et al.*, 1933) and glomerular filtration are increased (Herrmann *et al.*, 1932a,b, 1933; Earle *et al.*, 1949; Sinclair-Smith *et al.*, 1949; Baldwin *et al.*, 1950; Davison and Gaddie, 1951; Eichna *et al.*, 1951, 1953; Farber

et al., 1951). It must be noted that the changes in glomerular filtration may be small or even negligible; Borst (1948) found no change in urea clearance. The urine chloride concentration and total output rise (Falta and Quittner, 1917; Herrmann *et al.*, 1932*b*, 1933; Keith and Whelan, 1926; Steyrer, 1902; Stockton, 1932; Eichna *et al.*, 1951, 1953; Schroeder, 1951) and there is also an increased excretion of base (Steyrer, 1902; Keith and Whelan, 1926; Earle *et al.*, 1949; Sinclair-Smith *et al.*, 1949; Eichna *et al.*, 1951, 1953; Farber *et al.*, 1951). These derive mainly from the extracellular fluid. Variable changes in plasma chloride level were recorded by Herrmann *et al.* (1932*a,b*) and Farber *et al.* (1951), while other authors have reported that a fall in plasma chloride follows the diuresis (McLean, 1915; Stockton, 1932; Borst, 1948). The diuresis is followed by a decrease in plasma volume (Calvin *et al.*, 1940*a*; see also page 147) and a rise in plasma protein (Calvin *et al.*, 1940*b*; Borst, 1948) and specific gravity (Stewart, 1941). A slight initial rise in plasma volume (Calvin *et al.*, 1940*a*), accompanied by a decrease in plasma protein (Calvin *et al.*, 1940*b*) and specific gravity (Stewart, 1941), has been interpreted as evidences of mobilization of fluid from the edematous tissues; further studies will have to be made before this conclusion can be accepted. Output of water is greater than that of salt (Miller, 1951), as in the case of mercurial diuretics (page 275).

(5) *Oxygen as a diuretic.* — Occasionally edema disappears when the patient is given oxygen and reappears when the administration of oxygen is discontinued (Barach, 1931; Barach and Richards, 1931; Richards and Barach, 1934). The diuresis that occurs under such circumstances is accompanied by an increased urinary chloride excretion, a fall in plasma chloride level and a compensatory rise in bicarbonate concentration, according to these authors. The diuresis is followed by a rise in plasma protein level.

(6) *Urea.* — Studies on urea as a diuretic in man are scanty. Dean and McCance (1949) found an increase in urea clearance in normal men given urea; the change in clearance did not last as long as the diuresis and presumably is of secondary importance in causing it.

(7) *Other diuretic drugs.* — A uracil compound has been found to act as a diuretic in cardiac decompensation; sodium output is increased by its action (Kattus *et al.*, 1952).

A carbonic anhydrase inhibitor — one that acts mainly on renal carbonic anhydrase and less strongly on that of the blood and stomach — causes a large increase in the output of bicarbonate and also base; a state of mild acidosis results (Freidberg *et al.*, 1952). The drug appears to be a potent diuretic in cardiac decompensation.

Effects of rest. — Bed rest not only serves the obvious purpose of reducing activity to or toward a level that the heart can support, but it is also important because it enables patients who are in a continuous oxygen debt (page 93) to discharge that accumulated debt. Studies of the effects of bed rest in patients with congestive failure are scanty; the data of Kinsman and Moore (1935) show some fall in venous pressure and in a few cases slight acceleration of circulation time; Hussey (1936) also stressed the rapid fall in venous pressure which may occur with bed rest. In view of the known effects of activity and of straining on the venous pressure (page 36), it is to be expected that the rest and relaxation which the patient experiences after being put to bed will have this effect. An attempt should be made to ascertain whether bed rest alone can, after a time, so rest the heart as to enable it to recover somewhat and show an increase in output relative to the body's metabolic needs. Sinclair-Smith *et al.*, (1949) have made a careful study of electrolyte and water balance in cardiac patients at rest. The finding of Taylor *et al.* (1945) that prolonged bed rest causes a decrease in blood volume together with some hemoconcentration in normal subjects is of interest; the corresponding phenomenon has not been studied in chronic cardiac decompensation.

Role of diet. — The dietary management of cardiac patients is of great importance, but many of the diets suggested for use in cardiac decompensation are faulty because they emphasize only one aspect of the problem. The Karell diet, namely, 800 cc. of skim milk daily, should not be used for any length of time because it restricts fluids to an undesirable degree and is deficient in calories, thiamine, protein, and iron (Harrison, 1945). Starvation as a form of therapy in congestive failure is undesirable, since the published data show that it depletes the protein stores (Proger and Magendantz, 1936). Diets that limit salt intake to an extreme degree are generally unpalatable and are deficient in protein and often thiamine also. The effect of unwise restriction of salt intake in contributing to salt depletion and its undesirable consequences has been discussed (page 176). A study of salt and water metabolism in cardiac patients has been published by Iseri, Boyle, and Myers (1950). They showed that loss of edema in patients on low salt intakes was associated with a decline in venous pressure. They described also a loss of both intra- and extracellular water, loss of sodium from within and outside cells, and the entry of potassium into cells. However, Soloff et al. (1952) showed a potassium loss on this sort of regimen; the muscle sodium and potassium both decreased. The validity of some of the calculations used in studies of this type has been shaken by the discovery that bones contain large amounts of sodium. A large decrease in total body chloride occurs in cardiac decompensation treated with restricted intake of salt (Dunning et al., 1951). A negative nitrogen balance has been observed in normal subjects so treated (Black et al., 1950); it probably occurs in cardiac decompensation also. Many of the regimens suggested, including the acid-ash diet, are too complex to be used by the patient at home. The effects of the acid-ash diet can be secured with much less trouble by giving suitable quantities of ammonium chloride.

The diet for a patient with cardiac decompensation should be adequate in regard to calories and of high protein and vitamin B content. Since many of these patients are anoretic (Harrison, 1945), the diet should be varied, palatable, attractively prepared and concentrated in bulk. Salt intake should be limited to a moderate degree; little or none should be added in cooking, and none at the table. In the case of patients who are very ill, and in whom the rise in cardiac output that occurs with large food intake (Grollman, 1929) is undesirable, a regimen of six small meals per day may be helpful. Fluids should be adequate in amount; forcing fluids has no benefit (Gorham et al., 1947).

Exchange resins. — The use of ion exchange resins in congestive failure, with the removal of salt via the stool, gives rise to the interesting picture of loss of edema accompanied by a decrease in urinary excretion of sodium. The sodium loss may constitute a danger after a time. Loss of potassium and calcium, and induction of a state of acidosis, may follow the use of some types of resins. The number of reports describing the use of these substances is growing rapidly (Emerson et al., 1951; Weston et al., 1953; **84**).

The effects of such measures as venesection, injection of morphia, application of tourniquets, still-standing or sitting with feet dependent, and the use of positive-pressure apparatus are discussed elsewhere (page 320).

Physiologic status of the "adequately" treated cardiac patient. — A group of patients was studied some years ago in order to determine the physiologic status of the patient with chronic cardiac decompensation in whom the greatest possible improvement in symptoms was secured by treatment in the hospital (Altschule, 1938). These patients received the benefit of complete bed rest for several weeks, limitation of salt, full doses of digitalis, adequate diuresis with mercurial preparations, and in a few instances venesection or oxygen therapy as well. It was evident that striking symptomatic improvement had occurred; there was no edema and at most minimal dyspnea at rest. However, evidence of the persistence of an abnormal cardiovascular physiologic condition was shown by the somewhat decreased cardiac output, tendency toward an increased respiratory rate and minute volume, a slight decrease in arterial blood oxygen saturation, a lowering of the vital capacity, a prolongation of the pulmonary circulation time, and, in one patient, slight elevation of the venous pressure. These findings corroborated and extended the observations of other authors who have studied the cardiovascular system after recovery from congestive failure and have been corroborated by others since (Ferrer *et al.*, 1948). Evidence of failure of other functions to return to normal, such as the renal (page 162) and the hepatic (Layne *et al.*, 1950) is also available. An impressive study by Eichna *et al.* (1953) is the last word on this point. The persistence of physical abnormalities, such as cyanosis, cardiac enlargement and hepatic enlargement in the cases reported, is to be noted. *The symptoms of dyspnea, orthopnea and edema were controlled but the results of the cardiovascular physiologic measurements in each case failed to return to normal values.* Following discharge from the hospital all of the patients, except one who died, returned with fully developed cardiac decompensation within a year, in spite of the fact that their activities were markedly limited. It is clear that the improvement they experienced as a result of their hospital stay was due to the treatment of the secondary consequences of an inadequate cardiac output, as well as to an increase in the minute volume output of the heart; the latter, however, did not reach normal levels even with the patient at rest in bed.

This result explains not only the physiologic findings but the clinical course in chronic cardiac decompensation. Some patients, especially those with mild or moderate cardiac decompensation, find a level of activity at which they can avoid the signs and symptoms of congestive failure without much active treatment. In other cases, particularly those with more severe degrees of failure, continuous treatment, such as the frequent use of diuretics and repeated hospitalization, is necessary in spite of marked limitation of the patient's activity.

Bibliography

Chapter I — Section 36

AARON, R. S., and R. E. WESTON, Outpatient treatment of congestive heart failure with sodium-removing exchange resins, *Arch. Int. Med.* **90,** 182 (1952).   [84

AHMED, S., R. I. S. BAYLISS, W. A. BRISCOE, and J. McMICHAEL, The action of G-strophanthin on the circulation in man, and a comparison with digoxin, *Clin. Sc.* **9,** 1 (1950).   [59

ALSEVER, J. B., and S. A. LEVINE, The immediate effect of mercurial diuretics on the vital capacity of the lungs, *Am. Heart J.* **15,** 201 (1938).

ALTSCHULE, M. D., The pathological physiology of chronic cardiac decompensation, *Medicine* **17,** 75 (1938).

ALVERYD, A., and S. BRODY, Cardiovascular and respiratory changes in man during oxygen breathing, *Acta physiol. Scandinav.* **15,** 140 (1948).

ATCHLEY, D. W., and E. M. BENEDICT, Serum electrolyte studies in normal and pathological conditions, pneumonia, renal edema, cardiac edema, uremia and diabetic acidosis, *J. Clin. Investigation* **9,** 265 (1930).
                                                                    [75, 76

AXELROD, D. R., and R. F. PITTS, Anoxia as a factor in resistance to mercurial diuretics, *Am. J. Physiol.* **169,** 350 (1952).   [73, 74

BAIRD, M. M., C. G. DOUGLAS, J. B. S. HALDANE, and J. G. PRIESTLEY, Ammonium chloride acidosis, *J. Physiol.* **57,** xli (1923).   [65, 68

BALDWIN, D. S., J. H. SIROTA, and H. VILLARREAL, Diurnal variations in renal function in congestive heart failure, *Proc. Soc. Exper. Biol. & Med.* **74,** 578 (1950).

BARACH, A. L., The therapeutic use of oxygen in heart disease, *Ann. Int. Med.* **5,** 428 (1931).   [64

BARACH, A. L., M. ECKMAN, E. GINSBURG, A. E. JOHNSON, and R. D. BROOKES, The effect of ammonium chloride on altitude tolerance, *J. Aviation Med.* **17**, 123 (1946). [68, 69, 71

BARACH, A. L., and D. W. RICHARDS, JR., Effects of treatment with oxygen in cardiac failure, *Arch. Int. Med.* **48**, 325 (1931). [64

BARACH, A. L., and M. N. WOODWELL, Studies in oxygen therapy with determinations of the blood gases. I. In cardiac insufficiency and related conditions, *Arch. Int. Med.* **28**, 367 (1921).

BARKER, R. A., and I. R. MACKAY, Clinical effects of a cation-exchange resin (Zeo-karb-225), *Lancet* **2**, 758 (1951). [84

BARNES, A. R., and J. KNUTSON, Evidence of hemodilution during diuresis produced by salyrgan in patients with congestive heart failure and a discussion on its possible clinical implications, *Tr. A. Am. Physicians* **62**, 169 (1949).

BARRON, E. S. G., D. B. DILL, H. T. EDWARDS, and A. HURTADO, Acute mountain sickness; the effect of ammonium chloride, *J. Clin. Investigation* **16**, 541 (1937). [68, 69, 71

BARTRAM, E. A., Experimental observations on the effect of various diuretics when injected directly into one renal artery of a dog, *J. Clin. Investigation* **11**, 1197 (1932).

BAYLISS, R. I. S., M. J. ETHERIDGE, A. L. HYMAN, H. G. KELLY, J. McMICHAEL, and E. A. S. REID, The effect of digoxin on the right ventricular pressure in hypertensive and ischaemic heart failure, *Brit. Heart J.* **12**, 317 (1950). [59

BEAN, J. W., Effects of oxygen at increased pressure, *Physiol. Rev.* **25**, 1 (1945).

BEDDARD, A. P., and M. S. PEMBREY, Observations on pulmonary ventilation in disease, *Brit. M. J.* **2**, 580 (1908). [64

BEHNKE, A. R., F. S. JOHNSON, J. R. POPPEN, and E. B. MOTLEY, The effect of oxygen on man at pressures from 1 to 4 actual atmospheres, *Am. J. Physiol.* **110**, 565 (1935).

BERGLUND, H., and B. SUNDH, The effect of salyrgan, theophylline and caffeine on diuresis, glomerular filtration and proteinuria, *Acta med. Scandinav.* **86**, 216 (1935). [81, 82

BERGNER, G. E., J. H. HUTCHINSON, J. W. KOEHLER, and E. L. CZEBRINSKI, Metabolic problems arising in the management of congestive heart failure, *Arch. Int. Med.* **88**, 387 (1951). [69, 75

BERLINER, R. W., T. J. KENNEDY, JR., and J. G. HILTON, Salyrgan and renal tubular secretion of para-aminohippurate in the dog and man, *Am. J. Physiol.* **154**, 537 (1948). [73, 74

BERSEUS, S., The influence of heart glucosides, theophylline and analeptics on the cardiac output in congestive heart failure; with remarks on the acetylene methods for the determination of arteriovenous oxygen difference, *Acta med. Scandinav. Supp. No. 145* (1945). [59

BERSON, S. A., R. S. YALOW, A. AZULAY, S. SCHREIBER, and B. ROSWIT, The biological decay curve of P³² tagged erythrocytes. Application to the study of acute changes in blood volume, *J. Clin. Investigation* 31, 581 (1952). [77

BEST, M. M., W. F. HURT, J. E. SHAW, and J. D. WATHEN, Study of the mercurial diuretic, dicurin procaine (merethoxylline procaine) by subcutaneous injection, *Am. J. M. Sc.* 225, 132 (1953). [73, 74

BICKERS, W., and M. WOODS, Premenstrual tension. Its relation to abnormal water storage, *New England J. Med.* 245, 453 (1951).

BING, R. J., F. M. MARAIST, J. F. DAMMAN, JR., A. DRAPER, JR., R. HEIMBECKER, R. DALEY, R. GERARD, and P. CALAZEL, Effect of strophanthus on the coronary blood flow and cardiac oxygen consumption of normal and failing human hearts, *Circulation* 2, 513 (1950). [59

BLACK, A. B., and J. A. LITCHFIELD, Uraemia complicating low salt treatment of heart failure, *Quart. J. Med.* 20, 149 (1951). [75

BLACK, D. A. K., R. PLATT, and S. W. STANBURY, Regulation of sodium excretion in normal and salt-depleted subjects, *Clin. Sc.* 9, 205 (1950).

BLEYER, L., Erfahrungen über die Novasuroldiurese, *Klin. Wchnschr.* 1, 1940 (1922). [79

BLOOMFIELD, R. A., B. RAPOPORT, J. P. MILNOR, W. K. LONG, J. G. Mebane, and L. B. ELLIS, The effects of the cardiac glycosides upon the dynamics of the circulation in congestive heart failure I. Ouabain, *J. Clin. Investigation* 27, 588 (1948). [59, 61

BLUMGART, H. L., D. R. GILLIGAN, R. C. LEVY, M. G. BROWN, and M. C. VOLK, Action of diuretic drugs. I. Action of diuretics in normal persons, *Arch. Int. Med.* 54, 40 (1934). [73, 74, 79, 81, 82, 83

BLUMGART, H. L., D. R. GILLIGAN, and M. C. VOLK, Action of diuretic drugs. II. Effect of diuretic drugs on the acid-base equilibrium of the blood in patients with cardiac edema, *Medical Papers dedicated to Henry Asbury Christian* (Baltimore, 1936), p. 191.
[73, 74, 75, 76, 79, 82

BÖGER, A., and F. DIEHL, Das Verhalten des Schlag- und Minutenvolumens Herzkranker unter dem Einfluss der Digitalis- (Strophanthin-) Behandlung, *Arch. f. exper. Path. u. Pharmakol.* 172, 551 (1933). [59

BOHN, H., Experimentelle Studien über die diuretische Wirkung des Novasurols, *Ztschr. f. d. ges. exper. Med.* 31, 303 (1923). [78, 80

BOHN, H., Fortgesetzte Studien über Novasurol, seine Wirkung bei verschiedenen Lebensaltern und bei Diabetikern, sowie sein etwaiger Einfluss auf Ionenverscheibungen im Organismus, *Deutsches Arch. f. klin. Med.* 143, 225 (1923-24). [80

BONNER, C. D., Electrolyte-balance studies in normal volunteers and clinical observations on the effects of cation exchange resins in patients with cardiovascular disease and in subjects receiving pituitary adrenocorticotrophic hormone (ACTH), *New England J. Med.* **247**, 158 (1952). [84

BORNSTEIN, A., Ueber die Messung der Kreislaufzeit in der Klinik, *Verhandl. d. Kong. f. inn. Med.* **29**, 457 (1912). [60

BORST, J. G. G., The maintenance of an adequate cardiac output by the regulation of the urinary excretion of water and sodium chloride; an essential factor in the genesis of edema, *Acta med. Scandinav. Supp.* **207**, (1949). [61

BOUYOUCOS, B. G., La chlorurie, l'hydrurie, la chlorémie et l'hydrémie au cours de la diurèse par les sels mercuriels organiques, *Compt. rend. Soc. de biol.* **115**, 1170 (1934). [73

BOYER, P. K., and C. V. BAILEY, Concentration of carbon dioxide in expired air in heart disease, *Arch. Int. Med.* **71**, 529 (1943). [63

BRANDT, F., Die Abhangigkeit des Venendruckes von der Grosse der zirkulierenden Blutmenge, zugleich ein Beitrag zur Frage seiner klinischen Bedeutung, *Ztschr. f. klin. Med.* **116**, 398 (1931). [61

BRICKER, N. S., and L. G. WESSON, JR., Plasma electrolyte concentrations in ambulatory cardiac patients, *Circulation* **7**, 687 (1953).

BRUN, C., T. HILDEN, and F. RAASCHOU, On the effects of mersalyl on the renal function, *Acta pharmacol.* **3**, 1 (1947). [81

BRYAN, A. H., W. A. EVANS, JR., M. N. FULTON, and E. A. STEAD, JR., Diuresis following the administration of salyrgan. Its effect on the specific gravity, the total nitrogen and the colloid osmotic pressure of the plasma of normal and edematous dogs, *Arch. Int. Med.* **55**, 735 (1935). [76

BUDELMANN, G., Untersuchungen über den Venendruck, die Vitalkapazität der Lunge und das Herzminutenvolumen bei Gesunden und Herzkranken in Ruhe und bei Kreislaufbelastung, *Ztschr. f. klin. Med.* **127**, 15 (1935). [59, 61, 62

BURCH, G. E., and W. A. SODEMAN, The estimation of the subcutaneous tissue pressure by a direct method, *J. Clin. Investigation* **16**, 845 (1937).

CALLAHAN, E. J., III, N. R. FRANK, H. KRAUS, and L. B. ELLIS, Clinical use of cation exchange resins in the treatment of congestive heart failure, *Am. J. M. Sc.* **223**, 117 (1952). [84

CALVIN, D. B., G. DECHERD, and G. HERRMANN, Response of plasma volume to diuretics, *Proc. Soc. Exper. Biol. & Med.* **44**, 529 (1940a). [77

CALVIN, D. B., G. DECHERD, and G. HERRMANN, Plasma protein shifts during diuresis, *Proc. Soc. Exper. Biol. & Med.* **44**, 578 (1940b). [76

CAMPBELL, J. M. H., and E. P. POULTON, The effect on breathless subjects of residence in an oxygen chamber, *Quart. J. Med.* **20**, 141 (1926–27). [64

CAPPS, J. N., W. S. WIGGINS, D. R. AXELROD, and R. F. PITTS, The effect of mercurial diuretics on the excretion of water, *Circulation* **6**, 82 (1952).

CARDOZO, E. L., Invloed van salyrgan op het bloedvolume, *Nederl. tijdschr. v. geneesk.* **83**, 5528 (1939). [73, 76, 77

CATHCART, R. T., and D. W. BLOOD, Effect of digitalis on the clotting of the blood in normal subjects and in patients with heart failure, *Circulation* **1**, 1176 (1950).

CHASIS, H., H. A. RANGES, W. GOLDRING, and H. W. SMITH, The control of renal blood flow and glomerular filtration in normal man. *J. Clin. Investigation* **17**, 683 (1938).

CITRON, D., B. BERCU, R. LEMMER, and E. MASSIE, Congestive heart failure and hyponatremia: untoward effects of mercurial diuresis, *Ann. Int. Med.* **34**, 872 (1951).

CLAUSSEN, F., Ueber die Diurese der Herzkranken, *Ergeb. d. inn. Med. u. Kinderh.* **43**, 764 (1932). [73, 76, 80

COHN, D. J., L. N. KATZ, S. SOSKIN, and W. W. HAMBURGER, Observations on the effects of oxygen therapy. III. Blood chemical changes, *Am. J. M. Sc.* **184**, 818 (1932).

COURNAND, A., A. Discussion of the concept of cardiac failure in the light of recent physiologic studies in man, *Ann. Int. Med.* **37**, 649 (1952). [59

CRAWFORD, J. H., and J. F. McINTOSH, Observations on the use of novasurol in edema due to heart failure, *J. Clin. Investigation* **1**, 333 (1924–25). [73, 75, 76, 80

CULLEN, G. E., T. R. HARRISON, J. A. CALHOUN, W. E. WILKINS, and M. M. TIMS, Studies in congestive heart failure. XIII. The relation of dyspnea of exertion to the oxygen saturation and acid-base condition of the blood, *J. Clin. Investigation* **10**, 807 (1931). [69, 72

CURTIS, G. M., Die Wirkungsweise der specifischen Diuretica nebst Beitragen zur Lehre von der Harnabsonderung, *Biochem. Ztschr.* **163**, 109 (1925). [83

CURTIS, G. M., Fortgesetzte Untersuchungen über die Wirkungsweise der spezifischen Diuretica. Die Blockierung der normalen Reaktion durch die intraperitoneale Injektion von distilliertem Wasser, *Biochem, Ztschr.* **186**, 95 (1927).

CURTIS, G. M., The action of specific diuretics, *J. A. M. A.* **93**, 2016 (1929). [83

DAVIES, C. E., The effect of treatment on the renal circulation in heart-failure, *Lancet* **2**, 1052 (1951).

Davis, J. O., and N. W. Shock, The effect of theophylline ethylene diamine on renal function in control subjects and in patients with congestive heart failure, *J. Clin. Investigation* **28**, 1459 (1949).

Davison, P. H., and R. Gaddie, The influence of intravenous digoxin on renal function in congestive cardiac failure, *Quart. J. Med.* **20**, 389 (1951).   [61

Dean, R. F. A., and R. A. McCance, The renal response of infants and adults to the administration of hypertonic solutions of sodium chloride and urea, *J. Physiol.* **109**, 81 (1949).

Dennig, H., D. B. Dill, and J. H. Talbott, Bilanzuntersuchungen einer Salmiakazidose, *Arch. f. exper. Path. u. Pharmakol.* **144**, 297 (1929).
                                                    [65, 66, 67, 68, 69, 70, 71, 72

Dennig, H., J. H. Talbott, H. T. Edwards, and D. B. Dill, Effect of acidosis and alkalosis upon capacity for work, *J. Clin. Investigation* **9**, 601 (1930–31).   [68

de Thurzo, E., and S. Katzenelbogen, Alkali reserve in blood and in cerebrospinal fluid in experimental acidosis, *Arch. Neurol. & Psychiat.* **33**, 785 (1935).   [69

de Vries, A., Changes in hemoglobin and total plasma protein after injection of mercurophylline, *Arch. Int. Med.* **78**, 181 (1946).

Duggan, J. J., and R. F. Pitts, Studies on diuretics. I. The site of action of mercurial diuretics, *J. Clin. Investigation* **29**, 365 (1950).   [74

Duggan, J. J., and R. F. Pitts, Site of action of mercurial diuretics, *Federation Proc.* **8**, 37 (1949).   [74

Duncan, L. E., Jr., Treatment of edema by removal of body sodium by a cation exchange resin, *Am. J. Med.* **14**, 425 (1953).   [84

Dunning, M. F., J. M. Steele, and E. Y. Berger, Measurement of total body chloride, *Proc. Soc. Exper. Biol. & Med.* **77**, 854 (1951).   [65

Earle, D. P., Jr., S. J. Farber, J. D. Alexander, and L. W. Eichna, Effects of treatment on renal functions and electrolyte excretion in congestive heart failure, *J. Clin. Investigation* **28**, 778 (1949).   [61

Eichna, L., S. J. Farber, A. R. Berger, D. P. Earle, B. Rader, E. Pellegrino, R. E. Albert, J. D. Alexander, H. Taube, and S. Youngwirth, The interrelationship of the cardiovascular, renal and electrolyte effects of intravenous digoxin in congestive heart failure, *J. Clin. Investigation* **30**, 1250 (1951).   [59, 61

Eichna, L., S. J. Farber, A. R. Berger, D. P. Earle, B. Rader, E. Pellegrino, R. E. Albert, J. D. Alexander, H. Taube, and S. Youngwirth, Cardiovascular dynamics, blood volumes, renal functions and electrolyte excretions in the same patients during congestive heart failure and after recovery of cardiac decompensation, *Circulation* **7**, 674 (1953).   [59, 61

Eichna, L. W., and H. Taube, A comparison of the actions of four cardiac glycosides on a patient with congestive heart failure, *Am. Heart J.* **26,** 631 (1943).   [61

EICHNA, L. W., and H. TAUBE, The effect of intravenously administered digoxin and ouabain on the systemic venous pressure of patients with congestive heart failure, *Am. Heart J.* **27,** 641 (1944).   [61

ELIAKIM, M., and A. DE VRIES, Observations on the eosinophil count in congestive heart failure, *Cardiologia* **21,** 44 (1952).   [74

ELKINTON, J. R., R. D. SQUIRES, and L. W. BLUEMLE, JR., The distribution of body fluid in congestive heart failure. IV. Exchanges in patients, refractory to mercurial diuretics, treated with sodium and potassium, *Circulation* **5,** 58 (1952).

ELKINTON, J. R., R. D. SQUIRES, and W. C. KLINGENSMITH, JR., Cation exchange resin in the treatment of congestive heart failure. I. Electrolyte exchanges during initial periods of resin therapy, *Circulation* **5,** 747 (1952).   [84

EMERSON, K., JR., S. S. KAHN, J. W. VESTER, and K. D. NELSON, Oral use of cation-exchange resins in treatment of edema, *Arch. Int. Med.* **88,** 605 (1951).   [84

ESCHER, D. J. W., R. E. WESTON, G. LEINER, L. LEITER, and S. GOLDAT, The effect of aminophyllin on cardiac output and renal hemodynamics, *Federation Proc.* **7,** 31 (1948).

ETHRIDGE, C. B., D. B. MYERS, and M. H. FULTON, The modifying effect of various inorganic salts on the diuretic action of salyrgan, *Medical papers dedicated to Henry Asbury Christian* (Baltimore, 1936), p. 223.

EVANS, E. A., JR., The effect of changes in salt and water metabolism upon salyrgan diuresis (with special reference to the effect of permanent bile fistula), *Medical papers dedicated to Henry Asbury Christian* (Baltimore, 1936), p. 204.   [73

EVANS, W. E., JR., and J. G. GIBSON, II. The blood volume in diuresis. A study employing the colloidal blue dye T-1824 in dogs rendered edematous by plasmapheresis, *Am. J. Physiol.* **118,** 251 (1937).   [77

EWIG, W., and K. HINSBERG, Kreislaufstudien. II, *Ztschr. f. klin. Med.* **115,** 693 (1931).   [59

FALTA, W., and M. QUITTNER, Ueber den Chemismus verschiedener Oedemformen, *Wien. klin. Wchnschr.* **30,** 1189 (1917).

FARAH, A., T. S. COBBEY, and W. MOOK, Concentration changes in urinary electrolytes produced by mercurial diuretics, *Proc. Soc. Exper. Biol. & Med.* **81,** 601 (1953).   [73, 74

FARAH, A. and G. MARESH, The influence of sulfhydryl compounds on diuresis and renal and circulatory changes caused by mersalyl, *J. Pharmacol. & Exper. Therap.* **92,** 73 (1948).

FARBER, S. J., J. D. ALEXANDER, E. D. PELLEGRINO, and D. P. EARLE, The effect of intravenously administered digoxin on water and electrolyte excretion and on renal function, *Circulation* **4,** 378 (1951).   [59, 61

FARNSWORTH, E. B., Clearance of inulin, diodrast, chloride and phosphate under mercurial diuresis. Intensive study of a patient in severe cardiac failure, *Am. J. Med.* **1,** 246 (1946).   [81

FARNSWORTH, E. B., and J. S. KRAKUSIN, Electrolyte partition in patients with edema of various origins. Qualitative and quantitative definition of cations and anions in cardiac decompensation, *J. Lab. & Clin. Med.* **33,** 1534 (1948).   [66, 67, 74, 81

FEHER, S., Salyrgandiurese und zirkulierende Blutmenge, *Wien. klin. Wchnschr.* **42,** 964 (1929).

FEINBERG, A. W., and B. ROSENBERG, The use of a carboxylic cation exchange resin in the therapy of congestive failure, *Am. Heart J.* **42,** 698 (1951).   [84

FERRER, M. I., R. M. HARVEY, R. T. CATHCART, A. COURNAND, and D. W. RICHARDS, JR., Hemodynamic studies in rheumatic heart disease, *Circulation* **6,** 688 (1952).   [59

FERRER, M. I., R. M. HARVEY, R. T. CATHCART, C. A. WEBSTER, D. W. RICHARDS, JR., and A. COURNAND, Some effects of digoxin upon the heart and circulation in man. Digoxin in chronic cor pulmonale, *Circulation* **1,** 161 (1950).   [59

FERRER, M. I., R. M. HARVEY, L. WERKO, D. T. DRESDALE, A. COURNAND, and D. W. RICHARDS, JR., Some effects of quinidine sulphate on the heart and circulation in man, *Am. Heart J.* **36,** 816 (1948).

FERRER, M. I. and L. SOKOLOFF, The anti-diuretic effect of morphine and demerol in congestive heart failure, *Am. J. M. Sc.* **214,** 372 (1947).

FØLLING, A., On the mechanism of ammonium chloride acidosis, *Acta med. Scandinav.* **71,** 221 (1929).   [66, 67, 69, 70

FORSTER, R. P., An examination of some factors which alter glomerular activity in the rabbit kidney, *Am. J. Physiol.* **150,** 523 (1947).

FOWELL, D. M., A. P. BRIGGS, N. C. WHEELER, J. A. WINSLOW, JR., J. W. REMINGTON, and W. F. HAMILTON, Renal and circulatory factors in congestive failure of the circulation, *Federation Proc.* **7,** 35 (1948).

FOX, C. L., JR., C. K. FRIEDBERG, and A. G. WHITE, Electrolyte abnormalities in chronic congestive heart failure; effects of administration of potassium and sodium salt, *J. Clin. Investigation* **28,** 781 (1949).   [73, 74

FRANCO, A., and M. G. MARQUES, Digitalisation massive ou fractionée dans l'insuffisance cardiaque congestive chronique avec fibrillation auriculaire, *Cardiologia* **20,** 257 (1952).   [60, 61

FRANDSEN, J., and K. O. MØLLER, Untersuchungen über die Wirkung des Theophyllins auf die Chlorid- und Wasserausscheidung bei Kaninchen mit artifizial chronischer tubulärer Nephritis, *Acta med. Scandinav.* **68,** 385 (1928). [83

FRIEDBERG, C. K., and M. HALPERN, Effect of carbonic anhydrase inhibitor 6063 (2-acetylamino-1,3,4-thiadiazole-5-sulfonamide) on renal excretion of fluid and electrolytes in patients with congestive heart failure, *Federation Proc.* **11,** 49 (1952).

FRIEDBERG, C. K., M. HALPERN, and R. TAYMOR, The effect of intravenously administered 6063, the carbonic anhydrase inhibitor, 2-acetylamino-1,3,4,-thiadiazole-5-sulfonamide, on fluid and electrolytes in normal subjects and patients with congestive heart failure, *J. Clin. Investigation* **31,** 1074 (1952).

FRIEDMAN, B., G. CLARK, H. RESNIK, JR., and T. R. HARRISON, Effect of digitalis on the cardiac output of persons with congestive heart failure, *Arch. Int. Med.* **56,** 710 (1935*a*).

FRIEDMAN, B., H. RESNIK, JR., J. A. CALHOUN, and T. R. HARRISON, Effect of diuretics on the cardiac output of patients with congestive heart failure, *Arch. Int. Med.* **56,** 341 (1935*b*).

FRIEDMAN, I. S., Problems of cation-exchange-resin therapy, *Arch. Int. Med.* **89,** 99 (1952). [84

FRISK, A. R., L. WERKÖ, and G. WRANGE, A new mercurial diuretic "diurgin" (disodium salt of N-succinyl-, N^1 (8-carboxymethylmercapto-mercuri-B-methoxy) propylcarbamide), *Acta med. Scandinav.* **144,** 85 (1952). [52, 73, 74

FULTON, M. N., H. A. VAN AUKEN, R. J. PARSONS, and L. F. DAVENPORT, The comparative effect of various diuretics in dogs with special reference to the excretion of urine chloride and urea, *J. Pharmacol, & Exper. Therap.* **50,** 223 (1934). [66, 73, 75, 79, 83

GABRIEL, G., and H. KAHLER, Ueber den Einfluss des respiratorischen Quotienten auf die Höhe der Gewichtsabgabe. Zur Frage der perspiratio insensibilis bei Kreislaufkranken, *Wien. Arch. f. inn. Med.* **24,** 181 (1934).

GAMBLE, J. L., K. D. BLACKFAN, and B. HAMILTON, A study of the diuretic action of acid producing salts, *J. Clin. Investigation* **1,** 359 (1924–25). [66, 67

GARCIA, J. E., and B. A. GOLDMAN, The combined use of strophanthin-K and digitalis in the treatment of congestive heart failure. A preliminary report, *Am. Heart J.* **26,** 20 (1943). [60, 61

GILBERT, R. P., and J. K. LEWIS, Effect of exercise on the plasma volume of patients with heart failure, *Circulation* **2,** 403 (1950). [61

GILLIGAN, D. R., M. C. VOLK, and H. L. BLUMGART, Observations on the chemical and physical relation between blood serum and body fluids. I. The nature of edema fluids and evidence regarding the mechanism of edema formation, *J. Clin. Investigation* **13,** 365 (1934).

298   CHRONIC CARDIAC DECOMPENSATION

GOLDHAMMER, S., G. LEINER, and D. SCHERF, Ueber die zirkulierende
Blutmenge vor und nach der Quecksilberdiurese, *Klin. Wchnschr.* **14,**
1109 (1935). [77

GOLDRING, W., Edema in congestive heart failure. Effectiveness of
diuretics as a guide to prognosis, *Arch. Int. Med.* **44,** 465 (1929). [73

GORHAM, L. W., D. E. LESTER, A. V. WOLF, and H. H. SHULTZ, The
relative importance of dietary sodium chloride and water intake in
cardiac edema, *Ann. Int. Med.* **27,** 575 (1947).

GOVAERTS, P., Origine rénal ou tissulaire de la diurèse par un composé mercuriel organique, *Compt. rend. Soc. de Biol.* **99,** 647 (1928).

GRASSMANN, W., and F. HERZOG, Die Wirkung von Digitalis (Strophanthin) auf das Minuten- und Schlagvolumen des Herzkranken, *Arch.
f. exper. Path. u. Pharmacol.* **163,** 97 (1932). [59, 63

GREENMAN, L., J. B. SHALER, and T. S. DANOWSKI, Biochemical disturbances and clinical symptoms during prolonged exchange resin therapy
in congestive heart failure, *Am. J. Med.* **14,** 391 (1953). [84

GRIGGS, D. E., and V. J. JOHNS, Influence of mercurial diuretics on the
excretion of sodium, potassium and chloride, *California Med.* **69,** 133
(1948). [73, 74

GROLLMAN, A., Physiological variations in the cardiac output in man. III.
The effect of the ingestion of food on the cardiac output, pulse
rate, blood pressure, and oxygen consumption of man, *Am. J. Physiol.*
89, 366 (1929)

GROSSMAN, J., R. E. WESTON, I. S. EDELMAN, and L. LEITER, Studies on
thiomerin — a subcutaneously administerable mercurial diuretic, *Circulation* **1,** 502 (1950). [73, 74, 81

HALDANE, J. B. S., Experiments on the regulation of the blood's alkalinity.
II, *J. Physiol.* **55,** 265 (1921). [68, 70, 71, 72

HANDLEY, C. A., R. B. SIGAFOOS, and M. LAFORGE, Proportional changes
in renal tubular reabsorption of dextrose and excretion of p-aminohippurate with changes in glomerular filtration, *Am. J. Physiol.* **159,**
175 (1949). [81

HANDLEY, C. A., J. TELFORD, and M. LAFORGE, Xanthine and mercurial
diuretics and renal tubular transport of glucose and p-aminohippurate
in the dog, *Proc. Soc. Exper. Biol. & Med.* **71,** 187 (1949).

HANSEN, H. L., L. G. FOSDICK, and C. A. DRAGSTEDT, A study of the effect
of certain diuretics on the concentration of blood chlorides in dogs,
J. Pharmacol. & Exper. Therap. **41,** 325 (1931). [79

HARRIS, I., E. L. RUBIN, and J. S. LAWRENCE, Salyrgan and ammonium
chloride as diuretics in cardiac oedema, *Acta med. Scandinav.* **83,** 23
(1934). [65, 66, 69, 74, 75

HARRISON, J. V., Diet therapy in congestive heart failure, *J. Am. Dietet.
A.* **21,** 86 (1945).

HARTIALA, K., and M. KAROONEN, The influence of anoxia on the gastric HCl-secretion, *Acta physiol.* **11**, 85 (1946).

HARVEY, R. M., M. I. FERRER, R. T. CATHCART, D. W. RICHARDS, JR., and A. COURNAND, Some effects of digoxin upon the heart and circulation in man. Digoxin in left ventricular failure, *Am. J. Med.* **7**, 439 (1949). [59

HATZIEGANU, I., I. GAVRILA, and J. BORBIL, Action des diurétiques mer-curiels sur l'hydrémie, la chlorurémie, l'asotémie et les éliminations urinaires, *Compt. rend. Soc. de biol.* **99**, 1813 (1928).   [73, 78

HAY, S. H., and J. E. WOOD, JR., Cation exchange resins in the treatment of congestive heart failure, *Ann. Int. Med.* **33**, 1139 (1950).   [84

HAWTHORNE, B. E., and C. A. STORVICK, Effect of sodium bicarbonate and ammonium chloride on ascorbic acid metabolism of adults, *Proc. Soc. Exper. Biol. & Med.* **67**, 447 (1948).

HERRMANN, G., E. H. SCHWAB, and C. T. STONE, Further studies on the mechanism of diuresis in patients with congestive heart failure, *Tr. A. Am. Physicians* **48**, 364 (1933).   [73, 81, 82, 83

HERRMANN, G., C. T. STONE, and E. H. SCHWAB, Some studies in the mechanism of diuresis in patients with congestive heart failure, *Tr. A. Am. Physicians* **47**, 279 (1932a).   [75, 82

HERRMANN, G., C. T. STONE, E. H. SCHWAB, and W. W. BONDURANT, Diu-resis in patients with congestive heart failure, *J. A. M. A.* **99**, 1647 (1932b).   [73, 82, 83

HERRMANN, G. R., and G. M. DECHERD, Further studies on the mechan-ism of diuresis with especial reference to the action of some newer diuretics, *J. Lab. & Clin. Med.* **22**, 767 (1937).   [73, 74, 81, 82, 83

HILTON, J. G., Potentiation of diuretic action of mercuhydrin by ammo-nium chloride, *J. Clin. Investigation* **30**, 1105 (1951).   [67, 68

HITZENBERGER, K., and F. L. ENGELMANN, Ueber das spezifische Gewicht des Harnes bei Salyrgandiurese, *Ztschr. f. klin. Med.* **129**, 290 (1935). [73

HOEN, H., Pharmakologische Untersuchungen über das Minutenvolumen des menschlichen Herzens, *Arch. f. exper. Path. u. Pharmakol.* **184**, 67 (1936).

HOFF, F., Ueber Änderungen der seelischen Stimmungslage bei verschieb-ungen der Säurebasengleichgewichtes, *München. med. Wchnschr.* **82**, 1478 (1935).

HOFF, H., and P. WERNER, Untersuchungen über den Mechanismus der Diuresehemmung durch Pituitrin am Menschen, *Arch. exper. Path. u. Pharmakol.* **119**, 153 (1926).

HOFF, H., and P. WERNER, Untersuchungen über die Sekretion des Pituitrins unter dem Einfluss Harntreibender Mittel, *Arch. f. exper. Path. u. Pharmakol.* **133**, 84 (1928).

HOWARTH, S., J. McMICHAEL, and E. P. SHARPEY-SCHAFER, Effects of venesection in low output heart failure, *Clin. Sci.* **6**, 41 (1947). [59

HOWARTH, S., J. McMICHAEL, and E. P. SHARPEY-SCHAFER, The circulatory action of theophylline ethylene diamine, *Clin. Sci.* **6**, 125 (1947).

HOWARTH, S., J. McMICHAEL, and E. P. SHARPEY-SCHAFER, The effects of oxygen, venesection and digitalis in chronic heart failure from disease of the lungs, *Clin. Sc.* **6**, 187 (1947).

HUSSEY, H. H., Clinical application of venous pressure measurement, *M. Ann. District of Columbia* **5**, 232 (1936).

ISERI, L. T., A. J. BOYLE, and G. B. MYERS, Water and electrolyte balance during recovery from severe congestive failure on a 50 milligram sodium diet, *Am. Heart J.* **40**, 706 (1950).

JANSEN, K., H. W. KNIPPING, and K. STROMBERGER, Klinische Untersuchungen über Atmung und Blutgase, *Beitr. z. Klin. d. Tuberk.* **80**, 304 (1932). [64

JERVELL, O., Investigation of the concentration of lactic acid in blood and urine under physiologic and pathologic conditions, *Acta med. Scandinav. Supp. No. 24*, 5 (1928).

KATTUS, A., T. M. ARRINGTON, and E. V. NEWMAN, Clinical observations on a new oral diuretic 1-propyl-3-ethyl-6-aminouracil and preliminary studies on 1-allyl-3-ethyl-6-aminouracil, *Am. J. Med.* **12**, 319 (1952).

KARTUN, P., P. PARIS, J. NORY, and G. BOUSQUET, Action précoce sur la circulation de retour de l'injection intraveineuse d'un diurétique mercuriel, *Arch. d. mal. du cœur* **43**, 133 (1950).

KATZ, L. N., W. W. HAMBURGER, and S. H. RUBINFELD, Observations on the effects of oxygen therapy. II. Changes in the circulation and respiration, *Am. J. M. Sc.* **184**, 810 (1932). [64

KEITH, N. M., and M. WHELAN, A study of the action of ammonium chloride and organic mercury compounds, *J. Clin. Investigation* **3**, 149 (1926–27). [65, 66, 67, 68, 72, 73, 74, 76, 79, 83

KELLY, H. G., and R. I. S. BAYLISS, Influence of heart-rate on cardiac output. Studies with digoxin and atropin, *Lancet* **2**, 1071 (1949). [59

KETY, S. S., and C. F. SCHMIDT, Effects of alterations in the arterial tensions of carbon dioxide and oxygen on cerebral blood flow and cerebral oxygen consumption of normal young men, *Federation Proc.* **5**, 55 (1946).

KININMONTH, J. G., The circulation rate in some pathological states, with observations on the effect of digitalis, *Quart. J. Med.* **21**, 277 (1928). [59

KINSMAN, J. M., and J. W. MOORE, The hemodynamics of the circulation in hypertension, *Ann. Int. Med.* **9**, 649 (1935). [59, 60, 61, 62

KIRSTEIN, L., Studies on the diuretic effect of injectable xanthine derivatives, *Acta med. Scandinav.* **128**, 122 (1947). [83

KLINGENSMITH, W. C., JR., and J. R. ELKINTON, Cation exchange resin in the treatment of congestive heart failure. II. Clinical effectiveness and chemical complications during prolonged periods of use, *Circulation* **5**, 842 (1952). [84

KRASNOW, S., and M. I. GROSSMAN, Stimulation of gastric secretion in man by theophylline ethylenediamine, *Proc. Soc. Exper. Biol. & Med.* **71**, 335 (1949).

KROETZ, C. F., Messung des Kreislaufminutenvolumens mit Acetylen als Fremdgas. Ihre bisherigen Ergebnisse bei arteriellen Hochdruck und bei Dekompensation des Kreislaufs, *Klin. Wchnschr.* **9**, 966 (1930). [59

KUPFER, S., D. D. THOMPSON, and R. F. PITTS, The isolated kidney and its response to diuretic agents, *Am. J. Physiol.* **167**, 703 (1951).

KYLIN, E., Studien über den kolloidosmotischen (onkotischen) Druck. XVIII. Ueber die Einwirkung verschiedener Diuretica auf den kolloidosmotischen Drucke, *Arch. f. exper. Path. u. Pharmakol.* **164**, 33 (1932).

LA DUE, J. S., and G. FAHR, The effect of the intravenous administration of lanatoside C upon the output, diastolic volume, and mechanical efficiency of the failing human heart, *Am. Heart J.* **25**, 344 (1943). [59, 60, 61

LAGERLÖF, H., and L. WERKÖ, Studies on the circulation in man. V. The effect of cedilanid (lanatoside C) on cardiac output and blood pressure in the pulmonary circulation in patients with compensated and decompensated heart disease, *Acta cardiol.* **4**, 1 (1949). [59

LASSEN, H. C. A., Some investigations on the kidney function in heart lesions, *Acta med. Scandinav. Supp.* **50**, 413 (1932). [81

LAUTER, S., and H. BAUMANN, Zur Theorie der Herzinsufficienz und der Digitaliswirkung, *Klin. Wchnschr.* **8**, 263 (1929). [59

LAYNE, J. A., F. R. SCHEMM, and W. W. HURST, Further comparative studies on ascites in liver and heart disease, *Gastroenterol.* **16**, 91 (1950).

LEFKEN, E. B., D. K. HAWLEY, and A. IGLAUER, Ammonium and potassium cation exchange resin in treatment of congestive heart failure, *Postgrad. Med.* **12**, 537 (1952). [84

LESSER, G. T., M. F. DUNNING, F. H. EPSTEIN, and E. Y. BERGER, Mercurial diuresis in edematous individuals, *Circulation* **5**, 85 (1951). [73, 74, 75

LEVIN, E., Acción de los diuréticos mercuriales sobre el volumen sanguineo, *Rev. argent. de cardiol.* **8**, 267 (1941).

LIAN, C., and E. BARRAS, Intérêt clinique de la mesure de vitesse de la circulation par l'épreuve de la fluorescéine, *Bull. et mém. Soc. méd. d. hôp. de Paris* **46**, 179 (1930).   [60

LOEB, R. F., D. W. ATCHLEY, D. W. RICHARDS, JR., E. M. BENEDICT, and M. E. DRISCOLL, On the mechanism of nephrotic edema, *J. Clin. Investigation* **11**, 621 (1932).   [65, 66, 67

LYONS, R. H., N. L. AVERY, JR., and S. D. JACOBSON, Effect of dehydration, produced by mercupurin, on the plasma volume of normal persons, *Am. Heart J.* **28**, 247 (1944a).   [76

LYONS, R. H., S. D. JACOBSON, and N. L. AVERY, JR., The effect on the plasma volume of dehydration produced by a low-salt diet and ammonium chloride, *Am. Heart J.* **27**, 353 (1944b).

LYONS, R. H., S. D. JACOBSON, and N. L. AVERY, JR., The change in plasma volume and body weight in normal subjects after a low salt diet, ammonium chloride and mercupurin, *Am. J. M. Sc.* **211**, 460 (1946).   [76

MACKAY, E. M., A. N. WICK, H. O. CARNE, and C. P. BARNUM, The influence of alkalosis and acidosis upon fasting ketosis, *J. Biol. Chem.* **138**, 63 (1941).

MACKLER, B., H. LICHTENSTEIN, and G. M. GUEST, Effects of ammonium chloride acidosis on glucose tolerance in dogs, *Am. J. Physiol.* **168**, 126 (1952).

MACLAGLAN, N. F., The influence of the acid base equilibrium on gastric secretion, *J. Physiol.* **83**, 16 P (1935).   [68, 69, 71

MAGENDANTZ, H., and F. STRATMAN, Ueber die extrarenale Wasserausscheidung bei Herzinsufficienz, *Deutsches Arch. f. klin. Med.* **174**, 1 (1933).

MARTZ, B. L., K. G. KOHLSTAEDT, and O. M. HELMER, Use of a combination of anion and cation exchange resins in the treatment of edema and ascites, *Circulation* **5**, 524 (1952).   [84

MARVEL, R. J., and W. A. SHULLENBERGER, Thromboembolic phenomena associated with rapid diuresis in the treatment of congestive heart failure, *Am. Heart J.* **42**, 194 (1951).

MASSIE, E., H. S. STILLERMAN, C.-S. WRIGHT, and V. MINNICH, Effect of administration of digitalis on coagulability of human blood, *Arch. Int. Med.* **74**, 172 (1944).

McLEAN, F., The numerical laws governing the rate of excretion of urea and chlorides in man. II. The influence of pathological conditions and of drugs on excretion, *J. Exper. Med.* **22**, 366 (1915).

McMICHAEL, J., and E. P. SHARPEY-SCHAFER, The action of intravenous digoxin in man, *Quart. J. Med.* **13**, 123 (1944).   [59

MELVILLE, K. I., and R. L. STEHLE, Novasuroldiurese, *Arch. f. exper. Path. u. Pharmakol.* **123**, 175 (1927).   [73, 74

MERRILL, A. J., Edema and decreased renal blood flow in patients with chronic congestive failure. Evidence of "forward failure" as the primary cause of edema, *J. Clin. Investigation* **25**, 389 (1946).

MEYER, P., Untersuchungen über den kolloidosmotischen Druck des Blutes. II. Salyrgandiurese, *Ztschr. f. klin. Med.* **116**, 174 (1931a).
[76, 80

MEYER, P., Untersuchungen über den kolloidosmotischen Druck des Blutes. III. Die Euphyllindiurese, *Ztschr. f. klin. Med.* **116**, 687 (1931b).

MEYERS, J. H., and E. B. MAN, Artifactual values of serum precipitable iodine after clinical intramuscular injections of mercuhydrin, *J. Lab. & Clin. Med.* **37**, 867 (1951).

MIES, H., Ueber die Wirkung des Strophanthin auf die zirkulierende Blutmenge, *Ztschr. f. Kreislaufforsch.* **23**, 460 (1931).

MILLER, G. E., Water and electrolyte metabolism in congestive heart failure, *Circulation* **4**, 270 (1951). [73, 74, 75

MÖLLER, K. O., Flüssigkeits- und Chloridaustausch zwischen Blut und Geweben nach Theophyllineingabe, *Arch. f. exper. Path. u. Pharmakol.* **126**, 143 (1927). [83

MØLLER, K. O., Det teoretiske grundlag for den kliniske anvendelse af kviksølvholdige diuretika med saerligt henblik paa salyrgan, *Nord. med. tidskr.* **13**, 321 (1937). [73

MONTGOMERY, H., and O. HORWITZ, Oxygen tension of tissues by the polarigraphic method. I. Introduction: Oxygen tension and blood flow of the skin of human extremities, *J. Clin. Investigation* **29**, 1120 (1950).

MOUNSEY, J. P. D., L. W. RITZMAN, N. J. SELVERSTONE, W. A. BRISCOE, and G. A. McLEMORE, Circulatory changes in severe pulmonary emphysema, *Brit. Heart J.* **14**, 153 (1952).

MOYER, J. H., C. A. HANDLEY, and R. A. SIEBERT, Clinical diuretic studies on three new mercurial compounds, *Am. Heart. J.* **44**, 281 (1952).
[74

MOYER, J. H., S. I. MILLER, A. B. TASHNEK, and R. BOWMAN, The effect of theophylline with ethylenediamine (aminophylline) on cerebral hemodynamics in the presence of cardiac failure with and without Cheyne-Stokes respiration, *J. Clin. Investigation* **31**, 267 (1952).

MÜHLING, A., Studien über die diuretische Wirkungsweise von Quecksilber. Ausgefuhrt mit dem organischen Quecksilberpräparat Novasurol, *München. med. Wchnschr.* **68**, 1447 (1921). [73, 75, 79

NEWMAN, E. V., Function of the kidney and metabolic changes in cardiac failure, *Am. J. Med.* **7**, 490 (1949).

NIELSEN, M., Untersuchungen uber die Atemregulation beim Menschen besonders mit Hinblick auf die Art des chemischen Reiges, *Skandinav. Arch. f. Physiol., Supp. No. 10*, 83 (1936).   [68, 69, 70, 71

NONNEBRUCK, W., Ueber die Wirkung des Novasurols auf Blut und Diurese, *München. med. Wchnschr.* **68**, 1282 (1921).   [73, 74, 76

NORLIN, G., Das Minutenvolumen des Herzens bei experimenteller Azidose, *Skandinav. Arch. f. Physiol.* **67**, 170 (1933).   [70, 71

NOTHMANN, M., Beobachtungen bei der Salyrgandiurese, *Ztschr. f. klin. Med.* **120**, 158 (1932).   [73, 75

NOTHMANN, M., Weitere Untersuchungen über den Mineralstoffwechsel bei Salyrgandiurese, *Arch. f. exper. Path. u. Pharmakol.* **172**, 402 (1933).   [73, 75

NYLIN, G., L'influence de la digitale sur la dette relative d'oxygène dans l'insuffisance cardiaque latente à rhythme cardiaque normal, *Arch. d. mal. du cœur* **32**, 1010 (1939).

OELKERS, H. A., Untersuchungen über den kolloidosmotischen Druck des Serums, *Ztschr. f. klin. Med.* **115**, 854 (1931).

OTIS, A. B., H. RAHN, M. BRONTMAN, L. J. MULLINS, and W. O. FENN, Ballistocardiographic study of changes in cardiac output due to respiration, *J. Clin. Investigation* **25**, 413 (1946).

PAGE, I. H., The action of certain diuretics in the function of the kidney as measured by the urea clearance test, *J. Clin. Investigation* **12**, 737 (1933).

PERE, S. A. N., The effect of digitalis, strophanthin, and novurit on blood coagulation, *Acta med. Scandinav. Supp.* **251**, 1 (1950).

PETERSEN, A., Studier over Virkningen af kviksølvholdige diuretica Paa Ødematøse Patienter. Med. saerligt. henblik paa blodets vand- og cloridinhold, *Ugesk. f. læger* **102**, 46 (1940).   [73, 75, 79

PILCHER, C., G. CLARK, and T. R. HARRISON, Studies in congestive heart failure. III. The buffering power of the blood and tissues, *J. Clin. Investigation* **8**, 317 (1929–30).   [68, 69

PITTS, R. F., and J. J. DUGGAN, Filtration rate and sodium and water excretion following mercurial diuretics, *Federation Proc.* **8**, 127 (1949).   [74

PITTS, R. F., and J. J. DUGGAN, Studies on diuretics. II. The relationship between glomerular filtration rate, proximal tubular absorption of sodium and diuretic efficacy of mercurials, *J. Clin. Investigation* **29**, 373 (1950).   [74

PLATTS, M. M., The arterial blood gases in pulmonary heart failure, *Clin. Sc.* **12**, 63 (1953).

PROGER, S. H., and H. MAGENDANTZ, Effect of prolonged dietary restriction on patients with cardiac failure, *Arch. Int. Med.* **58**, 703 (1936).   [59, 62, 63

Pugh, L. C. G., and C. L. Wyndham, The circulatory effects of mercurial diuretics in congestive heart failure, *Clin. Sc.* **8,** 10 (1949).

Reaser, P. R., and G. E. Burch, Radiosodium tracer studies in congestive heart failure, *Proc. Soc. Exper. Biol. & Med.* **63,** 543 (1946).

Reveley, H. P., G. R. Herrmann, and J. A. Ortiz, Studies of factors in congestive heart failure during effective therapy, *Texas State J. Med.* **47,** 617 (1951). [74, 81

Reynolds, T., Sweat sodium levels in congestive heart failure, *Proc. Soc. Exper. Biol. & Med.* **79,** 118 (1952).

Richards, D. W., Jr., and A. L. Barach, Prolonged residence in high oxygen atmospheres. Effects on normal individuals and on patients with chronic cardiac and pulmonary insufficiency, *Quart. J. Med.* **3,** 457 (1934). [64

Ringer, M., and M. D. Altschule, Studies on the circulation. II. Cardiac output in diseases of the heart, and under the influence of digitalis therapy, *Am. Heart J.* **5,** 305 (1930). [59

Sartorius, O. W., J. C. Roemmelt, and R. F. Pitts, The renal regulation of acid-base balance in man. IV. The nature of the renal compensations in ammonium chloride acidosis, *J. Clin. Investigation* **28,** 423 (1949). [66, 67, 68, 69

Saxl, P., and R. Heilig, Ueber die diuretische wirkung von Novasurol und anderen Quecksilberinjektionen, *Wien. klin. Wchnschr.* **33,** 943 (1920). [73, 80

Saxl, P., and R. Heilig, Über die Novasuroldiurese, *Ztschr. f. d. ges. exper. Med.* **38,** 94 (1923). [75, 76, 78, 80

Scébat, L., P. Maurice, and J. Lenègre, L'action d'un diurétique mercuriel sur la pression sanguine des cavités droites du coeur chez les cardiaques, *Arch. d. mal. du cœur* **42,** 1149 (1949).

Schally, A. O., Veränderungen der Bluteiweisskörper bei der Salyrgandiurese, *Deutsches Arch. f. klin. Med.* **177,** 368 (1935).

Schieve, J. F., and W. P. Wilson, The changes in cerebral vascular resistance of man in experimental alkalosis and acidosis, *J. Clin. Investigation* **32,** 33 (1953).

Schmitz, H. L., Studies on the action of diuretics. I. The effect of euphyllin and salyrgan upon glomerular filtration and tubular reabsorption, *J. Clin. Investigation* **11,** 1075 (1932). [81, 82

Schmitz, H. L., Studies on the action of diuretics. II. The effect of salyrgan upon the water content of the plasma as measured by the refractive index, *J. Clin. Investigation* **12,** 741 (1933).

Schoen, R., and E. Derra, Untersuchungen über die Bedeutung der Zyanose als klinisches Symptom (I), *Deutsches Arch. f. klin. Med.* **168,** 52, (1930).

Schroeder, H. A., Studies on congestive circulatory failure. IV. The effect of various diuretics on the excretion of water and chlorides, *Circulation* **4**, 87 (1951).   [73, 75

SQUIRES, R. D., A. P. CROSLEY, JR., and J. R. ELKINTON, The distribution of body fluids in congestive heart failure. III. Exchanges in patients during diuresis, *Circulation* **4**, 868 (1951).   [73, 74, 75

SCHWARTZ, W. B., The role of electrolyte balance in the response to mercurial diuretics in congestive heart failure, *Bull. New England M. Center* **12**, 213 (1950).   [73, 74, 75

SCHWARTZ, W. B., and W. M. WALLACE, Electrolyte equilibrium during mercurial diuresis, *J. Clin. Investigation* **30**, 1089 (1951).
                                                            [65, 73, 74, 75

SEYMOUR, W. B., W. H., PRITCHARD, L. P. LONGLEY, and J. M. HAYMAN, JR., Cardiac output, blood and interstitial fluid volumes, total circulating serum protein, and kidney function during cardiac failure and after improvement, *J. Clin. Investigation* **21**, 229 (1942).

SHOCK, N. W., and A. B. HASTINGS, Studies of the acid-base balance of the blood. IV. Characterization and interpretation of displacement of the acid-base balance, *J. Biol. Chem.* **112**, 239 (1935).   [68, 69

SIMMERT, H., Über die diuretische Wirkung organischer Quecksilberverbindungen, *Klin. Wchnschr.* **14**, 530 (1935).   [73, 75, 78

SINCLAIR-SMITH, B., A. A. KATTUS, J. GENEST, and E. V. NEWMAN, The renal mechanism of electrolyte excretion and the metabolic balances of electrolytes and nitrogen in congestive cardiac failure; the effects of exercise, rest and aminophyllin, *Bull. Johns Hopkins Hosp.* **84**, 369 (1949).   [61, 83

SMITH, W. C., G. L. WALKER, and H. L. ALT, The cardiac output in heart disease. I. Complete heart block, auricular fibrillation before and after the restoration to normal rhythm, subacute rheumatic fever and chronic rheumatic valvular disease, *Arch. Int. Med.* **45**, 706 (1930).
                                                                [59, 63

SOKOLOFF, L., and M. I. FERRER, Effect of digitalization on the coagulation time in man, *Proc. Soc. Exper. Biol. & Med.* **59**, 309 (1945).

SOLOFF, L. A., J. ZATUCHNI, and J. H. BOUTWELL, The relationship of some electrolytes of the serum, edema fluid, and urine in a case of intractable heart failure, *Am. Heart J.* **44**, 766 (1952).

SPUHLER, V. O., K. WIESINGER, and E. MEILI, Diuretica und zirkulierende Plasmamenge, *Helvet. med. acta* **15**, 95 (1948).

SQUIRES, R. D., R. B. SINGER, G. R. MOFFITT, JR., and J. R. ELKINTON, The distribution of body fluids in congestive heart failure. II. Abnormalities in serum electrolyte concentration and in acid-base equilibrium, *Circulation* **4**, 697 (1951).   [75

STAPLETON, J. F., and W. P. HARVEY, Hypochloremic alkalosis induced by mercurial diuretics in congestive heart failure, *Arch. Int. Med.* **90,** 425 (1952). [75

STARR, I., C. J. GAMBLE, A. MARGOLIES, J. S. DONAL, JR., N. JOSEPH, and E. EAGLE, A clinical study of the action of 10 commonly used drugs on cardiac output, work and size; on respiration, on metabolic rate and on the electrocardiogram, *J. Clin. Investigation* **16,** 799 (1937). [59

STEAD, E. A., JR., J. V. WARREN, and E. S. BRANNON, Effect of lanatoside C on the circulation of patients with congestive failure. A study using catheterization of the right side of the heart, *Arch. Int. Med.* **81,** 282 (1948). [59, 61

STEWART, H. J., Mechanism of diuresis: alterations in the specific gravity of the blood plasma with onset of diuresis in heart failure, *J. Clin. Investigation* **20,** 1 (1941).

STEWART, H. J., and A. E. COHN, Studies on the effect of the action of digitalis on the output of blood from the heart. III. Part 2. The effect on the output of hearts in heart failure with congestion in human beings, *J. Clin. Investigation* **11,** 933 (1932). [59, 61, 62

STEWART, H. J., J. E. DEITRICK, N. F. CRANE, and C. H. WHEELER, Action of digitalis in uncompensated heart disease, *Arch. Int. Med.* **62,** 569 (1938). [59, 61, 62, 63

STEWART, H. J., W. F. EVANS, H. BROWN, and J. R. GERJUOY, Peripheral blood flow, rectal and skin temperature in congestive heart failure. The effects of rapid digitalization in this state, *Arch. Int. Med.* **77,** 643 (1946). [60, 61

STEWART, H. J., and N. B. JACK, The effect of aminophyllin on peripheral blood flow, *Am. Heart J.* **20,** 295 (1940).

STEYRER, A., Ueber osmotische Analyse des Harns, *Beitr. z. chem. Physiol. u. Path.* **2,** 312 (1902).

STOCK, R. J., G. H. MUDGE, and M. J. NURNBERG, Congestive heart failure. Variations in electrolyte metabolism with salt restriction and mercurial diuretics, *Circulation* **4,** 54 (1951). [73, 74, 75, 79

STOCKTON, A. B., Diuretic effects and changes in blood and urinary metabolites after digitalis in normal and edematous persons, *Arch. Int. Med.* **50,** 480 (1932).

STOCKTON, A. B., Action of diuretic drugs and changes in metabolites in edematous patients, *Arch. Int. Med.* **58,** 891 (1936). [73, 75, 78, 83

STORSTEIN, O., Measurement of the venous pressure and of the circulation time, *Acta med. Scandinav.* **136,** 122 (1949). [60, 61

SUTTON, G. C., Studies on blood coagulation and the effect of digitalis, *Circulation* **2,** 271 (1950). [52

SWIGERT, V. W., and R. FITZ, The effect of mersalyl (salyrgan) on plasma volume, *J. A. M. A.* **115**, 1786 (1940). [75

TAYLOR, H. L., L. ERICKSON, A. HENSCHEL, and A. KEYS, The effect of bed rest on the blood volume of normal young men, *Am. J. Physiol.* **144**, 227 (1945).

TEPPER, W., Die Wirkung des Strophanthins auf den Venendruck bei kardialer Insuffizienz, *Deutsche med. Wchnschr.* **75**, 142 (1950). [61

THOMSON, G., D. M. MITCHELL, and L. C. KOLB, The influence of variations in systemic acid-base balance upon carbohydrate tolerance in normal subjects, *Biochem. J.* **27**, 1253 (1933). [68

THREEFOOT, S., T. GIBBONS, and G. BURCH, Relationship of weight, venous pressure and radiosodium (Na^{22}) excretion in chronic congestive heart failure, *Proc. Soc. Exper. Biol. & Med.* **66**, 369 (1947).
[74

TRUITT, E. B., V. A. McKUSICK, and J. C. KRANTZ, JR., Theophylline blood levels after oral, rectal and intravenous administration and correlation with diuretic action, *J. Pharmacol. & Exper. Therap.* **100**, 309 (1950). [83

VAN LINGEN, B., J. H. GEAR, and J. WHIDBOURNE, Ballistocardiographic patterns in congestive cardiac failure before and after the intravenous administration of digitalis, *South African J. Clin. Sc.* **2**, 239 (1951).
[59

VOLINI, I. F., and R. O. LEVITT, Studies on mercurial diuresis. II. The immediate effect on the venous blood pressure, *Am. Heart J.* **17**, 187 (1939).

VOLINI, I. F., and R. O. LEVITT, Studies on mercurial diuresis. III. The alteration induced in the cerebrospinal fluid pressure, *Am. Heart J.* **19**, 566 (1940).

VOYLES, C., and E. S. ORGAIN, Prolonged cation-exchange resin therapy in congestive heart failure, *New England J. Med.* **245**, 808 (1951). [84

VOYLES, C. M., JR., and E. S. ORGAIN, The prolonged administration of cation exchange resin as a supplementary measure in congestive heart failure, *South. M. J.* **45**, 439 (1952). [84

WATT, J. G., P. R. DUMKE, and J. H. COMROE, JR., Effects of inhalation of 100 per cent and 14 per cent oxygen upon respiration of unanesthetized dogs before and after chemoreceptor denervation, *Am. J. Physiol.* **138**, 610 (1943).

WECHSLER, R. L., L. M. KLEISS, and S. S. KETY, The effects of intravenously administered aminophylline on cerebral circulation and metabolism in man, *J. Clin. Investigation* **29**, 28 (1950).

WERKÖ, L. and H. LAGERLÖF, Studies on the circulation of blood in man.

VII. The effects of a single intravenous dose of theophylline diethan-olamine on the cardiac output, pulmonary blood volume and systemic and pulmonary blood pressures in hypertensive cardiovascular disease, *Scandinav. J. Clin. & Lab. Investigation* 1, 181 (1949).

WESTON, R. E., and D. J. W. ESCHER, An analysis of the unresponsiveness of mercurial diuretics observed in certain patients with severe chronic congestive failure, *J. Clin. Investigation* 27, 561 (1948).

WESTON, R. E., D. J. W. ESCHER, J. GROSSMAN, and L. LEITER, Mechanisms contributing to unresponsiveness to mercurial diuretics in congestive failure, *J. Clin. Investigation* 31, 901 (1952).   [74, 81

WESTON, R. E., J. GROSSMAN, E. R. BORUN, H. A. GUERIN, H. MARK, T. D. ULLMAN, M. WOLFMAN, and L. LEITER, Metabolic studies on the effects of ion exchange resins in edematous patients with cardiac and renal disease, *Am. J. Med.* 14, 404 (1953).   [84

WESTON, R. E., J. GROSSMAN, I. S. EDELMAN, D. J. W. ESCHER, L. LEITER, and L. HELLMAN, Renal tubular action of diuretics. II. Effects of mercurial diuresis on glucose reabsorption, *Federation Proc.* 8, 164 (1949).

WESTON, R. E., J. GROSSMAN, and L. LEITER, The effect of mercurial diuretics on renal ammonia and titrable acidity production in acidotic human subjects with reference to site of diuretic action, *J. Clin. Investigation* 30, 1262 (1951).

WHITEHORN, W. V., A. EDELMANN, and F. A. HITCHCOCK, The cardiovascular response to the breathing of 100 per cent oxygen at normal barometric pressure, *Am. J. Physiol.* 146, 61 (1946).

WOLLHEIM, E., Untersuchungen zur Hämodynamik unter Digitalis und Strophanthin, *Deutsche med. Wchnschr.* 75, 482 (1950).   [60

WOOD, J. E., JR., D. FERGUSON, and P. LOWRANCE, The use of cation resins in the treatment of edema, *Virginia M. Monthly* 79, 300 (1952).   [84

WOOD, J. E., JR., D. H. FERGUSON, and P. LOWRANCE, Cation exchange resins as an adjunct in treatment of heart failure, *J. A. M. A.* 148, 820 (1952).   [84

WOOD, P., The action of digitalis in heart failure with normal rhythm, *Brit. Heart J.* 2, 132 (1940).   [60, 61

WOOD, P., and J. PAULETT, The effect of digitalis on the venous pressure, *Brit. Heart J.* 11, 83 (1949).   [59

ZIMMERMAN, H., A study of the pulmonary circulation in man, *Dis. of Chest* 20, 46 (1951).   [59

37. *"Backward" Failure. "Forward" Failure. A Generalization Concerning the Pathogenesis of the Signs and Symptoms of Congestive Heart Failure*

It is evident from all of the foregoing discussion that chronic cardiac decompensation is associated with a large number of complexly interrelated bodily changes. That other changes, as yet unrecognized, may occur is likely.

A low cardiac output is the rule in cardiac decompensation that is not complicated by anemia, fever, thyrotoxicosis, acidosis, cor pulmonale, severe thiamine deficiency, and so on. The few reported studies in which a normal cardiac output was found in the absence of these complicating diseases included patients in whom were found elevated metabolic rates as high as plus 85 per cent consequent solely to congestive failure itself. It is clear that under these circumstances the cardiac output is low in proportion to the metabolic needs of the body. The disproportion between circulation and metabolism in congestive failure is greatly aggravated by exercise, a factor which is responsible for increase in symptoms in all patients with myocardial insufficiency. Most patients with congestive failure have elevated venous pressures. The normal response to such increases in venous pressure is a considerable increase in cardiac output, but decompensated patients do not exhibit this response.

The widespread physiologic changes in congestive failure are all probably secondary to a cardiac output that is low in relation to the metabolic needs of the body and to the venous return. It must be borne in mind, however, that some of these secondary changes may overshadow the lowering of the cardiac output as the direct cause of one symptom or another in some patients. Thus, in some instances, intrapulmonary changes may be more important in the genesis of dyspnea, or lowering of the plasma protein level more important in the genesis of edema, than anoxemia consequent to an inadequate cardiac output. The low cardiac output of congestive failure may give rise to the signs and symptoms of cardiac decompensation in many ways. All or nearly all of these different mechanisms are present in all patients with congestive failure, but one or another may predominate in a given patient, or several may be equally important.

This concept is not new and has been expressed in various terms by other authors. Particularly pertinent is the conclusion of Weiss and Ellis (1930) that "evidence is available that a number of mechanisms are responsible for the clinical manifestations of cardiovascular diseases. Confusion exists, nevertheless, because results of experimental and clinical studies of a single aspect of the circulation are still offered as an explanation or index of the multiform nature of circulatory failure."

Any theory that attempts to explain the origin of all the signs and symptoms of congestive failure as *directly* consequent to "forward" failure (low cardiac output) or "backward" failure (increased peripheral and pulmonary venous pressures) is clearly inadequate. Back pressure can occur only if the blood fails to go forward; moreover, failure of the blood to go forward must result in back pressure, provided the volume of circulating blood does not decrease. An additional criticism of both theories is that both neglect the chemical changes that are potent factors in the genesis of various signs and symptoms of cardiac decompensation.

As stated previously (Altschule, 1938), a valid generalization concerning the origin of the signs and symptoms of chronic congestive failure is that they are due to summation of the effects of submaximal or even minimal changes in a multiplicity of complexly interrelated factors and that the degree of change in each of these factors, and consequently their importance, varies from patient to patient. The fundamental defect, however, is a cardiac output which, in relation to the metabolic requirements of the body and to the venous return, is abnormally lowered.

Bibliography

Chapter I — Section 37

ALTSCHULE, M. D., The pathological physiology of chronic cardiac decompensation, *Medicine* **17**, 75 (1938).

WEISS, S., and L. B. ELLIS, Circulatory measurements in patients with rheumatic heart disease before and after the administration of digitalis, *J. Clin. Investigation* **8**, 435 (1929–30).

II

ACUTE PULMONARY EDEMA. CARDIAC ASTHMA

The syndromes of acute pulmonary edema and cardiac asthma in patients with heart disease are considered by most clinicians to be caused by sudden weakening of the left ventricle, while the right ventricle continues normal function, at least for some time. This view receives little, if any, support from physiologic studies and is not accepted by physiologists; studies in animals, such as those of Modrakowski (1914) and those reviewed by Luisada (1940) by Henneman (1946), and by Cameron (1948), throw much doubt on the concept. The reviews of Luisada (1940), Henneman (1946), Cameron (1948), and Altschule (1954) bring forward strong evidence for the view that pulmonary edema is caused by the summation of submaximal changes in several complexly interrelated physiologic phenomena, with one mechanism or another playing a preponderant part in different situations; the fundamental disorder appears to be a rate of transudation from the pulmonary capillaries that exceeds the reabsorptive capacity of the pulmonary lymphatics. It must be borne in mind that pulmonary blood capillaries do not absorb protein-containing fluids and, since the latter must be taken up by lymphatics, the development of acute pulmonary edema is an indication that the lymphatics have been overwhelmed by the rate of diffusion from the blood capillaries that obtains at the time (Drinker and Hardenbergh, 1949).

The factors that contribute to this imbalance are:

I. Increased transudation
    A. Elevated capillary pressure in lungs
        1. Cardiac decompensation, mitral stenosis

 2. Venular constriction
    a. Neurogenic venoconstriction
    b. Histamine?
 B. Increased filtering area in lungs
    1. Increased blood volume
    2. Redistribution of blood
       a. Peripheral vasoconstriction
 C. Large blood flow in lungs
 D. Lowered plasma protein level
 E. Increased capillary permeability
    1. Anoxia
    2. Histamine?
    3. Toxins
 F. Bronchospasm
 II. Decreased reabsorption
 A. Impaired lymphatic function
    1. Elevated systemic venous pressure
    2. Inflammatory thrombosis?
III. Increased total extracellular fluid volume

In diseases in which lymphatic function is disturbed, such as some instances of interstitial pneumonia or of pulmonary fibrosis, or in conditions in which lymphatic pressure rises, such as congestive failure with high systemic venous pressure (Paine *et al.*, 1950), relatively small changes in blood capillary permeability or filtering pressure produce edema of the lungs. On the other hand, where pulmonary lymphatic function is not so impaired, changes in blood capillary permeability and in filtering pressure would have to be large to cause pulmonary edema to develop; in such circumstances, although the rate of filtration from the blood capillaries may greatly exceed the normal, pulmonary edema need not develop. Lowered plasma protein level is a contributing factor (Paine and Smith, 1949) in that it exaggerates the influence of capillary pressure. On the other hand, under conditions in which filtration from pulmonary capillaries is increased, such as anoxia or greatly increased pulmonary capillary pressure, pulmonary arteriolar constriction develops (page 64) and, by diminishing pulmonary blood flow, maintains filtration from the blood capillaries at a level at or near that which can be met by the lymphatics. In addition, the appearance of overt manifestations of pulmonary edema depends to some extent on salt and water metabolism. Edema fluid containing sodium accumulates mainly in collagenous tissue and the tissues proportionately richest in collagen are skin and lung; sodium retention must exert an important influence in determining the level at which the factors described above produce the syndrome. For instance, Merrill *et al.* (1950) have shown that dialysis of the blood via the artificial kidney relieves pulmonary edema irrespective of whether the blood volume is diminished by the procedure or not. It is evident from this brief analysis that to regard pulmonary edema as the same as left ventricular failure is not valid on physiologic grounds. Moreover, the concept that pulmonary edema is the same as left ventricular failure is not helpful therapeutically and may be misleading diagnostically; it should be abandoned. For the purposes of the present discussion, acute pulmonary edema will be considered a syndrome caused by mechanisms whose nature has not yet been established, although the precipitating factors are fairly well understood.

Cardiac output. — Lauter's (1930) observations in three patients, using cardiac puncture to obtain blood for estimating arteriovenous oxygen difference, showed that the blood flow through the lungs, that is, the output of the right ventricle, was diminished. That of the left ventricle was, therefore, also decreased in these patients. Weiss and Robb (1933) used the dye method to measure cardiac output and found it to be unchanged or decreased during the attack; however, some of their patients had low cardiac outputs and increased arteriovenous oxygen differences (measured by means of blood drawn from the femoral artery and vein) between attacks. Their data are not presented in detail; consequently it is impossible to analyze them further here. Moreover, the dye method used by them to estimate cardiac output is less accurate than the other methods commonly used. Lenègre *et al.* (1953) used intracardiac catheterization to study the circulation in acute pulmonary edema and found the output of the right ventricle to be low. The cardiac output and pulmonary blood flow in patients with mitral stenosis who develop pulmonary edema readily is low (page 413). However, in such cases, a further fall in cardiac output may be accompanied by disappearance of attacks of pulmonary edema.

Pulmonary vascular pressures. — Patients with mitral stenosis who develop pulmonary edema readily, or who exhibit it at the time of observation, have very high pulmonary capillary pressures (page 413). Lagerlöf and Werkö (1949) also found the pulmonary capillary pressure to be elevated above the oncotic pressure of blood in a patient with pulmonary edema associated with hypertensive heart disease. Lenègre et al. (1953) studied a series of such patients and obtained similar findings. There is no close parallelism between the pulmonary capillary pressure and the occurrence of pulmonary edema. The pulmonary arterial pressure is elevated, of course (Lenègre et al., 1953).

Circulation time. — The arm-to-tongue or arm-to-face time is uniformly reported increased in patients with cardiac asthma (1; Plotz, 1939). Stead and Ebert (1942), in a discussion of the shock syndrome in patients with heart disease, reported studies of patients in shock who also had pulmonary edema; the circulation time was increased to the same degree as in the other reported instances of edema of the lungs. According to Oppenheimer and Hitzig (1936), the arm-to-lung time, as measured by means of ether, is normal, but Plotz (1939) and Schuman and Simmons (1952) found it to be increased in most patients during attacks. The arm-to-tongue or -face time is also increased *between* attacks (Plotz, 1939; Tarr et al., 1933; Weiss and Robb, 1933), so that it must be concluded that pulmonary congestion exists at such times also, and apparently is not greatly increased during the attack itself. These findings throw doubt on the concept that cardiac asthma and pulmonary edema are caused by rapidly developing stasis in the lungs consequent to sudden weakening of the left ventricle. The long arm-to-tongue or -face circulation time of cardiac asthma is used to help differentiate it from bronchial asthma, where the circulation time is normal or somewhat shortened.

Venous pressure. — Although a few authors describe the venous pressure as unchanged (Oppenheimer and Hitzig, 1936; Weiss and Robb, 1933) or only occasionally and slightly elevated (Weiss and Robb, 1933; Wood, 1936), a majority record the finding of elevated venous pressures during and immediately after the attack (Villaret et al., 1923; Tornquist, 1932; Altschule, 1937; Perera and Berliner, 1943). The right auricular pressure is usually elevated during attacks (Sarnoff et al., 1952; Lenègre et al., 1953). Richards et al.

(1942) studied the intra-auricular and venous pressures in animals with spontaneous or induced pulmonary edema and found that both pressures were elevated, but the latter was raised relatively less, so that the normal gradient between the two disappeared. The cause of the elevation of venous pressure in attacks in man is not established, but it appears that diminished cardiac output, resistance to the flow of blood through the edematous lungs and probably also changes in intrapleural pressure are responsible for the peripheral venous engorgement. Actually the venous pressure may occasionally fall to very low levels in pulmonary edema; this may occur when the attack is complicated or terminated by the development of a state of shock (Altschule, 1937; Stead and Ebert, 1942).

Arterial pressure. — The arterial blood pressure may be unchanged, but is often elevated and occasionally depressed during the attack (Sonne and Hilden, 1950). Elevation of the blood pressure above its usual level may occur at the onset of the paroxysm even before dyspnea becomes marked or even apparent. This rise appears to be consequent to vasoconstriction due to sympathetic activity for, at such times, the patient appears pale and sweaty. A fall in arterial pressure of varying degree may occur in association with the development of a greater or lesser amount of shock (Stead and Ebert, 1942; Sonne and Hilden, 1950).

Respiratory dynamics. — Few data bearing on respiratory function in man during paroxysms of cardiac asthma or pulmonary edema have been reported. Respirations visibly increase in rate and become labored. The vital capacity, low between attacks (Weiss and Robb, 1933), becomes lower during paroxysms (Weiss and Robb, 1933; Perera and Berliner, 1943). This observation implies not only encroachment upon space available for respiration but also an increase in rigidity and loss of elasticity of the lungs, as more fluid accumulates in the interstitial tissues. Both of these phenomena give rise to dyspnea, but the change in rigidity may also activate the Hering-Breuer reflex and lead thereby to hyperpnea. Another consequence of impaired pulmonary elasticity is a rise in intrapleural pressure, which should be associated with a corresponding rise in venous pressure. Other subdivisions of the lung volume may show changes resembling those seen in chronic congestive failure (Weiss and Robb, 1933).

Blood gases; tissue gases. — The arterial blood oxygen saturation falls during attacks (Weiss and Robb, 1933; Penneys, 1952), often to very low levels, as a consequence of the above-described changes in the lungs. This arterial anoxia causes the cyanosis and contributes to the dyspnea seen in the syndrome. In addition, it aggravates the severity of the edema of the lungs itself (Gesell, 1928; Maurer, 1940; M. F. Warren *et al.*, 1942*a, b*). The arterial carbon dioxide content may be normal or increased (Porges *et al.*, 1913). Carbon dioxide is much more readily diffusible than oxygen and, accordingly, the hyperventilation that occurs during attacks should be enough to prevent the accumulation of carbon dioxide in any but very severe degrees of pulmonary edema. A single undetailed observation of the tissue gas tensions during an attack of pulmonary edema has been recorded by Sibree (1941*b*); increased tissue carbon dioxide tension and a normal oxygen tension are described. The accuracy of the latter observation may be questioned because the time required for equilibration of oxygen between the blood and the bubble of air introduced under the skin is longer than that for carbon dioxide; as is well known, attacks of cardiac asthma are usually of relatively short duration.

Blood lactate. — Harris, Jones, and Aldred (1935) reported elevation of the blood lactate at rest in a patient with cardiac asthma. This implies a high degree of tissue anoxia, apparently the consequence of the above-described changes in arterial blood oxygen saturation and possibly also of a decreased cardiac output. As pointed out previously, high blood lactate concentrations accentuate dyspnea (page 169).

Nocturnal occurrence of attacks. — A few patients have attacks of nocturnal dyspnea because they are orthopneic and slip down in bed while asleep; others have them in association with Cheyne-Stokes respiration, occurring spontaneously during sleep, or caused or exaggerated by sedatives that depress respiration. In most instances, the cause of the greater frequency of attacks of true cardiac asthma or pulmonary edema at night is not immediately apparent; this difficulty exists in large part because the cause of the paroxysms of pulmonary edema is not understood in general.

A phenomenon that bears on the problem is the fact that when an individual is up and about for a time, the plasma volume is about

ACUTE PULMONARY EDEMA

10 per cent less than when he is recumbent, apparently because of a loss of fluid into the legs (page 148); this fluid returns to the circulation during the hours spent in bed, presumably as a result of a fall in venous pressure (Hooker, 1914; Halmágyi et al., 1952). Accordingly, a patient with a tendency to pulmonary edema in effect receives an infusion of several hundred cubic centimeters of plasma when, after being up and about, he goes to bed. Convincing evidence in this direction, based on studies of vital capacity and plasma protein levels, has been published by Perera and Berliner (1943) and by Spealman et al. (1947). The observation of Harrison et al. (1934) that even bedridden patients exhibit a progressive fall in vital capacity and an increase in respiratory rate and minute volume toward evening is hard to explain; it has not been corroborated by other observers.

Another factor to be considered is the anoxia that normally develops during sleep (Doust and Schneider, 1952); this change increases transudation from the pulmonary capillaries.

Of great interest are the observations of Halmágyi et al. (1952, 1953); during sleep cardiac patients show a fall in pulmonary arterial, right auricular, and venous pressures, the pulmonary blood flow increasing somewhat. As has been shown in the case of mitral stenosis (page 413), an increase in pulmonary blood flow sometimes precipitates pulmonary edema.

Shock during pulmonary edema. — The occurrence of a marked fall in arterial and venous blood pressure, rise in pulse rate and appearance of clinical manifestations of shock as a complication or terminal event in pulmonary edema is not rare. Although this phenomenon has not been studied completely, it is possible to make tentative suggestions as to its origin. Profound anoxia and marked sympathetic overactivity may occur during attacks; both favor the occurrence of shock. In addition, it must be borne in mind that edematous lungs may, judging by their weight, contain as much as a liter or more of plasma, blood or other fluid, which are thus removed from the general circulation. In this connection, it is of interest that hemoconcentration has been found to occur during attacks of pulmonary edema (Lemierre and Bernard, 1926; Stead and Ebert, 1942; Perera and Berliner, 1943). Further loss of circulating blood volume may result from venesection. Usually, however, the veins are collapsed and the venous pressure is low at this time, so that vene-section is difficult or impossible. The importance of this factor may at times be demonstrable by means of the application of tourniquets; this may precipitate a fall in blood pressure, which may rise when the tourniquets are released. The occurrence of profound and per-sistent shock together with pulmonary edema almost always results fatally.

Wheezing. — Asthmatic wheezing may be a consequence of heart disease. It is considered to be similar in origin to acute pulmonary edema; instead, however, of an outpouring of edema fluid into the alveoli with the production of crackling and bubbling râles, there occurs spasm of the bronchi and the development of musical rhonchi. The bronchial spasm was shown to be reflex in origin by Weiss and Robb (1933); the origin of the reflex is obscure but it may be ini-tiated by accumulation of interstitial edema fluid in the lungs. The differentiation of cardiac asthma from bronchial asthma is of great importance since morphia in large doses relieves the first and may cause death in the second; contrariwise, epinephrine relieves bron-chial asthma and, in the doses used, may be fatal in cardiac asthma. If the differentiation cannot be made on clinical grounds, measure-ment of the circulation time is helpful (page 502). However, a severe paroxysm of wheezing may require immediate treatment before such measurements can be made; in such instances aminophylline, given intravenously, should be used since it controls both types of asthmatic paroxysm.

Effects of aminophylline. — The mechanism whereby aminophyl-line when given intravenously in doses of approximately 250 mg. relieves bronchospasm is not established. The drug is apparently a powerful relaxer of smooth muscle and this useful property results in relief of dyspnea and an increase in vital capacity in patients with cardiac asthma (Greene *et al.*, 1937; Heyer, 1946; Werkö and Lagerlöf 1949). However, the action of the drug also involves the smooth muscle of blood vessels and causes vasodilatation (Robertson and Faust, 1940). This phenomenon is useful in part because the resulting fall in venous pressure (Greene *et al.*, 1937; Robertson and Faust, 1940; Steinberg and Jensen, 1946; Sinclair-Smith *et al.*, 1949; Davis and Shock, 1949) causes a secondary decline in cerebrospinal fluid pressure (Greene *et al.*, 1937; Robertson and Faust, 1940); a change of this sort may alleviate dyspnea (page 259). On the other hand, the vasodilatation that occurs also causes the capillaries to dilate and the arterioles to relax (Robertson and Faust, 1940). Starr *et al.* (1937) and Werkö and Lagerlöf (1949) observed a decrease in peripheral resistance after the injection of theophylline and Werkö and Lagerlöf (1949), Zimmerman (1951), and Frisk *et al.* (1952) observed a fall in pulmonary arterial pressure and pulmonary vascular resistance. Werkö and Lagerlöf (1949) and Frisk *et al.* (1952) also observed a decrease in pulmonary capillary and right auricular pressures; a questionable decrease in pulmonary blood volume was also noted by the former. An increase in cardiac output (page 282), and in the volume of peripheral blood flow (Sewart and Jack, 1940) is known to occur, and a reduction in circulation time has also been described (Steinberg and Jensen, 1946; Werkö and Lagerlöf, 1949). Lowering of arterial pressure may act deleteriously on the heart in patients with coronary arteriosclerosis, and increased cardiac work may be dangerous in such individuals. Accordingly it is clear that aminophylline can be expected to cause cardiac pain or coronary failure in some patients with sclerotic coronary arteries, and collapse in any individual susceptible to the effects of generalized vasodilatation. It is fortunate that the administration of the drug intravenously at a slow rate avoids most of the circulatory effects while preserving the bronchodilating action of aminophylline.

The cerebral effect of aminophylline is a decrease in blood flow, owing apparently to cerebral vasoconstriction (Wechsler *et al.*, 1950; Moyer *et al.*, 1952). This phenomenon, although unexpected, may possibly explain in part the fall in spinal fluid pressure described above.

Effects of morphia. — It is widely held among clinicians that morphia, although not effective in every instance, is by far the most useful remedy for cardiac asthma and pulmonary edema. The reason for its effectiveness is not known. That it depresses the activity of the respiratory center, decreasing the respiratory minute volume (2; Dripps and Comroe, 1945) by decreasing respiratory rate, is established; changes in tidal air volume are variable. Harrison *et al.* (1934) reported that morphia increased the vital capacity in cardiac patients, but other observers (Resnik *et al.*, 1935a, b) found no such change. The metabolic rate falls slightly after the administration of morphia (Resnik and Friedman, 1935a; Wangeman and Hawk, 1942). The arterial blood oxygen content may fall to a variable degree and the carbon dioxide content may rise slightly (Fraser, 1927; Wortis et al., 1940); a fall in blood pH may also occur (Fraser, 1927). All of these slight but apparently deleterious changes in the blood may be associated with relief of dyspnea during an attack of pulmonary edema (Fraser, 1927). Changes in the cardiac output (Resnik et al., 1935b; Drew et al., 1946), the circulation time (Wortis et al., 1940) and the cerebral blood flow (Wortis et al., 1940) consequent to the action of morphia in therapeutic doses are not significant. The effect of morphia on respiration is partly to relieve dyspnea but this phenomenon is not sufficiently marked to explain the striking benefit that is associated with its use. Its beneficial action may include the allaying of anxiety in some patients. It is possible, however, that its effectiveness in controlling pulmonary edema may be due largely to its depressing action on the respiratory center or on reflex arcs that are activated when pulmonary edema occurs (Luisada, 1940).

Although morphine has no effect on the circulation with the patient flat, it has a hypotensive effect when the patient is upright (Drew et al., 1946; King et al., 1952).

Morphine elevates the cerebrospinal fluid pressure through some unknown mechanism (Kepes, 1952).

Although morphia depresses mercurial diuresis (page 281), it has no effect on the diuretic action of water (Walsh, 1949).

Effects of tourniquets. — The application of tourniquets at well above venous pressure has the obvious effect of impounding a considerable amount of blood in the extremities (Ebert and Stead, 1940); this is clearly visible in the veins and, to judge by the increase in capillary pressure that follows (Landis, 1930; Eichna and Bordley, 1939) it occurs in the capillaries also; the return of blood to the heart is therefore decreased. Measurements reveal decreased blood flow in limbs constricted by tourniquets (Friedland, et al., 1941; Wilkins et al., 1950; Fisch et al., 1950). This slowing of flow is only a temporary effect, lasting only as long as the tourniquets are in place. In addition, there is loss of fluid from the blood into the tissues of the limbs in which circulation is slowed (Ebert and Stead, 1940). Accordingly, there is an increase in plasma specific gravity or in plasma protein or hemoglobin concentration (3; Peters *et al.*, 1925, 1926); swelling of the limb occurs and lasts for a time after removal of the tourniquets (4; Landis *et al.*, 1932, 1933). The transudation of fluid is accompanied by a loss of chloride into the tissues; Dautrebande *et al.* (1923) reported a loss of bicarbonate as well, but this has been denied by Peters *et al.* (1926). Levitt *et al.* (1952) found no significant change in sodium, potassium, or chloride concentrations. The impounded blood shows an increase in carbon dioxide content and decrease in capacity (Dautrebande *et al.*, 1923; Peters *et al.*, 1926) so that the pH falls. The loss of fluid into the tissues is not, however, marked enough to raise the tissue pressure greatly (Burch and Sodeman, 1937).

The local rise in venous pressure and capillary pressure caused by the tourniquets is not the sole cause of this transudation of fluid and electrolyte, since it occurs even when the circulation to an extremity is cut off entirely (Dautrebande *et al.*, 1923). Studies on the cutaneous capillaries in man have shown (5; Friedland *et al.*, 1941) that tourniquets cause marked stasis and result in capillary dilatation, particularly in the venous limb; this increases the filtering surface. It has also been shown that the application of tourniquets in normal man causes an elevation of tissue carbon dioxide tension (Sibree, 1941*a*) and a lowering of venous blood oxygen (Friedland *et al.*, 1941; Wilkins *et al.*, 1950) and tissue oxygen tensions (Sibree, 1941*a*). The latter reduction might result in an increase in capillary permeability (page 227), although no increase in tissue fluid protein occurs until the tourniquet pressure reaches 80 mm-of-mercury (Landis *et al.*, 1932). It appears that the transudation of fluid into the tissues of the limbs is the consequence of the combined action of the elevated filtration pressure, increased filtering surface and possibly increased capillary permeability. The result of the impounding of blood and loss of fluid in the extremities is a decrease in venous pressure in the unconstricted limbs. This has been described both in normal subjects and in cardiac patients (von Tabora, 1910; Fuchs, 1921; Kountz *et al.*, 1942; McMichael and Sharpey-Shafer, 1944*a*; Warren and Stead, 1943; Davison and Gaddie, 1951); however, Brams and Golden report no fall in their patients (1935).

The right auricular pressure is also lowered (McMichael and Sharpey-Schafer, 1944*a*, *b*; Warren *et al.*, 1945). The lowered volume and pressure of the venous return flow results in an appreciable decrease in blood flow through the lungs, as observed by means of auricular catheterization in normal subjects by McMichael and Sharpey-Schafer (1944a); the left ventricular output must fall correspondingly. Roentgenographic studies by Kountz, Smith and Wright (1942) in dyspneic cardiac patients similarly indicate a fall in cardiac output. Warren et al. (1945), who also used auricular catheterization, observed no decrease in cardiac output. On the other hand, McMichael and Sharpey-Schafer (1944b), who found a decrease in the output of the heart when tourniquets were placed on normal subjects, found a slight rise in cardiac patients, an increase which is, however, not impressive. It is apparent that more work must be done in this field.

The application of tourniquets also results in a small rise in vital capacity or partially prevents the fall that occurs in the recumbent position (6; Asmussen et al., 1939). The action of tourniquets is, therefore, to decrease the inflow into the lungs, thereby reducing the rate of edema formation and allowing the resorptive processes to catch up; this effect is prolonged somewhat by a transitory reduction of blood volume.

The observation of Warren et al. (1945) that intrapleural pressure was not changed in one normal subject after application of tourniquets indicates the need for additional observations in this direction.

Sweating is decreased distal to the tourniquets and increased proximally (Ichihashi and Ogata, 1935). An interesting side effect of the application of tourniquets to all four extremities is a fall in skin temperature over these limbs and a rise in rectal temperature (Smirk, 1936; Steele, 1937; Wilkins et al., 1950); if the tourniquets are kept on for some time, the rise in rectal temperature may result in hyperpnea unless respiration is depressed with morphia.

The changes in renal function found by Wilkins et al. (1949), Chalmers et al. (1951), and Levitt et al. (1952), to follow the application of tourniquets to the extremities in normal subjects include decrease in renal blood flow and glomerular filtration rate, and diminshed excretion of sodium, potassium, and chloride. The changes in electrolyte excretion persist longer than those in blood flow, and so tubular function must be changed. Davison and Gaddie (1951) found no change in renal dynamics in patients with congestive failure in similar circumstances. Nevertheless the importance of phenomena of this type in relation to accumulation of edema during the use of tourniquets is evident.

Effects of positive pressure respiration. — Positive pressure respiration is often helpful in controlling pulmonary edema. It acts apparently in a manner similar to tourniquets, but at a higher level, namely, the great veins in the thorax. Breathing against resistance raises the intrapleural pressure, thereby impeding flow through the great veins and into the lungs. It has been shown in man and dogs that increased intrapleural pressure raises the peripheral venous pressure (7; Barach *et al.*, 1938, 1946). Studies in normal man show that positive pressure in the airway causes a fall in cardiac output (Richards, 1945; Otis *et al.*, 1946*a, b*; Cournand *et al.*, 1948; Werkö, 1947) and an increase in circulation time (Barach *et al.*, 1938, 1946); peripheral flow also decreases (Fenn and Chadwick, 1947). Pulmonary vascular resistance of course increases and accordingly the right ventricular pressure rises (Werkö, 1947). In the dog, slowing of peripheral blood flow has been found (Beecher *et al.*, 1943) and auricular pressures are elevated, the right more than the left (Opdyke and Brecher, 1949, 1950). Renal blood flow is apparently also decreased, for the urea clearance falls significantly (Drury *et al.*, 1947). Barach *et al.* (1938) found a fall in vital capacity in normal subjects breathing against positive pressure; a respiratory tracing reproduced by these authors (Barach *et al.*, 1938) suggests also that the functional residual air is increased, as later measurements showed (Barach *et al.*, 1946). Rahn *et al.* (1946) also demonstrated an increase in functional residual air volume due to an increase in supplemental air; the complemental air decreased so that in their experiments the vital capacity was unchanged. Further studies (Barach *et al.*, 1946; Rahn *et al.*, 1946) showed hyperventilation in normal subjects during at least part of the time when positive pressure was in force. No change in oxygen consumption occurred. The work of breathing was increased when pressures were elevated above any but the lowest levels.

Werkö (1947) found no fall in cardiac output in cardiac patients under positive pressure respiration. According to Barach *et al.* (1938), cardiac patients show a somewhat greater rise in venous pressure and more increase in the circulation time than do normal subjects, but the vital capacity rises. A possible explanation for the rise in vital capacity is a reduction in the rigidity of the lungs found in congestive failure; this rigidity is due to an increased amount of blood in the lungs, a factor which would be counteracted by the impounding of blood in the periphery by positive pressure in the airway (Fenn et al., 1947; Jacobs et al., 1948). It is of interest that positive pressure respiration results in hemoconcentration (Barach et al., 1946; Henry et al., 1948); this phenomenon is probably consequent to loss of fluid into the tissues and is comparable to the effect of tourniquets (page 321). However Henry et al. (1948) found no decrease in plasma volume except at very high pressures (Henry, 1951).

Effects of venesection. — The removal of 300 cc. or more of blood results in a fall in venous pressure in normal subjects and in cardiac patients (8; Loutit et al., 1942; Stead and Ebert, 1942). The right auricular pressure also falls in normal subjects (Barcroft et al., 1944; McMichael and Sharpey-Schafer, 1944a; Warren et al., 1945; Howarth et al., 1947), as does the right ventricular pressure (Richards, 1945; Bloomfield et al., 1946). These changes are accompanied by a considerable decrease in blood flow through the lungs in normal subjects (Barcroft et al., 1944; McMichael and Sharpey-Schafer, 1944a; Richards, 1945; Bloomfield et al., 1946); the left ventricular output must diminish correspondingly. Warren et al. (1945), Shenkin et al. (1944), and Lombardo et al. (1951) found no decrease in cardiac output in normal subjects after venesection; the last two groups used the ballistocardiograph. It is probable that the rate of withdrawal of blood, the effects of anxiety in increasing cardiac output by inducing vasodilation, and possibly other factors should be taken into account in considering the changes that occur. Little or no fall in cardiac output was found in cardiac patients by authors using older methods (Resnik et al., 1935b; McMichael, 1938), whatever decrease occurred apparently being a consequence of diminished oxygen consumption, since the arteriovenous oxygen difference did not change (Resnik et al., 1935b). Similarly, studies made by auricular catheterization (Howarth et al., 1946, 1947; Sharpey-Schafer, 1946) show only inconsequential changes in cardiac output after venesection. The circulation time is unchanged (Howarth et al., 1946). Any decrease in cardiac output that occurs is probably of short duration and is of no importance as a rule. Venesection at times gives rise to vasoconstriction so that the arterial blood pressure is maintained; accordingly the peripheral resistance remains unchanged (Richards, 1945) or is increased (Barcroft et al., 1944).

Studies by Barcroft et al. (1944) on the peripheral circulation after venesection are of interest in this regard. After removal of several hundred cubic centimeters of blood from a vein, the peripheral flow (Barcroft et al., 1944), like the cardiac output, is diminished somewhat. However, if the subject faints, this reaction is associated with a sudden vasodilatation manifested by a fall in peripheral resistance and an increase in peripheral flow.

If the venous return does fall appreciably during venesection, the inflow into the lungs is diminished and edema thereby influenced favorably. In addition, lowering of peripheral venous pressure improves pulmonary lymphatic function (page 313), thereby favoring resorption of edema fluid. The vital capacity in normal subjects (Glaser and McMichael, 1940) and in cardiac patients is increased by several hundred cubic centimeters (9; Platz, 1947). The precise nature of the change that occurs in the lungs after venesection is, however, difficult to state; Glaser and McMichael (1940) studied the subdivisions of the lung volume and found increases only in the complemental air and the measurements derived from it, namely, the vital capacity and total capacity. The respiratory minute volume (Resnik et al., 1935a, b) and with it the oxygen consumption falls in cardiac patients who have been bled. The changes in the lungs may occasionally result in an increase in arterial blood oxygen saturation (Grant, 1923). In addition, the hemodilution that follows venesection (Lemierre and Bernard, 1926; Ebert, Stead and Gibson, 1941) may in cardiac patients occur at the expense of the edema fluid. Following venesection the blood volume is restored to its previous level within twenty-four hours in normal subjects (Ebert, Stead and Gibson, 1941) and possibly more rapidly in decompensated cardiac patients. The cerebrospinal fluid pressure falls after venesection (Roberston and Fetter, 1935), a factor that may ameliorate dyspnea (page 259). It should be borne in mind that all of these favorable actions on the lungs and possibly also on the brain must be balanced against the possibility, not very strong but not to be ignored, that venesection may precipitate shock in a patient with pulmonary edema by too great a lowering cardiac output and consequent sudden vasodilatation.

After venesection, sodium retention may occur (Lombardo *et al.*, 1951). The fact that venesection (and also tourniquets) may favor the development of edema by modifying renal function should give pause to those who insist that the dyspnea of acute pulmonary edema subsides only after the right ventricle has failed as evidenced by the appearance of peripheral edema; the appearance of edema under these circumstances, as under any other, affords no specific information concerning the function of the right ventricle.

Effects of still-standing and sitting with feet dependent. — The venous pressure in the legs is higher during still-standing than during walking (page 36); consequently, the tendency toward filtration of fluid from the blood is increased in the former. Still-standing results in hemoconcentration and a decrease in blood volume in normal subjects (Thompson *et al.*, 1928; Waterfield, 1931; Youmans *et al.*, 1934; Asmussen *et al.*, 1940) and in cardiac patients also (Berson *et al.*, 1952). It is probable that sitting with the feet hanging has the same effect; the available data bearing on this point (de Flora and Ciravegna, 1931) are not acceptable. It has been shown clearly that venous pressure in the legs is elevated (Pollack and Wood, 1949). In addition, the observations made by Lagerlöf *et al.* (1951) on subjects on a tilt table revealed falls in pulmonary capillary, pulmonary arterial, and peripheral venous pressures due to diminution of venous return; pulmonary blood volume also decreased. Many of the effects of a small or moderate venesection are apparently reproduced by still-standing or sitting with feet dependent and, therefore, it is understandable why these procedures may give more relief in severe acute cardiac dyspnea than that afforded merely by sitting up in bed.

The view held by some clinicians that still-standing, or sitting or reclining with legs dependent, draws edema fluid into the legs from the lungs is based on unphysiologic reasoning. While gravity undoubtedly influences to a greater or lesser degree the distribution of edema fluid in a given organ or tissue, it is highly improbable that it will deflect it from one to another.

Effects of oxygen. — The administration of oxygen serves the obvious purpose of remedying the generalized anoxia that results from pulmonary edema (page 317). A further beneficial effect of oxygen therapy in pulmonary edema is that it tends to diminish the edema itself, for it has been shown (page 317) that anoxia increases the amount of transudation from the blood vessels of the lungs.

Summary. — Physiologic data bearing on acute pulmonary edema and cardiac asthma are not sufficiently complete to permit of generalizations as to the nature of these disorders. This unsatisfactory state is to some extent unavoidable, for attacks of pulmonary edema are relatively short in duration, frequently complicated by other disorders such as chronic congestive failure, arrhythmias or myocardial infarction, and often so severe as to make it impossible for patients to coöperate in studies. In addition, there exists a marked dichotomy of thought between clinicians, who study patients, and physiologists, who study mechanisms. The first named usually designate the condition by a physiologic term, namely, "left ventricular failure," which physiologists consider unacceptable. The physiologists, on the other hand, adhere to a simple clinical designation, namely, "acute pulmonary edema," realizing that their studies of mechanism in man are fragmentary. Pulmonary edema is poorly understood, but whatever the final causative mechanisms may prove to be, it is established (i) that morphia, a drug which, in the doses used, apparently acts only on nervous tissue, terminates most attacks; (ii) that the anoxia which develops during attacks is ameliorated by oxygen; (iii) that factors which diminish inflow into the lungs also decrease total blood flow for a time and accordingly, the use of these mechanisms, namely, tourniquets, venesection and positive pressure respiration, is not entirely without hazard; and (iv) that the element of bronchospasm which is present is helped by aminophylline.

There is nothing to prevent the development of attacks of acute pulmonary edema in patients with chronic congestive failure. Indeed, it is not uncommon to see the two together, the paroxysmal syndrome developing as the chronic disorder worsens and disappearing as the chronic failure improves. It is clear that, under these circumstances, the treatment of the two syndromes is identical. However, the treatment of individual attacks of pulmonary edema, whether isolated or in association with chronic myocardial insufficiency, is that outlined above.

Bibliography

Chapter II

ALTSCHULE, M. D., Venous pressure in pulmonary edema, *Unpublished data* (1937).

ALTSCHULE, M. D., *Acute pulmonary edema* (Grune and Stratton, New York, 1954).

ANDERSON, M. E., and J. S. LUNDY, Venous pressure in relation to blood volume in man, *Anesthesiol.* 10, 145 (1949). [8

ASMUSSEN, E., E. H. CHRISTENSEN, and M. NIELSEN, The regulation of circulation in different postures, *Surgery* 8, 604 (1940).

ASMUSSEN, E., E. H. CHRISTENSEN, and T. SJÖSTRAND, Ueber die Abhängigkeit der Lungenvolumen von der Blutverteilung, *Skandinav. Arch. J. Physiol.* 82, 193 (1939). [6

BARACH, A. L., M. ECKMAN, E. GINSBURG, C. C. RUMSEY, JR., I. KORR, I. ECKMAN, and G. BESSON, Studies on positive pressure respiration. I. General aspects and types of pressure breathing. II. Effects on respiration and circulation at sea level, *J. Aviation Med.* 17, 290 (1946). [7

BARACH, A. L., J. MARTIN, and M. ECKMAN, Positive pressure respiration and its application to the treatment of acute pulmonary edema, *Ann. Int. Med.* 12, 754 (1938). [7

BARCROFT, H., O. G. EDHOLM, J. MCMICHAEL, and E. P. SHARPEY-SCHAFER, Posthaemorrhagic failure. Study by cardiac output and forearm flow, *Lancet* 1, 489 (1944).

BECK, G. J., H. E. SEANOR, and A. L. BARACH, Effects of pressure breathing on venous pressure; a comparative study of positive pressure applied to the upper respiratory passageway and negative pressure to the body of normal individuals, *Am. J. M. Sc.* 224, 169 (1952). [7

BEECHER, H. K., H. S. BENNETT, and D. L. BASSET, Circulatory effects of increased pressure in the airway, *Anesthesiology* 4, 612 (1943). [7

BERRY, T. J., E. PERKINS, and P. JERNSTROM, The effect of venous compression on certain blood factors, *Am. J. Clin. Path.* 20, 765 (1950). [3

BERSON, S. A., R. S. YALOW, A. AZULAY, S. SCHREIBER, and B. ROSWIT, The biological decay curve of P³² tagged erythrocytes. Application to the study of acute changes in blood volume, *J. Clin. Investigation* 31, 581 (1952).

BLOOMFIELD, R. A., H. D. LAUSON, A. COURNAND, E. S. BREED, and D. W. RICHARDS, JR., Recording of right heart pressures in normal subjects and in patients with chronic pulmonary disease and various types of cardiocirculatory disease, *J. Clin. Investigation* 25, 639 (1946).

Böhme, A., Ueber die Schwankungen der Serumkonzentration beim gesunden Menschen, *Deutsches Arch. f. klin. Med.* **103**, 522 (1911).   [3

Bordley, J., III, M. H. Grow, and W. B. Sherman, Intermittent blood flow in the capillaries of human skin, *Bull. Johns Hopkins Hosp.* **62**, 1 (1938).   [5

Brams, W. A., and J. S. Golden, The early response to venesection with observations on so-called bloodless venesection, *Am. J. M. Sc.* **189**, 813 (1935).   [8

Budelmann, G., Untersuchungen über den Venendruck, die Vitalkapazität der Lunge und das Herzminutenvolumen bei Gesunden und Herzkranken in Ruhe und bei Kreislaufbelastung, *Ztschr. f. klin. Med.* **127**, 15 (1935).   [8, 9

Budelmann, G., Zur Beeinflussung der Vitalkapazität der Lunge durch Behinderung des venösen Abflusses aus den Extremitäten (Stauung), *Klin. Wchnschr.* **17**, 1009 (1938).

Burch, G. E., and W. A. Sodeman, The estimation of the subcutaneous tissue pressure by a direct method, *J. Clin. Investigation* **16**, 845 (1937).

Cameron, G. R., Pulmonary oedema, *Brit. Med. J.* **1**, 965 (1948).

Chalmers, T. M., A. A. G. Lewis, and G. L. S. Pawan, Relation between glomerular filtration rate and sodium excretion in man, *J. Physiol.* **115**, 17P (1951).

Chalmers, T. M., A. A. G. Lewis, and G. L. S. Pawan, The effect of acute reduction of the glomerular filtration rate on sodium excretion in man, *J. Physiol.* **117**, 218 (1951).

Clark, A. H., A study of the diagnostic and prognostic significance of venous pressure observations in cardiac disease, *Arch. Int. Med.* **16**, 587 (1915).   [7

Cottrell, J. D., and D. C. Cuddie, The arm-to-tongue circulation time in chronic asthma, *Brit. Med. J.* **1**, 70 (1942).   [1

Cournand, A., H. L. Motley, L. Werko, and D. W. Richards, Jr., Physiological studies of the effects of intermittent positive pressure breathing on cardiac output in man, *Am. J. Physiol.* **152**, 162 (1948).

Dautrebande, L., H. W. Davies, and J. Meakins, The influence of circulatory changes on the gaseous exchanges of the blood. III. An experimental study of circulatory stasis, *Heart* **10**, 133 (1923).   [3

Davis, J. O., and N. W. Shock, The effect of theophylline ethylene diamine on renal function in control subjects and in patients with congestive heart failure, *J. Clin. Investigation* **28**, 1459 (1949).

de Flora, G., and M. Ciravegna, Le variazione della massa sanguigna dei cardiopatici nei cambiamenti di decubito, *Cuore e circolaz.* **21**, 396 (1931).

Doust, J. W. L., and R. A. Schneider, Studies on the physiology of awareness: anoxia and the levels of sleep, *Brit. M. J.* **1,** 449 (1952).

Dow, P., The venous return as a factor affecting the vital capacity, *Am. J. Physiol.* **127,** 793 (1939). [6

Drew, J. H., R. D. Dripps, and J. H. Comroe, Jr., Clinical studies on morphine. II. The effect of morphine upon the circulation of man and upon the circulatory and respiratory responses to tilting, *Anesthesiol.* **7,** 44 (1946).

Drinker, C. K., and E. Hardenbergh, Acute effects upon the lungs of dogs of large intravenous doses of alpha-naphthyl thiourea (ANTU), *Am. J. Physiol.* **156,** 35 (1949).

Dripps, R. D., and J. H. Comroe, Clinical studies on morphine. I. The immediate effect of morphine administered intravenously and intramuscularly upon the respiration of normal man, *Anesthesiology* **6,** 462 (1945). [2

Drury, A. N., and N. W. Jones, Observations upon the rate at which edema forms when the veins of the human limb are congested, *Heart* **14,** 55 (1927). [4

Drury, D. R., J. P. Henry, and J. Goodman, The effects of continuous pressure breathing on kidney function, *J. Clin. Investigation* **26,** 945 (1947).

Ebert, R. V., and E. A. Stead, Jr., The effect of the application of tourniquets on the hemodynamics of the circulation, *J. Clin. Investigation* **19,** 561 (1940).

Ebert, R. V., E. A. Stead, Jr., and J. G. Gibson, II. Response of normal subjects to acute blood loss, with special reference to the mechanism of restoration of blood volume, *Arch. Int. Med.* **68,** 578 (1941).

Eichna, L. W., and J. Bordley, III. Capillary blood pressure in man. Comparison of direct and indirect methods of measurement, *J. Clin. Investigation* **18,** 695 (1939). [5

Eyster, J. A. E., Venous pressure and its clinical applications, *Physiol. Rev.* **6,** 281 (1926). [8

Eyster, J. A. E., Venous pressure in cardiac decompensation, *J. Am. M. A.* **89,** 428 (1927). [8

Eyster, J. A. E., and W. J. Meek, Studies on venous pressure, *Am. J. Physiol.* **95,** 294 (1930). [7

Eyster, J. A. E., and W. S. Middleton, Clinical studies on venous pressure, *Arch. Int. Med.* **34,** 228 (1924). [8

Eyster, J. A. E., and W. S. Middleton, Cardiovascular reactions to hemorrhage and transfusion in man, *Am. J. Physiol.* **68,** 581 (1924). [8

Eyster, J. A. E., and W. S. Middleton, Venous pressure as a guide to venesection in congestive heart failure, *Am. J. M. Sc.* **174,** 486 (1927). [8

FENN, W. O., and L. E. CHADWICK, Effect of pressure breathing on blood flow through the finger, *Am. J. Physiol.* **151,** 270 (1947).

FENN, W. O., A. B. OTIS, H. RAHN, L. E. CHADWICK, and A. H. HEGNAUER, Displacement of blood from the lungs by pressure breathing, *Am. J. Physiol.* **151,** 258 (1947).

FISCH, S., S. B. GILSON, and R. E. TAYLOR, Capillary circulation in human arms studied by venous congestion. A cutaneo-muscular vasomotor reflex, *J. Appl. Physiol.* **3,** 113 (1950).

FRASER, F. R., Goulstonian lectures on cardiac dyspnoea, *Lancet* **1,** 529, 589, 643 (1927).

FRIEDLAND, C. K., J. S. HUNT, and R. W. WILKINS, Effects of changes in venous pressure upon blood flow in the limbs, *Am. Heart J.* **25,** 631 (1941). [5

FUCHS, L., Ueber die Messung des Venendruckes und ihre klinische Bedeutung, *Deutsches Arch. f. klin. Med.* **135,** 68 (1921). [8

GESELL, R., Further observations on respiratory control, *Am. J. Physiol.* **85,** 373 (1928).

GLASER, E. M., and J. McMICHAEL, Effect of venesection on the capacity of the lungs, *Lancet* **2,** 230 (1940).

GRANT, S. B., Changes in the blood oxygen following therapeutic bleeding in cardiac patients, *J. Lab. & Clin. Med.* **9,** 160 (1923).

GRAWITZ, E., Klinisch-experimentelle Blutuntersuchungen, *Ztschr. f. klin. Med.* **21,** 459 (1892). [3

GREENE, J. A., W. D. PAUL, and A. E. FELLER, The action of theophylline with ethylenediamine on intrathecal and venous pressures in cardiac failure and on bronchial obstruction in cardiac failure and bronchial asthma, *J. A. M. A.* **109,** 1712 (1937).

HALMÁGYI, D., B. FELKAI, J. IVÁNYI, and G. HETÉNYI, JR. The role of the nervous system in the maintenance of venous hypertension in heart failure, *Brit. Heart J.* **14,** 101 (1952).

HALMÁGYI, D., B. FELKAI, J. IVÁNYI, T. ZSÓTER, M. TÉNYI, and S. SZÜCS, The role of the nervous system in the maintenance of pulmonary arterial hypertention in heart failure, *Brit. Heart J.* **15,** 15 (1953).

HAMILTON, W. F., and J. P. MAYO, Changes in the vital capacity when the body is immersed in water, *Am. J. Physiol.* **141,** 51 (1944). [6

HAMILTON, W. F., and A. B. MORGAN, Mechanism of the postural reduction in vital capacity in relation to orthopnea and storage of blood in the lungs, *Am. J. Physiol.* **99,** 526 (1932). [6

HARRIS, I., E. W. JONES, and C. N. ALDRED, Blood pH and lactic acid in different types of heart disease, *Quart. J. Med.* **28,** 407 (1935).

HARRISON, W. G., JR., J. A. CALHOUN, J. P. MARSH, and T. R. HARRISON, Congestive heart failure. XIX. Reflex stimulation of respiration as the cause of evening dyspnea, *Arch. Int. Med.* **53,** 724 (1934). [9

HENNEMAN, P. H., Acute pulmonary edema, with special reference to experimental studies, *New England J. Med.* **235,** 590, 619 (1946).

HENRY, J. P., The significance of the loss of blood volume into the limbs during pressure breathing, *J. Aviation Med.* **22,** 31 (1951).

HENRY, J. P., I. HENDRICKSON, E. MOVITT, and J. P. MEEHAN, Estimations of the decrease in effective blood volume when pressure breathing at sea level, *J. Clin. Investigation* **27,** 700 (1948).

HEYER, H. E., Abnormalities of the respiratory pattern in patients with cardiac dyspnea, *Am. Heart J.* **32,** 457 (1946).

HOLT, J. P., The effect of positive and negative intrathoracic pressure on peripheral venous pressure in man, *Am. J. Physiol.* **139,** 208 (1943). [7

HOLT, J. P., The effect of positive and negative intrathoracic pressure on cardiac output and venous pressure in the dog, *Am. J. Physiol.* **142,** 594 (1944). [7

HOOKER, D. R., Observations on the venous blood pressure in man, *Am. J. Physiol.* **35,** 73 (1914). [7

HOWARTH, S., J. MCMICHAEL, and E. P. SHARPEY-SCHAFER, Effects of venesection in low output heart failure, *Clin. Sc.* **6,** 41 (1946). [8, 9

HOWARTH, S., J. MCMICHAEL, and E. P. SHARPEY-SCHAFER, The effects of oxygen, venesection and digitalis in chronic heart failure from disease of the lungs, *Clin. Sc.* **6,** 187 (1947).

ICHIHASHI, T., and K. OGATA, The effect of a local obstruction of the blood flow on the sweat secretion in man, *J. Orient. Med.* **23,** 1 (1935).

JACOBS, H., A. KARSTENS, and J. P. HENRY, The effect of pressure breathing on circulationg blood volume (2). Distension of the venous reservoirs, *Federation Proc.* **7,** 60 (1948).

JANSEN, K., H. W. KNIPPING, and K. STROMBERGER, Klinische Untersuchungen über Atmung und Blutgase, *Beitr. z. Klin. d. Tuberk.* **80,** 304 (1932). [2

KAHLER, H., Ueber Veränderungen der Blutumlaufzeit, *Wien. Arch. f. inn. Med.* **19,** 1 (1930). [1

KEPES, E. R., Effect of demerol on the cerebrospinal fluid pressure, *Anesthesiol.* **13,** 281 (1952).

KING, B. D., J. D. ELDER, JR., and R. D. DRIPPS, The effect of the intravenous administration of meperidine upon the circulation of man and upon the circulatory response to tilt, *Surg. Gynec. & Obst.* **94,** 591 (1952).

KLEIN, O., and J. HEINEMAN, Zur Messung der Strömungsgeschwindigkeit des Blutes beim Menschen, *Zentralbl. f. inn. Med.* **50,** 490 (1929). [1

KNIPPING, H. W., W. LEWIS, and A. MONCRIEFF, Ueber die Dyspnoe, *Beitr. z. Klin. d. Tuberk.* **79**, 1 (1932). [2

KNIPPING, H. W., and A. MONCRIEFF, The ventilation equivalent for oxygen, *Quart. J. Med.* **1**, 17 (1932). [2

KOUNTZ, W. B., J. R. SMITH, and S. T. WRIGHT, Observations on the effect of tourniquets on acute cardiac crises, normal subjects, and chronic heart failure, *Am. Heart J.* **23**, 624 (1942).

KREIBICH, K., Ueber die refraktometrischen werte des Blutserums, *Folia haemat.* **4**, 795 (1907). [3

KROETZ, C., Die Koeffizienten des klinisch messbaren Venendruckes, *Deutsches Arch. f. klin. Med.* **139**, 325 (1922). [8

KROGH, A., E. M. LANDIS, and A. H. TURNER, The movement of fluid through the human capillary wall in relation to venous pressure and to the colloid osmotic pressure of the blood, *J. Clin. Investigation* **11**, 63 (1932). [4

LAGERLÖF, H., H. ELIASCH, L. WERKÖ, and E. BERGLUND, Orthostatic changes of the pulmonary and peripheral circulation in man. A preliminary report, *Scandinav. J. Clin. & Lab. Investigation* **3**, 85 (1951).

LAGERLÖF, H., and L. WERKÖ, Studies on the circulation of blood in man. VI. The pulmonary capillary venous pressure pulse in man, *Scandinav. J. Clin. & Lab. Investigation* **1**, 147 (1949).

LANDIS, E. M., Micro-injection studies of capillary blood pressure in human skin, *Heart* **15**, 209 (1930).

LANDIS, E. M., and J. H. GIBBON, JR., The effects of temperature and of tissue pressure on the movement of fluid through the human capillary wall, *J. Clin. Investigation* **12**, 105 (1933). [4

LANDIS, E. M., L. JONAS, M. ANGEVINE, and W. ERB, The passage of fluid and protein through the human capillary wall during venous congestion, *J. Clin Investigation* **11**, 717 (1932). [4

LANGE, K., and L. J. BOYD, Objective methods to determine the speed of blood flow and their results (fluorescein and acetylene), *Am. J. M. Sc.* **206**, 438 (1943). [1

LAUTER, S., Kreislaufprobleme, *München. med. Wchnschr.* **77**, 593 (1930).

LEMIERRE, A., and É. BERNARD, Recherches sur les indications et sur l'action physiologique de la soignée, *Presse méd.* **34**, 705 (1926). [8

LENÈGRE, J., L. SCÉBAT, H. BESSON, F. BENCHEMOUL, and J. DAMIEN, Étude de la pression capillaire pulmonaire dans différents types de cardiopathies, *Arch. d. mal. du cœur* **46**, 1 (1953).

LESCHKE, E., Kreislaufzeit und Blutgeschwindigkeit, *München. med. Wchnschr.* **78**, 2117 (1931). [1

LEVITT, M. F., L. B. TURNER, and A. Y. SWEET, The effect of experimental venous obstruction on salt and water distribution and excretion in man, *J. Clin. Investigation* **31**, 885 (1952). [3

LIAN, C., and E. BARRAS, Intérêt clinique de la mesure de vitesse de la circulation par l'épreuve de la fluorescéine, *Bull. et mém. Soc. méd. d. hôp. de Paris* **46**, 175 (1930). [1

LOMBARDO, T. A., S. EISENBERG, B. B. OLIVER, W. N. VIAR, E. E. EDDLE-MAN, and T. R. HARRISON, Effects of bleeding on electrolyte excretion and on glomerular filtration, *Circulation* **3**, 260 (1951).

LOUTIT, J. F., M. D. MOLLISON, and E. D. VAN DER WALT, Venous pressure during venesection and blood transfusion, *Brit. M. J.* **2**, 658 (1942). [8

LUISADA, A., The pathogenesis of paroxysmal pulmonary edema, *Medicine* **19**, 475 (1940).

MACKAY, I. F. S., The influence of posture on the pulmonary blood volume and the alveolar gas tensions, *J. Physiol.* **102**, 228 (1943). [6

MAURER, F. W., The effects of decreased blood oxygen and increased blood carbon dioxide on the flow and composition of cervical and cardiac lymph, *Am. J. Physiol.* **131**, 331 (1940).

McMICHAEL, J., The output of the heart in congestive failure, *Quart. J. Med.* **7**, 331 (1938). [8

McMICHAEL, J., and K. M. MORRIS, Acute oxygen lack and capillary permeability in man, *J. Physiol.* **87**, 74P (1936). [4

McMICHAEL, J., and E. P. SHARPEY-SCHAFER, Cardiac output in man by a direct Fick method. Effects of posture, venous pressure change, atropine and adrenaline, *Brit. Heart J.* **6**, 33 (1944).

McMICHAEL, J., and E. P. SHARPEY-SCHAFER, The action of intravenous digoxin in man, *Quart. J. Med.* **13**, 123 (1944).

MENDE, Ueber Hyperämie und Oedem bei der Hemmung des Rückflusses des venösen Blutes durch die Staubinde, *Deutsche Ztschr. f. Chir.* **150**, 379 (1919). [4

MERRILL, J. P., S. SMITH, III, E. J. CALLAHAN, III, and G. W. THORN, The use of an artificial kidney. II. Clinical experience, *J. Clin. Investigation* **29**, 425 (1950).

MODRAKOWSKI, G., Beobachtungen an der überlebenden Säugetierlungen. II. Mitt. Über die experimentelle Erzeugung von Lungenödem, *Arch. f. d. ges. Physiol.* **158**, 527 (1914).

MOYER, J. H., S. I. MILLER, A. B. TASHNEK, and R. BOWMAN, The effect of theophylline with ethylenediamine (aminophylline) on cerebral hemodynamics in the presence of cardiac failure with and without Cheyne-Stokes respiration, *J. Clin. Investigation* **31**, 267 (1952).

MULINOS, M., and I. SHULMAN, Vasoconstriction in the hand from a deep inspiration, *Am. J. Physiol.* **125**, 310 (1939). [5

NEUMANN, R., Kapillarstudien mittels der mikroskopischen Kapillarbeobachtungsmethode nach Müller-Weiss. I. Die Strömung in den Kapillaren, *Berl. klin. Wchnschr.* **57**, 826 (1920). [5

OLMER, D., A.-X. JOUVE, and J. VAGUE, Une épreuve fonctionelle de la circulation de retour, *Presse méd.* **46**, 1233 (1938).   [8

OPDYKE, D. F., and G. A. BRECHER, Effect of intrapulmonic and intra-thoracic pressure variations on left atrial pressure, *Federation Proc.* **8**, 121 (1949).

OPDYKE, D. F., and G. A. BRECHER, Effect of normal and abnormal changes of intrathoracic pressure on effective right and left atrial pressures, *Am. J. Physiol.* **160**, 556 (1950).

OPPENHEIMER, B. S., and W. M. HITZIG, The use of circulatory measurements in evaluating pulmonary and cardiac factors in chronic lung disorders, *Am. Heart J.* **12**, 257 (1936).   [1

OTIS, A. B., H. RAHN, M. BRONTMAN, L. J. MULLINS, and W. O. FENN, Ballistocardiographic study of changes in cardiac output due to respiration, *J. Clin. Investigation* **25**, 413 (1946a).

OTIS, A. B., H. RAHN, and W. O. FENN, Venous pressure changes associated with positive intrapulmonary pressures; their relationship to the distensibility of the lung, *Am. J. Physiol.* **146**, 307 (1946b).   [7

PAINE, R., H. R. BUTCHER, J. R. SMITH, and F. A. HOWARD, Observations on the role of pulmonary congestion in the production of edema of the lungs, *J. Lab. & Clin. Med.* **36**, 288 (1950).

PAINE, R., and J. R. SMITH, Observations on experimental pulmonary edema, *J. Clin. Investigation* **28**, 802 (1949).

PENNEYS, R., Studies with the Millikan oximeter at the bedside of patients with cardiac and pulmonary disease, *Bull. Johns Hopkins Hosp.* **90**, 192 (1952).

PERERA, G. A., and R. W. BERLINER, The relation of postural hemodilution to paroxysmal dyspnea, *J. Clin. Investigation* **22**, 25 (1943).

PETERS, J. P., JR., H. A. BULGER, A. J. EISENMAN, and C. LEE, Total acid-base equilibrium of plasma in health and disease. IV. The effects of stasis, exercise, hyperpnea and anoxemia; and the causes of tetany, *J. Biol. Chem.* **67**, 175 (1926).   [3

PETERS, J. P., JR., A. J. EISENMAN, and H. A. BULGER, The plasma proteins in relation to blood hydration. I. In normal individuals and in miscellaneous conditions, *J. Clin. Investigation* **1**, 435 (1924–25).   [3

PLASS, E. D., and M. D. ROURKE, The effect of venous stasis on the proteins of blood plasma and on the rate of sedimentation of the red blood corpuscles, *J. Lab. & Clin. Med.* **12**, 735 (1927).   [3

PLOTZ, M., Asthmatoid heart failure: a form of left ventricular failure and its differentiation from bronchial asthma by circulation time and other criteria, *Ann. Int. Med.* **13**, 151 (1939).   [1

PLOTZ, M., Bronchial spasm in cardiac asthma, *Ann. Int. Med.* **26**, 521 (1947).   [9

Pollack, A. A., and E. H. Wood, Venous pressure in the saphenous vein at the ankle in man during exercise and changes in posture, *J. Appl. Physiol.* **1**, 649 (1949).

Porges, O., A. Leimdörfer, and E. Markovici, Ueber die Kohlensäurespannung des Blutes in pathologischen Zuständen. II. Ueber die Kohlensäurespannung des Blutes in der kardialen und pulmonalen Dyspnoe, *Ztschr. f. klin. Med.* **77**, 446 (1913).

Price, H. L., B. D. King, J. D. Elder, B. H. Libien, and R. D. Dripps, Circulatory effects of raised airway pressure during cyclopropane anesthesia in man, *J. Clin. Investigation* **30**, 1243 (1951).   [7

Prinzmetal, M., and W. B. Kountz, Intrapleural pressure in health and disease and its influence on body function, *Medicine* **14**, 457 (1935).   [7

Pugh, L. C. G., and C. L. Wyndham, The circulatory effects of mercurial diuretics in congestive heart failure, *Clin. Sc.* **8**, 10 (1949).

Rahn, H., A. B. Otis, L. E. Chadwick, and W. O. Fenn, The pressure-volume diagram of the thorax and lung, *Am. J. Physiol.* **146**, 161 (1946).

Resnik, H., Jr., and B. Friedman, Studies on the mechanism of the increased oxygen consumption in patients with cardiac disease, *J. Clin. Investigation* **14**, 551 (1935a).   [2

Resnik, H., Jr., B. Friedman, and T. R. Harrison, Effect of certain therapeutic measures on the cardiac output of patients with congestive heart failure, *Arch. Int. Med.* **56**, 891 (1935b).   [2, 9

Richards, D. W., Jr., Cardiac output by the catheterization technique in various clinical conditions, *Federation Proc.* **4**, 215 (1945).

Richards, D. W., Jr., A. Cournand, R. C. Darling, W. H. Gillespie, and E. D. Baldwin, Pressure of blood in the right auricle in animals and in man: under normal conditions and in right heart failure, *Am. J. Physiol.* **136**, 115 (1942).

Robertson, H. F., and F. B. Faust, Theophylline with isopropanolamine in heart disease, with special reference to congestive failure, *J. Lab. & Clin. Med.* **25**, 1066 (1940).

Robertson, H. F., and F. Fetter, The effect of venesection on arterial, spinal fluid, and venous pressures with especial reference to failure of the left and right heart, *J. Clin. Investigation* **14**, 305 (1935).   [8

Rowe, A. H., The effect of venous stasis on the proteins of human blood serum, *J. Lab. & Clin. Med.* **1**, 485 (1915).   [3

Sarnoff, S. J., W. T. Goodale, and L. C. Sarnoff, Graded reduction of arterial pressure in man by means of a thiophanium derivative (R 02–2222), *Circulation* **6**, 63 (1952).

Schultz, W., and G. Wagner, Ueber den Flüssigkeitsaustauch zwischen

Blut und Geweben unter den Einwirkung von thermischen und anderen Einflüssen, *Folia serol.* **3**, 387 (1909).   [3

SCHUMAN, C., and H. G. SIMMONS, Cardiac asthma: its pathogenesis and response to aminophylline, *Ann. Int. Med.* **36**, 864 (1952).   [1

SCHUR, H., Mikroskopische Hautstudien am Lebenden, *Wien. klin. Wchnschr.* **32**, 1201 (1919).   [3

SCHWALM, H., and M. BRÖDER, Die Blutviskosimetrie in der Untersuchung des Wasserhaushaltes, *Deutsches Arch. f. klin. Med.* **191**, 455 (1943).   [3

SHARPEY-SCHAFER, E. P., 2-Thiouracil in the treatment of congestive heart failure, *Brit. M. J.* **2**, 888 (1946).

SHENKIN, H. A., R. H. CHENEY, S. R. GOVONS, J. D. HARDY, A. G. FLETCHER, and I. STARR, On the diagnosis of hemorrhage in man. A study of volunteers bled large amounts, *Am. J. M. Sc.* **208**, 421 (1944).   [8

SIBREE, E. W., Gas tensions in tissues in physiological conditions, *M. J. Australia* **1**, 42 (1941a).

SIBREE, E. W., Gas tensions in the tissues in pathological conditions, *M. J. Australia* **1**, 201 (1941b).

SINCLAIR-SMITH, B., A. A. KATTUS, J. GENEST, and E. V. NEWMAN, The renal mechanism of electrolyte excretion and the metabolic balance of electrolytes and nitrogen in congestive cardiac failure; the effects of exercise, rest and aminophyllin, *Bull. Johns Hopkins Hosp.* **84**, 369 (1949).

SMIRK, F. H., Observations on the causes of oedema in congestive heart failure, *Clin. Sc.* **2**, 317 (1936).

SONNE, I., and T. HILDEN, Clinical aspects of cardiac asthma and acute pulmonary edema with special reference to the blood pressure, *Acta med. Scandinav.* **138**, 354 (1950).

SPEALMAN, C. R., M. NEWTON, and R. L. POST, Influence of environmental temperature and posture on volume and composition of blood, *Am. J. Physiol.* **150**, 628 (1947).

STARR, I., C. J. GAMBLE, A. MARGOLIES, J. S. DONAL, JR., N. JOSEPH, and E. EAGLE, A clinical study of the action of 10 commonly used drugs on cardiac output, work and size; on respiration, on metabolic rate and on the electrocardiogram, *J. Clin. Investigation* **16**, 799 (1937).

STEAD, E. A., JR., and R. V. EBERT, Shock syndrome produced by failure of the heart, *Arch. Int. Med.* **69**, 369 (1942).

STEELE, J. M., Elevation of rectal temperature following mechanical obstruction to the peripheral circulation, *Am. Heart J.* **13**, 542 (1937).

STEINBERG, F. V., and J. JENSEN, The effect of theophylline aminoisobutanol on the circulation in congestive heart failure, *J. Lab. & Clin. Med.* **31**, 850 (1946).

STEWART, H. J., and N. B. JACK, The effect of aminophyllin on peripheral blood flow, *Am. Heart J.* **20**, 295 (1940).

TARR, L., B. S. OPPENHEIMER, and R. V. SAGER, The circulation time in various clinical conditions determined by the use of sodium dehydrocholate, *Am. Heart J.* **8**, 766 (1932–33). [1

TAYLOR, F. A., A. B. THOMAS, and H. G. SCHLEITER, A direct method for the estimation of venous blood pressure, *Proc. Soc. Exper. Biol. & Med.* **27**, 867 (1930). [8

THOMPSON, W. O., P. K. THOMPSON, and M. E. DAILEY, The effect of posture upon the composition and volume of the blood in man, *J. Clin. Investigation* **5**, 573 (1927–28).

TORNQUIST, H., Physiologische und klinische Studien über den Armvenendruck, *Ztschr. f. d. ges. exper. Med.* **81**, 227 (1932).

VILLARET, M., F. ST. GIRONS, and P. GRELLETY-BOSVIEL, La tension veineuse périphérique (P.V.) et ses modifications pathologiques, *Presse méd.* **31**, 318 (1923). [8

VON GÖNCZY, V. I., J. KISS, and Z. ENYEDY, Ueber den Venendruck und dessen Tagesschwankungen, *Ztschr. f. d. ges. exper. Med.* **70**, 236 (1930). [8

VON TABORA, D., Ueber den Aderlass bei Kreislaufstörungen und seinen unblutigen Ersatz, *München. med. Wchnschr.* **57**, 1265 (1910). [8

WALSH, E. G., The effect of smoking on water diuresis in man, *Quart. J. Med.* **18**, 51 (1949).

WANGEMAN, C. P., and M. H. HAWK, The effects of morphine, atropine and scopolamine in human subjects, *Anesthesiology* **3**, 24 (1942). [2

WARREN, J. V., E. S. BRANNON, E. A. STEAD, JR., and A. J. MERRILL, The effect of venesection and the pooling of blood in the extremities on the atrial pressure and cardiac output in normal subjects with observations on acute circulatory collapse in three instances, *J. Clin. Investigation* **24**, 337 (1945).

WARREN, J. V., and E. A. STEAD, JR., The effect of the accumulation of blood in the extremities on the venous pressure of normal subjects, *Am. J. M. Sc.* **205**, 501 (1943).

WARREN, M. F., and C. K. DRINKER, The flow of lymph from the lungs of the dog, *Am. J. Physiol.* **136**, 207 (1942a).

WARREN, M. F., D. K. PETERSON, and C. K. DRINKER, The effects of heightened negative pressure in the chest, together with further experiments upon anoxia in increasing the flow of lung lymph, *Am. J. Physiol.* **137**, 641 (1942b).

WATERFIELD, R. L., The effects of posture on the circulating blood volume, *J. Physiol.* **72**, 110 (1931).

WECHSLER, R. L., L. M. KLEISS, and S. S. KETY, The effects of intravenously administered aminophylline on cerebral circulation and metabolism in man, *J. Clin. Investigation* **29,** 28 (1950).

WEISS, S., and G. P. ROBB, Cardiac asthma (paroxysmal cardiac dyspnea) and the syndrome of left ventricular failure, *J. A. M. A.* **100,** 1841 (1933). [1

WERKÖ, L., The influence of positive pressure breathing on the circulation in man, *Acta med. Scandinav. Supp. No. 193* (1947).

WERKÖ, L., and H. LAGERLÖF, Studies on the circulation of blood in man. VII. The effect of a single intravenous dose of theophylline diethanolamine on the cardiac output, pulmonary blood volume and systemic and pulmonary blood pressures in hypertensive cardiovascular disease, *Scandinav. J. Clin. & Lab. Investigation* **1,** 181 (1949).

WILKINS, R. W., J. W. CULBERTSON, B. A. BURROWS, C. M. TINSLEY, W. E. JUDSON, and C. H. BURNETT, Antidiuresis and renal vasoconstriction following venous congestion of the limbs in normal, hypertensive and splanchnicectomized subjects, *J. Clin. Investigation* **28,** 819 (1949).

WILKINS, R. W., M. H. HALPERIN, and J. LITTER, The effects of various physical procedures on the circulation in human limbs, *Ann. Int. Med.* **33,** 1232 (1950).

WINTERNITZ, M., J. DEUTSCH, and Z. BRÜLL, Eine klinisch brauchbare Bestimmungsmethode der Blutumlaufzeit mittels Decholininjektion, *Med. Klin.* **27,** 986 (1931). [1

WOOD, P., Right and left ventricular failure. A study of circulation time and venous blood pressure, *Lancet* **2,** 15 (1936). [1

WORTIS, J., K. M. BOWMAN, and W. GOLDFARB, Human brain metabolism. Normal values and values in certain clinical states, *Am. J. Psychiat.* **97,** 552 (1940).

YOUMANS, J. B., H. S. WELLS, D. DONLEY, and D. G. MILLER, The effect of posture (standing) on the serum protein concentration and colloid osmotic pressure of blood from the foot in relation to the formation of edema, *J. Clin. Investigation* **13,** 447 (1934).

ZIMMERMAN, H., A study of the pulmonary circulation in man, *Dis. of Chest* **20,** 46 (1951).

III

ANGINA PECTORIS
MYOCARDIAL INFARCTION

1. *Angina Pectoris*

Most physicians agree that the fundamental cause of angina pectoris is, largely or entirely, disease of the coronary arteries; accordingly, many studies have been made of the function of the coronary arteries and myocardium in patients with angina pectoris. There are, therefore, few physiologic data on the status of the circulation as a whole in this syndrome.

Cardiac output. — The minute volume output of the heart has been reported normal between attacks in patients with angina pectoris (Starr and Gamble, 1935; Bazett *et al.*, 1941; Altschule, 1944; Berman *et al.*, 1950; Makinson, 1950). In 1935, Starr and Gamble (1935), summarizing their studies with the ethyl iodide method, stated that the cardiac output was normal in patients with angina pectoris. Later, however, Starr and Jonas (1940) and Starr and Wood (1943), using the ballistocardiograph to estimate cardiac output, found normal values in only five patients with angina pectoris and low values in nineteen, including fifteen whose cardiac output was 30 to 60 per cent below normal. Four of the latter group developed congestive failure while under observation, but no such complicating factor was present in the others. Accordingly, other explanations must be invoked to explain the markedly subnormal cardiac output in these patients.

One criticism of studies of the minute volume output of the heart made by means of the ballistocardiograph is that they afford no information on the relation of the volume of the cardiac output to the metabolic requirements of the body. The importance of considering this relation in studies of the circulation in disease has already been emphasized (page 6). It is clear, therefore, that the value of data on cardiac output is impaired by the absence of corresponding data on metabolism; this is especially true in patients with angina pectoris, since many of them have low metabolic rates (Riseman and Brown, 1937; Altschule, 1944). Actually some authors who used the ballistocardiogram (Berman et al., 1950; Makinson, 1950) found the cardiac output normal at rest in patients with angina pectoris. The weight of the evidence appears to favor the conclusion that the general circulation is normal in relation to metabolic requirements at rest and in the absence of anginal pain in patients with angina pectoris. During attacks of angina pectoris in two patients, the cardiac output was found by Starr et al. (1938) to be elevated; the attacks were precipitated by emotion in one instance and by the injection of epinephrine in the other. Scarborough et al. (1951) also found the cardiac output increased during anginal attacks precipitated by induced anoxia. The finding of Wolf and Wolff (1946) of a decrease in cardiac output during an attack of angina pectoris associated with feelings of discouragement arouses skepticism. The observation that cardiac output does not rise in patients with angina pectoris after meals (Berman et al., 1950) may be an artifact owing to abnormal changes in pulse rate. The occasional finding of elevated right ventricular pressure in angina pectoris by Lenègre and Maurice (1947) cannot be evaluated with the scanty data presented by those authors. Fragmentary data on cardiac efficiency in patients with angina pectoris have been published (Lombardo et al., 1953).

Circulation time. — Normal circulation time is reported in most instances of angina pectoris (Winternitz et al., 1931; Bernstein and Simkins, 1939; Wood, 1936; Altschule, 1944), though Winternitz et al. (1931) and Bain (1934) found it to be increased often; most of Bain's patients had evidence of congestive failure also. A recent analysis (Altschule, 1944) showed that increase of the circulation time in the absence of frank decompensation in angina pectoris was usually consequent to noncardiac factors.

Venous pressure. — The venous pressure is normal in patients with angina pectoris (Wood, 1936; Altschule, 1944).

Arterial pressure. — Approximately 50 per cent of patients are mild hypertensives (Riseman and Brown, 1937; Altschule, 1944).

Vital capacity. — The vital capacity is often somewhat low in patients with angina pectoris (Altschule, 1944) apparently as a consequence of such noncardiac factors as emphysema and obesity. The fact that inhalation of oxygen results in no increase in oxygen intake (Malinow *et al.*, 1950) indicates that patients with angina pectoris are not anoxic.

Occurrence of pain. — The circulation between attacks is normal in patients with angina pectoris, except for a high incidence of hypertension. In everyday life, attacks of angina pectoris commonly occur at times when the cardiac output is increased, that is, during exertion or emotional upsets, or after heavy meals. The increased cardiac output reported by Starr *et al.* (1938) during attacks of angina was caused by the factor precipitating the attack, rather than the attack itself; the precipitating factor was emotion in one case and the injection of epinephrine in the other. Both the former (Grollman, 1929; Stead *et al.*, 1945) and the latter (Field and Bock, 1924; von Euler and Liljestrand, 1927; Starr *et al.*, 1937; Altschule and Iglauer, 1940; McMichael and Sharpey-Schaefer, 1944; Cathcart *et al.*, 1953) have been shown to increase cardiac output. It is not valid, however, to conclude that attacks of angina pectoris are in every instance associated with increased cardiac output. For instance, sympathomimetic amines such as paredrine, which elevate blood pressure but do not increase cardiac output (Altschule and Iglauer, 1940), may cause anginal pain in patients with history of angina pectoris. A clinical counterpart of this phenomenon is angina pectoris associated with sudden hypertension (Lewis, 1931). It is clear from the formula * of Evans and Matsuoka (1915), $W = OP + \frac{1}{2} (w/g)V^2$, that an increase either in cardiac output or in blood pressure increases the work of the heart and, accordingly, it may be concluded that the occurrence of angina pectoris is usually related to increased cardiac work. On the other hand, angina may occur when the work of the heart is decreased, that is, in cardiac arrhythmias with marked tachycardia (page 362). The factor re-

---

* In this formula, W is the work done by the heart, O is the output of the heart, P is the mean blood pressure, w is the weight of blood, V is the velocity of the blood flow, and g is the acceleration due to gravity.

sponsible for angina in such situations appears to be myocardial anoxia consequent to inadequate flow through the coronary tree, a result of shortening of diastole. Evidence of impaired myocardial function is afforded by abnormal changes in QT interval during attacks (Yu *et al.*, 1950).

The precise mechanisms underlying the production of pain by myocardial ischemia is unknown. Lewis(1935) showed that exercising a muscle under conditions of ischemia causes pain, an observation amply confirmed by others; however, there is no precise information indicating whether oxygen lack, carbon dioxide excesss, or the excessive production of some other metabolite is the direct cause of the discomfort. At any rate it has been shown that the nerve fibers that carry coronary arterial pain run in the adventitia of these arteries (Katz *et al.*, 1935). They are carried in the middle and inferior cardiac nerves and the thoracic cardiac rami to the middle and inferior cervical and the first four thoracic posterior roots (White and Smithwick, 1941). These axones are small, poorly myelinated or unmyelinated, and their rate of conduction is slow (Heinbecker and Bishop, 1935); they therefore resemble sympathetic motor neurones except that they run to the cord as a simple fiber without any synapse in the ganglion between a pre- and postganglionic fiber. Other components of the pain of coronary disease, such as pain in the neck or jaw, are apparently carried in the vagus nerve (White and Smithwick, 1941). The fact that most of the pain-carrying fibers enter the cord in the first four or five thoracic segments accounts for the typical referred pain over the skin of the shoulder, arm, or inner fingers. Anginal pain may be referred to a phantom limb (Cohen and Jones, 1943). The skin temperature over the painful arm is low, owing to reflex vasoconstriction (Doret and Ferrero, 1951).

Anginal pain may be precipitated in patients with coronary sclerosis by induced anoxia. This phenomenon appears to be the consequence of (i) myocardial anoxia, and (ii) increased cardiac output and work due to lowered arterial blood oxygen saturation (page 70). It should be noted that one change induced by the inhalation of air containing low percentages of oxygen, namely, the fall in arterial blood oxygen level, is unpredictable (Graybiel *et al.*, 1937; Houston, 1946; Pennys and Thomas, 1950; Mathers and Levy, 1950). Consequently, changes in cardiac work and in vasomotor function are also variable. The use of anoxia in tests of the state of the coronary arteries has accordingly been criticized (Graybiel *et al.*, 1937; Houston, 1946).

A valid generalization based on physiologic data is a reaffirmation of the clinical concept that factors which increase cardiac work or decrease myocardial oxygenation lead to angina in patients with disease of the coronary arteries or their ostia. These considerations do not explain status anginosus, or recurrent angina at rest. Local spastic changes in the coronary arteries also appear to be important in the genesis of angina. That diseased arteries frequently show vasospastic phenomena is well known to students of peripheral artery disease; there is no reason to doubt that coronary arteries may react similarly. Indeed, Freedberg *et al.* (1944) have shown that reflexes from the skin control the occurrence of anginal pain to a large degree, apparently by influencing the caliber of the coronary vessels. Similarly, there is evidence that distension of abdominal viscera may cause reflex coronary vasoconstriction (von Bergmann, 1932; Gilbert *et al.*, 1940). Freedberg and Riseman's (1953) discussion of reflex factors in angina pectoris is of interest. The relief of pain experienced by some patients after taking vasodilator drugs, such as nitrates, in doses too small to affect the general circulatory dynamics, is further evidence for the importance of coronary spasm in the causation of anginal pain. Available data show that only large doses of nitroglycerine affect the cardiac output (Wegria *et al.*, 1951; Brandt *et al.*, 1952). The fundamental defect in angina pectoris is a decreased coronary circulation which, though adequate for the work of the heart when the patient is at rest, becomes inadequate when coronary filling is somewhat impaired by spasm or other factors, or when the cardiac work is increased.

It is of interest that many patients with the anginal syndrome hyperventilate during the occurrence of pain but do not experience dyspnea (Boyer and Bailey, 1943); this phenomenon suggests that dyspnea need not be perceived when hyperventilation is present if more severe discomfort of other types occurs.

2. *Myocardial Infarction*

Circulatory dynamics. — Data describing the circulation in patients following myocardial infarction are scanty. A few measurements of cardiac output by unreliable methods suggest that lowering of the output of the heart probably occurs (Grishman and Master, 1941; Starr and Wood, 1943; Fries *et al.*, 1952; Starr and Jonas, 1940; Hauss and Kopperman, 1950). The finding of decreased blood flow through the fingers recorded by Mendlowitz (1942) is difficult to interpret with certainty since the circulation in the hands is strongly influenced by neurogenic factors and may not indicate the state of the circulation as a whole. The circulation time is normal or increased (Bain, 1934; Fishberg *et al.*, 1934; Neurath, 1937; Selzer, 1945; Stead and Ebert, 1942; Agress *et al.*, 1950; Fries *et al.*, 1952; Wollheim, 1952); the venous pressure may be normal, low or elevated (Fishberg *et al.*, 1934; Griffith *et al.*, 1934; Stead and Ebert, 1942; Selzer, 1945; Wollheim, 1952; Agress *et al.*, 1950; Fink *et al.*, 1953; Fries *et al.*, 1952). Of special interest is the finding by all of these authors of low values for venous pressure in some instances, suggestive of a state of shock due to impaired peripheral vascular mechanisms. In this connection a single observation of temporary loss of tone in the small vessels recorded by Capps (1936) is particularly pertinent. The vital capacity is often diminished (Selzer, 1945). Fishberg, Hitzig and King (1934) found the blood volume markedly variable, but these authors used a method not now considered reliable. Stead and Ebert (1942) found the plasma volume slightly diminished and detected evidences of hemoconcentration, but all of their patients had some degree of pulmonary edema, which in itself may cause hemoconcentration (page 222); Cameron *et al.* (1947) found the blood volume normal, as did Fries *et al.* (1952) also. Agress *et al.* (1950) found the plasma volume low in those patients in shock and high in those in whom congestive failure developed; hematocrit values were normal or high in all. Wollheim (1952) also found hemoconcentration and a decrease in plasma volume in his cases.

Interpretation of these findings is difficult. It is impossible to characterize the circulatory phenomena consequent to myocardial infarction *per se*, for it is probable that the cardiovascular changes that have been found are largely determined by the occurrence of associated conditions such as shock, pulmonary edema, congestive heart failure, and cardiac arrhythmias.

In addition to the well-known electrocardiographic patterns associated with myocardial infarction there are changes in QT interval (Krasnoff, 1950) that indicate the existence of a generalized myocardial disturbance superimposed upon the localized disorders suggested by the patterns.

Shock. — The shock that occurs during or after myocardial infarction is properly regarded as neurogenic by Fishberg *et al.* (1934); it is probably not due solely or largely to cardiac weakness, as Stead and Ebert suggest (1942). Whatever its mechanism, it is often self-limited and, when more persistent, may be benefited by infusions of plasma, even in the presence of pulmonary edema.

Pulmonary edema. — This disorder is probably neurogenic in origin (page 218), for it occurs irrespective of whether the left or right ventricle is the seat of infarction. Stead and Ebert (1942) pointed out that the circulation time may show surprisingly little increase in patients with pulmonary edema following myocardial infarction. It is apparent that much work must be done in this field; the vast amount of theorizing that occupies space in the medical literature has little established validity.

The fact that the arterial blood oxygen saturation is lowered in many patients with myocardial infarction (Godfrey, Pond, and Wood, 1948; Borden *et al.*, 1952; Montgomery, Zinnser, and Horwitz, 1950) suggests that pulmonary edema is more commonly present than recognized. It must be remembered that interstitial pulmonary edema may cause no râles or wheezes but does impair oxygenation of blood.

Cardiac arrhythmias. — The occurrence of ventricular arrhythmias, that is, extrasystoles or tachycardia, after myocardial infarction is probably consequent to the formation of hyperirritable foci in the damaged ventricular myocardium. It is probable, however, that the other common arrhythmias in this disorder are vagal in origin. It has been shown that atropine may abolish partial heart block after myocardial infarction (Master *et al.*, 1938); available evidence also suggests that auricular fibrillation and flutter are due to vagal reflexes acting on the auricles (Klainer and Altschule, 1942; Altschule, 1945).

Septal perforation. — This complication causes physical signs and also changes in the circulation resembling those of congenital septal defects (Muller *et al.*, 1950).

Autonomic function. — Reference has already been made to the probable vagal origin of some cardiac arrhythmias after myocardial infarction; it is likely that pulmonary edema seen in this condition is also reflex. The gastric distention and vomiting may also be vagal in origin. Definite evidence of increased vagal tone is afforded by the development of hypersensitivity of the carotid sinus reflex after myocardial infarction (Sigler, 1942).

The occurrence of bluish pallor, cold skin, and also a reduction in peripheral blood flow (Mendlowitz, 1942), all suggest sympathetic stimulation. Additional evidence in this regard is the not uncommon finding of a level of arterial blood pressure above what is usual in a given patient early in the course of myocardial infarction. Excretion of break-down products of adrenal medullary hormones may increase (Forssman *et al.*, 1952; Nuzum and Bischoff, 1952).

Intermediary metabolism. — Data are available that suggest the occurrence of an "adaptation reaction" after myocardial infarction. Eosinopenia has been noted by Gabrilove (1950), Recant *et al.* (1950), Ellestad and Reed (1952), Forssman *et al.* (1952), Feldman *et al.* (1952), and Slapak (1953). Adrenal cortical hormones or their derivatives may be excreted in excess (Forssman *et al.*, 1952). Lymphopenia also occurs (Altschul, 1950, 1952). Creatinuria develops early (Herrmann and Decherd, 1934; Altschule and Rosenfeld, 1947); negative nitrogen balance and elevated blood amino acid levels soon become manifest also (Altschule and Rosenfeld, 1947; Tietze and Schulz, 1953). Similarly, disturbance of carbohydrate metabolism appears, with elevation of the blood lactate and pyruvate levels (Davidson *et al.*, 1946; Altschule and Rosenfeld, 1947); glycosuria and hyperglycemia are well known to occur, either *de novo* or as evidence of the making overt of latent diabetes mellitus. Ellenberg *et al.* (1952) have reviewed the literature bearing on this point. The elevated blood cholesterol levels (Morrison *et al.*, 1948, 1949, 1950, 1952) with normal cholesterol-ester percentages, probably are consequent to the "adaptation reaction." The cholesterol tolerance is normal (Wang, 1952). A small rise in serum potassium has been described (Willhelm, 1951). The findings of elevated serum mucoprotein concentrations (Simkin et al., 1949) has no evident significance. Other changes in plasma proteins have also been reported (Hauss and Leist, 1952). The plasma tocopherol level is normal (Klatskin and Krehl, 1950).

A fact of unknown significance is that the serum of patients with recent myocardial infarcts expands frog melanophores (Johnsson and Högberg, 1952).

Evidences of impaired hepatic function, of unknown mechanism, may occur (Evans et al., 1952; Schwalm and Hoogenboom, 1952).

Blood clotting. — A tendency toward intravascular clot formation is common after myocardial infarction. Blood clotting has been found to be accelerated by some authors (de Takats, 1943; Hines and Kessler, 1945; Ogura et al., 1946; Cameron et al., 1947; Rosenthal and Weaver, 1952). The responsible mechanisms are unknown but may include the effects of bodily injury *per se*, increased viscosity of the blood due to dehydration or the loss of plasma into or through edematous lungs, and slowing of the blood flow consequent to shock, congestive failure, or oversedation. The adhesiveness of blood platelets is normal (Eisen et al., 1951). Whether the increased blood fibrinogen level that occurs (Myers, 1948), and accounts for alteration in sedimentation rate, has any effect upon clotting is not known. Slight changes in prothrombin time (Overman and Wright, 1951) are probably insignificant. The thrombin recovery test yields increased values (Sternberger, 1952), and clot density is increased also (Losner et al., 1951).

Probably even more dangerous than the increased tendency toward clot formation is the increased fibrinolytic activity of plasma in myocardial infarction (Tietze and Schulz, 1953); this phenomenon may cause breaking loose of clots that are only slightly adherent.

Shoulder-hand syndrome. — The mechanism of this syndrome is obscure. The vasemotor changes associated with it have been studied by Mogensen (1953). An excellent review of the neurophysiology is available (Vaernet, 1952).

Bibliography

Chapter III

AGRESS, C. M., M. ROSENBURG, A. SCHNEIDERMAN, and E. J. BROTMAN, Blood volume studies in shock resulting from myocardial infarction. I. Studies with Evans Blue dye (T-1824), *J. Clin. Investigation* **29**, 1267 (1950).

ALTSCHUL, R., White blood cells in old age and arteriosclerosis, *Circulation* **2**, 470 (1950).

ALTSCHUL, R., Lymphocytopenia in heart disease, *Am. Heart J.* **43**, 653 (1952).

ALTSCHULE, M. D., Cardiovascular dynamics in patients with angina pectoris, *Am. Heart J.* **27**, 322 (1944).

ALTSCHULE, M. D., The relation between vagal activity and auricular fibrillation in various clinical conditions, *New England J. Med.* **233**, 265 (1945).

ALTSCHULE, M. D., and A. IGLAUER, The effect of benzedrine (B-phenyl-isopropylamine sulphate) and paredrine (p-hydroxy-α-methylphenyl-ethylamine hydrobromide) on the circulation, metabolism and respiration in normal man, *J. Clin. Investigation* **19**, 497 (1940).

ALTSCHULE, M. D., and F. M. ROSENFELD, Increased catabolism following acute myocardial infarction, *Arch. Int. Med.* **80**, 74 (1947).

BAIN, C. W. C., Observations on the speed of the circulation, *Quart. J. Med.* **27**, 237 (1934).

BAZETT, H. C., L. B. LAPLACE, and J. C. SCOTT, The estimation of cardiac output from blood pressure and pulse wave velocity measurements on subjects with cardiovascular disease. I. Cardiovascular disease other than aortic regurgitation, *Am. Heart J.* **22**, 737 (1941).

BERMAN, B., J. R. BRAUNSTEIN, and J. McGUIRE, The effect of meals on the electrocardiogram and ballistocardiogram in patients with angina pectoris, *Circulation* **1**, 1017 (1950).

BERNSTEIN, M., and S. SIMKINS, The use of magnesium sulfate in the measurement of circulation time, *Am. Heart J.* **17**, 218 (1939).

BORDEN, C. W., R. V. EBERT, and R. H. WILSON, Anoxia in myocardial infarction and indications for oxygen therapy, *J. A. M. A.* **148**, 1370 (1952).

BOYER, P. K., and C. V. BAILEY, Concentration of carbon dioxide in expired air in heart disease, *Arch. Int. Med.* **71**, 529 (1943).

BRANDT, J. L., A. CACCESE, and W. DOCK, Slit-kymographic evidence that nitroglycerine decreases heart volume and stroke volume, *Am. J. Med.* **12**, 650 (1952).

CAMERON, W. M., J. H. B. HILTON, S. R. TOWNSEND, and E. S. MILLS, The importance of blood changes in coronary occlusion, *Canad. M. A. J.* **56**, 263 (1947).

CAPPS, R. B., A method for measuring tone and reflex constriction of the capillaries, venules and veins of the human hand with the results in normal and diseased states, *J. Clin. Investigation* **15**, 229 (1936).

CATHCART, R. T., W. FIELD, and D. W. RICHARDS, JR., Comparison of cardiac output determined by the ballistocardiograph (Nickerson apparatus) and by the direct Fick method, *J. Clin. Investigation* **32**, 5 (1953).

COHEN, H., and H. W. JONES, The reference of cardiac pain to a phantom left arm, *Brit. Heart J.* **5**, 67 (1943).

DAVIDSON, C. S., J. H. LEWIS, H. J. TAGNON, M. A. ADAMS, and F. H. L. TAYLOR, Medical shock: abnormal biochemical changes in patients with severe acute medical illnesses, with and without peripheral vascular failure, *New England J. Med.* **234**, 279 (1946).

DE TAKATS, G., Heparin tolerance; test of clotting mechanism, *Surg., Gynec. & Obst.* **77**, 31 (1943).

DORET, J. P., and R. FERRERO, Inégalité de la température cutanée dans l'infarctus du myocarde et l'angine de poitrine, *Cardiologia* **19**, 80 (1951).

EISEN, M. E., M. C. TYSON, S. MICHAEL, and F. BAUMANN, Adhesiveness of blood platelets in arteriosclerosis obliterans, thromboangiitis obliterans, acute thrombophlebitis, chronic venous insufficiency and arteriosclerotic heart disease, *Circulation* **3**, 271 (1951).

ELLENBERG, M., K. E. OSSERMAN, and H. POLLACK, Hyperglycemia in coronary thrombosis, *Diabetes* **1**, 16 (1952).

ELLESTAD, M. H., and J. REED, Circulating eosinophils in cardiovascular stress, *Ann. Int. Med.* **36**, 562 (1952).

EVANS, C. L., and MATSUOKA, The effect of various mechanical conditions on the gaseous metabolism and efficiency of the mammalian heart, *J. Physiol.* **49**, 378 (1915).

EVANS, J. M., O. H. WOOD, and E. M. BREW, Increased urinary urobilinogen following acute myocardial infarction, *Circulation* **6**, 925 (1952).

FELDMAN, D., C. SILVERBERG, A. BIRENBAUM, and S. JICK, Changes in the circulating blood eosinophils following acute myocardial infarction, *Am. J. M. Sc.* **223**, 168 (1952).

FIELD, H., JR., and A. V. BOCK, The action of adrenalin chloride on the circulation in man, *J. Clin. Investigation* **1**, 581 (1924–25).

FINK, T. R., C. J. D'ANGIO, and S. BILOON, Clinical study of shock following myocardial infarction, *J. A. M. A.* **151**, 1163 (1953).

FISHBERG, A. M., W. M. HITZIG, and F. H. KING, Circulatory dynamics in myocardial infarction, *Arch. Int. Med.* **54**, 997 (1934).

FORSSMAN, O., G. HANSON, and C. C. JENSEN, The adrenal function in coronary thrombosis, *Acta med. Scandinav.* **142,** 441 (1952).

FREEDBERG, A. S., and J. E. F. RISEMAN, Observations on the carotid sinus reflex and angina pectoris, *Circulation* **7,** 58 (1953).

FREEDBERG, A. S., E. D. SPIEGL, and J. E. F. RISEMAN, Significance of effects of external heat and cold in patients with angina pectoris. Evidence for the existence of a reflex factor, *Am. Heart J.* **27,** 611 (1944).

FRIES, E. D., H. W. SCHNAPER, R. L. JOHNSON, and G. E. SCHREINER, Hemodynamic alterations in acute myocardial infarction. I. Cardiac output, mean arterial pressure, total peripheral resistance, "central" and total blood volumes, venous pressure and average circulation time, *J. Clin. Investigation* **31,** 131 (1952).

GABRILOVE, J. L., The level of the circulatory eosinophils following trauma, *J. Clin. Endocrinol.* **10,** 637 (1950).

GILBERT, N. C., G. K. FENN, and G. V. LEROY, The effect of distention of abdominal viscera on coronary blood flow and angina pectoris, *J. A. M. A.* **115,** 1926 (1940).

GODFREY, L., H. S. POND, and F. C. WOOD, The Millikan oximeter in the recognition and treatment of anoxemia in clinical medicine, *Am. J. M. Sc.* **216,** 523 (1948).

GRAYBIEL, A., W. MISSIURO, D. B. DILL, and H. T. EDWARDS, Experimentally induced asphyxiation in cardiac patients, with especial reference to certain hazards in air travel and to the use of asphyxiation as a cardiac functional test, *J. Aviation Med.* **8,** 178 (1937).

GRIFFITH, G. C., C. T. CHAMBERLAIN, and J. R. KITCHELL, Observation on the practical significance of venous pressure in health and disease, with a review of the literature, *Am. J. M. Sc.* **187,** 642 (1934).

GRISHMAN, A., and A. M. MASTER, Cardiac output in coronary occlusion studied by the Wezler-Boger physical method, *Proc. Soc. Exper. Biol. & Med.* **48,** 207 (1941).

GROLLMAN, A., Physiological variations in the cardiac output of man. The effect of psychic disturbances on the cardiac output, pulse, blood pressure and oyxgen consumption of man, *Am. J. Physiol.* **89,** 584 (1929).

HAUSS, W. H., and E. KOPPERMANN, Ueber das Minutenvolumen beim Myokardinfarkt, *Ztschr. f. Kreisslaufforsch.* **39,** 449 (1950).

HAUSS, W. H., and J. LEIST, Ueber Dysproteinämie nach Herzinfarkt, *Klin. Wchnschr.* **30,** 481 (1952).

HEINBECKER, P., and G. H. BISHOP, The mechanism of painful sensations, *Res. Publ. Assoc. Nerv. & Ment. Dis.* (1935), vol. 15, p. 226.

HERRMANN, G., and G. DECHERD, Creatine mobilization in myocardial damage, *Proc. Soc. Exper. Biol. & Med.* **32,** 477 (1934).

HINES, L. E., and D. L. KESSLER, Venesection for plethoric patients, *Arch. Int. Med.* **75,** 248 (1945).

HOUSTON, C. S., The effect of pulmonary ventilation on anoxemia, *Am. J. Physiol.* **146,** 613 (1946).

JOHNSSON, S., and B. HOGBERG, Observations on the connection between intermedin and adrenocorticotropic hormone, *Nature* **169,** 286 (1952).

KATZ, L. N., W. MAYNE, and W. WEINSTEIN, Cardiac pain: the presence of pain fibres in the nerve plexus surrounding the coronary vessels, *Arch. Int. Med.* **55,** 760 (1935).

KLAINER, M. J., and M. D. ALTSCHULE, Prolongation of the P-R interval in patients with paroxysmal auricular fibrillation and flutter following myocardial infarction, *Am. J. M. Sc.* **203,** 215 (1942).

KLATSKIN, G., and W. A. KREHL, The significance of the plasma tocopherol concentration and of tocopherol tolerance tests in liver disease, *J. Clin. Investigation* **29,** 1528 (1950).

KRASNOFF, S. O., The duration of the Q-T interval in myocardial infarction, *Am. Heart J.* **39,** 523 (1950).

LENÈGRE, J., and P. MAURICE, Recherches sur la pression sanguine dans la petite circulation chez l'homme, *Acta cardiol.* **2,** 1 (1947).

LEWIS, T., Angina pectoris associated with high blood pressure and its relief by amyl nitrite; with a note on Nothnagel's syndrome, *Heart* **15,** 305 (1931).

LEWIS, T., Pain in muscular ischemia: its relation to anginal pain, *Arch. Int. Med.* **55,** 760 (1935).

LOMBARDO, T. A., L. ROSE, M. TAESCHLER, S. TULUY, and R. J. BING, The effect of exercise on coronary blood flow, myocardial oxygen consumption and cardiac efficiency in man, *Circulation* **7,** 71 (1953).

LOSNER, S., B. W. VOLK, M. JACOBI, and S. NEWHOUSE, Spectrophotometric studies on clot density, *J. Lab. & Clin. Med.* **38,** 28 (1951).

MAKINSON, D. H., Changes in the ballistocardiogram after exercise in normal and abnormal subjects, *Circulation* **2,** 186 (1950).

MALINOW, M. R., B. MOIA, and M. MANGUEL, Efficacité de l'oxygénothérapie déterminée par la mesure de la consommation d'oxygène, *Acta cardiol.* **5,** 457 (1950).

MASTER, A. M., S. DACK, and H. L. JAFFE, Partial and complete heart block in acute coronary artery occlusion, *Am. J. M. Sc.* **196,** 513 (1938).

MATHERS, J. A. L., and R. L. LEVY, Correlation of the oxygen saturation of the blood and changes in the electrocardiogram, blood pressure, and heart rate during the anoxemia test. Observations on normal persons and patients with suspected and manifest coronary heart disease, *Circulation* **1,** 426 (1950).

McMICHAEL, J., and E. P. SHARPEY-SCHAFER, Cardiac output in man by a direct Fick method. Effects of posture, venous pressure change, atropine and adrenaline, *Brit. Heart J.* **6**, 33 (1944).

MENDLOWITZ, M., The digital blood flow, arterial pressure, and vascular resistance in arterial hypertension and in coronary thrombosis, *J. Clin. Investigation* **21**, 539 (1942).

MOGENSEN, E. F., Reflex vasodilatation test in patients with periarthrosis humero-scapularis and the "shoulder-hand syndrome," *Acta med. Scandinav.* **145**, 1 (1953).

MONTGOMERY, H., H. F. ZINSSER, JR., and O. HORWITZ, Oxygen tension of tissues by the polarographic method. II. Detection of right to left shunts by changes in skin oxygen tension resulting from inhalation of oxygen, *Circulation* **2**, 845 (1950).

MORRISON, L. M., The serum phospholipid-cholesterol ratio as a test for coronary atherosclerosis, *J. Lab. & Clin. Med.* **39**, 550 (1952).

MORRISON, L. M., and K. D. JOHNSON, Cholesterol content of the coronary arteries and blood in acute coronary artery thrombosis, *Am. Heart J.* **39**, 31 (1950).

MORRISON, L. M., L. HALL, and A. L. CHANEY, Cholesterol metabolism: blood serum cholesterol and ester levels in 200 cases of acute coronary thrombosis, *Am. J. M. Sc.* **216**, 32 (1948).

MORRISON, L. M., W. T. GONZALES, and L. HALL, The significance of cholesterol variations in human blood serum, *J. Lab. & Clin. Med.* **34**, 1473 (1949).

MYERS, L., Blood fibrinogen in myocardial infarction, *Arch. Int. Med.* **82**, 419 (1948).

MULLER, O., S. HUMERFELT, H. RASMUSSEN, and O. STORSTEIN, Perforation of the ventricular septum following myocardial infarction, *Acta cardiol.* **5**, 633 (1950).

NEURATH, O., Untersuchungen über die Bestimmung der Blutumlaufsgeschwindigkeit mit Magnesiumsulfat, *Ztschr. f. klin. Med.* **132**, 134 (1937).

NUZUM, F. R., and F. BISCHOFF, The urinary output of catechol derivatives including adrenaline in normal individuals, in essential hypertension, and in myocardial infarction, *Circulation* **7**, 96 (1952).

OGURA, J. H., N. R. FETTER, M. A. BLANKENHORN, and H. L. GLUECK, Changes in blood coagulation following coronary thrombosis measured by the heparin retarded clotting test (Waugh and Ruddick test), *J. Clin. Investigation* **25**, 586 (1946).

OVERMAN, R. S., and I. S. WRIGHT, Prothrombin time determinations on patients with myocardial infarction, *J. A. M. A.* **147**, 227 (1951).

PENNYS, R., and C. B. THOMAS, The relationship between the arterial oxygen saturation and the cardiovascular response to induced anoxemia in normal young adults, *Circulation* **1**, 415 (1950).

RECANT, L., D. M. HUME, P. FORSHAM, and G. W. THORN, Studies on the effect of epinephrine on the pituitary-adrenocortical system, *J. Clin. Endocrinol.* **10**, 187 (1950).

RISEMAN, J. E. F., and M. G. BROWN, An analysis of the diagnostic criteria of angina pectoris. A critical study of 100 proved cases, *Am. Heart J.* **14**, 331 (1937).

ROSENTHAL, R. L., and J. C. WEAVER, Acceleration of blood coagulation in acute myocardial infarction as demonstrated by the heparin clotting time; effect of dicoumeral therapy, *Circulation* **6**, 257 (1952).

SCARBOROUGH, W. R., R. PENNEYS, C. B. THOMAS, B. M. BAKER, and R. E. MASON, The cardiovascular effect of induced controlled anoxemia, *Circulation* **4**, 190 (1951).

SCHALM, L., and W. A. H. HOOGENBOOM, Blood bilirubin in congestive heart failure, *Am. Heart J.* **44**, 571 (1952).

SELZER, A., Circulation in acute myocardial infarction, *Arch. Int. Med.* **76**, 54 (1945).

SIGLER, L. H., The hyperactive cardio-inhibitory carotid-sinus reflex as an aid in the diagnosis of coronary disease; its value compared with that of the electrocardiogram, *New England J. Med.* **226**, 46 (1942).

SIMKIN, B., H. C. BERGMAN, and M. PRINZMETAL, Studies on coronary circulation. V. Quantitative changes in a serum mucoprotein following the occurrence of myocardial infarction, *Am. J. Med.* **6**, 734 (1949).

SLAPAK, L., Ueber das Verhalten der Leukocyten im peripheren Blutbild beim Myokardinfarkt, *Cardiologia* **22**, 101 (1953).

STARR, I., and C. J. GAMBLE, Cardiac output in common clinical conditions, and the diagnosis of myocardial insufficiency by cardiac output methods, *Ann. Int. Med.* **9**, 569 (1935).

STARR, I., C. J. GAMBLE, J. S. DONAL, and L. H. COLLINS, Estimations of the work of the heart during and between attacks of angina pectoris, *J. Clin. Investigation* **17**, 287 (1938).

STARR, I., C. J. GAMBLE, A. MARGOLIES, J. S. DONAL, JR., N. JOSEPH, and E. EAGLE, A clinical study of the action of 10 commonly used drugs on cardiac output, work and size; on respiration, on metabolic rate and on the electrocardiogram, *J. Clin. Investigation* **16**, 799 (1937).

STARR, I., and L. JONAS, Syndrome of subnormal circulation in ambulatory patients, *Arch. Int. Med.* **66**, 1095 (1940).

STARR, L., and F. C. WOOD, Studies with the ballistocardiograph in acute cardiac infarction and chronic angina pectoris, *Am. Heart J.* **25**, 81 (1943).

STEAD, E. A., JR., and R. V. EBERT, Shock syndrome produced by failure of the heart, *Arch. Int. Med.* **69**, 369 (1942).

STEAD, E. A., JR., J. V. WARREN, A. J. MERRILL, and E. S. BRANNON, The cardiac output in male subjects as measured by the technique of right atrial catheterization. Normal values with observations on the effect of anxiety and tilting, *J. Clin. Investigation* **24**, 326 (1945).

STERNBERGER, L. A., Preliminary clinical evaluation of thrombin recovery test, *J. A. M. A.* **150**, 1591 (1952).

TIETZE, K., and F. H. SCHULZ, Ueber den Stickstoffhaushalt beim Myokardinfarkt, *Schweiz. med. Wchnschr.* **83**, 34 (1953).

VAERNET, K., Two cases of shoulder-hand syndrome in meningioma affecting the premotor region, *Acta psychiat. et neurol.* **27**, 201 (1952).

VON BERGMANN, G., Das "epiphrenale Syndrom," eine Beziehung zur Angina pectoris und zum Kardiospasmus, *Deutsche med. Wchnschr.* **58**, 605 (1932).

VON EULER, U., and G. LILJESTRAND, Die Wirkung des Adrenalins auf das Minutenvolumen des Herzens beim Menschen, *Skandinav. Arch. f. Physiol.* **52**, 243 (1927).

WANG, I., Cholesterol tolerance in coronary thrombosis, *Brit. M. J.* **1**, 1278 (1952).

WÉGRIA, R., J. L. NICKERSON, R. B. CASE, and J. F. HOLLAND, Effect of nitroglycerine on the cardiovascular system of normal persons, *Am. J. Med.* **10**, 414 (1951).

WHITE, J. C., and R. H. SMITHWICK, *The autonomic nervous system; anatomy, physiology, and surgical applications* (New York, Macmillan, ed. 2, 1941).

WILHELM, S. K., Alterations in serum potassium and sodium in acute myocardial infarction, *Am. J. Clin. Path.* **21**, 146 (1951).

WINTERNITZ, M., J. DEUTSCH, and Z. BRÜLL, Eine klinisch brauchbare Bestimmungsmethode der Bluetumlaufzeit mittels Decholininjektion, *Med. Klin.* **27**, 986 (1931).

WOLF, G. A., JR., and H. G. WOLFF, Studies on the nature of certain symptoms associated with cardiovascular disorders, *Psychosom. Med.* **8**, 293 (1946).

WOLLHEIM, E., Gefässinsuffizienz, Schock, Kollaps, und Minus-Dekompensation, *Cardiologia* **20**, 327 (1952).

WOOD, P., Right and left ventricular failure. A study of circulation time and venous blood pressure, *Lancet* **2**, 15 (1936).

YU, P. N. G., R. A. BRUCE, F. W. LOVEJOY, JR., and R. PEARSON, Observations on the change of ventricular systole (Q-T interval) during exercise, *J. Clin. Investigation* **29**, 279 (1950).

IV

CARDIAC ARRHYTHMIAS

1. *Auricular Fibrillation. Action of Quinidine*

The effects of auricular fibrillation in man have been studied in most cases by observing the changes that follow the restoration of normal rhythm, either spontaneously or as a result of the administration of quinidine. The findings are colored by the fact that many of the patients so studied had, in addition to the arrhythmia, valvular heart disease or some degree of myocardial insufficiency, or both. Therefore, absolute uniformity in the findings is not to be expected.

Restoration of normal sinus rhythm is associated with a rise in cardiac output and a fall in arteriovenous oxygen difference in most instances (1; Stewart *et al.*, 1938); occasionally these evidences of improved cardiac function do not occur (Resnik *et al.*, 1935; Stewart *et al.*, 1938; Smith *et al.*, 1930). Patients with auricular fibrillation exhibit subnormal rises in cardiac output during exercise; this defect is usually ameliorated after restoration of normal rhythm (Hansen *et al.*, 1952; Hecht *et al.*, 1951; Kory and Meneely, 1951). Glomerular filtration may increase after restoration of normal rhythm (Newman, 1949). The right auricular and pulmonary arterial pressures change variably; the pulmonary blood volume may decrease (Hansen *et al.*, 1952). The venous blood oxygen content usually rises (Stewart, 1923); this finding indicates an improvement in peripheral blood flow and increased oxygen tension in the tissues. Often, however, the improvement in cardiac function after reversion is not great enough to be considered significant, especially in instances where the ventricular rate was not rapid during fibrillation. Quinidine also has a vasodilator action (Ferrer *et al.*, 1948; Harvey *et al.*, 1949). Changes in circulation time and venous pressure (Stewart *et al.*, 1938; Lequime, 1940; Hansen *et al.*, 1952; Phillips and Levine, 1949), and in vital capacity (Stewart, 1923; Stewart *et al.*, 1938; Phillips and Levine, 1949) are variable but generally favorable. The respiratory minute volume may fall somewhat with a consequent rise in alveolar air carbon dioxide content (Smith *et al.*, 1930); there is a simultaneous decrease in oxygen consumption (Stewart, 1923). The respiratory minute volume after exercise no longer shows the excessive rise seen with effort during auricular fibrillation (Hecht *et al.*, 1951). The observations of Crawford (1926) on the behavior of the cutaneous capillaries in patients with auricular fibrillation suggest that changes occur in the caliber of these vessels which are independent of the heart beat; the significance of this finding is not clear. Buchbinder and Sugarman (1940) made a thorough study of arterial pulses in auricular fibrillation. Lagerlöf and Werkö (1948) have shown again the absence of auricular contraction in observations on the auricular pressure pulse.

The cardiac rate in auricular fibrillation has been the subject of much study. That it is often increased, even in the absence of failure, is well known. Digitalis slows rapid rates in this disorder, but the circulation time, in the absence of failure, need not be changed (Levy and Boas, 1938). The cardiac rate increases abnormally in exercise (Blumgart, 1924; Knox, 1949; Modell *et al.*, 1941; Weinstein, 1940; Wetherbee *et al.*, 1952), a phenomenon that is partly but not wholly ameliorated by digitalization; the occurrence of the sudden onset of acceleration of rate approximately 12 seconds after the start of the exercise (Knox, 1949) warrants further study in that it may throw light on the mechanism underlying the vagal inhibition that occurs in exertion in patients with auricular fibrillation (Modell *et al.*, 1941).

To summarize, auricular fibrillation causes a variable degree of reduction in cardiac output, with the expected secondary changes in circulation and respiration. It may, therefore, precipitate congestive failure, or aggravate it if it is already present. In occasional instances the amount of impairment of cardiac function caused by the arrhythmia may be such as to exert a decisive role in determining the presence or absence of disability; it is not rare for patients with established heart disease and only mild discomfort to date the onset of severe symptoms from the hour of the development of auricular fibrillation. In other instances the only complaint may be palpitation. The common occurrence of auricular fibrillation in association with disease of the mitral valve is worthy of note (page 412).

2. *Auricular Flutter*

The circulation and respiration in auricular flutter have not been studied extensively. Although the mechanism of flutter closely resembles that of auricular fibrillation, the cardiovascular dynamics and symptoms are more nearly similar to those of the tachycardias, discussed in the following sections, because of the usual occurrence of a persistently rapid ventricular rate. Auricular flutter causes a fall in cardiac output with increase in arteriovenous oxygen difference and in circulation time, elevation of venous pressure and decrease in vital capacity (Lequime, 1940; Stewart *et al.*, 1938). Lagerlöf and Werkö (1948) have studied the auricular pressure pulse in this condition.

3. *Auricular Tachycardia*

Although at times the only discomfort associated with auricular tachycardia is palpitation, this arrhythmia often gives rise to more disabling complaints. Auricular tachycardia is of particular interest because it often affects the normal heart, and causes changes in the circulatory dynamics that resemble in varying degrees of severity those of chronic congestive failure. In some patients, however, the clinical manifestations and physiologic changes are those of collapse, while in still other instances cardiac pain may be the chief complaint.

Cardiac output. — All authors agree that a considerable decrease in cardiac output and increase in arteriovenous oxygen difference occur during paroxysms of auricular tachycardia (2; Stewart *et al.*, 1938). The lowered minute volume output appears to be partly due to marked shortening of diastole, so that inadequate filling of the heart occurs. Myocardial weakness may also occur as a consequence of shortened diastole, since recovery of the heart muscle after each beat may be incomplete and the coronary flow, maximal during diastole, is probably decreased; the fall in cardiac output varies roughly with the rise in rate above 150. In addition, a fall in blood pressure (see below) may further diminish the coronary flow. The output of the heart per beat is decreased considerably more than the output per minute because of the marked tachycardia; the output per beat may be decreased to one quarter or one fifth of the normal.

Circulation time. — The arm-to-tongue time is long (Winternitz *et al.*, 1931; Lequime, 1940; Stewart *et al.*, 1938). Neurath (1937) stated that it might be either short or long in paroxysmal tachycardia; he may have included patients with sinus tachycardia.

Venous pressure. — Venous engorgement is of frequent occurrence during paroxysms of auricular tachycardia and the venous pressure has been reported as elevated (Hooker and Eyster, 1908; Lequime, 1940; Stewart *et al.*, 1938); Tornquist (1932), however, found it to be normal.

Arterial pressure. — A profound fall in blood pressure with narrowing of the pulse pressure is not uncommon during paroxysms of this arrhythmia. Considerable decreases in blood pressure are often associated with collapse. When the blood pressure is not markedly lowered, variations in posture give rise to normal changes in arterial pressure (Kahn, 1919).

Vital capacity. — Decreases in vital capacity are the rule (McClure and Peabody, 1917; Carter and Stewart, 1923); however, they do not always occur (Stewart *et al.*, 1938). The occurrence of a lowered vital capacity indicates that an appreciable degree of pulmonary vascular engorgement may occur during paroxysm.

Blood gases. — The arterial blood oxygen saturation may be normal (Barcroft *et al.*, 1921; Meakins, 1922) or low (Carter and Stewart, 1923), depending presumably on the degree of pulmonary stasis that occurs. The venous blood oxygen content is uniformly markedly lowered (Barcroft *et al.*, 1921; Carter and Stewart, 1923), as is to be expected from the decrease in cardiac output. The low venous oxygen content implies peripheral stagnation and low tissue oxygen tensions. The carbon dioxide content of the arterial blood is low as a consequence of dyspnea, whereas that of the venous blood is normal under these conditions because of stasis (Carter and Stewart, 1923).

Congestive failure. — The cardiovascular dynamics of this arrhythmia are similar to those of chronic cardiac decompensation in that the cardiac output is low, the arteriovenous oxygen difference is increased, the circulation time is increased, venous blood oxygen content is decreased, arterial blood carbon dioxide content is lowered, venous pressure is elevated, and evidences of pulmonary congestion are present in the form of diminished vital capacity and, at times, lowering of arterial blood oxygen saturation. Dyspnea, orthopnea, cyanosis and gastro-intestinal disturbances are, therefore, to be expected where the circulatory changes consequent to arrhythmia are severe enough, or where they occur in a milder degree in a patient with a previously damaged heart. The fact that edema in visible amounts does not occur is probably consequent to the short duration of most paroxysms; some increase in extracellular fluid may occur but it is not enough to become apparent on clinical examination.

The cardiovascular physiology of auricular tachycardia shows two important differences, probably related, from those of chronic cardiac decompensation. One is the common occurrence of significant and often marked decreases in arterial blood pressure. Starr and Rawson (1940), basing their conclusions on observations made upon a mechanical model of the circulation, emphasized the fact that when cardiac output falls, the arterial pressure will do likewise unless either vasoconstriction or an increase in blood volume occurs. In some patients pallor and a cold, sweaty skin suggest the occurrence of vasoconstriction due to sympathetic activity. This phenomenon probably accounts for maintenance of the arterial blood pressures at or near normal levels in many instances. In other patients, however, vasoconstriction is inadequate and the blood pressure falls. It is unlikely that an increase in blood volume occurs during paroxysms of auricular tachycardia; the common occurrence of sudden hypotension suggests that this is so and, besides, the attacks are usually too short in duration to allow appreciable new formation of blood. The fact that elevation of venous pressure, occasionally in a striking degree, can occur without increase in blood volume is evidence against the concept (page 35) that the latter is the sole or most important factor in the venous hypotension of chronic cardiac decompensation;

the importance of back pressure from the failing heart seems to be established.

Collapse. — The low cardiac output, increased arteriovenous oxygen difference, low venous blood oxygen content and profound hypotension, together with clinical signs of collapse, emphasize the similarity between the dynamics of auricular tachycardia and those of shock. The development of the complete picture of shock, with suppression of cellular oxidations and fall in oxygen consumption, does not appear to occur in the collapse associated with arrhythmias; the decreased oxygen consumption described by Barcroft *et al.* (1921) in their patient was associated with a fall in respiratory minute volume, and may have been due to technical error or to the effects of large amounts of sedation given during the paroxysm. An important difference between the changes of surgical shock and those of collapse due to arrhythmia is the maintenance of venous pressure at high levels in auricular tachycardia. This rules out reduced venous return consequent to impaired peripheral vascular function as the cause of the collapse seen in this syndrome and shows that its origin is primarily cardiac. It would seem that the collapse associated with the arrhythmia would not be benefited by infusions.

Chest pain. — The occurrence of anginal pain in auricular tachycardia is not uncommon. Decreased coronary flow, caused either by a profound fall in blood pressure or by marked shortening of diastole, or both, is presumably the cause, for cardiac work is not increased but actually may be considerably diminished.

4. *Ventricular Tachycardia*

The circulatory and respiratory physiology of paroxysmal ventricular tachycardia is much like that of auricular tachycardia. The former arrhythmia, however, usually occurs in patients who have serious preëxisting heart disease, so that the change in cardiac rhythm as a rule is associated with very serious symptoms.

Circulation. — Marked decreases in cardiac minute volume output and increases in arteriovenous oxygen difference occur as a consequence of ventricular tachycardia (Dieuaide, 1924; Dogliotti *et al.*, 1937*b*; Stewart *et al.*, 1938). The arm-to-tongue time is increased, often markedly, and elevation of venous pressure is the rule during the paroxysm (Dogliotti *et al.*, 1937*b*; Stewart *et al.*, 1938). The right ventricular systolic pressure falls but the diastolic rises, as does the right auricular pressure also (Dow *et al.*, 1950). The capillaries show changes similar to those of congestive failure (Dogliotti *et al.*, 1937*b*) and the resting blood lactate level has been reported elevated in one patient (Hallock, 1939). The blood pressure usually falls, often to low levels.

Respiration. — The vital capacity is diminished during paroxysms of the arrhythmia (Stewart *et al.*, 1938). Respiratory rate and minute volume rise, with a consequent fall in alveolar carbon dioxide content (Dieuaide, 1924); there is also an increase in oxygen consumption (Dieuaide, 1924; Stewart *et al.*, 1938).

Blood gases. — The changes in the concentrations of the various blood gases are in accord with the observed changes in circulation and respiration. The pulmonary congestion that occurs gives rise to a fall in arterial blood oxygen saturation and the marked slowing of the circulation present causes an additional decrease in venous oxygen content (Dieuaide, 1924). A fall in alveolar carbon dioxide content occurs and is paralleled by a decrease in arterial blood carbon dioxide content, in the one case reported, to a marked degree (Dieuaide, 1924); so great was the dyspnea in this patient that enough carbon dioxide was washed out of the arterial blood to leave him with a slightly lowered venous carbon dioxide content also, in spite of the slowed circulation and increased oxygen consumption.

Symptoms. — As in the case of auricular tachycardia, ventricular tachycardia may manifest itself by dyspnea of varying degree, cardiac pain, or collapse. The relatively more common occurrence of ventricular tachycardia in association with serious heart disease, such as myocardial infarction, tends to make the picture of shock or of severe dyspnea more striking.

5. *Nodal Tachycardia*

Stewart *et al.* (1938) observed a slight decrease in cardiac output in one patient. Ferrer *et al.* (1949) found the output of the heart normal. The venous pressure, according to both, is normal, as are the right auricular and right ventricular pressures also (Ferrer *et al.*, 1949); the venous and right auricular pressures vary only a little in relation to attacks of the arrhythmia (Ferrer *et al.*, 1949).

6. *Complete Heart Block*

Although a number of studies of the general circulatory changes in patients with complete block have been published, uniformity in the findings is lacking. This is perhaps to be accounted for by the fact that heart block usually occurs as a complication of coronary artery disease, and the patients often manifest myocardial insufficiency in addition to the arrhythmia; indeed, in many instances, chronic congestive failure dominates the picture, the arrhythmia being only incidental.

Cardiac output. — The output of the heart per minute is reported as normal by most observers (3; Stewart *et al.*, 1938), while some record low values (4). Some of the patients described by the latter authors had gross congestive failure. The low values reported by Starr *et al.* (1934) and Stewart *et al.* (1938) were associated with low metabolic rates, so that the cardiac output was normal in relation to oxygen consumption. The stroke volume is of course very large, since the pulse rate is low. The cardiac output may increase slightly after the administration of atropine (Kelly and Bayliss, 1949).

Circulation time. — The arm-to-tongue or -face time has been described as normal or increased (5; Ellis and Weiss, 1931; Stewart *et al.*, 1938). Similarly, the ether time may be normal or long (Hitzig, 1935).

Intracardiac and pulmonary vascular pressures. — The right auricular pressure shows large variations with the cardiac cycle (Lagerlöf and Werkö, 1948, 1949). The right ventricular, pulmonary arterial, and pulmonary capillary pressures all are normal (Lagerlöf and Werkö, 1949).

Venous pressure. — Normal values of venous pressure are described in all reported cases (Dogliotti *et al.*, 1937*a*; Ellis and Weiss, 1931; Hitzig, 1935; Stewart *et al.*, 1938).

Renal function. — Renal plasma flow and urea and creatinine clearances are not remarkable (Aas and Blegen, 1949).

Arterial pressure. — The arterial blood pressure characteristically is markedly elevated in systole, usually to or above 200 mm-of-mercury, while the diastolic level is normal or only slightly elevated. The wide pulse pressure is probably to be accounted for by the very much increased output of blood with each heart beat.

Capillaries. — A single observation records dilatation and slow flow in the capillaries of the nailfold (Dogliotti *et al.*, 1937*a*); this may not be typical as the patient so studied also had a long circulation time.

Respiratory dynamics. — A single report records somewhat decreased values for vital capacity (Ellis and Weiss, 1931); in this age group the low values need not be due to pulmonary congestion, but may be associated with emphysema. The respiratory minute volume is usually normal, but may be somewhat increased when the cardiac output is lowered (Smith *et al.*, 1930); in the latter case, the alveolar carbon dioxide content is diminished; otherwise it is normal (Ringer and Altschule, 1930). The arterial blood oxygen saturation is normal in uncomplicated cases (Ellis and Weiss, 1931).

Effect of exercise and fever. — Alt *et al.* (1930) found a normal or almost normal increase in cardiac output when their patients did light exercise. Menne and Lauter (1931) and Stollreiter (1947) recorded an abnormally small increase. Ellis and Weiss (1931) found a normal femoral arteriovenous oxygen difference and a normal blood lactate curve in their patients after moderate exercise. The increase in pulse rate during fever is small in patients with heart block (Gilchrist, 1934).

Symptoms. — Although some of the physiologic studies record normal responses in patients with heart block during light or moderate exercise, it is not unlikely that in severe exertion the cardiac output may fail to increase normally; the possible rise in pulse rate is small, and the increase in stroke volume must be limited because the output per beat is almost maximal with the patient at rest. Accordingly, patients with heart block may during exertion exhibit dyspnea or weakness which, strictly speaking, are not evidences of myocardial insufficiency. Such patients show little benefit after digitalization. On the other hand, patients who already have valvular heart disease or some degree of myocardial disease may develop full-blown congestive failure with the onset of complete heart block. Such patients, their stroke output limited by disease, are able to maintain their circulations at approximately a normal level by means of an increased pulse rate, but when complete heart block supervenes the cardiac output falls and the manifestations of cardiac decompensation appear. These patients may benefit from digitalization by virtue of the fact that the drug gives rise to an increase in output per beat through increased force of contraction.

The problems involved in the various types of syncopal attack are many. Often these attacks are precipitated by a change from partial to complete block; presumably a marked fall in cardiac output occurs in such instances. In other cases, the syncopal attacks may develop even though complete block has been established for some time. Ventricular standstill or fibrillation may account for some of these, but others seem to be related to exercise or the ingestion of a particularly large meal. Presumably here a limited ability to increase cardiac output, together with increased demand for blood flow to the muscles or viscera, results in a decrease in cerebral blood flow.

Bibliography

Chapter IV

AAS, K., and E. BLEGEN, The renal blood flow and the glomerular filtration rate in congestive heart failure and some other clinical conditions. The effect of exercise and hypoxemia. A preliminary report, *Scandinav. J. Clin. & Lab. Investigation* 1, 22 (1949).

ALT, H. L., G. L. WALKER, and W. C. SMITH, The cardiac output in heart disease. II. Effect of exercise on the circulation in patients with chronic rheumatic valvular disease, subacute rheumatic fever and complete heart block, *Arch. Int. Med.* 45, 958 (1930).

BARCROFT, J., A. V. BOCK, and F. J. ROUGHTON, Observations on the circulation and respiration in a case of paroxysmal tachycardia, *Heart* 9, 7 (1921).   [2

BLUMGART, H. L., The reaction to exercise of the heart affected by auricular fibrillation, *Heart* 11, 49 (1924).

BUCHBINDER, W. C., and H. SUGARMAN, Arterial blood pressure in cases of auricular fibrillation, measured directly, *Arch. Int. Med.* 66, 625 (1940).

CARTER, E. P., and H. J. STEWART, Studies of the blood gases in a case of paroxysmal tachycardia, *Arch. Int. Med.* 31, 390 (1923).   [2

CRAWFORD, J. H., Studies on human capillaries. V. Observations in cases of auricular fibrillation, *J. Clin. Investigation* **2**, 365 (1926).

DEBLER, K., Zur Kenntnis des Minutenvolumens bei schweren Kreislauf-leiden, *Med. Klin.* **33**, 761 (1937).   [3

DIEUAIDE, F. R., Observations on the respiratory gases in ventricular paroxysmal tachycardia, *Bull. Johns Hopkins Hosp.* **35**, 229 (1924).

DOGLIOTTI, G. C., E. MONTUSCHI, and A. BERETTA, Studi di emodinamica in due casi di polso lento permanente. Scritti in onore del Prof. A. Ceconi, *Minerva Med.* (1937a).   [3, 5

DOGLIOTTI, G. C., E. MONTUCCHI, and A. BERETTA, Ricerche e considera-zioni sull' emodinamica nella tachicardia parossistica ventricolare, *Cuore e circolaz.* **21**, 265 (1937).

DOW, J. W., H. D. LEVINE, M. ELKIN, F. W. HAYNES, H. K. HELLEMS, J. W. WHITTENBERGER, B. G. FERRIS, W. T. GOODALE, W. P. HARVEY, E. C. EPPINGER, and L. DEXTER, Studies of congenital heart disease. IV. Uncomplicated pulmonic stenosis, *Circulation* **1**, 267 (1950).

ELLIS, L. B., and S. WEISS, Studies in complete heart block. I. The cardiac output and the peripheral circulatory mechanism, *Am. J. M. Sc.* **182**, 195 (1931).   [3, 5

FERRER, M. I., R. M. HARVEY, H. M. WEINER, R. T. CATHCART, and A. COURNAND, Hemodynamic studies in two cases of Wolff-Parkinson-White Syndrome with paroxysmal AV nodal tachycardia, *Am. J. Med.* **6**, 725 (1949).

FERRER, M. I., R. M. HARVEY, L. WERKO, D. T. DRESDALE, A. COURNAND, and D. W. RICHARDS, JR., Some effects of quinidine sulphate on the heart and circulation in man, *Am. Heart J.* **36**, 816 (1948).

GILCHRIST, A. R., The effects of bodily rest, muscular activity and in-duced pyrexia on the ventricular rate in heart block, *Quart. J. Med.* **3**, 381 (1934).

HALLOCK, P., Lactic acid production during rest and after exercise in sub-jects with various types of heart disease with special reference to congenital heart disease, *J. Clin. Investigation* **18**, 385 (1939).

HANSEN, W. R., R. L. MCCLENDON, and J. M. KINSMAN, Auricular fibrilla-tion. Hemodynamic studies before and after conversion with quini-dine, *Am. Heart J.* **44**, 499 (1952).   [1

HARVEY, R. M., M. I. FERRER, R. T. CATHCART, D. W. RICHARDS, JR., and A. COURNAND, Some effects of digoxin upon the heart and circulation in man. Digoxin in left ventricular failure, *Am. J. Med.* **7**, 439 (1949).

HECHT, H. H., W. J. OSHER, and A. J. SAMUELS, Cardiovascular adjust-ments in subjects with organic heart disease before and after con-version of atrial fibrillation to normal sinus rhythm, *J. Clin. Investi-gation* **30**, 647 (1951).   [1

HITZIG, W. M., The use of ether in measuring the circulation time from the antecubital veins to the pulmonary capillaries. *Am. Heart J.* **10**, 1080 (1934–35). [5

HOOKER, D. R., and J. A. E. EYSTER, An instrument for the determination of venous pressure in man, *Bull. Johns Hopkins Hosp.* **19**, 274 (1908).

KAHN, M. H., Tests of the functional capacity of the circulation, *Am. J. M. Sc.* **157**, 634 (1919).

KELLY, H. G., and R. I. S. BAYLISS, Influence of heart-rate on cardiac output. Studies with digoxin and atropin, *Lancet* **2**, 1071 (1949). [3

KERKHOF, A. C., Minute volume determinations in mitral stenosis during auricular fibrillation and after restoration of normal rhythm, *Am. Heart J.* **11**, 206 (1936). [1

KININMONTH, J. G., The circulation rate in some pathological states, with observations on the effect of digitalis, *Quart. J. Med.* **21**, 277 (1928). [3, 4

KINSMAN, J. M., J. W. MOORE, and W. F. HAMILTON, Studies on the circulation: an analysis of some problems of the circulation in man in the normal and in the pathological states, by the use of the injection method, *Kentucky State M. J.* **31**, 285 (1933). [4, 5

KNOX, J. A. C., The heart rate with exercise in patients with auricular fibrillation, *Brit. Heart J.* **11**, 119 (1949).

KORY, R. C., and G. R. MENEELY, Cardiac output in auricular fibrillation with observations on the effects of conversion to normal sinus rhythm. *J. Clin. Investigation* **30**, 653 (1951). [1

LAGERLÖF, H., and L. WERKÖ, Studies on the circulation in man. III. The auricular pressure pulse, *Cardiol.* **13**: 241, 1948.

LAGERLÖF, H., and L. WERKÖ, Studies on the circulation of blood in man. VI. The pulmonary capillary venous pressure pulse in man, *Scandinav. J. Clin. & Lab. Investigation* **1**, 147 (1949).

LAUTER, S., Kreislaufprobleme, *München. med. Wchnschr.* **77**, 593 (1930).

LEQUIME, J., Le débit cardiaque. Études expérimentales et cliniques, *Acta med. Scandinav., Supp. No. 107* (1940). [1, 2, 3, 5

LEVY, H., and E. P. BOAS, Clinical studies of gitalin and of digitalis in the treatment of auricular fibrillation, *Am. Heart J.* **15**, 643 (1938).

McCLURE, C. W., and F. W. PEABODY, Relation of vital capacity of lungs to clinical condition of patients with heart disease, *J. A. M. A.* **69**, 1954 (1917).

MEAKINS, J., The influence of circulatory disturbances on the gaseous exchange of the blood. I. The oxygen saturation of the arterial blood in tachycardia, *Heart* **9**, 185 (1922).

MEAKINS, J., L. DAUTREBANDE, and W. J. FETTER, The influence of circulatory disturbances on the gaseous exchange of the blood. IV. The blood gases and circulation rates in cases of mitral stenosis, *Heart* **10**, 153 (1923). [1

MENNE, T., and S. LAUTER, Beiträge zur Kreislaufdynamik des Herzblocks, *Ztschr. f. klin. Med.* **119**, 196 (1931). [3, 4

MOBITZ, W., Die Ermittlung des Herzschlagvolumens des Menschen durch Einatmung von Aethyljodiddampf. IV. Klinisch kompensierte Veränderungen des Herzens und der Gefässe und beginnende Kreislaufdekompensation ohne Lungenveränderungen, *Deutsches Arch. f. klin. Med.* **157**, 359 (1927). [3

MODELL, W., H. GOLD, and H. H. ROTHENDLER, Use of digitalis to prevent exaggerated acceleration of the heart during physical exercise in patients with auricular fibrillation, *J. A. M. A.* **116**, 2241 (1941).

NEURATH, O., Untersuchungen über die Bestimmung der Blutumlaufsgeschwindigkeit mit Magnesiumsulfat, *Ztschr. f. klin. Med.* **132**, 134 (1937).

NEWMAN, E. V., Function of the kidney and metabolic changes in cardiac failure, *Am. J. Med.* **7**, 490 (1949).

PHILLIPS, E., and S. A. LEVINE, Auricular fibrillation without other evidence of heart disease; cause of reversible heart failure, *Am. J. Med.* **7**, 478 (1949).

RESNIK, H., JR., B. FRIEDMAN, and T. R. HARRISON, Effect of certain therapeutic measures on the cardiac output of patients with congestive heart failure, *Arch. Int. Med.* **56**, 891 (1935). [1

RIGONI, M., Il ricambio respiratorio, la portata circolatoria e la gittata sistolica nelle cardiopatie compensate e nello scompenso di circolo. II. Portata circolatoria e gittata sistolica, *Cuore e circolaz.* **21**, 209 (1937). [3

RINGER, M., and M. D. ALTSCHULE, Studies on the circulation. II. Cardiac output in diseases of the heart, and under the influence of digitalis therapy, *Am. Heart J.* **5**, 305 (1930). [3, 4

SCHÖNE, G., Über die Zirkulationsgrösse bei der paroxysmalen Tachycardie, *Klin. Wchnschr.* **16**, 804 (1937). [2

SESSA, T., La velocità della corrente del sangue. III. Tempo di circolazione nelle varie affezioni morbose, *Cuore e circolaz.* **22**, 181 (1938). [5

SMITH, W. C., G. L. WALKER, and H. L. ALT, The cardiac output in heart disease. I. Complete heart block, auricular fibrillation before and after the restoration to normal rhythm, subacute rheumatic fever and chronic rheumatic valvular disease, *Arch. Int. Med.* **45**, 706 (1930). [3

STARR, I., JR., L. H. COLLINS, JR., and F. C. WOOD, Studies of the basal work and output of the heart in clinical conditions, *J. Clin. Investigation* **12**, 13 (1933). [2

STARR, I., J. S. DONAL, A. MARGOLIES, R. SHAW, L. H. COLLINS, and C. J. GAMBLE, Studies of the heart and circulation in disease; estimations of basal cardiac output, metabolism, heart size, and blood pressure in 235 subjects, *J. Clin. Investigation* **13**, 561 (1934).   [1, 2, 4

STARR, I., and A. J. RAWSON, Role of the "static blood pressure" in abnormal increments of venous pressure, especially in heart failure. I. Theoretical studies on an improved circulation schema whose pumps obey Starling's law of the heart, *Am. J. M. Sc.* **199**, 27 (1940).

STEWART, H. J., Observations on the blood gases in auricular fibrillation and after the restoration of the normal mechanism, *Arch. Int. Med.* **31**, 871 (1923).   [1

STEWART, H. J., J. E. DEITRICK, N. F. CRANE, and W. P. THOMPSON, Studies of the circulation in the presence of abnormal cardiac rhythms. Observations relating to (Part I) rhythms associated with rapid ventricular rate and to (Part II) rhythms associated with slow ventricular rate, *J. Clin. Investigation* **17**, 449 (1938).   [1, 2, 3, 4, 5

STOLLREITER, H., Uber die Leistungsbreite des Herzmuskels bei pathologischer Frequenzniedrigung, *Klin. Wchnschr.* **24–25**, 269 (1947). [3

TARR, L., B. S. OPPENHEIMER, and R. V. SAGER, The circulation time in various clinical conditions determined by the use of sodium dehydrocholate, *Am. Heart J.* **8**, 766 (1932–33).

TORNQUIST, H., Physiologische und klinische Studien über den Armvenendruck, *Ztschr. f. d. ges. exper. Med.* **81**, 227 (1932).

WEINSTEIN, W., J. PLAUT, and L. N. KATZ, Limitations of the use of digitalis for ambulatory patients with auricular fibrillation, *Am. J. M. Sc.* **199**, 498 (1940).

WEISS, R., Ueber die klinische Verwendbarkeit der Bestimmung des zirkulatorischen Minutenvolumens mit der Krogh-Lindhard'schen Stickoxydulmethode, *Wien. med. Wchnschr.* **77**, 1367 (1927).   [1

WETHERBEE, D. G., M. G. BROWN, and D. HOLZMAN, Ventricular rate response following exercise during auricular fibrillation and after conversion to normal sinus rhythm, *Am. J. M. Sc.* **223**, 667 (1952).

WINTERNITZ, M., J. DEUTSCH, and Z. BRÜLL, Eine klinisch brauchbare Bestimmungsmethode der Blutumlaufzeit mittels Decholininjektion, *Med. Klin.* **27**, 986 (1931).   [5

WOLLHEIM, E., and K. LANGE, Kreislaufszeit und ihre Beziehung zu anderen Kreislaufgrössen, *Verhandl. d. deutsch. Gesellsch. f. inn. Med.* **43**, 134 (1931).   [5

V

PERICARDITIS

Although many observers have noted abnormal elevation of the venous pressure at rest or after exercise (**1**), and also increased spinal fluid pressure (Porot, 1930) in pericarditis in general, it is more illuminating in discussing the cardiovascular dynamics of pericarditis to divide it into (i) that due to fibrous pericarditis or concretio cordis and (ii) that due to acute or subacute pericarditis with effusion.

1. *Concretio Cordis*

In concretio cordis the heart is encased in a tough shell which prevents dilation in diastole and may also, by virtue of fibrous bands, constrict the great veins as they enter the heart.

Cardiac output. — All authors report low values of cardiac output, associated with an increased arteriovenous oxygen difference (**2**; Burwell *et al.*, 1932, 1935, 1938; Sawyer *et al.*, 1952); in some instances, however, the decreases in minute volume output are not great, and one author found normal values in his case (Debler, 1937). Since the heart is usually not enlarged greatly, if at all, the output per minute in relation to size is not decreased as much as in chronic congestive failure, where cardiac enlargement is the rule. Following exercise an abnormally small increase in cardiac output has also been recorded (Burwell and Strayhorn, 1932; Sawyer *et al.*, 1952; Scannell *et al.*, 1952); similarly, no increase in the output of the heart occurred in one case after a large rapid intravenous infusion (Lyons and Burwell, 1946). The cause of the decreased minute volume output of the heart is not myocardial weakness, for after successful removal of the constricting shell or of fibrous bands, the cardiac output is usually restored to or toward normal. In some instances, however, extension of the fibrosis into the muscle causes myocardial insufficiency.

Peripheral blood flow. — A single observation records the finding of peripheral blood flow in the normal range (Stewart *et al.*, 1946). No increase occurred after digitalization, in contradistinction to chronic congestive failure, where a considerable increase occurred.

Circulation time. — The arm-to-tongue time is long (3; Stewart *et al.*, 1938*b*). Bellet *et al.* (1951) and Storstein (1949) found it to be normal. Stewart *et al.* (1938*b*, 1939*a,b*) found the ether time normal, but Bruce *et al.* (1949) found it to be slowed.

Venous pressure. — All authors report elevated values, usually between 20 and 40 cm-of-water, for venous pressure in concretio cordis (4; Burwell *et al.*, 1932, 1935, 1938; Stewart *et al.*, 1938*b*); this includes the femoral venous pressure (Burwell and Flickinger, 1935). An excessive rise during exertion or intravenous infusions has been noted (Burwell and Blalock, 1938; Lyons and Burwell, 1946; Sawyer *et al.*, 1952). Increased salt intake also increased the venous pressure somewhat in one instance (Lyons and Burwell, 1946). After successful operation the venous pressure returns to or toward normal. An interesting phenomenon which should be further investigated is that described by Veal and Hussey (1940); these authors reported that rapidly repeated squeezing of a rubber bulb — too little exertion to raise the venous pressure in myocardial insufficiency — will elevate it greatly in the exercising limb if there exists an obstruction to venous flow such as that caused by pericarditis or superior vena caval occlusion. If corroborated, this may afford a helpful diagnostic test to assist in differentiating between chronic congestive failure and pericardial disease.

Intracardiac and pulmonary vascular pressures. — The right intra-auricular pressure is elevated and the normal gradient between the venous and right auricular pressures is absent (Richards *et al.*, 1941, 1942; Bloomfield *et al.*, 1946; Bruce *et al.*, 1949; Eliasch *et al.*, 1950; Hansen *et al.*, 1951; Hultgren, 1950; Sawyer *et al.*, 1952; Scannell *et al.*, 1952; Yu *et al.*, 1953; Fowler, 1953; Ehrenhaft and Taber, 1952; Burwell, 1951); this finding suggests that outflow from the lungs is also obstructed. The right auricular pressure rises abnormally after exercise (Hultgren, 1950). The elevated right ventricular pressure that has been noted (Bloomfield et al., 1946; Eliasch et al., 1950; Hansen et al., 1950; Kartun et al., 1950; Burwell, 1951; Ehrenhaft and Taber, 1952; Yu et al., 1953; Fowler, 1953; Sawyer et al., 1952) has the same significance; it may also indicate myocardial insufficiency. Hansen et al. (1950), Scannell et al. (1952), and Yu et al. (1953) described typical pressure curves in this disease. Operation ameliorates all these abnormal findings. The pulmonary arterial pressure is also increased (Eliasch et al., 1950; Burwell, 1951; Ehrenhaft and Taber, 1952; Fowler, 1953; McGuire et al., 1951; Sawyer et al., 1952; Scannell et al., 1952; Westcott et al., 1951). The pulmonary arterial pressure rises excessively during exercise (Scannell et al., 1952; Sawyer et al., 1952), a change accompanied by an excessive rise in right ventricular pressure (Sawyer et al., 1952). The pulmonary arterial pressure rises normally during induced anoxia (Westcott et al., 1951). The pulmonary capillary pressure is elevated (Eliasch et al., 1950; Burwell, 1951; Ehrenhaft and Taber, 1952; McGuire et al., 1951; Sawyer et al., 1952; Scannell et al., 1952; Westcott et al., 1951); it rises excessively during exercise (Sawyer et al., 1952) but not during induced anoxia (Westcott et al., 1951). The left auricular pressure is also increased (Sawyer et al., 1952).

Arterial pressure. — A low arterial blood pressure with small pulse pressure is characteristic of the syndrome, and pulsus paradoxicus occurs in most instances also. The arterial blood pressure and pulse pressure often return to normal after operation, but many exceptions to this finding occur.

Lung volume. — The vital capacity is often low, usually rising after operation (Beck and Cushing, 1934; Beck and Griswold, 1930; Burwell and Strayhorn, 1932; Lyons and Burwell, 1946; Chambliss et al., 1951); other authors found that a postoperative increase did not occur in every instance (Heuer and Stewart, 1939; Stewart et al., 1938b, 1939a,b; Bruce et al., 1949; Taquini et al., 1949). Possibly the effects of an extensive intrathoracic operation are sufficient to mask the increase in vital capacity which might otherwise occur. The decreased vital capacity, together with the above-described changes in intracardiac pressure, indicate that some degree of stasis exists in the lungs in concretio cordis. The residual air volume is normal (Taquini et al., 1949).

Respiratory dynamics. — The respiratory minute volume is usually elevated both absolutely and relative to oxygen intake (Taquini *et al.*, 1949; Sawyer *et al.*, 1952). Accordingly, expiratory and alveolar carbon dioxide contents are low (Taquini *et al.*, 1949). These changes disappear after operation. The arterial blood oxygen saturation is normal or slightly lowered (Bruce *et al.*, 1949; Eliasch *et al.*, 1949; Fowler, 1953; Sawyer *et al.*, 1952). Exercise resulted in a normal oxygen debt in the one patient described by Bruce *et al.* (1949).

The pulmonary blood volume is normal or increased (Bing *et al.*, 1951).

Blood volume. — The plasma volume, red cell volume and total circulating blood volume are increased (Burwell and Blalock, 1938; Lyons and Burwell, 1946; Smith and McKisack, 1902; Eliasch *et al.*, 1950; Chambliss *et al.*, 1951; Aikawa, 1952). This change is compensatory to the low cardiac output and resembles that seen in chronic cardiac decompensation, although it may be less marked.

Cerebrospinal fluid pressure. — The spinal fluid pressure is elevated, as is to be expected in the presence of increased venous pressure (Burwell and Blalock, 1938). Nevertheless, signs of increased intracranial pressure do not occur.

Hepatic function. — Icterus is not uncommon in concretio cordis and elevations of the plasma bilirubin and dye retention have been recorded (Ottenberg *et al.*, 1924). The early development of severe liver damage in this syndrome is well known and appears to be associated with very high venous pressure, for it also occurs in patients with severe disease of the tricuspid valve.

Extracellur fluid volume. — The sodium and thiocyanate spaces are increased when edema is present (Aikawa, 1952).

Blood carbonic anhydrase. — A single observation records the finding of normal values of blood carbonic anhydrase in one patient (Lambie, 1938).

Symptoms. — The occurrence of symptoms resembling those of congestive failure is not surprising. The low cardiac output, evidences of stasis in the lungs, high spinal fluid pressure, increased blood volume, venous engorgement, and increased venous blood deoxygenation readily explain dyspnea on exertion, edema, orthopnea and cyanosis, such as occur in this disorder. On the other hand, dyspnea is usually not severe, edema of the ankles may be absent and orthopnea is often mild or absent in patients with constrictive pericarditis, even though the cardiovascular dynamics in this condition resemble those of chronic congestive failure; in addition, the early development of ascites some time before the appearance of ankle edema is the rule.

Although the cardiac output is often quite low in concretio cordis, in some patients it is not greatly decreased. In most instances, the lungs do not become as markedly congested as in patients with chronic cardiac decompensation. The lessened degree of dyspnea enables the patients to be fairly active, so that the lowering of venous pressure which occurs with walking (page 231) and maintenance of normal tissue tension through good muscle tone may act to inhibit the development of peripheral edema; an additional factor is the persistently normal plasma protein level (Burwell and Blalock, 1938; Biörck et al., 1948). However, the latter finding is not universal (Chambliss et al., 1951). Denning and Leutscher (1950) found urinary salt-retaining corticoids normal in one patient, but Lasché et al. (1951) found their concentration to be abnormally low; their role in the edema formation is not clear.

The early development of ascites (ascites precox) often makes the patient seek medical attention long before embarrassment of cardiac function becomes severe. Ascites precox is explained by the early development of severe hepatic disease where, as in other cardiac disorders, venous pressures are markedly elevated; a very high thoracic duct pressure associated with concretio cordis is also a factor (Blalock and Burwell, 1935). The common absence of severe orthopnea in spite of very high venous and spinal fluid pressures is puzzling; one explanation is the absence of severe pulmonary changes in most cases. Also, it is the author's impression that patients with very high cerebrospinal fluid pressures consequent to marked elevations of venous pressure usually have a good deal of clouding of the sensorium, so that they are likely to be less troubled by symptoms than are other individuals.

2. Pericardial Effusion

Cardiac output. — The output of the heart has been reported as diminished, with a return to or toward normal after paracentesis

(McGuire *et al.*, 1937; Stewart *et al.*, 1938a; Warren *et al.*, 1946). On the other hand, Ewig and Hinsberg (1931) found it normal in their case before and after pericardial tap. Fletcher (1945) also found no rise in the output of the heart after a pericardial tap in his patient with pericarditis, but the patient was apparently moribund, for he died of pulmonary infarction within a few hours. In addition, LeBlanc (1922) found the arterial and venous blood gas contents to be normal in his case, implying a normal cardiac output also. It is understandable that variations might occur from case to case, depending upon the amount of pericardial fluid and the degree of tamponade.

Circulation time. — The arm-to-tongue time is usually reported as increased; it decreases after paracentesis (Duras, 1944; Esser and Berliner, 1943; Stewart *et al.*, 1938a; Neurath, 1937). McGuire *et al.* (1937) found the circulation time normal in their patient.

Venous pressure. — The venous pressure is elevated and falls after paracentesis (Fletcher, 1945; McGuire *et al.*, 1937; Stewart *et al.*, 1938a; Neurath, 1937; Elkin and Campbell, 1951; Fowler, 1953); Stewart *et al.* (1938a) demonstrated the close relation that exists between the intrapericardial pressure and the peripheral venous pressure during paracentesis in a patient with a pericardial effusion.

Right cardiac pressures. — The pressure in the right auricle is high and also falls after paracentesis (Fletcher, 1945; Warren *et al.*, 1946; Elkin and Campbell, 1951); it rises abnormally during intravenous infusions (Elkin and Campbell, 1951). The right ventricular pressure is increased also (Fowler, 1953).

Arterial pressure; peripheral resistance. — Depending upon the degree of tamponade, there is a variable reduction in the arterial blood pressure and pulse pressure. They usually, but not invariably, return to normal after pericardial tap (Stewart *et al.*, 1938a). The peripheral resistance is elevated before paracentesis (Warren *et al.*, 1946).

Vital capacity. — The vital capacity is low (McGuire *et al.*, 1937; Stewart *et al.*, 1938a; Neurath, 1937), either as a consequence of encroachment on the lungs by the distended pericardium, or because of pulmonary stasis secondary to compression of the pulmonary veins, or both.

Cutaneous capillaries. — Freedlander and Lenhart (1922) found in the cutaneous capillaries the changes described above for chronic cardiac decompensation (page 71).

Symptoms. — The prominent symptoms in patients with pericardial effusion are usually those of the traumatic or febrile manifestations of the disorder that causes it, and also the local pain or other discomfort. In addition, if the degree of tamponade is appreciable, a state of shock develops and must be treated. This type of shock is of interest because of the venous engorgement that is part of the picture. Here, as in the cardiac arrhythmias, the fall in cardiac output is usually too rapid to be compensated by an increase in blood volume, so that shock, rather than congestive failure, is the rule. When the effusion develops slowly, however, a syndrome resembling in many ways that of chronic congestive failure may result. It must be remembered that when the heart is dilated or hypertrophied by antecedent disease, a relatively small pericardial effusion may cause symptoms out of proportion to its size, since there is a limit beyond which the pericardium will not stretch.

Bibliography

Chapter V

AIKAWA, J., Comparison of the thiocyanate and radiosodium spaces in disease states, *Am. J. M. Sc.* **224,** 632 (1952).

BECK, C. S., and E. H. CUSHING, Circulatory stasis of intrapericardial origin. The clinical and surgical aspects of the Pick syndrome, *J. A. M. A.* **102,** 1543 (1934).   [2, 4

BECK, C. S., and R. A. GRISWOLD, Pericardiectomy in the treatment of the Pick syndrome. Experimental and clinical observations, *Arch. Surg.* **21,** 1064 (1930).

BELLET, S., C. S. NADLER, and W. A. STEIGER, The circulation time (arm to tongue time) in large pericardial effusions: an aid in the differential diagnosis between large pericardial effusion and cardiac dilatation, *Ann. Int. Med.* **34,** 856 (1951).   [3

BING, R. J., R. HEIMBECKER, and W. FALHOLT, An estimation of the residual volume of blood in the right ventricle of normal and diseased hearts in vivo, *Am. Heart J.* **42,** 483 (1951).   [2

BIÖRCK, G., S. HEDLUND, J. KARNELL, and H. KARNI, Serum proteiner vid Hjärtsjukdomar, *Nord. Med.* **38,** 1179 (1948).

BLALOCK, A., and C. S. BURWELL, Thoracic duct lymph pressure in concretio cordis, *J. Lab. & Clin. Med.* **21,** 296 (1935).

BLOOMFIELD, R. A., H. D. LAUSON, A. COURNAND, E. S. BREED, and D. W. RICHARDS, JR., Recording of right heart pressures in normal subjects and in patients with chronic pulmonary disease and various types of cardiocirculatory disease, *J. Clin. Investigation* **25**, 639 (1946).

BRUCE, R. A., F. W. LOVEJOY, JR., P. N. G. YU, R. PEARSON, and E. B. EMERSON, Recent developments in the physiologic study of patients with chest diseases, *New York State J. Med.* **49**, 2133 (1949). [2, 3, 4

BURWELL, C. S., Some effects of pericardial disease on the pulmonary circulation, *Tr. A. Am. Physicians* **64**, 74 (1951). [4

BURWELL, C. S., and A. BLALOCK, Chronic constrictive pericarditis. Physiologic and pathologic considerations, *J. A. M. A.* **110**, 265 (1938). [2, 3, 4

BURWELL, C. S., and D. FLICKINGER, Obstructing pericarditis. Effect of resection of the pericardium on the circulation of a patient with concretio cordis, *Arch. Int. Med.* **56**, 250 (1935). [2, 4

BURWELL, C. S., and W. D. STRAYHORN, Concretio cordis. I. A clinical study with observations on the venous pressure and cardiac output, *Arch. Surg.* **24**, 106 (1932). [2, 4

CHAMBLISS, J. R., E. J. JARUSZEWSKI, B. L. BROFMAN, J. F. MARTIN, and H. FEIL, Chronic cardiac compression (chronic constrictive pericarditis). A critical study of sixty-one operated cases with follow-up, *Circulation* **4**, 816 (1951). [2, 3, 4

DEBLER, K., Zur Kenntnis des Minutenvolumens bei schweren Kreislaufleiden, *Med. Klin.* **33**, 761 (1937).

DEMING, Q. B., and J. A. LUETSCHER, JR., Bioassay of desoxycorticosterone-like material in urine, *Proc. Soc. Exper. Biol. & Med.* **73**, 171 (1950).

DURAS, F. P., Measurement of the circulation time with saccharin, *Lancet* **1**, 303 (1944). [3

EHRENHAFT, J. L., and R. E. TABER, Hemopericardium and constrictive pericarditis, *J. Thoracic Surg.* **24**, 355 (1952). [2

ELIASCH, H., H. LAGERLÖF, and L. WERKÖ, Diagnos av adhesiv peridardit med särskild hänsyn till hjärtkatetrisering, *Nord. med.* **44**, 1128 (1950). [2

ELKIN, D. C., and R. E. CAMPBELL, Cardiac tamponade: treatment by aspiration, *Ann. Surg.* **133**, 623 (1951).

ESSER, K. H., and K. BERLINER, Duplicate measurements of circulation time made with the saccharin method, *Ann. Int. Med.* **19**, 64 (1943).

EWIG, W., and K. HINSBERG, Kreislaufstudien II, *Ztschr. f. klin. Med.* **115**, 693 (1931).

FERRIS, E. B., JR., and R. W. WILKINS, The clinical value of comparative measurements of the pressure in the femoral and cubital veins, *Am. Heart J.* **13**, 431 (1937). [1

FLETCHER, C. M., Cardiac output in a case of pericardial effusion with a note on pericardial pain, *Brit. Heart J.* **1**, 143 (1945). [2, 4

FOWLER, N. O., Cardiac catheterization in the diagnosis of adult heart disease, *Ann. Int. Med.* **38**, 478 (1953). [2, 4

FREEDLANDER, S. O., and C. H. LENHART, Clinical observations on the capillary circulation, *Arch. Int. Med.* **29**, 12 (1922).

GAERTNER, G., Die Messung des Drucks im rechten Vorhof, *München. med. Wchnschr.* **50**, 2038 (1903). [1

GRISWOLD, R. A., Chronic cardiac compression due to constricting pericarditis. Relief by pericardiectomy, with a note on the value of the roentgenkymogram, *J. A. M. A.* **106**, 1054 (1936). [2, 4

HANSEN, A. T., P. ESKILDSEN, and H. GÖTZSCHE, Pressure curves from the right auricle and the right ventricle in chronic constrictive pericarditis, *Circulation* **3**, 881 (1951).

HEUER, G. J., and H. J. STEWART, The surgical treatment of chronic constrictive pericarditis, *Surg., Gynec. & Obst.* **68**, 979 (1939). [2, 3, 4

HOOKER, D. R., and J. A. E. EYSTER, An instrument for the determination of venous pressure in man, *Bull. Johns Hopkins Hosp.* **19**, 274 (1908). [1

HULTGREN, H. N., The effect of increased venous return on the venous pressure of patients with congestive heart failure, *Am. Heart J.* **39**, 593 (1950). [4

HUSSEY, H. H., Clinical application of venous pressure measurement, *M. Ann. District of Columbia* **5**, 232 (1936). [1

KARTUN, P., P. PARIS, J. NORY, and G. BOUSQUET, Action précoce sur la circulation de retour de l'injection intraveineuse d'un diurétique mercuriel, *Arch. d. mal. du cœur* **43**, 133 (1950). [4

KOPPERMANN, E., Concretio pericardii: Beurteilung der Perikardektomie bei 4 Panzerherzen an Hand der Mechanischen Kreisslaufanalyse, *Ztschr. f. Kreisslaufforsch.* **38**, 598 (1949). [2, 4

KOPPERMANN, E., Zur concretio pericardii, *Ztschr. f. Kreisslaufforsch.* **39**, 167 (1950). [2, 4

LAMBIE, C. G., Observations on the carbonic anhydrase of the blood in anaemia and in other pathological conditions, *Edinburgh M. J.* **45**, 373 (1938).

LASCHÉ, E. M., W. H. PERLOFF, and T. M. DURANT, Some aspects of adrenocortical function in cardiac decompensation, *Am. J. M. Sc.* **222**, 459 (1951).

LEBLANC, E., Repiratorischer Gasaustausch und Lungendurchblutung unter normalen und krankhaften Zuständen der Atmungsorgane. Untersuchungen am arteriellen und venösen Blut von Mensch und Tier, *Beitr. z. Klin. d. Tuberk.* **50**, 21 (1922).

LEQUIME, J., Le débit cardiaque. Études expérimentales et cliniques, *Acta med. Scandinav., Supp. No. 107* (1940). [2, 3, 4

LYONS, R., and C. S. BURWELL, Induced changes in the circulation in constrictive pericarditis, *Brit. Heart J.* **8**, 33 (1946). [2, 3, 4

McGUIRE, J., V. HAUENSTEIN, and R. SHORE, Cardiac output in heart disease determined by the direct Fick method, including comparative determinations by the acetylene method, *Arch. Int. Med.* **60**, 1034 (1937).

McGUIRE, J., R. N. WESTCOTT, and N. O. FOWLER, Anoxia and human pulmonary vascular resistance, *Tr. A. Am. Physicians* **64**, 404 (1951).

MOORE, R. D., JR., The diagnostic value of venous pressure determinations in certain diseases, *South. M. J.* **30**, 1007 (1937). [1

MORTENSEN, V., and E. WARBURG, Chronic constrictive pericarditis, *Acta med. Scandinav.* **131**, 203 (1948). [4

NEURATH, O., Untersuchungen über die Bestimmung der Blutumlaufsgeschwindigkeit mit Magnesiumsulfat, *Ztschr. f. klin. Med.* **132**, 134 (1937).

OTTENBERG, R., S. ROSENFELD, and L. GOLDSMITH, The clinical value of the serum-tetrachlorphenolphthalein test for liver function, *Arch. Int. Med.* **34**, 206 (1924).

POROT, M. A., Les fortes hypertensions céphalo-rachidiennes d'origine veineuse. Leur latence. La discordance manométrique et clinique, *Rev. neurol.* **1**, 1173 (1930). [1

RESNIK, H., B. FRIEDMAN, and T. R. HARRISON, Effect of certain therapeutic measures on the cardiac output of patients with congestive heart failure, *Arch. Int. Med.* **56**, 891 (1935). [2

RICHARDS, D. W., JR., A. COURNAND, R. C. DARLING, and W. H. GILLESPIE, Pressure in the right auricle of man, in normal subjects and in patients with congestive heart failure, *Tr. A. Am. Physicians* **56**, 218 (1941). [4

RICHARDS, D. W., JR., A. COURNAND, R. C. DARLING, W. H. GILLESPIE, and E. D. BALDWIN, Pressure of blood in the right auricle in animals and in man: under normal conditions and in right heart failure, *Am. J. Physiol.* **136**, 115 (1942). [4

SAWYER, C. G., C. S. BURWELL, L. DEXTER, E. C. EPPINGER, W. T. GOODALE, R. GORLIN, D. E. HARKEN, and F. W. HAYNES, Chronic constrictive pericarditis: further consideration of the pathologic physiology of the disease, *Am. Heart J.* **44**, 207 (1952). [2, 4

SCANNELL, J. G., MYERS, G. S., and A. L. FRIEDLICH, Significance of pulmonary hypertension in constrictive pericarditis. A pre- and post-operative study, *Surgery* **32,** 184 (1952). [2, 4

Scébat, L., J. Lenègre, B. Ranson-Bitker, F. Benchemoul, and J. Damien, Étude des gaz du sang et du débit cardiaque dans les différents types de cardiopathies, *Arch. d. mal. du cœur* **46,** 18 (1953). [2

Schott, E., Die Erhöhung des Druckes im venösen System bei Anstrengung als Mass für die Funktionstüchtigkeit des menschlichen Herzens, *Deutsches Arch. f. klin. Med.* **108,** 537 (1912). [1

Smith, J. L., and H. L. McKisack, On a case in which cyanosis and plethora occurred in association with adherent pericardium, *Tr. Path. Soc. London* **53,** 136 (1902).

Stewart, H. J., N. F. Crane, and J. E. Deitrick, Studies of the circulation in pericardial effusion, *Am. Heart J.* **16,** 189 (1938*a*).

Stewart, H. J., W. F. Evans, H. Brown, and J. R. Gerjuoy, Peripheral blood flow, rectal and skin temperature in congestive heart failure. The effects of rapid digitalization in this state, *Arch. Int. Med.* **77,** 643 (1946).

Stewart, H. J., and G. J. Heuer, Chronic constrictive pericarditis. Dynamics of the circulation and results of surgical treatment, *Arch. Int. Med.* **63,** 504 (1939*a*). [2, 3, 4

Stewart, H. J., and G. J. Heuer, Measurement of the circulation in chronic constrictive pericarditis before and after resection of the pericardium, *New York State J. Med.* **39,** 2183 (1939*b*). [2, 3, 4

Stewart, H. J., G. J. Heuer, J. E. Deitrick, N. F. Crane, R. F. Watson, and C. H. Wheeler, Measurements of the circulation in constrictive pericarditis before and after resection of the pericardium, *J. Clin. Investigation* **17,** 581 (1938*b*). [2, 3, 4

Storstein, O., Measurement of the venous pressure and of the circulation time, *Acta med. Scandinav.* **136,** 122 (1949). [4

Taquini, A. C., J. R. E. Suarez, and J. M. Gonzales Fernandez, Las funciones circulatoria y respiratoria en la pericarditis constrictiva, *Medicina* **8,** 391 (1948). [2, 4

Veal, J. R., and H. H. Hussey, The use of "exercise tests" in connection with venous pressure measurements for the detection of venous obstruction in the upper and lower extremities. A preliminary report, *Am. Heart J.* **20,** 308 (1940).

Volhard and Schmieden, Ueber Erkennung und Behandlung der Umklammerung des Herzens durch schwielige Perikarditis, *Klin. Wchnschr.* **2,** 5 (1923). [4

Wall, H. C., Measurement of circulation time with calcium gluconate in patients receiving digitalis, with electrocardiographic studies, *Am. Heart J.* **18,** 228 (1939). [3

WARREN, J. V., E. S. BRANNON, E. A. STEAD, JR., and A. J. MERRILL, Pericardial tamponade from stab wound of the heart and pericardial effusion or empyema: a study utilizing the method of right heart catheterization, *Am. Heart J.* **31,** 418 (1946).

WESTCOTT, R. N., N. O. FOWLER, R. C. SCOTT, V. D. HAUENSTEIN, and J. McGUIRE, Anoxia and human pulmonary vascular resistance, *J. Clin. Investigation* **30,** 957 (1951).

WOOD, P., Right and left ventricular failure. A study of the circulation time and venous pressure, *Lancet* **2,** 15, (1936). [3, 4

YU, P. N. G., F. W. LOVEJOY, JR., H. A. JOOS, R. E. NYE, JR., and E. B. Mahoney, Right auricular and ventricular patterns in constrictive pericarditis, *Circulation* **7,** 102 (1953).

VI

CONGENITAL AND ACQUIRED
CARDIAC DEFECTS

1. *Patent Ductus Arteriosus*

The circulation in patients with patent ductus arteriosus is not distributed in a normal manner. The output of the right ventricle is equal to the amount of blood brought to it and is, therefore, identical with the peripheral (systemic) flow. However, this volume of flow is not the same as that which passes through the lungs, since the latter consists of the output of the right ventricle, to which is added a portion of the flow from the left. The left ventricular output comprises the volume shunted through the lungs together with that sent to the periphery, the latter equaling the output of the right ventricle. In effect, therefore, the output of the left ventricle is equal to the volume of blood flow through the lungs.

Cardiac output. — A few studies by older methods of measuring cardiac output have been recorded. Lequime (1940) and Richards (1931) investigated by means of rebreathing methods the concentration of respiratory gases in blood in the lungs and obtained data that indicated a very large flow of blood through the lungs in their patients; the patient described by Richards (1931) had other anomalies also. Keys (1941) attempted to justify on mathematical grounds the use of the acetylene method for measuring the systemic (nonpulmonary) flow in patients with this disorder; he concluded that the peripheral flow was usually normal and occasionally diminished. The data of Starr and Jonas (1943), obtained by means of the ballistocardiograph, are probably not reliable when the ductus is open. These authors themselves recognize the fact that their method leads to overestimates of cardiac output under these circumstances, and their conclusion that it measures systemic flow alone does not appear to be justified. They found normal values for cardiac output in their patients with the ductus closed; these data are as reliable as any obtained by that method.

In 1941, Eppinger, Burwell, and Gross published studies based on samples of blood obtained from appropriate arteries at the time of operation. Subsequently, Dexter et al. (1946a,b; 1947) made studies by means of the catheter and since then many others have done the same. Pulmonary flow is far above the normal range (Eppinger et al., 1941; Dexter et al., 1946a,b; 1947; 1) while the systemic flow at rest is normal or somewhat diminished. Ligation of the ductus eliminates these abnormalities. During exercise the normal increase in pulmonary blood flow does not occur in patients with patent ductus arteriosus (Gorlin and Gorlin, 1951).

Circulation time. — Reference may be found in the literature to normal circulation times in noncyanotic patients with congenital heart disease of unspecified types. In addition, Eppinger et al. (1941), Ziegler (1951a), and Gasul et al. (1949) described it as normal in patent ductus arteriosus. Johnson et al. (1950) found the arm-to-lung and arm-to-tongue times slowed in one patient in mild failure.

Venous pressure. — Peripheral venous pressure is normal (Eppinger et al., 1941; Brown et al., 1949; Borst and Molhuysen, 1952; Levinson et al., 1951; Ziegler, 1952b). Johnson et al. (1950) found it elevated in one patient in a state of mild decompensation.

Pulmonary arterial pressure. — The pulmonary arterial blood is exposed to aortic pressures in varying degree, depending on the size of the ductus. Accordingly, pulmonary arterial pressures are usually elevated (Dexter et al., 1947; 2), although values in the normal range may occur in some cases. The pulmonary diastolic, but not the systolic, pressure may equal the aortic. When the pulmonary arterial diastolic pressure rises and the aortic diastolic pressure falls so that the two are equal, the diastolic murmur may be absent (Myers et al., 1951). If pulmonary arterial pressure rises excessively, as in the one patient described by Johnson et al. (1950), reversal of flow may occur. Denolin et al. (1952), Bothwell et al. (1952), and Hultgren et al. (1953) have since reported similar cases.

Right heart pressures. — The right ventricular pressure is usually

elevated (Brown *et al.*, 1949; Dexter, 1947; Dexter *et al.*, 1946*a,b*;
3); where systolic and diastolic pressures are presented separately,
it is evident that the former is elevated while the latter is normal.
In some instances both are reported to be within the normal range.
The right auricular pressure is normal or slightly elevated (**4**; Dexter
et al., 1947; Adams *et al.*, 1950).

Arterial pressure and pulse. — Many patients with patent ductus
arteriosus show the peripheral signs of aortic insufficiency, including
the changes in arterial blood pressure (**5**; Eppinger *et al.*, 1941);
with exercise the pulse pressure increases greatly owing to a rise in
systolic, a fall in diastolic, or both (Bohn, 1938; Gilchrist, 1945,
1946; Bayer and Landen, 1950; Cassels *et al.*, 1950; Chapman *et al.*,
1950; Lewicki, 1940). Lewicki (1940) found the change only in the
arms; Lewes (1952) denied its occurrence. A specific pulse wave
pattern was noted by Megibow and Feitelberg (1948, 1951), Grover
et al. (1949), and Levinson *et al.* (1951). The abnormalities are
ameliorated by litigation of the ductus.

Vital capacity. — In spite of the shunting of large amounts of
blood through the lungs, no reduction in vital capacity occurs according to Eppinger *et al.* (1941); Bayer and Landen (1950) found it
low before and increased after ligation of the ductus.

Respiratory dynamics. — A few observations record normal or
somewhat increased respiratory minutes volumes at rest (Vandam
et al., 1947; Bayer and Landen, 1950). Bayer and Landen (1950)
reported a decrease in respiratory minute volume when the patients
were given oxygen. A normal change in the ratio of oxygen intake to
respiratory volume occurs in exercise (Vandam *et al.*, 1947), in contradistinction to the findings in some other types of congenital heart
disease. Denolin *et al.* (1952) found an excessive rise in respiratory
minute volume during exercise.

Blood oxygen contents. — Caval (Dexter, 1947; **6**), right auricular
(Dexter, 1947; **7**), and right ventricular (Dexter, 1947; **8**) blood
oxygen contents are normal; Johnson *et al.* (1950) found the last
relatively high in one patient. The pulmonary arterial blood oxygen
content is always increased (Dexter, 1947; **9**) owing to admixture
of blood from the aorta; this change is diagnostic of the condition.
Since the shunt is largely or entirely from left to right, the femoral
arterial oxygen content is in or near the normal range (Vandam *et al.*,

1947; **10**); what lowering occurs is indicative of some shunting from right to left. In exercise, the femoral arterial oxygen saturation falls to a variable degree (Vandam *et al.*, 1947; Callebaut *et al.*, 1949; Bothwell *et al.*, 1952; Denolin *et al.*, 1952; Lurie *et al.*, 1952) owing to a reversal of the usual shunt associated with the lowering of diastolic arterial pressure that occurs at this time. Standing causes no change in arterial blood oxygen saturation (Callebaut *et al.*, 1949). The pulmonary capillary blood is completely oxygenated (Dexter, 1947), indicating no serious impairment of respiratory function.

Blood carbon dioxide and pH. — Blood carbon dioxide content and tension and blood pH are normal (Cassels *et al.*, 1950).

Blood lactate and pyruvate. — Values for blood lactate and pyruvate are normal in patients at rest (Havel and Watkins, 1950); during exercise the rise in the former is normal, although a slightly excessive rise in pyruvate occurs.

Blood volume. — Although the blood volume is within the normal range in patients with this disorder, a slight decrease occurs after ligation of the patent shunt (Eppinger *et al.*, 1941; Nylin and Biörck, 1947; Cassels *et al.*, 1950; Nelson *et al.*, 1947).

Symptoms. — The manifestations of persistence of a patent ductus arteriosus depend in large measure upon the size of the fistula between the aorta and the pulmonary artery. This is true not only of the loudness and character of the murmurs but also of the other clinical features as well. Thus, with a large ductus, the peripheral signs of aortic insufficiency, namely, wide pulse pressure, Duroziez's sign, and capillary pulsation, may be present at rest; with smaller defects they may appear only after exercise or may even be absent entirely. Similarly, the diastolic murmur ordinarily heard at rest may, in occasional instances, appear only after exercise.

The mechanisms underlying these changes are clear; the aortic systolic and diastolic pressures, higher than those in the pulmonary artery, result in a flow of blood from the former into the latter in diastole as well as in systole. Accordingly, in an attempt to maintain peripheral flow, an increased systolic aortic pressure must be produced, and since the diastolic aortic pressure falls because of the runoff of blood into the ductus, the blood pressure measurements obtained are those of aortic insufficiency; the peripheral vascular changes must also be the same (page 415). Where the ductus is small, the increases in blood flow caused by exercise may be necessary to bring out the murmur; some peripheral vasodilatation may occur also, giving rise to reversal of flow during part of the cycle. When the pulmonary arterial and aortic diastolic pressures are equal, the diastolic murmur may disappear. When the pulmonary arterial pressure rises owing to congestive failure, reversal of flow in the shunt may occur.

The right ventricular work is increased to a variable degree by the increase in pressure within it, but no increase in work owing to increased output occurs since the shunted blood does not pass through the right heart; the work of the right ventricle is increased slightly or moderately while that of the left is increased markedly. Accordingly, left-sided cardiac enlargement and left-axis deviation in the electrocardiogram occur as a rule. The systemic manifestations of the disorder depend on how much of the blood is shunted off into useless circulation through the lungs, with the resultant deprivation to the peripheral tissues. The patients may exhibit retarded growth and development and may complain of variable amounts of exertional weakness and dyspnea. The dynamic changes of the disorder and their physical consequences are reversed by ligation of the patent ductus.

An unexplained finding in patients with patent ductus arteriosus is the abnormal change in QT interval that occurs during exercise (Yu et al., 1950).

Other cardiovascular anomalies may occur with patent ductus arteriosus and distort the physiologic pattern (Richards, 1945; Taylor et al., 1950a,b; Campbell et al., 1949; Johnson et al., 1951). The fact that ventricular septal defect may simulate patent ductus arteriosus at times has been pointed out (page 393).

2. Pulmonic Stenosis

Cardiac output. — The blood flow through the lungs is normal or slightly decreased, depending to some degree upon the amount of narrowing (Dow et al., 1950; **11**). Its increases with exercise are normal or somewhat below it (Dow et al., 1950; Gorlin and Gorlin, 1951; Greene et al., 1949).

Circulation time. — The circulation time is in the normal range

(Adams *et al.*, 1951; Ziegler, 1951) and, except when shunts are present in addition, does not show the changes seen in cyanotic congenital heart disease (page 401).

Right heart and pulmonary vascular pressures. — The pulmonary capillary pressure is normal at rest and in exercise (Dow *et al.*, 1950; Pannier *et al.*, 1953) and the pulmonary arterial pressure is normal or sometimes low beyond the stenosis (Adams *et al.*, 1951; **12**). Since the cardiac output is about normal, it is evident that pulmonary total vascular resistance must be normal also. The right ventricular pressure is elevated (Dow *et al.*, 1950; **13**) and rises excessively with exercise (Dow *et al.*, 1950; Gorlin and Gorlin, 1951). The rise in systolic pressure is much greater than in diastolic; indeed, the latter commonly is in the normal range. The discrepancy between the levels of right ventricular and pulmonary arterial pressures establishes the diagnosis of pulmonic stenosis. The right auricular pressure is normal or occasionally slightly increased (Dow *et al.*, 1950; Larsson *et al.*, 1951; **14**); it does not rise excessively with exercise (Greene *et al.*, 1949).

Venous pressure. — Venous pressure is normal (Hyman *et al.*, 1951; Van Buchem *et al.*, 1951, 1952).

Blood oxygen content. — Blood drawn from the right auricle or ventricle, the vena cava, and the pulmonary artery contains normal amounts of oxygen (Adams *et al.*, 1951; **15**) except in the presence of shunts. The femoral arterial oxygen saturation likewise is normal when no shunt is present (Maraist *et al.*, 1951; **16**). The arterial oxygen saturation does not fall during exercise in the uncomplicated cases (Callebaut *et al.*, 1949; Gøtsche *et al.*, 1951; Larsson *et al.*, 1951; Mannheimer, 1949; Maraist *et al.*, 1951; van Buchem *et al.*, 1952; van Lingen and Whidbourne, 1952). Posture does not influence the level of saturation (Callebaut *et al.*, 1949), nor does oxygen or hyperventilation (van Lingen and Whidbourne, 1952; van Buchem *et al.*, 1951).

When auricular or ventricular septal defects are present, the presence of pulmonic stenosis causes a reversal of the usual left-to-right flow in these shunts, and cyanosis, with its consequent changes in arterial oxygen saturation, appears (Adams *et al.*, 1951; **17**).

Respiratory dynamics. — The respiratory minute volume at rest is normal relative to oxygen consumption (Lequime and Denolin,

1949; Mannheimer *et al.*, 1949; Maraist *et al.*, 1951; Vandam *et al.*, 1947). During exercise the respiratory minute volume does not increase as much as oxygen consumption, a normal finding and in contradistinction to the change in cyanotic heart disease where the opposite occurs (page 400). The rise in oxygen consumption in work is normal (Mannheimer *et al.*, 1949).

Blood volume. — The blood volume is normal (Lagerlöf *et al.*, 1946).

Symptoms. — The symptoms may be negligible in the absence of shunts. A cardiac murmur may call attention to the lesion, or, in some instances, exertional dyspnea may be present if the stenosis is of very high degree. In this situation, so much work is expended by the right ventricle in developing pressure enough to maintain adequate blood flow as to encroach seriously on the ability of the ventricle to add to its work by increasing cardiac output during exercise. Growth is normal in children with uncomplicated congenital pulmonic stenosis (Galligan *et al.*, 1952).

The presence of pulmonic stenosis probably gives rise to the development of collateral circulation via the bronchial arteries; this phenomenon has been demonstrated in dogs (Bloomer *et al.*, 1949).

When shunts are present, the stenosis of the pulmonary valve causes the development of permanent cyanosis, the effects of which are discussed below (page 397). A case of patent ductus arteriosus and pulmonic stenosis was studied by Taylor and DuShane (1950).

3. *Auricular Septal Defect*

Cardiac output. — The outputs of the two ventricles are not equal; that of the right ventricle is greatly increased in the absence of pulmonic stenosis (Brannon *et al.*, 1945; **18**) while that of the left ventricle is normal or low (Brannon *et al.*, 1945; Dexter *et al.*, 1950; **19**). This occurs owing to the direction of the shunt, which is left to right. When pulmonic stenosis is present, the direction of the shunt is reversed and the pulmonary blood flow is diminished (page 388).

Circulation time. — As long as the shunt is left to right, the circulation time remains in the normal range (Gasul *et al.*, 1949; Lequime *et al.*, 1950; Donzelet *et al.*, 1951; Gross *et al.*, 1953; Ziegler, 1951).

Intracardiac and pulmonary vascular pressures. — The right auricular pressure is normal or occasionally slightly increased (Brannon *et al.*, 1945; Hickam, 1949; **20**) as is the left auricular pressure also (Calazel *et al.*, 1951; Cournand *et al.*, 1947; Gorlin and Gorlin, 1951; Hickam, 1949; Lagerlöf and Werkö, 1948, 1949; Nahas *et al.*, 1950; Bailey *et al.*, 1952; Cosby *et al.*, 1952). However, the latter normally is slightly above the former, so that the shunt is from left to right. When the shunt is in the opposite direction, the right auricular pressure is the higher during part of the cycle (Calazel *et al.*, 1951).

The right ventricular pressure is normal or somewhat increased (Brannon *et al.*, 1945; Dexter, 1947; **21**); it rises in exercise (Hickam, 1949). The increase is in the systolic pressure and is owing in part to the great increase in right ventricular output, although increased pulmonary vascular resistance may be the more important factor. The pulmonary arterial pressure is normal or increased (Hickam, 1949; Dexter *et al.*, 1950; **22**). The total pulmonary vascular resistance is in the normal range, although it may rise with exercise, as Hickam (1949) showed. Vasoconstriction plays a part in the observed changes in pulmonary arterial pressure and pulmonary vascular resistance, but in addition there is a large element of organic vascular disease present in some instances; in the latter circumstances, the pulmonary arterial and right ventricular pressures are very high.

The pulmonary capillary pressure is normal (Calazel *et al.*, 1951; Dexter *et al.*, 1950; Lagerlöf and Werkö, 1949; Lenègre *et al.*, 1953); if the blood flow through the lungs is greatly increased, the pulmonary capillary pressure may be elevated slightly (Dexter *et al.*, 1950). The pulmonary venous pressure is normal (Calazel *et al.*, 1951; Cournand *et al.*, 1947; Dexter, 1947; Hickam, 1949; Nahas *et al.*, 1950; Cosby *et al.*, 1952; Lenègre *et al.*, 1953). An artifact in the measurement of the pulmonary capillary-venous pressure has been described (Weissel *et al.*, 1952).

When pulmonic stenosis is present in addition to the septal defect, the pressure changes are those of the former condition (page 388).

Blood oxygen contents. — Pulmonary venous blood is normally oxygenated (Handelsman *et al.*, 1948; Cosby *et al.*, 1952), as is the blood in the left auricle (Bailey *et al.*, 1952), except in those instances in which the shunt is in both directions (Barber *et al.*, 1950; Hickam, 1949; Lagerlöf and Werkö, 1949). Since the shunt usually is from left to right predominately or entirely, the right auricle receives blood of high oxygen content and accordingly the blood is arterialized (Brannon *et al.*, 1945; Dexter, 1947; **23**). The right ventricular and pulmonary arterial bloods show the same oxygen content as that of the right auricle (Brannon *et al.*, 1945; Handelsman *et al.*, 1948; **24**). These findings are diagnostic of the condition.

The femoral arterial blood is normally saturated, unless some right-to-left shunting exists (Brannon *et al.*, 1945; **25**). Callebaut *et al.* (1949) reported that it might rise somewhat on standing and fall with exercise. Lurie *et al.* (1952), Ordway (1952), and van Lingen and Whidbourne (1952) found normal values after exercise for the most part. Rises after administration of oxygen are small (Lequime *et al.*, 1951; Ordway, 1952; van Lingen and Whidbourne, 1952).

When pulmonic stenosis is present, the direction of the shunt is changed to right to left; the arterialization of right auricular blood does not occur and the femoral arterial saturation is lowered (Adams *et al.*, 1951; **26**). In such instances the arterial oxygen saturation falls even more with exercise (Burchell *et al.*, 1950).

Coronary sinus blood is reported as normal in auricular septal defect (Soulié *et al.*, 1949).

Venous pressure. — The venous pressure is normal (Borst and Molhuysen, 1952; Cosby *et al.*, 1952; Gross *et al.*, 1953).

Respiratory dynamics. — The respiratory minute volume is normal or slightly increased (Handelsman *et al.*, 1948; Lequime *et al.*, 1950, 1951). It does not increase as much as oxygen consumption in exercise. Bruce *et al.* (1949) described a normal oxygen debt after exercise in one patient.

Blood volume. — In uncomplicated cases the blood volume is normal (Nelson *et al.*, 1947; Gross *et al.*, 1953), as is the hemoglobin level also.

Symptoms. — The prevailing left-to-right shunt prevents the occurrence of cyanosis unless the pressures in the right heart rise, as with pulmonic stenosis, congestive failure, or pulmonary vascular sclerosis. Temporary reversal of the direction of the shunt may, however, occur during episodes that raise pulmonary arterial pressure. The enormous increase in right ventricular work accounts for the finding of right axis deviation. That the whole heart is affected is suggested by the abnormal QT interval at rest and on exertion (Yu *et al.*, 1950). Depending on the size of the shunt and the strain upon the heart, congestive failure may develop sooner or later. When congestive failure occurs, cyanosis is likely to be marked and polycythemia present. On the other hand, a small defect is compatible with a long and active life. When the septal defect is very large, so much of the blood may pass via the shunt as to result in a diminution of peripheral flow with retardation of growth and development.

4. *Ventricular Septal Defect*

Cardiac output. — The two ventricles have equal outputs: the left delivers blood to the periphery and gives up some to the right, while the right pumps into the lungs the blood received from the periphery and that received directly from the left. The pulmonary flow accordingly is increased (Dexter *et al.*, 1947; **27**) while that to the periphery is normal or decreased. When pulmonic stenosis is present, the direction of flow in the shunt may be reversed (page 388).

Circulation time. — In the absence of shunts the circulation time is normal (Gasul *et al.*, 1949; Donzelot *et al.*, 1951; Lasser *et al.*, 1952; Ziegler, 1951).

Intracardiac and pulmonary vascular pressures. — The presence of an opening between the two ventricles results in an increase in pressure within the right (Dexter, 1947; **28**); the rise is mainly or entirely in the systolic pressure, which approaches the aortic in some cases. The pulmonary arterial pressure is normal or elevated, depending on the amount of blood traversing that vessel (Dexter, 1947; **29**). The pulmonary capillary pressure is normal, or, if the pulmonary flow is greatly increased, somewhat elevated (Gorlin and Gorlin, 1951; Fowler, 1953).

The right auricular pressure is normal or slightly elevated (Chapman *et al.*, 1949; **30**). The cause for the increase when present is not apparent.

Blood oxygen content. — The right auricular blood is normally oxygenated but that of the right ventricle is arterialized, owing to the prevailing direction of the shunt (Dexter *et al.*, 1947; **31**). When pulmonic stenosis is present this difference may be obliterated owing to a change in the direction of the shunt (page 388).

In rare instances, when the defect is high in the septum the differences in oxygen content of the various bloods, instead of following the typical pattern, may resemble those of patent ductus arteriosus (Morgan and Burchell, 1950; Soulié *et al.*, 1949; Adams, 1952; Adams *et al.*, 1952).

The arterial blood oxygen saturation is normal or lowered, depending upon whether the shunt is left to right or in both directions (Burchell *et al.*, 1950; Dexter, 1947; **32**). It may fall slightly in exercise (Callebaut *et al.*, 1949; Ordway, 1952; Joly *et al.*, 1951).

Respiratory dynamics. — The respiratory minute volume is normal or slightly elevated and in exercise increases less than does the oxygen consumption, that is, the reaction is normal (Handelsman *et al.*, 1948; Joly *et al.*, 1951).

Pulse wave pattern. — Those patients with high septal defects may show a peripheral pulse wave pattern similar to that of patent ductus arteriosus (Megibow and Feitelberg, 1951).

Blood volume. — The blood volume is normal in the absence of shunts (Nelson *et al.*, 1947).

Symptoms. — The work of both ventricles is increased owing to the abnormally large outputs of each, but the right ventricle has an additional increase in work owing to increased pressure. Right axis deviation may occur. In many respects the clinical course of ventricular septal defect resembles that of auricular septal defect. Renal vascular dynamics may be impaired in ventricular septal defect (Varnauskas *et al.*, 1952).

5. *Tetralogy of Fallot*

Cardiac output. — Workers in earlier days, using methods available at the time, attempted to study the cardiac output and calculate the amount of shunting in patients with the tetralogy of Fallot (**33**); the methods used were not adequate for these complex tasks, and the diagnoses, based often on clinical findings alone, were not always established. With the introduction of intracardiac catheterization these difficulties were obviated. It is now known that the pulmonary flow is small (Bing *et al.*, 1947*a*; Dexter *et al.*, 1947; **34**) and that the peripheral flow derived from both ventricles is about normal. The flow through the lungs represents not only that received via the pulmonary artery but a variable amount that enters via the bronchial arteries and other branches of the aorta. The situation exists owing to the effects of pulmonic stenosis in preventing normal blood flow through the pulmonary artery in patients in whom there is a large alternative pathway leading out of the right ventricle owing to the overriding aorta.

Intracardiac and pulmonary vascular pressures. — The right ventricular pressure is increased to the level of the aortic (Bing *et al.*, 1947*a*; Dexter *et al.*, 1947; **35**). The pulmonary arterial pressure distal to the stenosis is normal or low (Bing *et al.*, 1947*a*; Dexter *et al.*, 1947; **36**); even when in the normal range it may rise after operation designed to relieve the obstruction (Downing *et al.*, 1951; Glover *et al.*, 1950).

The right auricular pressure is normal or slightly elevated (Brock and Campbell, 1950; Holling and Zak, 1950; Lagerlöf *et al.*, 1949; Gordon and Goldberg, 1951; Soulié *et al.*, 1951, 1952). It is in normal relation to the slightly higher left auricular pressure (Lagerlöf *et al.*, 1949).

Venous pressure. — The venous pressure is normal (Talbott *et al.*, 1941).

Intracardiac and pulmonary blood oxygen contents. — The blood in the pulmonary capillaries is fully oxygenated (Dexter *et al.*, 1946*b*, 1947; Handelsman *et al.*, 1947; Hellems *et al.*, 1949; Hertz, 1951; Vandam *et al.*, 1947). The right auricular blood oxygen content is similar to the caval, while that of the right ventricle is the same or somewhat higher (Chapman *et al.*, 1949; Dexter, 1949; Lagerlöf *et al.*, 1949; Soulié *et al.*, 1951, 1952; **37**). The latter indicates the passage of some blood from the left ventricle to the right.

Symptoms. — Aside from the effects of the great strain put upon the right ventricle owing to the large increase in pressure within it, most of the consequences of the tetralogy of Fallot are consequent to the shunt that gives rise to chronic anoxia from infancy. Similar changes occur in association with some other cardiac lesions and all will be discussed together below (page 397).

The percentage of right ventricular output that is shunted depends on the resistance in the pulmonary and peripheral circuits. Instituting vasodilatation in the peripheral circuit by means of tetraethyl ammonium was shown by Hamilton, Winslow, and Hamilton (1950) to cause an increase in the amount of blood diverted to the periphery, with a resulting decrease in arterial oxygen saturation.

6. *Eisenmenger's Complex*

Cardiac output. — The blood flow through the lungs is low (Bing et al., 1947; Deuchar and Knebel, 1952; **38**); the systemic flow, derived from both the right and left ventricles, is higher. There appears to be a collateral circulation from the aorta via the bronchial arteries (Bing et al., 1947).

Intracardiac and pulmonary vascular pressures. — The right ventricular pressure is elevated to the level of the aortic (Cosby et al., 1951; Dexter, 1950; **39**) and the pulmonary arterial pressure is also greatly increased (Cosby et al., 1951; Dexter, 1950; **40**). The pulmonary capillary pressure, however, is normal so that an unusually large gradient between pulmonary arterial and pulmonary capillary pressure exists (Dexter et al., 1950; Fowler, 1953; Fowler et al., 1952), indicating a very large rise in pulmonary arteriolar resistance.

The right auricular pressure is normal or close to it (Bing et al., 1947; Brown et al., 1949; Charlier, 1949; Cosby et al., 1951; Holling and Zak, 1950; Lehmann et al., 1951; Lagerlöf et al., 1949; Varnauskas et al., 1952; Voci et al., 1952). The left auricular pressure is slightly higher but still normal (Lagerlöf et al., 1949; Voci et al., 1952).

Venous pressure. — The peripheral and coronary venous pressures are normal (Cosby et al., 1951).

Intracardiac and pulmonary blood oxygen contents. — The right auricular blood oxygen content is the same as the caval but the right ventricular is commonly higher (Cosby et al., 1951; **41**). Shunting from left to right is evident. The occasional finding of pulmonary arterial blood oxygen values higher than the right ventricular (Bing et al., 1947; Cosby et al., 1951; Holling and Zak, 1950) indicates the existence of a shunt high in the ventricles. The coronary sinus blood has been studied (Cosby et al., 1951).

Symptoms. — The greatly increased right ventricular work may lead to failure of the heart. However, peripheral anoxia accounts for the manifestations of the disorder for the most part. An unexplained phenomenon is reduction in glomerular filtration associated with decreased renal flow (Varnauskas *et al.*, 1952).

The origin of the marked increase in pulmonary arteriolar resistance that characterizes this disorder is not clear. It is possible that it is a mechanism designed to protect the pulmonary capillaries from the very high pulmonary arterial pressures consequent to the anatomical changes associated with the malformation.

In Eisenmenger's complex, exercise results in an increase in cardiac output but the percentage of blood shunted increases also, and so anoxia is exacerbated (Burchell *et al.*, 1950; Lurie *et al.*, 1952).

7. *Complex and Rare Anomalies*

The use of intracardiac catheterization has made possible studies during life that yield accurate diagnoses in a variety of congenital disorders formerly recognized only at autopsy; the use of special roentgenographic techniques has been helpful in many instances. These studies will not be described in detail since almost each case reported is unique. Some, however, may be grouped in an informing manner.

The aberrant entry of pulmonary veins into the right auricle may, by causing an admixture of arterialized blood, cause changes in blood oxygen contents similar to those seen in patients with uncomplicated interauricular septal defects (Adams *et al.*, 1950; Friedlich *et al.*, 1950; Grishman *et al.*, 1951; Hwang *et al.*, 1950; Knutson *et al.*, 1950; Nahas *et al.*, 1950; Limon Lason and Rubio Alvarez, 1949; Snellen and Albers, 1952; Nieveen *et al.*, 1952; Goldberg *et al.*, 1951; Cosby *et al.*, 1952; Campbell, 1951). Included in some of the above reports, and also in the papers of Dotter *et al.* (1949) and Cooke *et al.* (1951) are discussions of other anomalies of the pulmonary veins.

Defects of the aortic septum have been found to give changes in pressures and blood oxygen content identical with those of patent ductus arteriosus (page 384).

Tricuspid atresia, associated with other defects, including shunting of blood past the right ventricle, gives rise to a type of cyanotic heart disease (Denolin *et al.*, 1950; Holling, 1952; Engle *et al.*, 1950; Lequime *et al.*, 1949; Burchell *et al.*, 1950; Bayer and Landen, 1951; Blount *et al.*, 1951; van Lingen *et al.*, 1952; van Lingen and Whidbourne, 1952). As in normal subjects, the cardiac output falls when the patient stands (Burchell *et al.*, 1950). Unlike the findings in other types of cyanotic heart disease, the percentage of blood shunted does not increase in exercise and the arterial oxygen saturation does not fall (Burchell *et al.*, 1950; van Lingen *et al.*, 1952).

Cor triloculare has been studied (Brown *et al.*, 1949; Miller *et al.*, 1950) and the findings caused by transpositions of vessels, dextrocardia, and situs inversus have been described (Campbell *et al.*, 1949; Denolin and Lequime, 1950; Lequime *et al.*, 1948; Young and Griswold, 1951; Braun *et al.*, 1952; Campbell and Suzman, 1951; Martin and Lewis, 1952; Moscovitz *et al.*, 1952).

Studies on other complicated or rare congenital disorders may be found in the papers of Biörck *et al.* (1952), Campbell *et al.* (1952), Cosby *et al.* (1952), Holling (1952), Limon Lason *et al.* (1950, 1951), Lurie *et al.* (1952), and Metianu *et al.* (1953).

Brofman and Feil (1952) have described changes in pulse waves in subaortic stenosis.

8. *Morbus Caeruleus*

During the past half century a large number of physiologic studies have been made in patients with permanent cyanosis. In many instances reports are based upon observations in patients in whom no anatomic diagnosis could be made or if made could be proven with methods available at the time. The present discussion is based in part upon some of the data obtained in such cases. Diagnoses can now be made that are valid, if not always complete in all details. It has become evident that the tetralogy of Fallot, Eisenmenger's complex, septal defects in patients with pulmonic stenosis, tricuspid atresia with associated anomalies, and certain rare or complex anomalies involving shunts all may give rise to permanent cyanosis owing to the passage of blood from the right chambers of the heart directly into the left chambers or the aorta, and that certain physiologic changes are common to all.

Peripheral blood oxygen. Tissue oxygen. — The peripheral arterial blood oxygen content is either normal or low, but the saturation uniformly is lowered (Taussig and Blalock, 1947; **42**). Tension is very low (Ernsting and Shepard, 1951). Operations that remedy the underlying condition ameliorate this state. The peripheral venous blood oxygen content is of course lower than the arterial if peripheral circulation is normal, but it may be higher or lower than expected depending upon whether the peripheral circulation is abnormally high or decreased (Dautrebande *et al.*, 1929; Hitzenberger and Tuchfeld, 1930; Holling, 1952; Mainzer, 1928; Pijoan and Berard, 1936; Segal, 1933; Ernsting and Shepard, 1951). Capillary blood oxygen values and tension are very low also (Hertz, 1951; Hultgren, 1950; Ernsting and Shepard, 1951). Tissue oxygen tension likewise is lowered (Montgomery *et al.*, 1950).

During exercise the arterial blood oxygen saturation regularly falls (Burchell *et al.*, 1950; **43**), owing to increased shunting of blood in some instances and in others to decreased oxygen content of the venous blood resulting from inadequacy of circulation to the exercising muscles; lowered peripheral venous blood oxygen contents were found by Segal (1933) and Burch and Wood (1949) after exercise.

Bodily position influences arterial blood oxygen saturation in that standing often lowers the values somewhat (Montgomery *et al.*, 1948; Callebaut *et al.*, 1949; McGregor *et al.*, 1952) while squatting may raise it (Callebaut *et al.*, 1949). These changes represent variations in the per cent of blood shunted under these circumstances.

Oxygen inhalation usually has little or no effect on the blood oxygen saturation (Burchell *et al.*, 1950; Burchell and Wood, 1949; Denolin *et al.*, 1950; Gullickson *et al.*, 1948; Kremer, 1934; van Lingen and Whidbourne, 1952; Lurie *et al.*, 1952; McGregor *et al.*, 1952; Rassmussen and Storstein, 1951; Myer, 1932; Suarez *et al.*, 1949). What increase does occur was explained by Burchell and Wood (1949) as consequent to decreased shunting, owing to peripheral vasoconstriction caused by high concentrations of oxygen. Positive pressure respiration has no effect on oxygen saturation in morbus caeruleus (Burchell and Wood, 1949).

The blood oxygen dissociation curve is described as showing insignificant changes or it may exhibit a slight shift to the right (Dautrebande *et al.*, 1929; Ernsting and Shepard, 1951; Holling, 1952; Hitzenberger and Tuchfeld, 1930; Morse *et al.*, 1950; Suarez *et al.*, 1949; Talbott *et al.*, 1949). The shift to the right disappears after surgical repair of the anomaly (Morse *et al.*, 1950). The change in the curve in cyanotic patients has the effect of increasing oxygen tension for a given level of saturation; it resembles that seen in the presence of acidosis.

Blood carbon dioxide content, combining power, and pH. Blood carbonic anhydrase. — All authors agree that the carbon dioxide content of the blood is low (Dautrebande *et al.*, 1929; Richards, 1931; **44**). The carbon dioxide combining power of blood must also be low, as several have shown (Bing *et al.*, 1948; Morse *et al.*, 1950; Suarez *et al.*, 1949; Talbott *et al.*, 1949). Lowered blood carbon dioxide combining power always occurs where hematocrit values are elevated since a given volume of erythrocytes contains only two-thirds as much carbon dioxide as the same volume of plasma. In addition, lactic acidosis may be present (page 401). Bing *et al.* (1948) described lowering of carbon dioxide tension of arterial blood; Pearce (1921) found that the values for peripheral venous blood were normal.

The arterial blood pH has been studied most thoroughly by Morse *et al.* (1950). The pH is normal or low (Morse *et al.*, 1950; **45**). The significance of the finding of a lowered pH in this condition is not clear. Although some patients with morbus caeruleus have elevated blood lactate levels even at rest (page 401), the amount of increase is not enough to explain the change in hydrogen ion concentration. It is possible that marked polycythemia may cause an error in estimation of pH by calculation from carbon dioxide tension and combining power. Although a given mass of erythrocytes has only about two-thirds the combining power of plasma, it holds the carbon dioxide at a pH much lower than that of plasma, that is, at about pH 7.1 to 7.2, by some mechanism as yet not completely understood. Morse and Cassels (1953) have recently published a comprehensive study of acid-base balance in morbus caeruleus.

Stevenson (1943) reported the occurrence of a normal blood carbonic anhydrase level in a cyanotic infant with congenital heart disease, but Adams and Hansen (1950) and Adams and Cunningham (1952) in extensive studies, showed that carbonic anhydrase activity parallels the hematocrit value.

Lung volumes. — All measurements of subdivisions of the lung volume yield values in or close to the normal (Richards, 1931; Myers, 1932; Suarez et al., 1949; Talbott et al., 1941; Braun et al., 1952).

Respiratory dynamics. — The respiratory rate and minute volume are increased, the tidal air remaining normal (Dautrebande et al., 1929; **46**). Inhalation of oxygen does not lower the minute volume (Campbell and Poulton, 1927). Inhalation of carbon dioxide causes abnormally great hyperpnea (Suarez et al., 1949). During exercise the respiratory minute volume increases much more than the oxygen consumption (Bing et al., 1947; Charlier, 1949; Maraist et al., 1951; Denolin et al., 1950; Braun et al., 1952; Mannheimer et al., 1952; Soulié et al., 1952b). Maximal respiration is low (Braun et al., 1952).

In keeping with the hyperpnea that occurs in morbus caeruleus is the lowering of expired air carbon dioxide (Dautrebande et al., 1929; Suarez et al., 1949) and alveolar air carbon dioxide contents (Dautrebande et al., 1929; Suarez et al., 1949; **47**).

Blood volume and viscosity. Erythrocytes. Iron metabolism clotting. — The bone marrow is anoxic (Schwartz and Stats, 1949). Elevated erythrocyte counts, hemoglobin levels, hematocrit values, and oxygen capacities are uniformly found in morbus caeruleus (Prader and Rossi, 1949; Taussig and Blalock, 1947; **48**). The relation between degree of anoxia and erythrocyte count was stressed by Blalock and Taussig (1947); approximately 70 per cent oxygen saturation is a critical level. The blood viscosity of course is increased (Hitzenberger and Tuchfeld, 1930). The cell size follows no specific pattern (Adams and Cunningham, 1952).

Evidence of increased rate of turnover of erythrocytes is afforded by the slight reticulocytosis (Josephs, 1950; Myers, 1932; Prader and Rossi, 1950a), increased erythrocyte fragility (Greenthal and O'Donnell, 1921; Myers, 1932; Adams and Cunningham, 1951, 1952; Prader and Rossi, 1950b), increased urobilogen output (Josephs, 1950; Prader and Rossi, 1950a), and occasional bilirubinemia (Prader and Rossi, 1950a). Plasma iron concentrations are elevated (Prader and Rossi, 1950a) and the iron turnover is much accelerated (Huff *et al.*, 1950). However, Adams and Cunningham (1951, 1952) observed no abnormal reticulocytosis. Hemoglobin is normal in type (Adams and Cunningham, 1952).

The leukocyte count tends to be elevated and there may be a reduction in eosinophil and lymphocyte counts (Prader and Hollander, 1950).

An unexplained clotting disorder is present in many cases. Prothrombin is reduced in the blood (Bahnson and Ziegler, 1950; Favre-Gilly *et al.*, 1951; Hartman, 1952). Platelets often are low in number and clot retraction is poor (Hartman, 1952; Adams and Cunningham, 1952). Bleeding time and fibrinolysin activity are normal but fibrinogen is decreased in the blood (Hartman, 1952).

The plasma volume is normal or slightly lowered, so that the total blood volume is increased (Berlin *et al.*, 1950; **49**). This pattern is identical with that seen in simple anoxia and differs from that observed in congestive failure (page 147).

Blood lactate and pyruvate. — Although resting levels for lactate and pyruvate are normal or only slightly increased (Hallock, 1938, 1939; Havel and Watkins, 1950; Suarez *et al.*, 1949), the values during exercise are abnormally elevated (Hallock, 1938, 1939; Havel and Watkins, 1950). This is a common finding in anoxia (page 122). Havel and Watkins (1950) have also pointed out that an increase in lactic dehydrogenase occurs in the presence of polycythemia.

Basal metabolic rate. Respiratory quotient. — Although Bing *et al.* (1948) found the metabolic rate low in morbus caeruleus, others found it to be normal (Hitzenberger and Tuchfeld, 1930; Holling, 1952; Holling and Zak, 1950; Ernsting and Shepard, 1951; Mainzer, 1928; Myer, 1932; Suarez *et al.*, 1949; Talbott *et al.*, 1941).

The respiratory quotient likewise is normal (Dautrebande *et al.*, 1929; Hitzenberger and Tuchfeld, 1930; Mainzer, 1928; Myer, 1932).

Circulation time. — When much of the blood enters the aorta without passing through the lungs, the circulation time is shortened (Bain, 1934; Adams *et al.*, 1951; **50**). If ether is used, a sufficient concentration may be present in the blood to cause tingling of the face. When, however, marked polycythemia is present, the circulation time may not be accelerated (Allanby, 1949; Bing *et al.*, 1947; Engle *et al.*, 1950; Myer, 1932; Suarez *et al.*, 1949; Talbott *et al.*,

1941). Dye dilution curves, which depend on the circulation time in large measure, are often abnormal (Swan *et al.*, 1953).

Venous pressure. — In the absence of congestive failure the venous pressure is normal (Suarez *et al.*, 1949; Talbott *et al.*, 1941).

Cutaneous capillaries. — Findings similar to those of cardiac decompensation (page 71) were recorded by Rominger (1920) and by Rossi *et al.* (1950). On the other hand, Blumenfeldt and Wollheim (1937) and Schuller (1934) found no marked deviation from the normal.

Renal circulation. — A study by Scott and Elliott (1950) revealed an increased renal blood flow, but since the hematocrit value was elevated, the plasma flow was somewhat diminished. Glomerular filtration was moderately lowered and the filtration fraction was increased.

Symptoms. — The manifestations of anoxia include exertional dyspnea, hyperventilation, lactic acidosis, compensatory polycythemia, and impaired exercise tolerance. The last was studied by Mannerheim *et al.* (1952); these authors also emphasized the abnormally small oxygen intake in exercise, not an unexpected finding in view of the lactic acidosis that occurs. Lund (1952), who used the Wetzel grid, found retardation of growth and development. The finding of eosinopenia or lymphopenia in some instances may also be ascribed to anoxia. Cyanosis has been well discussed by Lundsgaard and Van Slyke (1923). The observation that some patients with morbus caeruleus prefer a squatting position may be explainable on the basis of the improvement in oxygen saturation that occurs in that position (page 398). That the anoxia influences the heart itself is suggested by the finding of abnormal changes in QT interval (Yu *et al.*, 1950); it is probable that anoxia is one of the factors that causes the cardiac decompensation that ultimately develops. Cerebral anoxia explains the nonspecific electroencephalographic changes that sometimes occur in morbus caeruleus (Stuhl *et al.*, 1952).

9. *Coarctation of the Aorta of the Adult Type*

Coarctation (stenosis of the isthmus) of the aorta of the adult type, formerly considered a rare anomaly, is now being recognized with increasing frequency. It is often associated with other congenital cardiovascular malformations but is compatible with a long and active life. The condition is of interest not only because of the extensive and complicated collateral circulation which develops, but also because of the changes in cardiovascular dynamics it causes. Relief by operation has been described (Crafoord and Nylin, 1945).

Cardiac output. — The output of the heart at rest is normal or somewhat increased (Lequime, 1940; Grollman and Ferrigan, 1934; Stewart and Bailey, 1941; Bing *et al.*, 1948, 1949*a,b*; Beard *et al.*, 1951; Griswold *et al.*, 1949; Taylor *et al.*, 1950); when increases occur they are associated with a high basal metabolic rate, so that the arteriovenous oxygen difference remains normal. Stewart *et al.* (1938, 1941) reported a slight decrease in cardiac output in one patient. Coronary blood flow is normal or somewhat increased, as is myocardial oxygen consumption; cardiac efficiency is normal (Bing *et al.*, 1949*a,b*).

The ballistocardiographic pattern is abnormal owing to the sudden shutting off of the flow of blood in the aorta (Brown *et al.*, 1949; Megibow and Feitelberg, 1948, 1951; Nickerson *et al.*, 1950).

Circulation time. — The arm-to-tongue time is within the normal range usually (Blumgart *et al.*, 1931; Stewart *et al.*, 1938, 1941, 1944; Beard *et al.*, 1951); the arm-to-leg time tends to be prolonged (Blumgart *et al.*, 1931; Stewart and Bailey, 1941; MacGregor and Wayne, 1951; Beard *et al.*, 1951). The latter finding appears to be the consequence of the long, winding path which blood from the heart must traverse to reach the foot.

Venous pressure. — The venous pressure is normal in the absence of congestive failure (Stewart *et al.*, 1944; Borst and Molhuysen, 1952). The latter authors also measured the right auricular pressure and found it normal.

Peripheral blood flow. — The peripheral blood flow as a whole is, like the cardiac output, normal or somewhat increased (Stewart *et al.*, 1944). The flows through the arm (Lewis, 1933; Pickering, 1935; Printzmetal and Wilson, 1936; Wakim *et al.*, 1948) and leg (Lewis, 1933; Wakim *et al.*, 1948; Wilson, 1951), measured plethysmographically, are normal, as are the arteriovenous oxygen differences in the arm and leg (Blumgart *et al.*, 1931). Bing *et al.* (1948) found arm blood flow much increased and leg blood flow somewhat lowered. Accordingly, it must be concluded that although blood going to the legs takes a long route, the volume of blood flowing through the lower extremities is normal, at least at rest. That it may be inadequate during exertion is suggested by the fact that intermittent claudication of the leg muscles may occur; measurements made during or shortly after walking are, however, not available.

Tissue gas tensions. — Fragmentary studies in one patient record low oxygen and high carbon dioxide tensions in the tissues (Seevers *et al.*, 1936).

Skin temperature. — The vascular disorder does not impair temperature regulation (Boden *et al.*, 1951).

Femoral arterial pulse. — The pulse over the femoral artery is, as expected, retarded (Lewis, 1933; Railsbach and Dock, 1929; Woodbury *et al.*, 1940; Galdston and Steele, 1948; Bjork and Liedholm, 1949; Brown *et al.*, 1948*a,b*; Hallenbeck *et al.*, 1951; Wood *et al.*, 1948; Fuller *et al.*, 1951), and the pulse wave is flat and smooth (Woodbury *et al.*, 1940; Megibow and Feitelberg, 1948; Bjork and Liedholm, 1949). The pulse may feel weak or be impalpable. The distal aortic pulse shows the same features (Salans *et al.*, 1951).

Renal vascular dynamics. — The renal blood flow is normal or somewhat lowered (Friedman *et al.*, 1941; Genest *et al.*, 1948; Grossman *et al.*, 1950; Harris *et al.*, 1950). However, the glomerular filtration rate is about normal, owing apparently to efferent vasoconstriction. Tubular function is normal (Harris *et al.*, 1950).

Cerebral blood flow. — Cerebral blood flow apparently is normal (Hafkenschiel *et al.*, 1949; Scheinberg, 1950). The data are too fragmentary to be analyzed with confidence.

Arterial blood pressure. — A diagnostic finding in patients with coarctation of the aorta is systolic hypertension in the arms and normal systolic pressure or systolic hypotension in the legs; in rare instances the various arterial pressures may all be normal (King, 1937). The brachial systolic pressure is usually between 140 and 170 mm-of-mercury. The diastolic blood pressure, on the other hand, is the same, or not markedly different, in the arms and legs (**51**; Woodbury *et al.*, 1940; Galdston and Steele, 1948); it usually ranges between 85 and 100 mm-of-mercury. On the other hand Crafoord and Nylin (1945), Grob and Stockman (1949), and Bing *et al.* (1948) found no elevation of diastolic pressure in the leg. Steele (1939) showed in animals that a clamp on the aorta above the renal veins resulted in an elevation of the diastolic pressure in the legs as well as in the upper parts. Studies of intra-aortic pressure show a considerable distal decrease in the systolic, the diastolic showing a smaller difference from the proximal values (Salans *et al.*, 1951; Fuller *et al.*, 1952). Immediately after operation the proximal values decrease slightly, whereas the distal levels rise appreciably (Fuller *et al.*, 1952).

In patients with coarctation of the aorta, the brachial arterial pressure is elevated abnormally after work (Eskilden *et al.*, 1949) but that in the legs is unchanged (Crafoord and Nylin, 1945); after relief of the condition by operation, the pressure in the legs also rises during exertion. Lewis (1933) felt that the hypertension in the arteries above the stenosis developed in order to maintain an adequate flow of blood distal to the constriction, but against this concept is the fact that hypertension does not develop in patients with circulatory insufficiency in the legs consequent to arterial disease.

A considerable body of work done on animals shows that when the arch of the aorta is clamped, an immediate rise in brachial blood pressure occurs (Barcroft, 1931*a, b*, 1933; Barcroft and Formijne, 1934; Brotchner, 1939; Gupta and Wiggers, 1951); however, Page (1940) showed this rise to be temporary. If, however, the clamp is allowed to remain on the aorta for some weeks, changes in pressures result that resemble those of coarctation of the aorta in man (Sealey, 1949; Sealey *et al.*, 1950). The concept that the changes are owing solely to damping of the aortic wave was advanced by Hull (1948), whose experiments can be criticized because measurements of diastolic pressure by means of a cuff are not sufficiently accurate for the purpose for which he used them. Rytand (1938) concluded, on the basis of the results of experiments in animals, that the persistent generalized diastolic hypertension of coarctation of the aorta was a Goldblatt phenomenon, that is, a humoral phenomenon, which occurred as a consequence of renal ischemia. This concept is supported by the finding of similarly elevated diastolic blood pressure levels in the brachial and femoral arteries of patients with coarctation of the aorta and also by the fact that after operation approximately a month must elapse before the hypertension disappears. Although a neurogenic mechanism for the hypertension of the coarctation was suggested by Prinzmetal and Wilson (1936), Pickering (1935) concluded that a humoral mechanism was responsible, which is consistent with the view expressed by Rytand (1938). This mechanism could account for the brachial systolic hypertension; the low systolic pressure found in the legs, however, must be due to the stenosis in the aorta. On the other hand Bing *et al.* (1948), who found no elevation of femoral diastolic pressure in their patients, concluded that the hemodynamic changes found in the legs were entirely due to the effects on blood flow of the obstruction itself. Recent experiments in animals, involving transplanting a kidney to an area proximal to an induced coarctation, are important in reference to this question; hypertension did not occur (Scott and Bahnson, 1951) and the humoral mechanism seems established as the cause of elevation of blood pressure in coarctation of the aorta.

Basal metabolic rate. — The basal metabolic rate is normal or elevated (Blackford, 1928; Grollman and Ferrigan, 1934; Stewart and Bailey, 1941; Ulrich, 1932; Goldman and Schroeder, 1949); although the mechanism responsible for this finding is unknown, it may be similar to that which often causes elevation of metabolic rate in patients with essential hypertension.

Symptoms. — Aside from clinical manifestations of associated congenital anomalies, the complaints and physical signs of coarctation of the aorta fall into two main groups: (i) those of hypertension, including headache, palpitation, cardiac enlargement, generalized arteriosclerosis and congestive failure and (ii) those of mild or moderate peripheral vascular insufficiency, including cold feet, intermittent claudication and decreased or absent pulsations in the arteries of the legs; gangrene does not develop. Although many patients with this disorder live long normal lives, many others die, principally of congestive failure and cerebral hemorrhage. Coarctation of the aorta may occur with patent ductus arteriosus (page 396) or with other anomalies (Muller and Dammann, 1952).

10. *Acquired Valvular Disease*

Precise characterization in *quantitative* terms of the dynamic effects of acquired, or any other, valvular lesions in man is beset with difficulty. Estimation of the severity of a lesion from physical signs is often grossly inaccurate. The common association with valvular lesions of myocardial damage or insufficiency confuses the picture, as do the facts that in a majority of instances more than one valve is involved and more than one type of damage to each valve exists. Accordingly, the interpretation of many of the published data is most insecure.

On the other hand, it is possible to formulate certain conclusions as to the effects of valvular lesions in general. For instance, it is apparent that stenotic lesions place a variable amount of strain on the ventricle which is situated in a retrograde position; it has actually been shown (page 388) that the right ventricular pressure is elevated in patients with pulmonic stenosis and also in those with mitral stenosis (pages 408 and 409). Therefore, according to the formula of Evans and Matsuoka (1915), $W = OP + \frac{1}{2} (w/g)V^2$, the work W of the ventricle is increased because the pressure P is greater. In this equation, O is the output of the heart, so that the term OP represents the output and pressure factors in blood flow and the term $\frac{1}{2} (w/g)V^2$ represents the velocity factor. Ordinarily, the latter is equal to only approximately 2 per cent of the total cardiac work, but, in the presence of stenotic lesions, interference with the ability of the ventricle to impart velocity to the blood results in an increase in the velocity factor, so that it may rise to 20 per cent of the work of the heart (Evans and Matsuoka, 1915). These factors become exaggerated during exertion, so that during work the cost to the heart of maintaining the necessary increases in blood flow and blood pressure may be so much greater than normal as to render its attainment impossible. In addition, the fact that the cardiac work is increased at rest reduces the reserve to be used during exertion.

These theoretical considerations have had ample verification in the demonstration in man that patients with valvular disease often exhibit a subnormal increase in cardiac output during work (page 408) and an increased oxygen debt (page 411) and flow debt after it (page 415). A similar state results in patients with regurgitant lesions, but here the strain on a ventricle is a consequence of the fact that it must put out more blood and develop a higher pressure than normal in order to maintain a normal flow ahead.

Another fact to be borne in mind is that the organ immediately retrograde to a damaged valve usually shows the greatest and the earliest evidence of damage.

Mitral stenosis. Cardiac output. — A number of older authors studied the circulatory dynamics in patients with mitral stenosis (**52**; Stewart *et al.*, 1938); some have stated that the cardiac output is often low. It is difficult, however, to evaluate these data, since the dynamic effects of the valve lesion are identical with some of those that occur as a consequence of myocardial insufficiency, and the latter may have been present in some of the patients studied. Studies by means of the catheter also show that the cardiac output is normal or low (Gorlin *et al.*, 1951*a,b,c*; **53**). In either case the increase in exertion is likely to be abnormally small or may be absent (Bayliss *et al.*, 1950; Bland and Sweet, 1949; Draper *et al.*, 1950; Gorlin and Gorlin, 1951; Gorlin *et al.*, 1951*a,b,c*; Harken *et al.*, 1948, 1950; **54**). Stevenson *et al.* (1949) and Makinson (1950), using the ballisto-cardiograph, found good increases in cardiac output in exercise.

Observations on coronary venous blood gases were reported by Soulié *et al.* (1949); Lombardo *et al.* (1953) also discussed myocardial efficiency.

Circulation time. — The circulation times are normal or somewhat slowed (Bailey *et al.*, 1950; Ball *et al.*, 1952; Facquet *et al.*, 1952; Eliasch, 1952; Borden *et al.*, 1949; Blumgart and Weiss, 1927; Harken *et al.*, 1948, 1950; Doyle *et al.*, 1953; Kopelman and Lee, 1951; Nathanson and Elek, 1947; Robb and Weiss, 1934; Weiss and Ellis, 1930). A slowed circulation time may be found in the absence of overt evidences of failure at rest; it does not become accelerated during exercise.

Venous pressure. — The venous pressure is usually normal but occasionally may be elevated slightly in the absence of detectable congestive failure (Bailey *et al.*, 1950; Blumgart and Weiss, 1927; Harken *et al.*, 1948, 1950; Facquet *et al.*, 1952; Bloomfield *et al.*, 1952; Gerbode *et al.*, 1952). The very high values reported by Cossio and Berconsky (1939) have not been found by others.

Intracardiac and pulmonary vascular pressures. — The left auricular pressure was measured by an indirect and inaccurate method by Staudacher (1932), who found high values. Direct measurements made at the time of operative exposure have yielded markedly elevated values that are even higher than expected from measurements of pulmonary capillary pressures (Bland and Sweet, 1949; Keown et al., 1951; Cooley and Chapman, 1952; Gerbode et al., 1952; Lam, 1953; Munnell and Lam, 1951). Insertion of a needle into the left auricle by way of a bronchoscope also permits measurement of the left auricular pressure, revealing high values in mitral stenosis (Facquet et al., 1952; Allison and Linden, 1953; Wynn et al., 1952). Studies by means of the catheter have shown that the pulmonary capillary pressure is usually elevated, although normal values may be found in patients without symptoms (Gorlin et al., 1951a,b,c; **55**). In exercise a further rise occurs, except in those instances where the output of the right ventricle does not increase (Draper et al., 1950; Araujo and Lukas, 1952; Carlotti et al., 1952; Cooley and Chapman, 1952; Crafoord et al., 1951; Eliasch, 1952; Eliasch et al., 1952; Ellis et al., 1951; Lukas and Dotter, 1952; Soulié et al., 1951a; Wulff et al., 1953; Gorlin and Gorlin, 1951; Gorlin et al., 1951a,b). The pulmonary arterial pressure is increased (Gorlin et al., 1951a,c; **56**). As pulmonary capillary pressure increases, the pulmonary arterial rises with it at first, but with higher capillary pressure the pulmonary arterial pressure rises disproportionately; vasoconstriction occurs. In exercise the rise in pulmonary arterial pressure is marked (Bayliss et al., 1950; Bland and Sweet, 1949; Draper et al., 1950; **57**) and the gradient between capillary and arterial pressure is greater; arteriolar constriction is more marked. Since the total vascular resistance equals the blood pressure divided by the cardiac output, it is evident that the pulmonary vascular resistance is often elevated — sometimes markedly so — in mitral stenosis. Exercise normally causes a fall in pulmonary vascular resistance; a marked rise occurs in mitral stenosis. Induced anoxia causes further pulmonary vasoconstriction in mitral stenosis (Doyle et al., 1952); the cardiac output does not increase and the pulmonary capillary pressure falls slightly. Administering oxygen in mitral stenosis lowers the pulmonary arterial pressure (Dressler et al., 1952). The right ventricular systolic pressure accordingly is elevated likewise, the diastolic showing little or no change (Bayliss et al., 1950; **58**) and rises excessively in exercise (Bayliss et al., 1950; Cooley and Chapman, 1952). Since the diastolic right ventricular pressure is not elevated greatly as a rule, there is no need for the right auricular pressure to increase in most instances (Bloomfield *et al.*, 1946; Draper *et al.*, 1950; Eliasch *et al.*, 1950; Gorlin *et al.*, 1951c, **59**). It may, however, rise abnormally in exercise (Gorlin *et al.*, 1951c; Ellis *et al.*, 1951). The pulmonary arterial pressure falls when the patient sits up (Donald *et al.*, 1953); this does not occur in normal subjects.

Arterial pressure. — Hypertension is not excessively common in mitral stenosis (Boas and Fishberg, 1926; Brumm and Smith, 1941; Horns, 1944; Roseman and Wasserman, 1951); Levine and Fulton (1928) opposed this view. The pressure often rises after valvulotomy (Denk, 1953). Changes during the Valsalva maneuver are often abnormal (Elisberg *et al.*, 1953).

Vital capacity and respiratory dynamics. — The vital capacity is normal or somewhat low (Berglund *et al.*, 1949; Blumgart and Weiss, 1927; Borden *et al.*, 1950; Gardam, 1950; Castaing *et al.*, 1952; Andrus *et al.*, 1952; Cash and Zimmerman, 1952; Mathieu *et al.*, 1952; Carroll *et al.*, 1953; Welch *et al.*, 1950; Wier *et al.*, 1952). The residual air volume is increased (Castaing *et al.*, 1952; Welch *et al.*, 1952). These changes apparently are owing to increased pulmonary rigidity caused by high capillary pressures, since the pulmonary blood volume is normal or close to it (Berglund *et al.*, 1949; Borden *et al.*, 1949; Kopelman and Lee, 1951; Lagerlöf *et al.*, 1949; Ball *et al.*, 1952; Bing *et al.*, 1951; Doyle *et al.*, 1952, 1953; Eliasch, 1952; Eliasch *et al.*, 1952; Tompkins *et al.*, 1952; Wade *et al.*, 1952). Little or no change occurs during exercise (Ball *et al.*, 1952; Eliasch, 1952; Eliasch *et al.*, 1952). The respiratory minute volume at rest is normal or slightly increased (Draper *et al.*, 1950; Castaing *et al.*, 1952; Landen and Bayer, 1952; Blount *et al.*, 1952; Eliasch, 1952; Wier *et al.*, 1952); it rises out of proportion to the increase in oxygen consumption of exercise (Draper *et al.*, 1950; Eliasch, 1952; Wier *et al.*, 1952). The maximal ventilation is low (Andrus *et al.*, 1952; Mathieu *et al.*, 1952; Wier *et al.*, 1952). During exertion the tidal air falls (Mathieu *et al.*, 1952), respiration thereby becoming less efficient. Mixing is impaired in many instances but not all (Castaing *et al.*, 1952; Carroll *et al.*, 1953; Andrus *et al.*, 1952). A recent study by West *et al.* (1953) correlates these measurements. Diffusion across alveolar walls may be impaired, judging from the oxygen gradient (Kroetz, 1931; Andrus *et al.*, 1952; Carroll *et al.*, 1953; Blount *et al.*, 1952). It seems to increase further in exercise (Blount *et al.*, 1952). Some venous admixture into arterial blood appears to occur (Blount *et al.*, 1952; Andrus *et al.*, 1952; Carroll *et al.*, 1953). Alveolar oxygen tensions are normal (Kroetz, 1931; Blount *et al.*, 1952); carbon dioxide tensions are lowered owing to hyperventilation (Kroetz, 1931). The observations of Blount *et al.* (1953) indicate that both impaired diffusion across the capillary walls and venous admixture of blood in the lungs may occur.

The arterial blood oxygen saturation is normal or close to it (Baker *et al.*, 1950; Gorlin *et al.*, 1951*c*; Montgomery *et al.*, 1950; 60) and does not change much in exercise (Gorlin *et al.*, 1951*c,e*; Castaing *et al.*, 1952; Blount *et al.*, 1952; Miller *et al.*, 1952; Soulié *et al.*, 1951*a*). Arterial carbon dioxide values are often low (Kroetz, 1931; Castaing *et al.*, 1952; Wier *et al.*, 1952) and usually decrease further during exercise.

Resting oxygen consumption is normal (Carlotti *et al.*, 1952; Eliasch, 1952; Miller *et al.*, 1952; Mills *et al.*, 1952; Raine and Twelmeyer, 1952; Wier *et al.*, 1952; Landen and Bayer, 1952) but does not rise normally in exercise, according to the last three. It does increase when oxygen is inhaled (Landen and Bayer, 1952).

The increased rigidity of the lungs impairs pulmonary function in mitral stenosis but it is evident that, since pulmonary congestion does not increase during exercise, the main difficulty during work is increased anoxia caused by failure of the cardiac output to increase normally (page 408); another factor may be activation of reflexes by marked increases in pulmonary vascular pressures (page 409).

Renal blood flow. — Aas and Blegen (1950) and Werkö *et al.* (1952) found changes typical of cardiac decompensation (page 159) in the absence of that state in patients with mitral valvular disease.

Hepatic function. — Kissane *et al.* (1950) found that some tests of hepatic function often were abnormal in patients with mitral stenosis.

Blood volume. — The blood volume in the absence of cardiac decompensation is normal (Uhlenbruck and Vogels, 1931; Borden *et al.*, 1949*e*; Doyle *et al.*, 1952; Eliasch, 1952; Wade *et al.*, 1952; Werkö *et al.*, 1952).

The symptoms of mitral stenosis are, as expected, dyspnea on exertion even before myocardial insufficiency develops. Such exertional dyspnea may be present for years, or even decades, before frank failure makes itself manifest; in some instances, the circulation time through the lungs may be prolonged because of pulmonary stasis, even in the absence of myocardial weakness. This dyspnea due to mechanical factors need not have the same unfavorable significance as dyspnea consequent to myocardial insufficiency. It is worthy of note that even though pulmonary engorgement and increased pulmonary vascular pressure may be present to a marked degree, severe enough to cause recurrent hemoptyses, attacks of acute pulmonary edema are relatively uncommon. The prolonged pulmonary congestion of mitral stenosis may ultimately result in lesions in the pulmonary vascular tree (Parker and Weiss, 1936) or in fibrotic perivascular lesions (Moschcowitz, 1930; Parker and Weiss, 1936) known to pathologists as "brown induration of the lungs." The brown coloration is probably due to the presence of pigment either free or in phagocytes, that is, the "heart failure cells." When fibrosis of the lungs develops in significant degree, clubbing of the fingers, polycythemia and the manifestations of pulmonary fibrosis in general (page 457) may appear.

Auricular fibrillation is recognized as common in mitral stenosis. The origin of this arrhythmia in general is not clearly understood by many clinicians. Auricular fibrillation develops when auricular conduction is slowed and the refractory period of the auricular myocardium is shortened. How the first of these is brought about is not known, but it is established that vagal action accomplishes the second. Evidence for the role of vagal hyperactivity in inducing auricular fibrillation in general and in mitral stenosis in particular is presented in detail elsewhere (Altschule, 1939, 1945). It has been pointed out that a majority of patients have other evidences of vagal hyperactivity before the onset of auricular fibrillation. The origin of these vagal impulses is obscure, but it is possible that they are reflex and arise from overdistention of the great veins, active rheumatic lesions in the great veins or aorta, congestion of the lungs, or other sources of vagal reflexes. The effects of auricular fibrillation on the circulation in mitral stenosis were studied by Ferrer et al. (1952) and Wade et al. (1952); the changes resemble those described previously (page 357).

Pulmonary edema theoretically should occur in every patient in whom pulmonary capillary pressure is elevated above plasma oncotic pressure; it occurs in some but not all. It is probable that although the rate of transudation from the capillaries is increased in such circumstances, the pulmonary lymphatics are able to remove the excess of fluid presented to them; this is especially likely to be true when pulmonary blood flow is diminished. Pulmonary arteriolar constriction appears to be the mechanism that limits pulmonary blood flow at rest and more especially in exercise and thereby prevents the pulmonary lymphatics from being overwhelmed in most instances. When pulmonary edema does occur in uncomplicated mitral stenosis, it is evident that left ventricular failure cannot be considered its cause, since not enough blood is delivered to that ventricle to raise the question of its being put under enough strain to make it fail. In occasional instances pulmonary edema may disappear when the pulmonary capillary pressure rises, if the cardiac output falls (Ellis et al., 1951). The correlation between the occurrence of pulmonary edema and the level of the pulmonary capillary pressure is far from close in the data of Araujo and Lukas (1952), Ellis et al. (1951), Lukas and Dotter (1952), Soulié et al. (1951a), and Gorlin et al. (1951). Nanson and Walker (1952) found circulatory changes in a patient with ball-valve thrombus that resembled those seen in mitral stenosis.

Mitral insufficiency. — Studies of cardiac output (Gorlin et al., 1952; Gorlin and Dexter, 1952; Burchell, 1953), of right auricular, right ventricular, and pulmonary arterial pressures (Burchell, 1953; Gorlin et al., 1952), of pulmonary capillary pressure (Biörck et al., 1953; Correll et al., 1952; Gorlin and Dexter, 1952; Gorlin et al., 1952), and of left auricular pressure (Allison and Linden, 1953; Facquet et al., 1952; Wynn et al., 1952) show changes generally similar to those of mitral stenosis, but less marked. The left auricular pressure rises synchronously with the ventricular beat in mitral insufficiency (Wynn et al., 1952). Typical changes in the pulmonary venous pulse wave occur (Allison and Linden, 1953; Biörck et al., 1953; Carlotti et al., 1952; Correll et al., 1952; van Bogaert et al., 1952). Calculations of valve cross-sectional area made by Gorlin and Dexter (1952) have been criticized by Burton (1953).

Aortic stenosis. — In addition to the typical murmur, which requires no discussion, there are striking peripheral signs in patients with marked aortic stenosis, namely, bradycardia, small pulse pressure, systolic hypotension, diastolic hypertension, small pulse and a flat pulse wave. The bradycardia cannot be explained, although prolongation of the period of ventricular ejection may be important in that it would necessarily tend to decrease the number of systoles possible per minute, if diastole remained unchanged. The other signs are so strikingly like those that obtain below the constriction in coarctation of the aorta as to suggest a similar mechanism (page 404). The low systolic pressure is due to the presence of the stricture itself, but the elevated diastolic pressure may be the consequence of a Goldblatt phenomenon, much like the one that Rytand (1938) discussed in relation to coarctation. The result is a decreased pulse pressure and a small pulse. Attacks of syncope, not infrequently in relation to exertion, may occur. During exertion the muscles drain off an increased portion of the circulation and, since increases in cardiac output are limited, other parts of the body, including the brain, suffer. Other mechanisms, as yet not understood, may also play a part. Angina pectoris is also common; this is probably related to narrowing of the coronary ostia by scar tissue.

Studies of the physiology of the disorder in man are few. Brofman and Feil (1952) recently discussed the pulse wave.

Aortic insufficiency. — Although patients with compensated aortic insufficiency show a normal cardiac output at rest, the output of the left ventricle is actually increased in order to compensate for regurgitation of blood past the damaged valves. Bazett *et al.* (1941) and Keys and Freidell (1939a, b) have attempted to estimate the amount of regurgitation by comparing the output of the right ventricle, as measured with a foreign gas by means of the Fick principle, with the output of the left ventricle, measured by other means; normally the two are equal. Since none of the methods used by these authors yields results of absolute accuracy, their conclusions must be accepted with a good deal of reservation. The amount of regurgitation in aortic insufficiency has been calculated by these authors to range between 15 and 40 per cent of the output of the left ventricle. Zimmerman (1950) introduced a catheter into the left ventricle and found the left ventricular systolic pressure normal or high, that is, equal to the aortic systolic pressure. The left ventricular diastolic pressure surprisingly was normal, except in the presence of failure, and the right ventricular systolic pressure elevated in one of the three patients not in failure. It is evident that more work is needed to elucidate these confusing findings. Limón Lason (1950) has also published a few data obtained by means of the catheter. The increase in cardiac work that occurs with aortic regurgitation favors the development of failure, although myocardial weakness due to damage to the heart muscle itself is more important in many instances. The inefficiency of the heart in aortic insufficiency probably limits the increase in cardiac output that occurs in exercise, for Abramson et al., (1942) found that work led to a more persistent increase in peripheral flow than normal, as if a debt had to be discharged. Fragmentary data on myocardial efficiency are available (Lombardo et al., 1953) and also on respiratory dynamics (Bruce et al., 1952).

The peripheral vascular phenomena of aortic insufficiency have interested clinicians for many decades. The low diastolic pressure is a direct consequence of regurgitation. The collapsing pulse has been studied extensively and, contrary to the opinion held by most clinicians, it is not the direct result of regurgitation of blood from the aorta and main arteries. Stewart (1908) showed that most of the sharp fall in blood pressure in aortic insufficiency occurs during systole, and this has recently been corroborated by studies made in man by means of arterial puncture (Kotte et al., 1944). This finding led Hewlett and Van Zwaluwenburg (1913), and many others since, to conclude that peripheral vasodilatation is present in aortic insufficiency, so that blood quickly runs off into the periphery. This conclusion is reasonable, for in effect the left ventricle and the peripheral circulation are in competition for the blood in the aorta in patients with aortic insufficiency; peripheral vasodilatation would favor the flow of blood to the periphery. However, Hewlett and Van Zwaluwenburg (1913) found a regurgitant rather than a forward flow in the arteries. The fact that Abramson et al. (1942) and Wilkins and Bradley (1946) observed no constant deviation from the normal value for total flow through the arm or leg in aortic insufficiency is not helpful in this regard. Wiggers (1931) reviewed the experimental data available and concluded that peripheral vasodilatation does not occur in this disease; he felt that aortic regurgitation results in a change in ventricular dynamics so that the curve of intraventricular pressure rises more steeply and to a higher level than normal, with an almost equally steep fall so that the pressure is well on its way back to the base line before the end of systole.

The concept that peripheral vasodilatation occurs in aortic insufficiency outwardly receives support from the common finding of capillary pulsation in this disease. Lewis (1924) and Heimberger (1925) showed that vasodilatation caused the appearance of this phenomenon. Wiggers (1931), on the other hand, demonstrated by means of artificial model circulatory systems that aortic insufficiency can cause capillary and even venous pulsation in spite of the absence of any change in peripheral resistance. There has been some controversy as to which vessels give rise to the phenomenon of capillary pulsation; Boas (1922), Fischl (1923) and Hisinger-Jägerskiöld (1924) found no abnormal pulsations in the capillaries on direct microscopic examination in patients with aortic insufficiency. Secher (1922) and a later report by Boas (1924) describe such pulsations as inconstant. However, the observation of pulsation, pulsatile flow and even regurgitation in the capillaries, made by means of direct miscroscopy by Jürgensen (1920), Freedlander and Lenhart (1922), Sumball (1923), Weiss and Dieter (1920), and Lewis (1924), are convincing. Accordingly, it must be concluded that the rhythmic flushing of aortic insufficiency is consequent largely to changes in capillary circulation; the abnormal pulsations seen in venules must also play an important role. Duroziez' sign and pistol-shot sounds may be produced in normal subjects by marked local vasodilatation (Myerson et al., 1938).

The concept of "free aortic regurgitation," based on the finding by auscultation of a diastolic blood pressure at or near zero, is probably erroneous, for direct arterial puncture has shown that values obtained by the auscultatory method are much too low in many or most patients with aortic valvular insufficiency (Kotte et al., 1944; Ragan and Bordley, 1941). Another clinically accepted concept, namely, that a femoral arterial pressure higher than the brachial is diagnostic of aortic insufficiency (Hill, 1909; Friedlander, 1927), has been negated by the work of Kotte, Iglauer and McGuire (1944), who showed that this difference also exists in a majority of normal individuals. An excessive fall in systolic pressure may occur on standing (Kahn, 1919); changes on a tilt table are normal according to Howard and Leathart (1951).

An excellent study of the aortic pulse wave was made by Salans
et al. (1951).

Symptoms in patients with aortic insufficiency include severe discomfort due to palpitation, probably consequent to widened pulse
pressure. Angina pectoris is also common and is probably related to
myocardial ischemia secondary to low diastolic arterial pressures;
filling of the coronary vessels is considered to be governed largely by
diastolic aortic pressure. The occurrence of attacks of pulmonary
edema and, in many instances, the rapid progression of congestive
failure when it occurs are both not well understood. Paroxysmal attacks of sinus tachycardia together with hypertension may be very
distressing (Lewis, 1931); their mechanism is obscure but may be
related to the apparent loss of depressor reflex mechanisms found in
patients (Hamilton et al., 1944) and also in experimental animals
(Brewer et al., 1934) with aortic insufficiency.

Rheumatic tricuspid disease. — Organic disease of the tricuspid
valve is of interest to clinicians because of the striking clinical manifestations, including marked venous pulsations, early development of
cirrhosis and the unusual coloration of the skin consequent to the
simultaneous occurrence of icterus and cyanosis. In addition, this
valve lesion is of considerable theoretical importance since it causes
very high venous pressure which may persist for years without giving
rise to edema, and it may be associated with some degree of orthopnea, even in the absence of myocardial insufficiency. The condition
is relatively uncommon; hence, data bearing on cardiorespiratory
function are scanty.

(1) *Cardiac output.* Normal values of cardiac output obtain when
the heart is compensated (Altschule et al., 1937, 1940); when congestive failure develops the usual fall in cardiac minute volume output occurs. Gorlin and Gorlin (1951) and Doyle et al. (1953) found
the resting cardiac output to be low in the absence of failure.

(2) *Circulation time.* The arm-to-tongue time is long in the absence of congestive failure and becomes longer when failure supervenes (Altschule et al., 1937, 1940; Aceves and Carral, 1947). The
increase that occurs before the onset of failure is probably entirely
in the venous segment; there are, however, no data bearing on this
point. Doyle et al. (1953) found the circulation time normal.

(3) *Right heart pressures.* The right ventricular diastolic pressure

is normal or elevated (Ferrer *et al.*, 1952), but the systolic is reported as normal by Gorlin and Gorlin (1951) or elevated by Bloomfield *et al.* (1947), Soulié *et al.* (1952*a*), and McCord and Blount (1952). These discrepancies may be due to mitral stenosis; organic rheumatic tricuspid disease without mitral disease is rare (Altschule and Budnitz, 1940). The right auricular pressure is also elevated (Bloomfield *et al.*, 1946; Gorlin and Gorlin, 1951; Lagerlöf and Werkö, 1948; Soulié *et al.*, 1952; McCord and Blount, 1952); the gradient between auricular and ventricular pressure may be reversed during part of the cardiac cycle. The right auricular pressure rises in inspiration for reasons not known (Lauson *et al.*, 1946). The right auricular pulse wave shows a distinctive form (McCord and Blount, 1952). The pressure rises excessively during exercise (McCord and Blount, 1952).

(4) *Venous pressure.* High venous pressures are found in all patients with well-marked stenosis or insufficiency (Robb and Weiss, 1934; Friedlander and Kerr, 1936; Altschule *et al.*, 1937, 1940; Bloomfield *et al.*, 1946; Aceves and Carral, 1947; Tenzer, 1949; Eliasch *et al.*, 1950), rising higher with congestive failure. The veins pulsate with each beat of the heart, the degree of pulsation varying roughly with the amount of valvular insufficiency; pulsations may cause a rise in pressure of 2 cm-of-water or more. The pulsations may be damped by the occurrence of myocardial insufficiency, with consequent overfilling of the veins even in diastole, and also by the development of pericardial tamponade (Altschule and Budnitz, 1940). The pulsations usually manifest two phases, presystolic and systolic; since the former are due to auricular contraction, they may disappear in the presence of such arrhythmias as auricular fibrillation or standstill, and nodal rhythm or tachycardia (Friedlander and Kerr, 1936). Changes in the phlebogram occur (Messer *et al.*, 1950).

(5) *Arterial blood pressure.* Tricuspid disease in itself does not influence the arterial blood pressure. Such changes as occur in patients with this disease are consequent to the commonly associated aortic valvular disease, or the pericardial tamponade that may also occur.

(6) *Vital capacity; respiratory dynamics.* The vital capacity may be low in patients with tricuspid disease (Altschule *et al.*, 1937,

1940); interpretation of this finding, however, is difficult, since it may be consequent to weakness, to the reduction of pulmonary expansibility by the presence of an enormously dilated heart, or to pulmonary stasis due to the mitral stenosis that occurs in almost all instances of rheumatic tricuspid disease. The respiratory dynamics in the absence of myocardial insufficiency are normal at rest (Altschule and Budnitz, 1940).

(7) *Hepatic function.* Visible icterus as well as elevation of the serum bilirubin are of common occurrence in patients with organic tricuspid disease; the galactose tolerance test is normal (Altschule and Budnitz, 1940). Dye excretion may be diminished (Aceves and Carral, 1947), and prothrombin time may be prolonged.

(8) *Symptoms.* The persistently high venous pressures and the occurrence of marked venous pulsations in tricuspid disease are readily understandable. The cardiac output at rest may, nevertheless, remain normal, enough pressure being built up in the veins to overcome the obstruction to the inflow of blood into the right ventricle. It is doubtful, however, that normal increases in cardiac output occur during exertion. In spite of the marked elevation of venous pressures persisting for years, visible edema may be minimal or even absent in some patients (Friedlander and Kerr, 1936; Altschule and Budnitz, 1940); this finding negates the concept that cardiac edema is due solely to failure of the right ventricle with consequent rise in venous pressure. Reasons for the failure of edema to occur in patients with tricuspid disease include normal cardiac output and renal blood flow, absence of tissue anoxia, and maintenance of normal plasma protein levels. When congestive failure develops, not only does peripheral edema appear, but a large amount of fluid — over a liter — may accumulate in the pericardial space (Altschule and Budnitz, 1940). This accumulation of fluid may be consequent in part to the very high venous pressures in the coronary sinus, which drains into the right auricle; the coronary sinus may be found greatly dilated at autopsy. The accumulation of these large volumes of fluid in the pericardium may give rise to signs of pericardial tamponade, with falling arterial blood pressure and pulse pressure, increasing venous pressures and diminution of the force of venous pulsations. An interesting observation on the orthopnea that may occur in triscupid disease in the absence of myocardial insufficiency has been reported (Altschule and

Blumgart, 1937); in a patient studied, lowering the head of the bed caused a smothering sensation when the visible venous engorgement rose to a level corresponding approximately to that of the respiratory centers in the brain.

The cyanosis of tricuspid disease is not due to abnormal deoxygenation of capillary blood, but rather to increased prominence of cutaneous veins and venules (Altschule and Blumgart, 1937). It has been stated that the presence of the tricuspid lesion protects the patient from the consequences of the commonly associated mitral stenosis, as evidenced by the long life with relative comfort that patients with a combination of the two lesions may enjoy when apparently in congestive failure. This view, however, neglects the fact that venous engorgement, exertional dyspnea and even edema and orthopnea are the consequences not of myocardial insufficiency but rather of a nonprogressive or very slowly progressive physical impediment to the entry of blood into the right ventricle, so that it is erroneous to diagnose myocardial insufficiency in such instances. When the latter finally occurs, dyspnea, orthopnea and edema are extreme, treatment is commonly ineffectual and the course is short. Tricuspid disease is another example of the utility of differentiating between valvular incompetence or some other physical impediment to flow, which is very slowly progressive, and myocardial insufficiency, which in most instances is very disabling and is more rapidly progressive; it is to be understood, of course, that the first may give rise to the second with little or no change in the character but only in the severity of the manifestations.

In the early stages of the syndrome the enlarged liver pulsates synchronously with the neck veins; later, as fibrosis progresses, the liver becomes firmer and smaller and pulsations diminish. In some instances, the clinical manifestations of cirrhosis may dominate the picture, or at least precede those of congestive failure. The occurrence of purpura in a significant proportion of patients with tricuspid disease may be consequent to prothrombin deficiency (Aceves and Carral, 1947).

Bibliography

Chapter VI

ABRAHAMS, D. G., and P. WOOD, Pulmonary stenosis with normal aortic root, *Brit. Heart J.* **13,** 519 (1951). [12, 13, 14, 17

ABRAMSON, D. I., S. M. FIERST, and K. FLACHS, Effect of muscular exercise upon the peripheral circulation in patients with valvular heart disease, *J. Clin. Investigation* **21,** 747 (1942).

ACEVES, S., and R. CARRAL, The diagnosis of tricuspid valve disease, *Am. Heart J.* **34,** 114 (1947).

ADAMS, F. H., Pulmonary hypertension in children due to congenital heart disease, *J. Pediat.* **40,** 42 (1952). [1, 2, 3, 21, 22, 27, 28, 29

ADAMS, F. H., and S. C. CUNNINGHAM, Fragility of red blood cells from newborn infants and children with cyanotic congenital heart disease, *J. Pediat.* **39,** 180 (1951).

ADAMS, F. H., and S. C. CUNNINGHAM, Further studies on the blood of children with cyanotic heart disease with special reference to the hemoglobin, *J. Pediat.* **41,** 424 (1952). [48

ADAMS, F. H., A. DIEHL, J. JORGENS, and L. G. VEASY, Right heart catheterization in patent ductus arteriosus and aortic-pulmonary septal defect, *J. Pediat.* **40,** 49 (1952). [1, 2, 3, 6, 7, 8, 9, 10

ADAMS, F. H., and D. M. HANSEN, Carbonic anhydrase in congenital heart disease, *Proc. Soc. Exper. Biol. & Med.* **73,** 642 (1950). [48

ADAMS, F. H., J. W. LABREE, J. JORGENS, and L. G. VEASY, Right heart catheterization of anomalous pulmonary veins emptying into the right atrium, *Radiology* **55,** 834 (1950).

ADAMS, F. H., J. LABREE, and H. M. STAUFFER, Right heart catheterization of the aorta through a patent ductus arteriosus. Report of two cases, *Pediatrics* **5,** 390 (1950). [2, 4, 5, 7, 9

ADAMS, F. H., L. G. VEASY, J. JORGENS, A. DIEHL, J. W. LABREE, M. J. SHAPIRO, and P. F. DWAN, Congenital valvular pulmonary stenosis with or without an interatrial communication: physiologic studies as diagnostic aids, *J. Pediatrics* **38,** 431 (1951). [10, 11, 12, 13, 15, 24, 35, 43

ALLANBY, K. D., Circulation times in congenital heart disease, *Brit. Heart J.* **11,** 165 (1949). [50

ALLISON, P. R., and R. J. LINDEN, The bronchoscopic measurement of left auricular pressure, *Circulation* **7,** 669 (1953). [55

ALTSCHULE, M. D., The relation between prolonged P-R interval and auricular fibrillation in patients with rheumatic heart disease, *Am. Heart J.* **18,** 1 (1939).

ALTSCHULE, M. D., The relation between vagal activity and auricular fibrillation in various clinical conditions, *New England J. Med.* **233**, 265 (1945).

ALTSCHULE, M. D., and H. L. BLUMGART, The circulatory dynamics in tricuspid stenosis. Their significance in the pathogenesis of edema and orthopnea, *Am. Heart J.* **13**, 589 (1937).

ALTSCHULE, M. D., and E. BUDNITZ, Rheumatic disease of the tricuspid valve, *Arch. Path.* **30**, 7 (1940).

ANDRUS, E. C., A. BLALOCK, and R. J. BING, The surgical treatment of mitral stenosis and its physiological consequences, *Tr. A. Am. Physicians* **64**, 334 (1951).

ANDRUS, E. C., E. V. NEWMAN, R. L. RILEY, L. E. SHULMAN, and H. T. BAHNSON, The preoperative and postoperative management of some of the pulmonary complications of mitral stenosis, *Tr. A. Am. Physician* **65**, 268 (1952). [53, 54, 56, 57

ARAUJO, J., and D. S. LUKAS, Interrelationships among pulmonary "capillary" pressure, blood flow and valve size in mitral stenosis. The limited regulatory effects of the pulmonary vascular resistance, *J. Clin. Investigation* **31**, 1082 (1952). [53, 54, 55

AZPITARTE, A., and A. SANCHEZ AGESTA, Sobre la prueba de Puddu en el diagnostico de las cardiopatias congenitas, *Rev. clin. españ.* **2**, 254 (1941). [50

BAHNSON, H. T., and R. F. ZIEGLER, A consideration of the causes of death following operation for congenital heart disease of the cyanotic type, *Surg., Gynec. & Obst.* **90**, 60 (1950).

BAILEY, C. P., D. F. DOWNING, G. D. GECKELER, W. LIKOFF, H. GOLDBERG, J. C. SCOTT, O. JANTON, and H. P. REDONDO-RAMIREZ, Congenital interatrial communications: Clinical and surgical considerations with a description of a new surgical technique: Atrio-septo-pexy, *Ann. Int. Med.* **37**, 888 (1952). [20, 21, 22, 23, 24, 27, 28, 29, 30, 31, 32

BAILEY, C. P., R. P. GLOVER, and T. J. E. O'NEILL, The surgery of mitral stenosis, *J. Thoracic Surg.* **19**, 16 (1950).

BAILEY, C. P., M. H. LACY, W. B. NEPTUNE, R. WELLER, C. S. ARVANITIS, and J. KARASIC, Experimental and clinical attempts at correction of interventricular septal defects, *Ann. Surg.* **136**, 919 (1952).

BAIN, C. W. C., Observations on the speed of the circulation, *Quart. J. Med.* **27**, 237 (1934). [50

BAKER, C., R. C. BROCK, and M. CAMPBELL, Valvulotomy for mitral stenosis. Report of six successful cases, *Brit. M. J.* **1**, 1283 (1950). [53, 56, 58

BAKER, C., R. C. BROCK, M. CAMPBELL, and P. WOOD, Valvotomy for mitral stenosis. A further report, on 100 cases, *Brit. M. J.* **1**, 1043 (1952). [56, 57

BALDWIN, E. DE F., L. V. MOORE, and R. P. NOBLE, The demonstration of ventricular septal defect by means of right heart catheterization, *Am. Heart J.* **32,** 153 (1946).   [31

BALL, J. D., H. KOPELMAN, and Λ. C. WITHAM, Circulatory changes in mitral stenosis at rest and on exercise, *Brit. Heart J.* **14,** 363 (1952).   [53, 54, 56, 57, 58, 59

BANSI, H. W., and G. GROSCURTH, Kreislauffunktionsprüfung bei Herzkranken, *Deutsche med. Wchnschr.* **57,** 1276 (1931).   [52

BARBER, J. M., O. MAGIDSON, and P. WOOD, Atrial septal defect. With special reference to the electrocardiogram, the pulmonary artery pressure and the second heart sound, *Brit. Heart J.* **12,** 277 (1950).   [18, 20, 21, 22, 23, 24

BARCROFT, H., Cardiac output and blood distribution, *J. Physiol.* **71,** 280 (1931a).

BARCROFT, H., Properties of the peripheral vascular system and their relation to the systemic output, *J. Physiol.* **72,** 186 (1931b).

BARCROFT, H., Observations on the pumping action of the heart, *J. Physiol.* **78,** 186 (1933).

BARCROFT, H., and D. FORMIJNE, The relation of the central nervous system to the increase in systemic flow produced by occlusion of the thoracic aorta, *J. Physiol.* **82,** 377 (1934).

BAYER, O., and H. C. LANDEN, Zur Diagnostik des offenen Ductus arteriosus (Botalli), *Schweiz. med. Wchnschr.* **80,** 261 (1950).   [5

BAYER, O., and H. C. LANDEN, Tricuspidalatresie mit linksmünderer Vena cava superior sinistra unter besonderer, Berücksichtigung der Verhaltnisse in der Lungenstrombahn, *Cardiologia* **18,** 297 (1951).   [42, 48

BAYER, O., H. H. WOLTER, I. TEIGE, and R. RIPPERT, Die Berechnung der Öffnungsflache stenosierter Herzklappen demonstriert am Beispiel der Stenose der Mitralis und Pulmonalis, *Ztschr. f. Kreislaufforsch.* **41,** 926 (1952).   [1, 2, 3, 53, 55, 56, 58

BAYLISS, R. I. S., M. J. ETHERIDGE, and A. L. HYMAN, Pulmonary hypertension in mitral stenosis, *Lancet* **2,** 889 (1950).   [53, 55, 56, 58

BAZETT, H. C., L. B. LAPLACE, and J. C. SCOTT, The estimation of cardiac output from blood pressure and pulse wave velocity measurements on subjects with cardiovascular disease. II. Aortic regurgitation, *Am. Heart J.* **22,** 749 (1941).

BEARD, E. F., E. H. WOOD, and O. T. CLAGETT, Study of hemodynamics in coarctation of the aorta using dye dilution and direct intra-arterial pressure recording methods, *J. Lab. & Clin. Med.* **38,** 858 (1951).   [51

BENENSON, W., and W. M. HITZIG, The diagnosis of venous-arterial shunt by ether circulation time method, *Proc. Soc. Exper. Biol. & Med.* **38**, 256 (1938). [50

BERGLUND, H., H. LAGERLÖF, L. WERKÖ, and H. BUCHT, The relation between pulmonary capillary venous pressure, pulmonary blood volume, and vital capacity, *Tr. A. Am. Physicians* **62**, 124 (1949). [55

BERLIN, N. I., J. H. LAWRENCE, and J. GARLAND, Blood volume in polycythemia as determined by P^{32} labeled red blood cells, *Am. J. Med.* **9**, 747 (1950). [48, 49

BING, R. J., M. HAMMOND, J. HANDELSMAN, S. R. POWERS, F. SPENCER, J. ECKENHOFF, W. GOODALE, J. HAFKENSCHIEL, and S. KETY, Coronary blood flow, cardiac oxygen consumption and efficiency in man, *J. Clin. Investigation* **28**, 771 (1949).

BING, R. J., M. M. HAMMOND, J. C. HANDELSMAN, S. R. POWERS, F. C. SPENCER, J. E. ECKENHOFF, W. T. GOODALE, J. H. HAFKENSCHIEL, and S. S. KETY, The measurement of coronary blood flow, oxygen consumption, and efficiency of the left ventricle in man, *Am. Heart J.* **38**, 1 (1949).

BING, R. J., J. C. HANDELSMAN, J. A. CAMPBELL, H. E. GRISWOLD, and A. BLALOCK, The surgical treatment and physiopathology of coarctation of the aorta, *Ann. Surg.* **128**, 803 (1948).

BING, R. J., R. HEIMBECKER, and W. FALHOLT, An estimation of the residual volume of blood in the right ventricle of normal and diseased hearts in vivo, *Am. Heart J.* **42**, 483 (1951). [53

BING, R. J., T. A. LOMBARDO, L. M. BARGERON, M. TAESCHLER, and S. TULUY, Congenital heart disease: A clinical and physiologic correlation, *Ann. Int. Med.* **37**, 664 (1952). [12, 13, 15, 23, 24, 31, 39, 40

BING, R. J., L. D. VANDAM, and F. D. GRAY, JR., Physiological studies in congenital heart disease. II. Results of preoperative studies in patients with tetralogy of Fallot, *Bull. Johns Hopkins Hosp.* **80**, 121 (1947a). [34, 35, 36

BING, R. J., L. D. VANDAM, and F. D. GRAY, JR., Physiological studies in congenital heart disease. III. Results obtained in five cases of Eisenmenger's complex, *Bull. Johns Hopkins Hosp.* **80**, 323 (1947b). [38, 40, 42, 46

BING, R. J., L. D. VANDAM, J. C. HANDELSMAN, J. A. CAMPBELL, R. SPENCER, and H. E. GRISWOLD, Physiological studies in congenital heart disease. VI. Adaptations to anoxia in congenital heart disease with cyanosis, *Bull. Johns Hopkins Hosp.* **83**, 439 (1948). [42, 44, 45, 46, 48

BIÖRCK, G., O. AXÉN, H. KROOK, L. ANDRÉN, and H. B. WULFF, Studies in mitral stenosis. IV. The relative merits of various diagnostic methods in mitral valvular disease, *Am. Heart J.* **45**, 13 (1953). [55

BJÖRCK, S., and K. LIEDHOLM, The femoral pulse curve in coarctation of the aorta, *Acta med. Scandinav.* **136,** 97 (1949).   [51

BLACKFORD, L. M., Coarctation of the aorta, *Arch. Int. Med.* **41,** 702 (1928).   [51

BLALOCK, A., Physiopathology and surgical treatment of congenital cardiovascular defects, *Bull. New York Acad. Med.* **22,** 57 (1946).
[12, 17, **42, 43, 48**

BLALOCK, A., and R. F. KIEFFER, Valvulotomy for the relief of congenital valvular pulmonic stenosis with intact ventricular septum. Report of nineteen operations by the Brock method, *Ann. Surg.* **132,** 496 (1950).
[**12, 13, 16, 17,** 26

BLALOCK, A., and H. B. TAUSSIG, The surgical treatment of malformations of the heart in which there is pulmonary stenosis or pulmonary atresia, *J. A. M. A.* **128,** 189 (1945).   [17, **42, 44, 48**

BLAND, E. F., and R. H. SWEET, A venous shunt for advanced mitral stenosis, *J. A. M. A.* **140,** 1259 (1949).   [53, 56

BLEGEN, E., and K. AAS, Renal blood flow and glomerular filtration rate in patients with valvular heart disease, *Acta med. Scandinav.* **138,** 391 (1950).

BLOOMER, W. E., W. HARRISON, G. E. LINDSKOG, and A. A. LIEBOW, Respiratory function and blood flow in the bronchial artery after ligation of the pulmonary artery, *Am. J. Physiol.* **157,** 317 (1949).

BLOOMFIELD, R. A., H. D. LAUSON, A. COURNAND, E. S. BREED, and D. W. RICHARDS, JR., Recording of right heart pressures in normal subjects and in patients with chronic pulmonary disease and various types of cardiocirculatory disease, *J. Clin. Investigation* **25,** 639 (1946).   [58

BLOOMFIELD, R. A., B. RAPAPORT, J. P. MILNOR, W. K. LONG, J. G. MEBANE, and L. B. ELLIS, Studies in mitral stenosis. III. The effect of ouabain on the circulation in patients with pulmonary disability, *Arch. Int. Med.* **89,** 970 (1952).   [53, 56, 58

BLOUNT, S. G. JR., C. FERENCZ, A. FRIEDLICH, J. G. MUDD, D. G. CARROLL, and R. J. BING, Physiological studies in congenital heart disease. XII. The circulatory dynamics in patients with tricuspid atresia, *Bull. Johns Hopkins Hosp.* **89,** 235 (1951).   [**42, 48**

BLOUNT, S. G., S. KOMESU, and M. McCORD, Asymptomatic isolated pulmonary valvular stenosis. Diagnosis by clinical methods, *New England J. Med.* **248,** 5 (1953).   [**11, 12, 13, 14, 16**

BLOUNT, S. G., JR., M. C. McCORD, and L. L. ANDERSON, The alveolar-arterial oxygen pressure gradient in mitral stenosis, *J. Clin. Investigation* **31,** 840 (1952).   [53, 54, 60

BLOUNT, S. G., JR., M. C. McCORD, L. L. ANDERSON, and S. KOMESU, The analysis of the alveolar-arterial oxygen pressure gradient in mitral stenosis, *J. Lab. & Clin. Med.* **42,** 108 (1953).   [60

BLUMENFELDT, E., and E. WOLLHEIM, Zur klinischen Beurteilung angeborner Herzfehler, *Klin. Wchnschr.* **6,** 396 (1927).   [**46, 47, 48, 49**

BLUMGART, H. L., J. S. LAWRENCE, and A. C. ERNSTENE, The dynamics of the circulation in coarctation (stenosis of the isthmus) of the aorta of the adult type. Relation to essential hypertension, *Arch. Int. Med.* **47,** 806 (1931).   [**51**

BLUMGART, H. L., and S. WEISS, Studies on the velocity of blood flow and its relation to other aspects of the circulation in patients with rheumatic and syphilitic heart disease, *J. Clin. Investigation* **4,** 149 (1927).

BOAS, E. P., The nature of the so-called "capillary pulse," *Arch. Int. Med.* **29,** 763 (1922).

BOAS, E. P., Clinical "capillary pulsation," *Heart* **11,** 57 (1924).

BOAS, E. P., and M. H. FINEBERG, Hypertension in its relationship to mitral stenosis and aortic insufficiency, *Am. J. M. Sc.* **172,** 648 (1926).

BODEN, E., O. BAYER, and F. LOOGEN, Zur Diagonstik angeborener Herzund Gefassmissbildungen. IV. Mitt. Ueber die Isthmusstenose der Aorta, *Arch. f. Kreisslaufforsch.* **17,** 28 (1951).   [**51**

BOHN, H., Ein wichtiges diagnostisches Phänomen zur Erkennung des offenen Ductus art. Botalli, *Klin. Wchnschr.* **17,** 907 (1938).

BORDEN, C. W., R. V. EBERT, R. H. WILSON, and H. S. WELLS, Studies of the pulmonary circulation. II. The circulation time from the pulmonary artery to the femoral artery and the quantity of blood in the lungs in patients with mitral stenosis and in patients with left ventricular failure, *J. Clin. Investigation* **28,** 1138 (1949).   [**53, 56, 58**

BORDEN, C. W., R. V. EBERT, R. H. WILSON, and H. S. WELLS, Pulmonary hypertension in heart disease, *New England J. Med.* **242,** 529 (1950).   [**53, 56**

BORST, J. G. G., and J. A. MOLHUYSEN, Exact determination of the central venous pressure by a simple clinical method, *Lancet* **2,** 304 (1952).   [**14, 20**

BOTHWELL, T. H., B. VAN LINGEN, J. WHIDBORNE, J. KAYE, M. McGREGOR, and G. A. ELLIOTT, Patent ductus arteriosus with partial reversal of the shunt. Study of two cases, *Am. Heart J.* **44,** 360 (1952).   [**2, 3, 4, 6, 7, 8, 9, 10**

BRANNON, E. S., H. S. WEENS, and J. V. WARREN, Atrial septal defect. Study of the hemodynamics by the technique of right heart catheterization, *Am. J. M. Sc.* **210,** 480 (1945).   [**18, 19, 20, 21, 23, 24, 25**

BRAUN, K., A. DE VRIES, D. S. FEINGOLD, N. E. EHRENFELD, J. FELDMAN, and S. SCHORR, Complete dextra-position of the aorta, pulmonary stenosis, interventricular septal defect, and patent foramen ovale, *Am. Heart J.* **43,** 773 (1952).   [**42, 43**

BREWER, G., W. F. HAMILTON, and I. BROTMAN, Pressure pulse contours in the intact animal. II. Femoral pressure pulses in the normal dog and in the dog with aortic regurgitation; effect of certain drugs, *Am. J. Physiol.* **107**, 436 (1934).

BROCK, R. C., Direct cardiac surgery in the treatment of congenital pulmonary stenosis, *Ann. Surg.* **136**, 63 (1952).   [35, 36

BROCK, R. C., Congenital pulmonary stenosis, *Am. J. Med.* **12**, 706 (1952).
                                                                    [12, 13

BROCK, R. C., and M. CAMPBELL, Valvulotomy for pulmonary valvular stenosis, *Brit. Heart J.* **12**, 377 (1950).   [11, 12, 13, 14, 15, 26

BROCK, R. C., and M. CAMPBELL, Infundibular resection or dilatation for infundibular stenosis, *Brit. Heart J.* **12**, 403 (1950).   [34, 35, 36, 37

BROFMAN, B. L., and H. FEIL, The diagnosis of congenital subaortic stenosis. Application of hemodynamic principles, *Circulation* **6**, 817 (1952).

BROTCHNER, R. J., Etiology of hypertension resulting from coarctation of the aorta, *Arch. Path.* **28**, 676 (1939).

BROWN, B. C., N. J. ENGLAND, P. P. HAUCH, and J. A. LEWIS, A study of congenital heart disease by cardiac catheterization, *Canad. M. A. J.* **60**, 50 (1949).   [2, 4, 7, 8, 9, 39, 40

BROWN, G. E., JR., O. T. CLAGETT, H. B. BURCHELL, and E. H. WOOD, Preoperative and postoperative studies of intraradial and intrafemoral pressures in patients with coarctation of the aorta, *Proc. Staff Meet., Mayo Clin.* **23**, 352 (1948).   [51

BROWN, G. E., JR., A. A. POLLACK, O. T. CLAGETT, and E. H. WOOD, Intraarterial blood pressure in patients with coarctation of the aorta, *Proc. Staff Meet., Mayo Clin.* **23**, 129 (1948).   [51

BROWN, H. R., M. J. HOFFMAN, and V. DeLALLA, Ballistocardiograms in coarctation of the aorta. Observations before and after operation, *New England J. Med.* **240**, 715 (1949).

BRUCE, R. A., F. W. LOVEJOY, JR., P. N. G. YU, and M. E. McDOWELL, Observations of cardiorespiratory performance in normal subjects under unusual stress during exercise, *Arch. Indust. Hyg. & Occupat. Med.* **6**, 105 (1952).

BRUCE, R. A., F. W. LOVEJOY, JR., P. N. G. YU, R. PEARSON, and E. B. EMERSON, Recent developments in the physiologic study of patients with chest diseases, *New York State J. Med.* **49**, 2133 (1949).
                                                                [18, 19, 25

BRUMM, H. J., and H. L. SMITH, Hypertension associated with mitral stenosis: report of 44 cases, *Minnesota Med.* **24**, 664 (1941).

BURCHELL, H. B., Rheumatic mitral insufficiency, *Circulation* **7**, 747 (1953).

BURCHELL, H. B., B. E. TAYLOR, J. R. B. KNUTSON, and E. H. WOOD, Circulatory adjustments to the hypoxemia of congenital heart disease of the cyanotic type, *Circulation* **1**, 404 (1950).   [26, 31, 42, 43, 48

BURCHELL, H. B., and E. H. WOOD, Reproducibility of values for oxygen saturation of arterial blood, and magnitude of venous-arterial shunts in patients with congenital cardiac malformations, *J. Appl. Physiol.* **1**, 560 (1949). [42, 43

BURTON, A. C., Peripheral circulation, *Ann. Rev. Physiol.* **15**, 213 (1953).

CALAZEL, P., R. GERARD, R. DALEY, A. DRAPER, J. FOSTER, and R. J. BING, Physiological studies in congenital heart disease. XI. A comparison of the right and left auricular, capillary, and pulmonary artery pressures in nine patients with auricular septal defect, *Bull. Johns Hopkins Hosp.* **88**, 20 (1951). [22, 55, 56

CALLEBAUT, C., H. DENOLIN, and J. LEQUIME, Recherches oxymétriques dans les cardiopathies congénitales, *Acta cardiol.* **4**, 324 (1949). [16, 31, 42, 43

CAMPBELL, J. A., R. J. BING, J. C. HANDELSMAN, H. E. GRISWOLD, and M. HAMMOND, Physiological studies in congenital heart disease. VIII. The physiological findings in two patients with complete transposition of the great vessels, *Bull. Johns Hopkins Hosp.* **84**, 269 (1949).

CAMPBELL, J. M. H., G. H. HUNT, and E. P. POULTON, An examination of the blood gases and respiration in disease, with reference to the cause of breathlessness and cyanosis, *J. Path. & Bact.* **26**, 234 (1923). [42, 44, 45, 48

CAMPBELL, J. M. H., and E. P. POULTON, The effect on breathless subjects of residence in an oxygen chamber, *Quart. J. Med.* **20**, 141 (1926–27). [46

CAMPBELL, M., Visible pulsation in relation to blood flow and pressure in the pulmonary artery, *Brit. Heart J.* **13**, 438 (1951). [1, 2, 18, 22, 27, 29, 53, 56

CAMPBELL, M., F. GARDNER, and G. REYNOLDS, Cor biloculare, *Brit. Heart J.* **14**, 317 (1952).

CAMPBELL, M., and S. SUZMAN, Transposition of the aorta and pulmonary artery, *Circulation* **4**, 329 (1951). [42, 48

CARLOTTI, J., F. JOLY, J.-R. SICOT, G. VOCI, and F. CAZALS, Étude physio-pathologique de la petite circulation au cours du rétrécissement mitral (travail basé sur 50 cas), *Arch. d. mal. du cœur* **45**, 412 (1952). [53, 54, 55, 56, 57, 58, 59, 60

CARLOTTI, J., J. R. SICOT, and F. JOLY, Cardiopathies congénitales. III. Étude de la dynamique des grosses artères pulmonaires, *Arch. d. mal. du cœur* **43**, 705 (1950). [21, 22, 28, 29, 38, 39, 40, 53, 56, 58

CARROLL, D., J. E. COHN, and R. L. RILEY, Pulmonary function in mitral valvular disease: distribution and diffusion characteristics in resting patients, *J. Clin. Investigation* **32**, 510 (1953). [53, 55, 56

CASH, H. R., and H. A. ZIMMERMAN, An evaluation of the effect of Khellin

on the pulmonary circulation in man, *Dis. of Chest* **21**, 137 (1952).
[53, 56

CASTAING, R., BRICAUD, P. BROUSTET, and MARTY, Le mesure de l'air residual chez les mitraux, *Arch. d. mal. du cœur* **45**, 725 (1952). [60

CASSELS, D. E., M. MORSE, and W. E. ADAMS, Effect of patent ductus arteriosus on the pulmonary blood flow, blood volume, heart rate, blood pressure, arterial blood gases and pH, *Pediatrics* **6**, 557 (1950).
[1, 5

CHAPMAN, D. W., D. M. EARLE, L. J. GUGLE, R. A. HUGGINS, and W. ZIMDAHL, Intravenous catheterization of the heart in suspected congenital heart disease. Report of seventy-two cases, *Arch. Int. Med.* **84**, 640 (1949). [5, 9, 20, 21, 23, 28, 30, 31, 35, 36, 37, 42

CHARLIER, R., Observations de physiologie circulatoire dans un cas de communication interventriculaire isolée (Maladie de Roger), *Rev. belge de Path. et de med. Exper.* **19**, 175 (1949). [27, 28, 29, 31

CHARLIER, R., Cardiopathies congénitales cyanogènes. Importance du cathétérisme du cœur pour leur diagnostic différentiel, *Acta cardiol.* **4**, 68 (1949). [31, 39, 42

CLAY, R. C., S. R. ELLIOTT, II, and H. W. SCOTT, JR., Changes in blood volume following operation for pulmonic stenosis: studies with Evans blue and radioactive phosphorus, *Bull. Johns Hopkins Hosp.* **89**, 377 (1951). [49

COELHO, E., M. FONSECA, R. PINTO, and A. NUNES, Pulmonary stenosis with large interatrial septum defect and severe cyanosis, *Cardiologia* **18**, 183 (1951). [13, 17, 42, 48, 50

COOKE, F. N., J. M. EVANS, A. B. KISTIN, and B. BLADES, An anomaly of the pulmonary veins. A case study, *J. Thoracic Surg.* **21**, 452 (1951).

COOLEY, D. A., and D. W. CHAPMAN, Mitral commissurotomy during pregnancy, *J. A. M. A.* **150**, 1113 (1952). [53, 54, 55, 56, 57, 58

CORRELL, H. I., N. GROSSMAN, A. R. BAIER, T. R. MURPHY, and P. G. LA BISSONIERE, Selection of candidates for mitral valve surgery, *Wisconsin M. J.* **51**, 997 (1952). [55

COSBY, R. S., G. C. GRIFFITH, W. J. ZINN, D. C. LEVINSON, S. P. DIMITROFF, R. W. OBLATH, and G. JACOBSON, Cardiac catheterization in interatrial septal defect, *Am. J. Med.* **14**, 4 (1953).
[20, 21, 22, 23, 24, 25, 26, 39

COSBY, R. S., D. C. LEVINSON, G. C. GRIFFITH, W. J. ZINN, and S. P. DIMITROFF, Clinical and cardiac catheterization studies in four cases of Eisenmenger's complex, *Am. J. Med.* **11**, 31 (1951). [39, 40, 41

COSBY, R. S., D. C. LEVINSON, W. J. ZINN, S. P. DIMITROFF, and G. C. GRIFFITH, Congenital heart disease: An analysis of electrocardiographic patterns in forty-four patients, *Am. Heart J.* **44**, 581 (1952).
[11, 13, 18, 21, 27, 28, 34, 35

Cossio, P., and I. Berconsky, The cyanosis in mitral stenosis, *Am. Heart J.* **17**, 1 (1939). [52

Cournand, A., H. L. Motley, A. Himmelstein, D. Dresdale, and J. Baldwin, Recording of blood pressure from the left auricle and the pulmonary veins in human subjects with interauricular septal defect, *Am. J. Physiol.* **150**, 267 (1947). [18

Crafoord, C., F. Berglund, H. Eliasch, and L. Werkö, Kirurgisk behandling av mitralisstenos, *Nord. med.* **45**, 831 (1951).
[53, 54, 55, 56, 57, 60

Crafoord, C., and G. Nylin, Congenital coarctation of the aorta and its surgical treatment, *J. Thoracic Surg.* **14**, 347 (1945).

Dammann, J. F., Jr., and C. G. Sell, Patent ductus arteriosus in the absence of a continuous murmur, *Circulation* **6**, 110 (1952).
[2, 3, 4, 6, 7, 8, 9, 10

Dautrebande, L., W. R. Marshall, and J. C. Meakins, Studies of the circulation in three cases of morbus caeruleus, *J. Clin. Investigation* **8**, 123 (1929–30). [33, 42, 44, 45, 46, 47, 48

Davis, F. W., Jr., W. R. Scarborough, R. E. Mason, M. L. Singewald, and B. M. Baker, Jr., The ballistocardiogram in mitral stenosis, *Circulation* **4**, 503 (1953). [56

Debler, K., Zur Kenntnis des Minutenvolumens bei schweren Kreislauf-leiden, *Med. Klin.* **33**, 761 (1937). [33

Deglaude, L., and P. Laurens, Recherches vectorographiques dans les cardiopathies congénitales, *Semaine méd.* **28**, 17 (1952).
[12, 13, 21, 22, 26, 35, 36, 39, 40

Denk, W., Weitere Erfahrungen mit der chirurgischen Behandlung der Mitralstenose, *Wien. klin. Wchnschr.* **65**, 38 (1953). [53

Dennig, H., and S. H. Proger, Herzkranke bei Arbeit, *Deutsches Arch. f. klin. Med.* **175**, 170 (1933). [52

Denolin, H., and J. Lequime, Dextrocardie avec situs inversus total et malformations cardiovasculaires associées, *Acta clin. belg.* **5**, 168 (1950).

Denolin, H., J. Lequime, F. Goksel, and R. Pannier, L'atrésie tricuspidienne. Étude clinique et physiopathologique de deux cas, *Acta cardiol.* **5**, 400 (1950). [42, 43, 46, 48

Denolin, H., J. Lequime, and M. Segers, La dynamique circulatoire au cours de la persistance du canal artériel et le problème de l'hypertension artérielle pulmonaire, *Cardiologia* **21**, 1 (1952).
[1, 2, 3, 4, 8, 9, 10

Denolin, H., J. Lequime, M. Wybauw, and A. Bollaert, Communication inter-auriculaire avec hypertension pulmonaire et vein pulmonaire aberrante, *Acta cardiol.* **8**, 64 (1953). [18, 20, 21, 22, 25, 42

DEUCHAR, D. C., and R. KNEBEL, The pulmonary and systemic circulations in congenital heart disease, *Brit. Heart J.* **14**, 225 (1952).
[18, 19, 22, 27, 29, 38, 40

DEXTER, L., Venous catheterization of the heart. II. Results, interpretations and value, *Radiology* **48**, 451 (1947).
[1, 2, 4, 6, 7, 8, 9, 18, 20, 21, 22, 23, 25, 28, 29, 31, 34, 35, 36

DEXTER, L., Cardiac catheterization in the diagnosis of congenital heart disease, *Bull. New York Acad. Med.* **26**, 93 (1950).
[8, 9, 11, 12, 13, 18, 22, 23, 31, 35, 36, 37, 39, 40

DEXTER, L., C. S. BURWELL, F. W. HAYNES, and R. E. SEIBEL, Venous catheterization for the diagnosis of congenital heart disease, *Bull. New England M. Center* **8**, 113 (1946a).
[1, 2, 4, 5, 6, 7, 8, 9, 34, 35, 36

DEXTER, L., C. S. BURWELL, F. W. HAYNES, and R. E. SEIBEL, Oxygen content of pulmonary "capillary" blood in unanesthetized human beings, *J. Clin. Investigation* **25**, 913 (1946b).

DEXTER, L., J. W. DOW, F. W. HAYNES, J. L. WHITTENBERGER, B. G. FERRIS, W. T. GOODALE, and H. K. HELLEMS, Studies of the pulmonary circulation in man at rest. Normal variations and the interrelations between increased pulmonary blood flow, elevated pulmonary arterial pressure, and high pulmonary "capillary" pressures, *J. Clin. Investigation* **29**, 602 (1950).   [1, 2, 18, 21, 38, 39, 40, 53, 55, 56

DEXTER, L., F. W. HAYNES, C. S. BURWELL, E. C. EPPINGER, M. C. SOSMAN, and J. M. EVANS, Studies of congenital heart disease. III. Venous catheterization as a diagnostic aid in patent ductus arteriosus, tetralogy of Fallot, ventricular septal defect and auricular septal defect, *J. Clin. Investigation* **26**, 561 (1947).
[1, 2, 4, 5, 6, 7, 8, 9, 18, 19, 23, 27, 28, 29, 31, 34, 35, 36, 37

DONALD, K. W., J. M. BISHOP, G. CUMMING, and O. L. WADE, The effect of nursing positions on the cardiac output in man. With a note on the repeatability of measurements of cardiac output by the direct Fick method, and with data on subjects with a normal cardiovascular system, *Clin. Sc.* **12**, 199 (1953).   [53, 56, 58

DONZELOT, E., Valeur de l'épreuve à l'éther pour le diagnostic de shunt veino-arterial. Résultats dans 500 cas de cardiopathies congénitales, *Arch. d. mal. du cœur* **42**, 601 (1949).   [50

DONZELOT, E., P. VLAD, M. DURAND, and C. METIANU, Un nouveau moyen diagnostique dans les cardiopathies congénitales: l'épreuve à l'éther sélective au cours du cathéterisme cardiaque, *Arch. d. mal. du cœur* **44**, 638 (1951).   [50

DOTTER, C. T., N. M. HARDISTY, and I. STEINBERG, Anomalous right pulmonary vein entering the inferior vena cava. Two cases diagnosed during life by angiocardiography and cardiac catheterization, *Am. J. M. Sc.* **218**, 31 (1949).

Dow, J. W., L. Dexter, F. W. Haynes, J. L. Whittenberger, and B. G. Ferris, Pulmonary circulatory dynamics in mitral stenosis and left heart failure, *J. Clin. Investigation* 28, 778 (1949). [55, 56

Dow, J. W., H. D. Levine, M. Elkin, F. W. Haynes, H. K. Hellems, J. W. Whittenberger, B. G. Ferris, W. T. Goodale, W. P. Harvey, E. C. Eppinger, and L. Dexter, Studies of congenital heart disease. IV. Uncomplicated pulmonic stenosis, *Circulation* 1, 267 (1950). [11, 12, 13, 14

Downing, D. F., C. P. Bailey, and R. P. Glover, Brock procedure for the relief of pulmonary stenosis in the tetralogy of Fallot, *Pediatrics* 7, 230 (1951). [36, 48

Doyle, J. T., J. S. Wilson, C. Lépine, and J. V. Warren, An evaluation of the measurement of the cardiac output and of the so-called pulmonary blood volume by the dye-dilution method, *J. Lab. & Clin. Med.* 41, 29 (1953). [53

Doyle, J. T., J. S. Wilson, and J. V. Warren, The pulmonary vascular responses to short-term hypoxia in human subjects, *Circulation* 5, 263 (1952). [53, 55, 56

Draper, A., R. Heimbecker, R. Daley, D. Carroll, G. Mudd, R. Wells, W. Falholt, E. C. Andrus, and R. J. Bing, Physiologic studies in mitral valvular disease, *Circulation* 3, 531 (1950). [53, 55, 56, 58

Dressler, S. H., N. B. Slonim, O. J. Balchum, G. J. Bronfin, and A. Ravin, The effect of breathing 100% oxygen on the pulmonary arterial pressure in patients with pulmonary tuberculosis and mitral stenosis, *J. Clin. Investigation* 31, 807 (1952). [56, 60

Eliasch, H., The pulmonary circulation at rest and on effort in mitral stenosis, *Scandinav. J. Clin. & Lab. Investigation* 4, *Supp. No. 4* (1952). [53, 54, 55, 56, 57

Eliasch, H., H. Lagerlöf, and L. Werkö, Diagnos av adhesiv peridardit med särskild hänsyn till hjärtkatertrisering, *Nord. Med.* 44, 1128 (1950). [47, 48, 49

Eliasch, H., G. Wade, and L. Werkö, The effects of work on the pulmonary circulation in mitral stenosis, *Circulation* 5, 271 (1952). [53, 54, 55, 56, 57

Elisberg, E., E. Singian, G. Miller, and L. N. Katz, The effect of the Valsalva maneuver on the circulation. II. The influence of heart disease on the expected poststraining overshoot, *Circulation* 7, 880 (1953). [53

Ellis, L. B., R. A. Bloomfield, G. K. Graham, D. J. Greenberg, H. N. Hultgren, H. Kraus, G. Maresh, J. G. Mebane, P. H. Pfiffer, L. A. Selverstone, and J. A. Taylor, Studies in mitral stenosis. I. The correlation of physiologic and clinical findings, *Arch. Int. Med.* 88, 515 (1951). [53, 54, 55, 56, 57, 59, 60

ENGLE, M. A., T. P. B. PAYNE, C. BRUINS, and H. B. TAUSSIG, Ebstein's anomaly of the tricuspid valve. Report of three cases and analysis of clinical syndrome, *Circulation* 1, 1246 (1950). [42, 48

ENGLE, M. A., and H. B. TAUSSIG, Valvular pulmonic stenosis with intact ventricular septum and patent foramen ovale. Report of illustrative cases and analysis of clinical syndrome, *Circulation* 2, 481 (1950). [11, 12, 13, 14, 15

EPPINGER, E. C., C. S. BURWELL, and R. E. GROSS, The effects of the patent ductus arteriosus on the circulation, *J. Clin. Investigation* 20, 127 (1941). [1, 5

EPPS, R. G., and R. H. ADLER, Left atrial and pulmonary capillary venous pressures in mitral stenosis, *Brit. Heart J.* 15, 298 (1953). [55, 56

ERNSTING, J., and R. J. SHEPARD, Respiratory adaptations in congenital heart disease, *J. Physiol.* 112, 332 (1951). [34, 42, 48

ESKILDEN, P., The circulation in Fallot's tetralogy, *Acta med. Scandinav.* 117, 488 (1944). [33, 42

ESKILDEN, P., H. GOTZSCHE, and A. J. HANSEN, Measuring of the intra-arterial blood pressure during exercise, *Acta cardiol.* 4, 199 (1949).

EVANS, C. L., and MATSUOKA, The effect of various mechanical conditions on the gaseous metabolism and efficiency of the mammalian heart, *J. Physiol.* 49, 378 (1915).

EWIG, W., and K. HINSBERG, Kreislaufstudien II, *Ztschr. f. klin. Med.* 115, 693 (1931). [45

FACQUET, J., J.-M. LEMOINE, P. ALHOMME, and J. LEFEBVRE, La mesure de la pression auriculaire gauche par la voi transbronchique, *Arch. d. mal. du cœur* 45, 740 (1952).

FAVRE-GILLY, J., J. BRET, and J. BORHEL-MILHET, Un trouble inattendu de la coagulation dans la maladie bleue: l'hypoprothrombinémie, *Sang* 22, 278 (1951).

FELL, E. H., O. PAUL, J. CAMPBELL, C. B. DAVIS, JR., L. SELVERSTONE, and R. GRISSOM, Mitral stenosis. Physiological studies, diagnosis and treatment, *Arch. Surg.* 65, 128 (1952). [53, 54, 56, 57

FERRER, M. I., R. M. HARVEY, R. T. CATHCART, A. COURNAND, and D. W. RICHARDS, JR., Hemodynamic studies in rheumatic heart disease, *Circulation* 6, 688 (1952). [53, 54, 56, 57, 60

FISCHL, F., Kapillarbeobachtung am Lebenden, *Med. Klin.* 19, 980 (1923).

FOWLER, N. O., Cardiac catheterization in the diagnosis of adult heart disease, *Ann. Int. Med.* 38, 478 (1953). [2, 3, 6, 7, 8, 9, 12, 13, 14, 15, 29, 30, 31, 32, 39, 40, 41

FOWLER, N. O., JR., R. N. WESTCOTT, and R. C. SCOTT, Pulmonary artery diastolic pressure: its relationship to pulmonary arteriolar resistance and pulmonary "capillary" pressure, *J. Clin. Investigation* 31, 72 (1952). [38, 40, 53, 55, 56, 60

FREEDLANDER, S. O., and C. H. LENHART, Clinical observations on the capillary circulation, *Arch. Int. Med.* **29**, 12 (1922).

FRENCH, H. S., M. S. PEMBREY, and J. H. RYFFEL, Observations on cases of cyanosis due to congenital heart disease, *J. Physiol.* **39**, ix (1909). [46, 47

FRIEDENBERG, R., and A. J. SOKOL, Coarctation of aorta. A report of two cases, *New England J. Med.* **234**, 552 (1946). [51

FRIEDLANDER, A., Hypotension, *Medicine* **6**, 143 (1927).

FRIEDLANDER, R. D., and W. J. KERR, The clinical diagnosis of tricuspid stenosis. Report of a case complicated by paroxysmal nodal tachycardia and A-V dissociation, *Am. Heart J.* **11**, 357 (1936).

FRIEDLICH, A., R. J. BING, and S. G. BLOUNT, JR., Physiological studies in congenital heart disease. IX. Circulatory dynamics in the anomalies of venous return to the heart including pulmonary arteriovenous fistula, *Bull. Johns Hopkins Hosp.* **86**, 20 (1950).

FRIEDMAN, M., A. SELZER, and H. ROSENBLUM, The renal blood flow in coarctation of the aorta, *J. Clin. Investigation* **20**, 107 (1941).

FULLER, J., B. E. TAYLOR, O. T. CLAGETT, and E. H. WOOD, Blood pressure in the aorta during resection and repair of coarctation of the aorta, *J. Lab. & Clin. Med.* **39**, 10 (1952). [51

GALDSTON, M., and J. M. STEELE, Arterial pressure pulse waves in a patient with coarctation of the aorta, *Am. J. Physiol.* **152**, 554 (1948). [51

GALLIGAN, J. J., F. H. ADAMS, and J. JORGENS, Congenital pulmonary stenosis without cyanosis, *J. Pediat.* **41**, 562 (1952). [12, 13, 16

GARDAM, J. D., Vital capacity in adults with heart disease in relation to age, degree of cardiac enlargement and type of valvular lesion, *Am. J. M. Sc.* **219**, 76 (1950).

GASUL, B. M., J. J. MARINO, and J. R. CHRISTIAN, Fluorescein circulation time in normal and pathological conditions in infants and children, including various types of congenital malformations of the heart, *J. Pediat.* **34**, 460 (1949). [50

GEIGER, A. J., H. C. ANDERSON, A. W. WINKLER, and H. S. KAPLAN, Cardiovascular catheterization as an aid in diagnosis of abnormal cardiovascular communications, *Connecticut State M. J.* **10**, 895 (1946). [23

GENEST, J., E. V. NEWMAN, A. A. KATTUS, B. SINCLAIR-SMITH, and A. GENECIN, Renal function before and after surgical resection of coarctation of the aorta, *Bull. Johns Hopkins Hosp.* **83**, 429 (1948).

GERBODE, F., E. HOLMAN, and H. HULTGREN, Treatment of mitral stenosis by finger fracture valvulotomy, *Arch. Surg.* **65**, 113 (1952). [53, 54, 56, 58

GIBSON, S., W. J. POTTS, and W. H. LANGEWISCH, Aortic-pulmonary communications due to localized congenital defect of the aortic septum, *Pediatrics* **6**, 357 (1950).

GILCHRIST, A. R., Patent ductus arteriosus and its surgical treatment, *Brit. Heart J.* **7**, 1 (1945). [5

GILCHRIST, A. R., Ligation of the ductus arteriosus. *Edinburgh M. J.* **53**, 346 (1946). [5

GLOVER, R. P., C. P. BAILEY, and T. J. E. O'NEILL, Surgery of stenotic valvular disease of the heart, *J. A. M. A.* **144**, 1049 (1950). [36

GLOVER, R. P., C. P. BAILEY, T. J. E. O'NEILL, D. F. DOWNING, and C. R. E. WELLS, The direct intracardiac relief of pulmonary stenosis in the tetralogy of Fallot, *J. Thoracic Surg.* **23**, 14 (1952). [48

GLOVER, R. P., T. J. E. O'NEILL, J. S. C. HARRIS, and O. H. JANTON, The indications for and the results of commissurotomy for mitral stenosis, *J. Thoracic Surg.* **25**, 55 (1953). [56, 58

GOLDBERG, H., E. I. ELISBERG, and L. N. KATZ, The effect of the Valsalva-like maneuver upon the circulation in normal individuals and patients with mitral stenosis, *Circulation* **5**, 38 (1951). [53, 56

GOLDBERG, H., E. N. SILBER, A. GORDON, and L. N. KATZ, The dynamics of Eisenmenger's complex. An integration of the pathologic, physiologic and clinical features, *Circulation* **4**, 343 (1951). [39, 40, 41

GOLDMAN, M. L., and H. A. SCHROEDER, Coarctation of the aorta. Photoelectric plethysmography and direct arterial blood pressure measurement as an aid in diagnosis, *Am. J. Med.* **7**, 454 (1949). [51

GORDON, A., and H. GOLDBERG, Correlation of the electrocardiographic pattern of right heart strain and evidence of right ventricular hypertension in congenital heart disease, *Am. Heart J.* **42**, 226 (1951). [2, 3, 4, 12, 13, 14, 28, 29, 30, 35, 36

GORLIN, R., and L. DEXTER, Hydraulic formula for the calculation of the cross-sectional area of the mitral valve during regurgitation, *Am. Heart J.* **43**, 188 (1952).

GORLIN, R., and S. G. GORLIN, Hydraulic formula for calculation of the area of the stenotic mitral valve, other cardiac values, and central circulatory shunts. I, *Am. Heart J.* **41**, 1 (1951). [1, 2, 11, 12, 13, 18, 20, 27, 28, 29, 30, 53, 55

GORLIN, R., F. W. HAYNES, W. T. GOODALE, C. G. SAWYER, J. W. DOW, and L. DEXTER, Studies of the circulatory dynamics in mitral stenosis. II. Altered dynamics at rest, *Am. Heart J.* **41**, 720 (1951). [53, 55, 56, 58

GORLIN, R., B. M. LEWIS, F. W. HAYNES, and L. DEXTER, Studies of the circulatory dynamics at rest in mitral valvular regurgitation with and without stenosis, *Am. Heart J.* **43**, 357 (1952). [53, 55, 56

GORLIN, R., B. M. LEWIS, F. W. HAYNES, R. J. SPIEGL, and L. DEXTER,

Factors regulating pulmonary "capillary" pressure in mitral stenosis. IV., *Am. Heart J.* **41**, 834 (1951). [53, 55

GORLIN, R., C. G. SAWYER, F. W. HAYNES, W. T. GOODALE, and L. DEXTER, Effects of exercise on circulatory dynamics in mitral stenosis. III, *Am. Heart J.* **41**, 192 (1951). [53, 55, 56

GØTZSCHE, H., P. ESKILDEN, and A. T. HANSEN, Isolated pulmonary stenosis, *Acta med. Scandinav.* **139**, 431 (1951). [12, 13, 16, 17

GOVAERTS, J., J. ENDERLE, E. HENROTIN, and A. VAN WIEN, La place de la valvulotomie dans les stenoses pulmonaires congénitales, *Acta cardiol.* **7**, 440 (1952). [35, 36, 37, 42, 48

GRASSMANN, W., and F. HERZOG, Die Wirkung von Digitalis (Strophanthin) auf das Minuten- und Schlagvolumen des Herzkranken, *Arch. f. exper. Path. u. Pharmakol.* **163**, 97 (1932). [45

GREENE, D. G., E. DeF. BALDWIN, J. S. BALDWIN, A. HIMMELSTEIN, C. E. ROH, and A. COURNAND, Pure congenital pulmonary stenosis and idiopathic congenital dilatation of the pulmonary artery, *Am. J. Med.* **6**, 24 (1949). [11, 12, 13, 14, 15, 16

GREENTHAL, R. M., and W. S. O'DONNELL, Studies on the fragility of the red blood cells, *Am. J. Physiol.* **58**, 271 (1921).

GRISHMAN, A., S. A. BRAHMS, A. GORDON, and F. H. KING, Aberrant insertion of pulmonic veins, *J. Mt. Sinai Hosp.* **17**, 336 (1951).

GRISWOLD, H. E., R. J. BING, J. C. HANDELSMAN, J. A. CAMPBELL, and E. LeBRUN, Physiological studies in congenital heart disease. VII. Pulmonary arterial hypertension in congenital heart disease, *Bull. Johns Hopkins Hosp.* **84**, 76 (1949). [1, 2, 4, 18, 20, 22, 27, 29, 30

GROB, M., and M. STOCKMANN, Ueber Isthmusstenose der Aorta, *Helvet. paediat. Acta* **4**, 294 (1949).

GROLLMAN, A., and J. P. FERRIGAN, JR., Cardiac output. Its related functions in a case of coarctation of the aorta, *Arch. Int. Med.* **53**, 35 (1934). [51

GROSS, R. E., E. WATKINS, JR., A. A. POMERANZ, and E. I. GOLDSMITH, A method for surgical closure of interauricular septal defects, *Surg. Gynec. & Obst.* **96**, 1 (1953). [18, 19, 20, 23

GROSSMAN, J., R. E. WESTON, I. S. EDELMAN, and L. LEITER, Studies on thiomerin — a subcutaneously administerable mercurial diuretic, *Circulation* **1**, 502 (1950).

GROVER, R. F., H. SWAN, and C. A. MAASKE, Pressure changes in the pulmonary artery and aorta before and after ligation of the patent ductus arteriosus, *Federation Proc.* **8**, 63 (1949). [2

GULLICKSON, G., J. O. ELAM, M. HAMMOND, J. R. PAINE, and R. L. VARCO, Oxygenation studies in congenital pulmonary stenosis, *Am. Heart J.* **35**, 940 (1948). [42, 43

GUPTA, T. C., and C. J. WIGGERS, Basic hemodynamic changes produced by aortic coarctation of different degrees, *Circulation* **3**, 17 (1951).

HAFKENSCHIEL, J. H., JR., C. W. CRUMPTON, and J. H. MOYER, Blood flow and oxygen consumption of the brain in coarctation of the aorta, *Proc. Soc. Exper. Biol. & Med.* **71**, 165 (1949).

HALLENBECK, G. A., E. H. WOOD, H. B. BURCHELL, and O. T. CLAGETT, Coarctation of the aorta. The relationship of clinical results to cardiovascular dynamics studied before, during and after surgical treatment, *Surg. Gynec. & Obst.* **92**, 75 (1951). [51

HALLOCK, P., Blood lactic acid after exercise; with particular reference to polycythemia rubra vera, *Proc. Soc. Exper. Biol. & Med.* **38**, 587 (1938). [48

HALLOCK, P., Lactic acid production during rest and after exercise in subjects with various types of heart disease with special reference to congenital heart disease, *J. Clin. Investigation* **18**, 385 (1939). [48

HALLOCK, P., Polycythemia of morbus caeruleus (cyanotic type of congenital heart disease), *Proc. Soc. Exper. Biol. & Med.* **44**, 11 (1940). [48, 49

HAMILTON, W. F., J. A. WINSLOW, and W. F. HAMILTON, JR., Notes on a case of congenital heart disease with cyanotic episodes, *J. Clin. Investigation* **29**, 20 (1950). [42

HAMILTON, W. F., R. A. WOODBURY, and H. T. HARPER, JR., Arterial, cerebrospinal and venous pressures in man during cough and strain, *Am. J. Physiol.* **141**, 42 (1944).

HANDELSMAN, J. C., R. J. BING, J. A. CAMPBELL, and H. E. GRISWOLD, Physiologic studies in congenital heart disease V. Circulation in patients with isolated septal defects, *Bull. Johns Hopkins Hosp.* **82**, 615 (1948). [22, 23, 24, 29, 31

HARKEN, D. E., L. B. ELLIS, and L. R. NORMAN, The surgical treatment of mitral stenosis. I. Progress in developing a controlled valvuloplastic technique, *J. Thoracic Surg.* **19**, 1 (1950). [53, 55, 56

HARKEN, D. E., L. B. ELLIS, P. F. WARE, and L. R. NORMAN, The surgical treatment of mitral stenosis. I. Valvuloplasty, *New England J. Med.* **239**, 801 (1948). [53, 58

HARRIS, J. S., W. C. SEALY, and W. DeMARIA, Hypertension and renal dynamics in aortic coarctation, *Am. J. Med.* **9**, 734 (1950). [51

HARTMANN, R. C., A hemorrhagic disorder occurring in patients with cyanotic congenital heart disease, *Bull. Johns Hopkins Hosp.* **91**, 49 (1952). [48

HAVEL, R. J., and E. WATKINS, JR., The metabolism of lactate and pyruvate in children with congenital heart disease, *Circulation* **2**, 536 (1950).

HEALEY, R. F., L. DEXTER, M. ELKIN, and M. C. SOSMAN, Roentgenographic changes in pulmonic stenosis. A report of nine cases, *Am. J. Roentgenol.* **63**, 813 (1950). [12, 13

HEALEY, R. F., J. W. Dow, M. C. SOSMAN, and L. DEXTER, The relationship of the roentgenographic appearances of the pulmonary artery to pulmonary hemodynamics, *Am. J. Roentgenol.* **62**, 777 (1949).
[1, 2, 11, 12, 13, 18, 22, 27, 28, 34, 35, 36, 38, 40, 53, 56

HEALEY, R. F., J. W. Dow, M. C. SOSMAN, and L. DEXTER, The roentgenographic appearance of interatrial septal defect, *Am. J. Roentgenol.* **63**, 646 (1950). [18, 19, 20, 21, 22

HEIMBERGER, H., Beiträge zur Physiologie der menschlichen Capillaren, *Ztschr. f. d. ges. exper. Med.* **46**, 519 (1925).

HELLEMS, H. K., F. W. HAYNES, and L. DEXTER, Pulmonary "capillary" pressure in man, *J. Appl. Physiol.* **2**, 24 (1949). [22

HENDERSON, L. J., Sur l'application de la méthode nomographique à l'étude des phénomènes respiratoires dans le sang, *Compt. rend. Acad. d. sc.* **180**, 2066 (1925). [42, 44, 45, 47, 48

HERTZ, C. W., Zur Entstehung der Cyanose bei angebornen Herzfehlern, *Klin. Wchnschr.* **29**, 15 (1951). [34, 37, 42, 48

HEWLETT, A. W., and J. G. VAN ZWALUWENBURG, The pulse flow in the brachial artery. III. Aortic insufficiency, *Arch. Int Med.* **12**, 18 (1913).

HICKAM, J. B., The pulmonary vascular resistance, *J. Clin. Investigation* **28**, 788 (1949). [22

HICKAM, J. B., Atrial septal defect. A study of intracardiac shunts, ventricular outputs, and pulmonary pressure gradient, *Am. Heart J.* **38**, 801 (1949). [20, 22, 25

HILL, L., The measurement of systolic blood pressure in man, *Heart* **1**, 73 (1909).

HISINGER-JÄGERSKIÖLD, E., Einige Untersuchungen des Kapillarpulses nach der Müller-Weiss'schen Methode, *Acta med. Scandinav.* **60**, 7 (1924).

HITZENBERGER, K., and F. TUCHFELD, Die zirkulierende Blutmenge bei Kreislaufserkrankungen im kompensierten und dekompensierten Zustand, *Wien. Arch. f. inn. Med.* **18**, 171 (1929).
[33, 42, 44, 45, 46, 47, 48, 49

HITZENBERGER, K., and F. TUCHFELD, Der CO_2-Gehalt des arteriellen Blutes, *Ztschr. f. klin. Med.* **116**, 603 (1931). [42, 44, 48

HOLLING, H. E., Compensatory mechanisms for the anoxia of cyanotic congenital heart disease, *Clin. Sc.* **11**, 283 (1952).
[11, 15, 34, 37, 38, 41, 42, 48

HOLLING, H. E., and G. A. ZAK, Cardiac catheterization in the diagnosis of congenital heart disease, *Brit. Heart J.* **12**, 153 (1950).
[1, 4, 5, 7, 9, 11, 12, 13, 14, 15, 17, 18, 20, 21, 22, 23, 25, 34, 35, 36, 37, 38, 39, 40

HORNS, H. L., Association of hypertension and mitral stenosis, *Am. Heart J.* **28**, 435 (1944).

HOWARTH, S., J. MCMICHAEL, and E. P. SHARPEY-SCHAFER, Cardiac catheterization in cases of patent interauricular septum, primary pulmonary hypertension, Fallot's tetralogy and pulmonary stenosis, *Brit. Heart J.* **9**, 242 (1947). [2, 4, 5, 9, 20, 21, 23, 24, 25, 28, 31

HUFF, R. L., T. G. HENNESSY, R. E. AUSTIN, J. F. GARCIA, B. M. ROBERTS, and J. H. LAWRENCE, Plasma and red cell iron turnover in normal subjects and in patients having various hematopoietic disorders, *J. Clin. Investigation* **29**, 1041 (1950). [48

HULL, E., On the evidence for generalized arteriolar constriction in co-arctation of the aorta, *Am. Heart J.* **35**, 980 (1948).

HULTGREN, H. N., and A. J. HACKETT, Determination of the oxygen content of capillary blood in congenital heart disease, *Pediatrics* **6**, 93 (1950).

HULTGREN, H., A. SELZER, A. PURDY, E. HOLMAN, and F. GERBODE, The syndrome of patent ductus arteriosus with pulmonary hypertension, *Circulation* **8**, 15 (1953).

HWANG, W., O. PREC, K. KURAMOTO, S. SEGALL, and L. N. KATZ, Hemodynamic study of a case of anomalous pulmonary venous drainage, *Circulation* **2**, 553 (1950).

HYMAN, A. L., L. LEVY, II, R. BAGNETTO, N. K. ORDWAY, and E. HULL, Isolated disease of the pulmonary valve and artery, *Ann. Int. Med.* **34**, 90 (1951). [12 13, 14, 15

IHAYA, H., Studien über die Alveolarluft, Blutgase, Vitalkapazität und Minuten- und Schlagvolumen des Herzens bei Beriberi, Herzklappenfehler und Pleuritis, *Mitt. d. med. Gesellsch. zu Tokyo* **48**, 2167 (1934). [52

JANTON, O. H., R. P. GLOVER, T. J. E. O'NEILL, J. E. GREGORY, and G. F. FROIO, Results of the surgical treatment for mitral stenosis. Analysis of one hundred consecutive cases, *Circulation* **6**, 321 (1952). [56

JOHNSON, A. L., C. FERENCZ, F. W. WIGGLESWORTH, and D. L. MCRAE, Coarctation of the aorta complicated by patency of the ductus arteriosus. Physiologic considerations in the classification of coarctation of the aorta, *Circulation* **4**, 242 (1951).

JOHNSON, A. L., D. G. WOLLIN, and J. B. ROSS, Heart catheterization in the investigation of congenital heart disease, *Canad. M. A. J.* **56**, 249 (1947). [9, 23, 31

JOHNSON, R. E., P. WERMER, M. KUSCHNER, and A. COURNAND, Intermittent reversal of flow in a case of patent ductus arteriosus. A physiologic study with autopsy findings, *Circulation* **1**, 1292 (1950). [2, 6, 7, 8, 9

JOLY, F., J. CARLOTTI, and J.-R. SICOT, Les communications interven-

triculaires (diagnostic par cathétérisine). Étude clinique et physiologique, *Arch. d. mal. du cœur* **44**, 602 (1951).
[**27, 28, 29, 31, 32, 38, 39, 40, 41, 42**

JOLY, F., J. CARLOTTI, J.-R. SICOT, and A. PITON, Cardiopathies congénitales. II. Les trilogies de Fallot, *Arch. d. mal. du cœur* **43**, 687 (1950). [**11, 12, 13, 15, 16, 17, 26**

JORDAN, P., JR., and H. K. HELLEMS, Mitral valve surgery. A critical analysis, *Surg., Gynec. & Obst.* **95**, 689 (1952). [**55, 56**

JOSEPHS, H. W., The mechanism of the reduction of red cells and hemoglobin following operation for tetralogy of Fallot, *Bull. Johns Hopkins Hosp.* **86**, 1 (1950). [**42, 48**

JÜRGENSEN, E., Mikrokapillarbeobachtungen. Ein Beitrag zur pathologischen Physiologie des Kreislaufsystems, *Deutsches Arch. f. klin. Med.* **132**, 204 (1920).

KAHN, M. H., Tests of the functional capacity of the circulation, *Am. J. M. Sc.* **157**, 634 (1919).

KEITH, J. D., and C. C. FORSYTH, Auricular septal defects in children, *J. Pediat.* **38**, 172 (1951). [**23, 24**

KEOWN, K. K., D. D. GROVE, and H. S. RUTH, Anesthesia for commissurotomy for mitral stenosis, *J. A. M. A.* **146**, 446 (1951).

KERKHOF, A. C., Minute volume determinations in mitral stenosis during auricular fibrillation and after restoration of normal rhythm, *Am. Heart J.* **11**, 206 (1936). [**52**

KEYS, A., Estimation by the foreign gas method of the net (systemic) cardiac output in conditions where there is recirculation through the lungs, *Am. J. Physiol.* **134**, 268 (1941).

KEYS, A., and H. L. FRIEDELL, Quantitative measurement of valvular efficiency of the human heart, *Proc. Soc. Exper. Biol. & Med.* **40**, 556 (1939*a*).

KEYS, A., and H. L. FRIEDELL, Measurement of the stroke volume of the human heart from roentgenograms; simultaneous roentgenkymographic and acetylene-rebreathing experiments, *Am. J. Physiol.* **126**, 741 (1939*b*).

KING, F. H., A. GORDON, S. BRAHMS, R. LASSER, and R. BORUN, Aortic septal defect simulating patent ductus arteriosus, *J. Mt. Sinai Hosp.* **17**, 310 (1951).

KING, J. T., The blood pressure in stenosis at the isthmus (coarctation) of the aorta: Case reports, *Ann. Int. Med.* **10**, 1802 (1937).

KININMONTH, J. G., The circulation rate in some pathological states, with observations on the effect of digitalis, *Quart. J. Med.* **21**, 277 (1928).
[**52**

KIRKLIN, J. W., C. R. OPENSHAW, and R. G. TOMPKINS, Surgical treatment of infundibular stenosis with intact ventricular septum, *Ann. Surg.* **137**, 229 (1953). [12, 13

KISSANE, R. W., R. S. FIDLER, T. E. CLARK, and J. J. CONN, Cephalin-cholesterol flocculation reaction in rheumatic heart disease. I, *Am. J. M. Sc.* **219**, 48 (1950).

KNUTSON, J. R. B., B. E. TAYLOR, R. D. PRUITT, and T. J. DRY, Anomalous pulmonary venous drainage diagnosed by catheterization of the right side of the heart: Report of 3 cases, *Proc. Staff Meet., Mayo Clin.* **25**, 52 (1950).

KOPELMAN, H., and G. DE J. LEE, The intrathoracic blood volume in mitral stenosis and left ventricular failure, *Clin. Sc.* **10**, 383 (1951). [53

KOTTE, J. H., A. IGLAUER, and J. McGUIRE, Measurements of arterial blood pressure in the arm and leg: comparison of sphygmomanometric and direct intra-arterial pressures, with special attention to their relationship to aortic regurgitation, *Am. Heart J.* **28**, 476 (1944).

KREMER, M., Blood gas in a case of Fallot's tetralogy, *J. Physiol.* **80**, 26P (1934). [33, 42

KROETZ, C., Physiologische und pathologische Schwankungen der Sauerstoffdurchlässigkeit der Lungen, *Verhandl. d. deutsch. Gesellsch. f. inn. Med.* **43**, 105 (1931). [60

KROOP, I. G., E. R. BORUN, R. P. LASSER, A. J. GORDON, S. A. BRAHMS, and F. H. KING, Isolated interventricular septal defect with dilatation of the pulmonary artery, an entity, *J. Mt. Sinai Hosp.* **17**, 317 (1951). [28

LAGERLÖF, H., H. BUCHT, L. WERKÖ, and A. HOLMGREN, Bestämning av hjärtats minutvolym samt blodvolymen i hjärthalvorna och i lungorna med hjälp av färgutspadningskurvor, *Nord. med.* **41**, 446 (1946).

LAGERLÖF, H., E. MANNHEIMER, and L. WERKÖ, *Morbus caeruleus: An analysis of 114 cases of congenital heart disease with cyanosis* (S. Karger, Basel, 1949). [21, 22, 25, 28, 29, 31, 34, 35, 36, 37, 38, 39, 40

LAGERLÖF, H., and L. WERKÖ, Studies on the circulation in man. III. The auricular pressure pulse, *Cardiologia* **13**, 241 (1948). [20

LAGERLÖF, H., and L. WERKÖ, Studies on the circulation of blood in man. VI. The pulmonary capillary venous pressure pulse in man, *Scandinav. J. Clin. & Lab. Investigation* **1**, 147 (1949). [20, 21, 22, 23, 24, 55

LAGERLÖF, H., L. WERKÖ, H. BUCHT, and A. HOLMGREN, Separate determination of the blood volume of the right and left heart and the lungs in man with the aid of the dye injection method, *Scandinav. J. Clin. & Lab. Investigation* **1**, 114 (1949).

LAM, C. R., The surgical treatment of mitral stenosis, *Michigan State M. Soc. J.* **52**, 48 (1953). [56

LANDEN, H. C., and O. BAYER, Die Lungenfunktion bei Kranken mit Mitralstenose vor und nach operativer Sprengung der Klappe, *Ztschr. f. Kreisslaufforsch.* **41**, 561 (1952). [60

LARSSON, Y., E. MANNHEIMER, T. MÖLLER, H. LAGERLÖF, and L. A. WERKÖ, Congenital pulmonary stenosis without overriding aorta. A clinical study, *Am. Heart J.* **42**, 70 (1951). [11, 12, 13, 14, 15, 16

LASSER, R. P., A. J. GORDON, R. BORUN, and F. H. KING, The use of an oximetrically determined circulation time from the right ventricle to the ear in congenital heart disease, *Circulation* **6**, 106 (1952). [50

LAUSON, H. D., R. M. BLOOMFIELD, and A. COURNAND, The influence of the respiration on the circulation in man. With special reference to pressures in the right auricle, right ventricle, femoral artery and peripheral veins, *Am. J. Med.* **1**, 315 (1946).

LAWRENCE, J. S., L. M. HURXTHAL, and A. V. BOCK, Variations in blood flow with changes in position in normal and pathologic subjects, *J. Clin. Investigation* **3**, 613 (1926–27). [52

LEHMANN, J. H., A. D. JOHNSON, W. C. BRIDGES, J. MICHEL, and D. M. GREEN, Cardiac catheterization — a diagnostic aid in congenital heart disease, *Northwest Med.* **50**, 170 (1951).
[2, 4, 6, 7, 8, 9, 20, 21, 22, 23, 28, 29, 30, 31, 39, 40

LENÈGRE, J., and P. MAURICE, Recherches sur la pression sanguine dans la petite circulation chez l'homme, *Acta cardiol.* **2**, 1 (1947). [58

LENÈGRE, J., L. SCÉBAT, H. BESSON, F. BENCHEMOUL, and J. DAMIEN, Étude de la pression capillaire pulmonaire dans différents types de cardiopathies, *Arch. d. mal. du cœur* **46**, 1 (1953). [20, 22, 55, 56

LEQUIME, J., Le débit cardiaque. Études expérimentales et cliniques, *Acta med. Scandinav., Supp. No. 107* (1940). [33

LEQUIME, J., and H. DENOLIN, Le coefficient d'utilisation d'oxygène au cours de l'effort. Son application à l'étude des cardiopathies congénitales, *Acta cardiol.* **4**, 159 (1949).

LEQUIME, J., H. DENOLIN, F. GÖKSEL, L. JONNART, and M. WYBAUW, La circulation au cours de la communication interauriculaire, *Arch. d. mal. du cœur* **44**, 539 (1951). [18, 21, 22, 23, 24, 25

LEQUIME, J., H. DENOLIN, and R. PANNIER, La cathétérisme du sinus coronaire chez l'homme, *Arch. d. mal. du cœur* **42**, 811 (1949).
[42, 48

LEQUIME, J., H. DENOLIN, and A. VERNIORY, Dextrocardie et malformations septales (Étude physiopathologique de deux cas), *Acta cardiol.* **3**, 56 (1948).

LEVINE, S. A., and M. P. FULTON, The relation of hypertension to mitral stenosis, *Am. J. M. Sc.* **176**, 465 (1928).

LEVINSON, D. C., R. S. COSBY, G. C. GRIFFITH, J. P. MEEHAN, W. J. ZINN, and S. P. DIMITROFF, A diagnostic pulmonary artery pulse pressure contour in patent ductus arteriosus found during cardiac catheterization, *Am. J. M. Sc.* **222,** 46 (1951).   [**2, 3, 6, 7, 8, 9**

Lewes, D., The exercise test in patent ductus arteriosus, *Brit. Heart J.* **14,** 357 (1952).   [**5**

Lewicki, E., Zur Diagnostik des offenen Ductus arteriosus Botalli, *Wien. klin. Wchnschr.* **53,** 1029 (1940).   [**5**

Lewis, B. M., R. Gorlin, H. E. J. Houssay, F. W. Haynes, and L. Dexter, Clinical and physiological correlations in patients with mitral stenosis. V, *Am. Heart J.* **43,** 2 (1952).   [**53, 55, 56, 59**

Lewis, T., Studies of capillary pulsation with special reference to vasodilatation in aortic regurgitation and including observations on the effects of heating the human skin, *Heart* **11,** 151 (1924).

Lewis, T., Angina pectoris associated with high blood pressure and its relief by amyl nitrite; with a note on Nothnagel's syndrome, *Heart* **15,** 305 (1931).

Lewis, T., Material relating to coarctation of the aorta of the adult type, *Heart* **16,** 205 (1933).   [**51**

Limón Lason, R., F. Bouchard, V. Rubio Alvarez, P. Cahen, and S. Novelo, El cateterismo intracardiaco. III. Persistencia del conducto arterioso con hallazgos clinicos atipicos. Presentacion de 8 casos, 5 de los cuales tenian cianosis. Pruebas de la existencia de "Shunt" invertido y cruzado, *Arch. Inst. cardiol. de Mexico* **20,** 147 (1950).

Limón Lason, R., and V. Rubio Alvarez, El cateterisino intracardiaco. I. Diagnostico de la communicacion interauricular y estudio de la direccion del flujo a traves del defecto septal por medio de la cateterizacion de las venas pulmonares; presentacion de un caso de desembrocadura anomala de venas pulmonares en la auricula derecha como comparacion, *Arch. Inst. cardiol. de Mexico* **19,** 545 (1949).   [**18, 23, 24, 25**

Limón Lason, R., V. Rubio Alvarez, and F. Bouchard, El cateterismo intracardiaco. V. Cateterizacion de las cavidades izquierdas en el hombre. Registro simultaneo de presion y electrocardiograma intracavitarios, *Arch. Inst. cardiol. de Mexico* **20,** 271 (1950).

Limón Lason, R., V. Rubio, H. Rodriguez, J. Espino, and S. Novelo, Asociacion de coartacion aortica con aorta biventricular aislada (el llamado complejo de Eisenmenger), *Arch. Inst. cardiol. de Mexico* **21,** 469 (1951).

Logan, A., and R. Turner, The diagnosis of mitral incompetence accompanying mitral stenosis. Review of eleven cases treated surgically, *Lancet* **2,** 599 (1952).   [**56, 57**

Lukas, D. S., and C. T. Dotter, Modifications of the pulmonary circulation in mitral stenosis, *Am. J. Med.* **12,** 639 (1952).
                                                      [**53, 54, 55, 56, 57**

LUND, G. W., Growth study of children with the tetralogy of Fallot, *J. Pediat.* **41,** 572 (1952).

LUNDSGAARD, C., Untersuchungen über das Minutenvolumen des Herzens bei Menschen. II. Patienten mit Herzklappenfehlern, *Deutsches Arch. f. klin. Med.* **118,** 513 (1916). [53

LUNDSGAARD, C., and D. D. VAN SLYKE, Cyanosis, *Medicine* **2,** 1 (1923).

LURIE, P. R., F. D. GRAY, JR., and R. WHITTEMORE, Cardiac catheterization and other physiological studies in fifty cases of congenital heart disease, *Angiology* **3,** 98 (1952).
[6, 7, 8, 9, 10, 17, 23, 24, 25, 37, 41, 42, 43

MACGREGOR, A. G., and E. J. WAYNE, Fluorescein test of circulation time in peripheral vascular disease, *Brit. Heart J.* **13,** 80 (1951).

MAIER, C., and M. VOLKMANN, Die Bedeutung der Gasanalyse in der Diagnostik der kongenitalen Herzvitien, *Helvet. pædiat. Acta* **4,** 260 (1949). [2, 7, 8, 9, 23, 24, 31, 37

MAINZER, F., Analyse eines kongenitalen Herzfehlers (Zugleich ein Beitrag zur Bedeutung der Hämoglobinvermehrung bei Sauerstoffmangel), *Ztschr. f. klin. Med.* **108,** 489 (1928). [42, 44, 45, 48

MAKINSON, D. H., Changes in the ballistocardiogram after exercise in normal and abnormal subjects, *Circulation* **2,** 186 (1950).

MANNHEIMER, E., The diagnostic value of cardiac catheterization in isolated pulmonary stenosis and large interventricular septal defects, *Arch. Dis. Childhood* **24,** 264 (1949).
[8, 9, 12, 13, 15, 16, 27, 28, 29, 30, 31

MANNHEIMER, E., Y. LARSSON, T. MÖLLER, H. LAGERLÖF, and L. WERKÖ, Congenital isolated pulmonary stenosis. A clinical study of seven cases diagnosed by heart catheterization, *Acta pædiat.* **38,** 484 (1949).
[12, 13, 15, 16

MANNHEIMER, E., B. LANDTMAN, and T. HEDQVIST, Postoperative course in morbus caeruleus, *Acta pædiat.* **41,** 518 (1952). [34, 35, 36

MARAIST, F., R. DALEY, A. DRAPER, JR., R. HEIMBECKER, J. F. DAMMANN, JR., R. KIEFFER, JR., J. T. KING, C FERENCZ, and R. J. BING, Physiological studies in congenital heart disease. X. The physiological findings in thirty-four patients with isolated pulmonary valvular stenosis, *Bull. Johns Hopkins Hosp.* **88,** 1 (1951).
[11, 12, 13, 14, 15, 16, 17, 26, 42, 43, 46

MARTIN, J. A., and B. M. LEWIS, Transposition of the aorta and levoposition of the pulmonary artery, *Am. Heart J.* **43,** 621 (1952).

MATHIEU, L., GRILLIAT, and PILLOT, Considerations diagnostiques sur la fonction ventilatoire des cardiaques, *Arch. d. mal. du cœur* **45,** 21 (1952).

MAYER, C. P., and J. E. ISRAEL, La cianosis de una cardiopatía congénita.

Estudio de los gases alveolares y de la sangre, *Rev. Asoc. méd. argent.* **48,** 113 (1934). [42, 44

McCord, M. C., and S. G. Blount, Jr., The hemodynamic pattern in tricuspid valve disease, *Am. Heart J.* **44,** 671 (1952).

McGregor, M., B. van Lingen, T. H. Bothwell, J. Kaye, J. Greenstein, J. Whidborne, J. L. Braudo, H. D. Jacobs, and G. A. Elliott, Fallot's tetralogy. Its differentiation from pulmonic stenosis with intact ventricular septum and an inter-auricular communication (Fallot's trilogy), *South African J. Clin. Sc.* **3,** 154 (1952).
[12, 13, 17, 26, 35, 36, 37, 42, 43, 48

McGuire, J., and F. Goldman, Apparent increased velocity of blood flow in cases of congenital heart disease with septal defects having right-to-left shunt, *Am. Heart. J.* **14,** 230 (1937). [50

Meakins, J., L. Dautrebande, and W. J. Fetter, The influence of circulatory disturbances on the gaseous exchange of the blood. IV. The blood gases and circulation rate in cases of mitral stenosis, *Heart* **10,** 153 (1923). [52

Means, J. H., and L. H. Newburgh, Studies of the blood flow by the method of Krogh and Lindhard, *Tr. A. Am. Physicians* **30,** 51 (1915).
[52

Megibow, R. S., and S. Feitelberg, Application of microplethysmography to the diagnosis of patent ductus arteriosus and coarctation of the aorta, *Am. J. Med.* **4,** 798 (1948).

Megibow, R. S., and S. Feitelberg, Further experiences with microplethysmography in the study of congenital heart disease, *J. Mt. Sinai Hosp.* **17,** 303 (1951).

Messer, A. L., J. W. Hurst, M. B. Rappaport, and H. B. Sprague, A study of the venous pulse in tricuspid valve disease, *Circulation* **1,** 388 (1950).

Métianu, C., M. Durand, R. Guillemot, and R. Heim de Balsac, Un nouveau cas de syndrome de Tanssig-Bing diagnostiqué in vivo et verifié anatomiquement, *Acta cardiol.* **8,** 76 (1953).

Métianu, C., and B. Latscha, Enregistrements des pressions intracardiaques par ponction direct au cœur, *Semaine d. hôp. de Paris* **28,** 1730 (1952). [13, 35, 58

Miller, A. J., O. Prec, L. Akman, L. N. Katz, and S. Gibson, A case of congenital heart disease. Truncus aorticus solitarius, single ventricle, and aberrant coronary drainage into the common ventricle, *Am. Heart J.* **39,** 607 (1950).

Miller, G., H. Goldberg, E. I. Elisberg, G. L. Snider, M. Toor, and L. N. Katz, Cardiopulmonary studies in patients with mitral stenosis. I. Cardiovascular dynamics, *J. Lab. & Clin. Med.* **40,** 390 (1952).
[53, 54, 55, 56, 57, 58, 59, 60

MILLS, F. H., J. K. MADDOX, R. B. BLACKET, and A. J. PALMER, The surgical relief of mitral stenosis. A preliminary report, *M. J. Australia* **1,** 385 (1952). [53, 54, 55, 56, 58, 60

MOBITZ, W., Ergebnisse von 200 Herzschlagvolumbestimmungen beim Menschen, *Verhandl. d. deutsch. Gesellsch. f. inn. Med.* **38,** 314 (1926). [52

MOBITZ, W., Die Ermittlung des Herzschlagvolumens des Menschen durch Einatmung von Aethyljodiddampf. IV. Klinisch kompensierte Veränderungen des Herzens und der Gefässe und beginnende Kreislaufdekompensation ohne Lungenveränderungen, *Deutsches Arch. f. klin. Med.* **157,** 359 (1927). [52

MONTGOMERY, G. E., JR., E. H. WOOD, H. B. BURCHELL, T. J. DRY, R. L. PARKER, and H. F. HELMHOLZ, JR., Continuous observations of the arterial oxygen saturation at rest and during exercise in congenital heart disease, *Am. Heart J.* **36,** 668 (1948). [42, 43

MONTGOMERY, H., H. F. ZINSSER, JR., and O. HORWITZ, Oxygen tension of tissues by the polarographic method. II. Detection of right to left shunts by changes in skin oxygen tension resulting from inhalation of oxygen, *Circulation* **2,** 845 (1950). [16, 25, 42

MORGAN, E. H., and H. B. BURCHELL, Ventricular septal defect simulating patent ductus arteriosus, *Proc. Staff Meet., Mayo Clin.* **25,** 69 (1950).

MORSE, M., and D. E. CASSELS, Arterial blood gases and acid-base balance in cyanotic congenital heart disease, *J. Clin. Investigation* **32,** 837 (1953). [43, 44, 45

MORSE, M., D. E. CASSELS, and M. HOLDER, The position of the oxygen dissociation curve of the blood in cyanotic congenital heart disease, *J. Clin. Investigation* **29,** 1098 (1950). [42, 45, 48

MOSCHCOWITZ, E., The pathogenesis of brown induration of the lung, *Am. Heart J.* **6,** 171 (1930–31).

MOSCOVITZ, H. L., A. J. GORDON, and L. SCHERLIS, Levocardia, *Am. Heart J.* **44,** 184 (1952).

MULLER, W. H., and J. F. DAMMANN, JR., The surgical significance of pulmonary hypertension, *Ann. Surg.* **136,** 495 (1952). [2

MUNNELL, E. R., and C. R. LAM, Cardiodynamic effects of mitral commissurotomy, *Circulation* **4,** 321 (1951). [56

MYER, P., Hämodynamik und Hämophysikochemie bei einem Fall von Ventrikelseptumdefekt mit Pulmonalstenose, *Ztschr. f. klin. Med.* **120,** 341 (1932). [17, 33, 42, 44, 45, 47, 48, 49

MYERS, G. S., J. G. SCANNELL, S. M. WYMAN, E. G. DIMOND, and J. W. HURST, Atypical patent ductus arteriosus with absence of the usual aortic-pulmonary pressure gradient and of the characteristic murmur, *Am. Heart J.* **41,** 819 (1951). [2, 4, 7, 8, 9

MYERSON, A., J. LOMAN, M. RINKEL, and M. F. LESSES, Human autonomic pharmacology. XVIII. Effects of the intra-arterial injection of acetyl-choline, acetyl-beta-methylcholine chloride, epinephrine, and benze-drine sulphate, *Am. Heart J.* **16**, 329 (1938).

NAHAS, G. G., E. H. MORGAN, and H. B. BURCHELL, Pressure gradients in the atria and pulmonary veins in man, *Proc. Soc. Exper. Biol. & Med.* **74**, 737 (1950). [20

NANSON, E. M., and R. M. WALKER, A case of thrombus in the left auricle simulating mitral stenosis, *Thorax* **7**, 263 (1952).

NATHANSON, M. H., and S. R. ELEK, The influence of heart size on the circulation time, *Am. Heart J.* **33**, 464 (1947). [52

NELSON, W., H. S. MAYERSON, J. H. CLARK, and C. LYONS, Studies of blood volume in the tetralogy of Fallot and in other types of con-genital heart disease, *J. Clin. Investigation* **26**, 860 (1947). [41, 42

NEWBURGH, L. H., and J. H. MEANS, Blood flow in a patient with double aortic and double mitral disease, *J. Pharmacol. & Exper. Therap.* **7**, 441 (1915). [52

NICKERSON, J. L., G. H. HUMPHREYS, R. A. DETERLING, T. C. FLEMING, and J. A. L. MATHERS, Diagnosis of coarctation of the aorta with the aid of the low frequency, critically damped ballistocardiograph, *Circulation* **1**, 1032 (1950).

NIEVEEN, J., B. P. A. A. HOMAN, W. E. MARRING, and F. S. P. VAN BUCHEM, Pénétration dans l'oreillette droite des veines pulmonaires, *Arch. d. mal. du cœur* **45**, 636 (1952).

NYLIN, G., and G. BIÖRCK, Circulatory corpuscle and blood volume in a case of patent ductus arteriosus before and after ligation, *Acta med. Scandinav.* **127**, 434 (1947).

ORDWAY, N. K., Studies in congenital cardiovascular disease. IV. Impaired pulmonary diffusion of oxygen in persons with left-to-right shunts, *Yale J. Biol. & Med.* **24**, 292 (1952). [25, 32

ORDWAY, N. K., L. LEVY, II, A. L. HYMAN, and R. L. BAGNETTO, Pul-monary stenosis with patent foramen ovale, *Am. Heart J.* **40**, 271 (1950). [12, 13, 14, 15, 17, 26

ORME, H. W., and F. H. ADAMS, The relationship of intracardiac pressures and electrocardiographic findings in cases of congenital heart disease, *J. Pediat.* **41**, 53 (1952). [12, 13, 35, 36

PAGE, I. H., The effect of chronic constriction of the aorta on arterial blood pressure in dogs: an attempt to produce coarctation of the aorta, *Am. Heart J.* **19**, 218 (1940).

PANNIER, R., A. VAN LOO, K. VUYLSTEEK, J. VERSTRAETEN, C. VAN BEYLEN, and BLANCQUAERT, Étude clinique et physiopathologique de huit cas de stenose pulmonaire isolée, *Acta cardiol.* **8**, 8 (1953). [12, 13, 14, 15, 16

PARKER, F., JR., and S. WEISS, The nature and significance of the structural changes in the lungs in mitral stenosis, *Am. J. Path.* **12,** 573 (1936).

PEARCE, R. G., The cardiorespiratory mechanism in health and disease, *Arch. Int. Med.* **27,** 139 (1921). [46, 47

PETERSEN, O. V. C. E., N. R. CHRISTOFFERSEN, and J. LINDHARD, Observations on a case of morbus caeruleus. Grave congenital malformations of the heart. Its clinic, pathology, and physiology, *Acta med. Scandinav.* **54,** 395 (1921). [33

PICKERING, G. W., The peripheral resistance in persistent arterial hypertension, *Clin. Sc.* **2,** 209 (1935).

PIJOAN, M., and BÉRARD, Une nouvelle méthode de diagnostic des communications cardiaques artério-veneuses, dans les cardiopathies congénitales, *Compt. rend. Soc. de biol.* **122,** 411 (1936). [42, 48, 50

PRADER, A., and L. HOLLÄNDER, Blutuntersuchungen beim Morbus Caeruleus. IV. Leukocyten und weisses Blutbild, *Helvet. pædiat. acta* **5,** 185 (1950).

PRADER, A., and E. ROSSI, Blutuntersuchungen beim Morbus Caeruleus. II. Eisen- und Hämoglobinstoffwechsel, *Helvet. pædiat. acta* **5,** 159 (1950). [48

PRADER, A., and E. ROSSI, Blutuntersuchungen beim Morbus Caeruleus. III. Erythrocyteneigenschaften, *Helvet. pædiat. acta* **5,** 172 (1950). [48

PRADER, A., E. ROSSI, and M. WODENEGG, Blutuntersuchungen beim Morbus coeruleus. I. Plasma- und Blutvolumen, *Helvet. pædiat. acta* **4,** 267 (1949). [48, 49

PRINZMETAL, M., Calculation of the venous-arterial shunt in congenital heart disease, *J. Clin. Investigation* **20,** 705 (1941). [50

PRINZMETAL, M., and C. WILSON, The nature of the peripheral resistance in arterial hypertension with special reference to the vasomotor system, *J. Clin. Investigation* **15,** 63 (1936).

PROGER, S. H., and C. KORTH, Effect of light muscular training on patients with heart disease. Rheumatic heart disease; changes at rest and during exercise, *Arch. Int. Med.* **55,** 204 (1935). [52

PROUDFIT, W. L., and A. C. ERNSTENE, The diagnosis of coarctation of the aorta, *J. A. M. A.* **139,** 985 (1949). [51

PUDDU, V., Ein besonderes Ergebnis mit der Ätherprobe in zwei Fällen mit angeborenem Herzfehler, *Ztschr. f. Kreisslaufforsch.* **32,** 689 (1940). [50

RABB, W., R. WEISS, B. LÖWBEER, and J. RIHL, Untersuchungen über einen Fall von kongenitalem Herzvitium, *Wien. Arch. f. inn. Med.* **7,** 367 (1923). [42, 48

RAGAN, C., and J. BORDLEY, III, The accuracy of clinical measurements of arterial blood pressure. With a note on the auscultatory gap, *Bull. Johns Hopkins Hosp.* **69,** 504 (1941).

RAILSBACH, O. C., and W. DOCK, Erosions of the ribs due to stenosis of the isthmus (coarctation) of the aorta, Radiology **12,** 58 (1929).

RAINE, F., and H. F. TWELMEYER, Mitral stenosis. Surgical treatment, *Wisconsin M. J.* **51,** 994 (1952). [53, 54, 56, 58, 59

RASMUSSEN, H., and O. STORSTEIN, Studies in oxygen therapy. Part II. On the effect of oxygen therapy on the oxygen unsaturation of the arterial blood, *Acta med. Scandinav.* **141,** 52 (1951). [42, 48

RAVIN, A., N. B. SLONIM, O. J. BALCHUM, S. H. DRESSLER, and J. B. GROW, Diagnosis of tight mitral stenosis, *J. A. M. A.* **149,** 1079 (1952). [53, 56

RICHARDS, D. W., JR., Congenital heart disease. Measurements of the circulation, *Arch. Int. Med.* **47,** 484 (1931). [33, 42, 44, 47, 48

ROBB, G. P., and S. WEISS, The velocity of pulmonary and peripheral venous blood flow and related aspects of the circulation in cardiovascular disease. Their relation to clinical types of circulatory failure, *Am. Heart J.* **9,** 742 (1934).

ROMINGER, C., Ein Fall von morbus caeruleus mit Demonstration der Hautkapillaren am Lebenden nach Weiss und elektrokardiographischen Untersuchungen, *Deutsche med. Wchnschr.* **46,** 168 (1920).

ROSEMAN, M. D., and E. WASSERMAN, The incidence of hypertension in mitral stenosis, *New England J. Med.* **245,** 450 (1951).

ROSSI, E., M. GROB, and J. GUTEWA, Ueber Prä- und Postoperative Kapillaroskopie bei angeborenen Herzfehlern, *Helvet. pædiat. acta* **5,** 279 (1950).

RYTAND, D. A., The renal factor in arterial hypertension with coarctation of the aorta, *J. Clin. Investigation* **17,** 391 (1938).

SALANS, A. H., L. N. KATZ, G. R. GRAHAM, A. GORDON, E. I. ELISBERG, and A. GERBER, A study of the central and peripheral arterial pressure pulse in man. Correlation with simultaneously recorded electrokymograms, *Circulation* **4,** 510 (1951).

SCÉBAT, L., J. LENÉGRE, B. RANSON-BITKER, F. BENCHEMOUL, and J. DAMIEN, Étude des gaz du sang et du débit cardiaque dans les différents types de cardiopathies, *Arch. d. mal. du cœur* **46,** 18 (1953). [53, 55, 56, 59, 60

SCHEINBERG, P., Simultaneous bilateral determinations of cerebral blood flow and arterial-cerebral venous oxygen and glucose differences, *Proc. Soc. Exper. Biol. & Med.* **74,** 575 (1950).

SCHOEN, R., and E. DERRA, Untersuchungen über die Bedeutung der Zyanose als klinisches Symptom (1), *Deutsches Arch. f. klin. Med.* **168,** 52 (1930). [42, 44, 45, 47, 48

Schiller, M., Capilläruntersuchungen bei Schulkindern. (Unter Besonderer Berücksichtigung der Frage: Sind Beziehungen zwischen Intelligenz und Capillärbild vorhanden?), *Ztschr. f. d. ges. Neurol. u. Psychiat.* **151,** 700 (1934).

Schwartz, B. A., and D. Stats, Oxygen saturation of sternal marrow blood in polycythemia vera, *J. Clin. Investigation* **28,** 736 (1949).

Schwartz, B. M., A. J. Gordon, S. A. Brahms, and F. H. King, Uncomplicated pulmonary stenosis, *J. Mt. Sinai Hosp.* **17,** 323 (1951).
[13, 15

Scott, H. W., Jr., and H. T. Bahnson, Evidence for a renal factor in the hypertension of experimental coarctation of the aorta, *Surgery* **30,** 206 (1951).

Scott, H. W., Jr., and S. R. Elliott, II, Renal hemodynamics in congenital cyanotic heart disease, *Bull. Johns Hopkins Hosp.* **86,** 58 (1950). [48

Scott, H. W., Jr., S. R. Elliott, II, and R. C. Clay, Blood volume in congenital cyanotic heart disease: simultaneous measurements with Evans blue and radioactive phosphorus, *Bull. Johns Hopkins Hosp.* **89,** 121 (1951). [48, 49

Sealey, W. C., Arterial hypertension produced by experimental stenosis of the thoracic aorta, *Proc. Soc. Exper. Biol. & Med.* **71,** 174 (1949).

Sealey, W. C., W. DeMaria, and J. Harris, Studies of the development and nature of the hypertension in experimental coarctation of the aorta, *Surg. Gynec. and Obst.* **90,** 193 (1950).

Secher, K., Klinische Kapillaruntersuchungen, *Acta med. Scandinav.* **56,** 295 (1922).

Seevers, M. H., H. R. Hathaway, and R. T. Stormont, Tissue gas studies in respiratory and circulatory disease, *Am. J. Physiol.* **116,** 140 (1936).

Segall, H. N., A case of tetralogy of Fallot: Clinicopathological observations. Quantitative studies of circulation rate and the right-to-left shunt, *Am. Heart J.* **8,** 628 (1933). [33, 42, 43, 48

Sekelj, P., A. L. Johnson, H. E. Hoff, and M. P. Schuerch, A photoelectric method for the determination of arterial oxygen saturation in man, *Am. Heart J.* **42,** 826 (1951). [42, 48

Shapiro, M. J., Clinical studies on twenty-one cases of coarctation of the aorta, *Am. Heart J.* **37,** 1045 (1949). [51

Sicot, J.-R., F. Joly, and J. Carlotti, Les courbes de pression ventriculaires et vasculaires chez l'homme, *Semaine d. hôp. de Paris* **27,** 38 (1951). [13, 35, 39, 56, 58

Silber, E. N., O. Prec, N. Grossman, and L. N. Katz, Dynamics of isolated pulmonary stenosis, *Am. J. Med.* **10,** 21 (1951). [11, 12, 13

Smith, W. C., G. L. Walker, and H. L. Alt, The cardiac output in heart disease. I. Complete heart block, auricular fibrillation before and after the restoration to normal rhythm, subacute rheumatic fever and chronic rheumatic valvular disease, *Arch. Int. Med.* **45**, 706 (1930). [52

SNELLEN, H. A., and F. H. ALBERS, The clinical diagnosis of anomalous pulmonary venous drainage, *Circulation* **6**, 801 (1952).

SOULIÉ, P., Y. BOUVRAIN, and J. DI MATTEO, Les tricuspidites et l'insuffisance tricuspidienne fonctionelle au cours du rétrécissement mitral, *Bull. et mém. Soc. méd. d. hôp. de Paris* **68**, 332 (1952).

SOULIÉ, P., J. CARLOTTI, F. JOLY, and J.-R. SICOT, Cathétérisme du sinus coronaire. (Étude detaillée de 11 cas), *Arch. d. mal. du cœur* **42**, 818 (1949).

SOULIÉ, P., J. CARLOTTI, J.-R. SICOT, and F. JOLY, Étude hémodynamique du rétrécissement mitral, *Semaine d. hôp. de Paris* **27**, 67 (1951). [53, 54, 55, 56, 57, 59, 60

SOULIÉ, P., P. CHICHE, G. VOCI, J. NOUAILLE, and A. PITON, Voie infundibulaire et tétrade de Fallot (Considérations anatomo-radiologiques et chirurgicales), *Semaine méd.* **28**, 1 (1952). [35, 36, 37, 42

SOULIÉ, P., J. DI MATTEO, R. TRICOT, and L. MOREAU, Commissurotomie pour rétrécissement mitral. (Résultats, indications opératoires). *Bull. et mém. Soc. méd. d. hôp. de Paris* **68**, 871 (1952). [53, 55

SOULIÉ, P., F. JOLY, J. CARLOTTI, and J.-R. SICOT, Contribution à l'étude des shunts dans les communications inter-auriculaires, *Arch. d. mal. du cœur* **43**, 97 (1950). [11, 12, 13, 18, 19, 21, 23, 24, 25, 28, 29, 31

SOULIÉ, P., F. JOLY, J. CARLOTTI, and J.-R. SICOT, Étude comparée de l'hémodynamique dans les tétralogies et dans les trilogies de Fallot (Étude de 43 cas), *Arch. d. mal. du cœur* **44**, 577 (1951). [12, 13, 17, 26, 34, 35, 37, 42

SOULIÉ, P., F. JOLY, J. CARLOTTI, J.-R. SICOT, and G. VOCI, Étude physiopathologique post-opératoire de la trilogie de Fallot. (Étude de neuf cas apres valvulotomie pulmonaire), *Arch. d. mal. du cœur* **45**, 387 (1952). [42

SOULIÉ, P., J. NOUAILLE, O. SCHWEISGUTH, F. JOLY, J. CARLOTTI, and J.-R. SICOT, Le rétrécissement pulmonaire avec communication inter-auriculaire (Trilogie ou triade de Fallot), *Bull. et mém. Soc. méd. d. hôp. de Paris* **67**, 495 (1951). [12, 13, 17, 26, 42, 48

SOULIÉ, P., D. ROUTIER, and P. BERNAL, Communication interventriculaire avec insuffisance cardiaque (Diognostique différentiel de la persistance due caval artériel), *Arch. d. mal. du cœur* **42**, 765 (1949).

STARR, I., and L. JONAS, Supernormal circulation in resting subjects (hyperkinemia). With a study of the relation of kinemic abnormalities to the basal metabolic rate, *Arch. Int. Med.* **71**, 1 (1943).

452 CARDIAC DEFECTS

STAS, R., P. SOULIÉ, M. SERVELLE, and J. ROUGEULLE, Commissurotomie et rétrécissement mitral, *Acta cardiol.* **7,** 587 (1952). [55, 56, 58, 59

STAUDACHER, W., Ueber oszillatorische Druckmessung am linken Vorhof des Menschen. II Mitt. Der Vorhofdruck des Insuffizienten und des Ventilgestörten Herzens, *Ztschr. f.d.ges. exper. Med.* **84,** 548 (1932).

STEELE, J. M., Effect of partial clamping of aorta in dogs upon diastolic pressure in carotid and femoral arteries, *Proc. Soc. Exper. Biol. & Med.* **41,** 86 (1939).

STEELE, J. M., Evidence for general distribution of peripheral resistance in coarctation of the aorta: Report of three cases, *J. Clin. Investigation* **20,** 473 (1941). [51

STEELE, J. M., and A. E. COHN, The nature of hypertension in coarctation of the aorta, *J. Clin. Investigation* **17,** 514 (1938). [51

STEVENSON, I. P., C. H. DUNCAN, and H. G. WOLFF, Circulatory dynamics before and after exercise in subjects with and without structural heart disease during anxiety and relaxation, *J. Clin. Investigation* **28,** 1535 (1949).

STEVENSON, S. S., Carbonic anhydrase in newborn infants, *J. Clin. Investigation* **22,** 403 (1943).

STEWART, H. A., Experimental and clinical investigation of the pulse and blood pressure changes in aortic insufficiency, *Arch. Int. Med.* **1,** 102 (1908).

STEWART, H. J., and R. L. BAILEY, JR., The cardiac output and other measurements of the circulation in coarctation of the aorta, *J. Clin. Investigation* **20,** 145 (1941).

STEWART, H. J., J. E. DEITRICK, R. F. WATSON, C. H. WHEELER, and N. F. CRANE, The effect of valvular heart disease on the dynamics of the circulation. Observations before, during and after the occurrence of heart failure, *Am. Heart J.* **16,** 477 (1938). [52

STEWART, H. J., H. S. HASKELL, and W. F. EVANS, The peripheral blood flow and other observations in coarctation of the aorta, *Am. Heart J.* **28,** 133 (1944).

STORSTEIN, O., S. HUMERFELT, O. MÜLLER, and H. RASMUSSEN, Studies in catheterization of the heart in cases of patent ductus arteriosus Botalli, *Acta med. Scandinav.* **141,** 419 (1952). [1, 2, 3, 4

STUHL, M. L., CLOCHE, and M. P. KARTUN, Intérêt de l'électroencephalographic dans l'étude des insuffisances cardiaques avec cyanose, *Arch. d. mal. du cœur,* **45,** 921 (1952).

SUÁREZ, J. R. E., H. CHIODI, J. C. FASCIOLO, and A. C. TAQUINI, Respiration and circulation in morbus coeruleus, *Acta cardiol.* **4,** 439 (1949). [33, 42, 44, 45, 46, 47, 48, 49

SUÁREZ, J. R. E., J. C. FASCIOLO, and A. C. TAQUINI, Cardiac output in heart failure, *Am. Heart J.* **32,** 339 (1946). [52

Sumball, J. J., The vessels concerned in clinical "capillary pulsation," *Heart* **10**, 271 (1923).

Swan, H. J. C., J. Zapata-Diaz, and E. H. Wood, Dye dilution curves in cyanotic congenital heart disease, *Circulation* **8**, 70 (1953).

Talbott, J. H., F. S. Coombs, B. Castleman, F. L. Chamberlain, W. V. Consolazio, and P. D. White, A record case of tetralogy of Fallot, with comments on metabolic and pathologic studies, *Am. Heart J.* **22**, 754 (1941). [42, 44, 45, 46, 47, 48

Taussig, H. B., and A. Blalock, Observations on the volume of the pulmonary circulation and its importance in the production of cyanosis and polycythemia, *Am. Heart J.* **33**, 413 (1947). [42, 48

Taylor, B. E., D. T. Clagett, H. B. Burchell, and E. H. Wood, Repetitive studies of intra-arterial pressures after resection for coarctation in man, *Federation Proc.* **8**, 154 (1949). [51

Taylor, B. E., and J. W. DuShane, Patent ductus arteriosus associated with pulmonary stenosis, *Proc. Staff Meet., Mayo Clin.* **25**, 60 (1950). [13, 15

Taylor, B. E., J. R. B. Knutson, H. B. Burchell, G. W. Daugherty, and E. H. Wood, Patent ductus arteriosus associated with coarctation of the aorta: Report of 2 cases studied before and after surgical treatment, *Proc. Staff Meet., Mayo Clin.* **25**, 62 (1950). [2, 51

Taylor, B. E., A. A. Pollack, H. B. Burchell, O. T. Clagett, and E. H. Wood, Studies of the pulmonary and systemic arterial pressure in cases of patent ductus arteriosus with special reference to the effects of surgical closure, *J. Clin. Investigation* **29**, 745 (1950). [1, 5

Tenzer, C., A propos d'un cas de stenose tricuspidienne, *Acta cardiol.* **4**, 499 (1949).

Tompkins, R. G., H. B. Burchell, and E. H. Wood, Dye dilution curves associated with mitral valvular disease, *Federation Proc.* **11**, 163 (1952). [53

Touroff, A. S. W., and H. Vesell, Experiences in the surgical treatment of subacute streptococcus viridans endarteritis complicating patent ductus arteriosus, *J. Thoracic Surg.* **10**, 59 (1940). [5

Tricot, R., F. Bouchard, M. Caramanian, and A. Samaras, Étude clinique et hémodynamique de la persistance du canal artériel. (A propos de 77 cas), *Semaine méd.* **28**, 32 (1952). [1, 2, 3, 8, 9

Tricot, R., A. Piton, M. Cotlenko, and M. Degeorges, Erosions costales unilatérales, associées à une tétrade de Fallot sans coarctation aortique, *Semaine méd.* **28**, 48 (1952). [35, 36, 37, 42, 48

Uhlenbruck, P., Untersuchungen an einem autoptisch kontrollierten Fall von Pulmonalstenose, *Ztschr. f. Kreislaufforsch.* **19**, 601 (1927). [42, 44, 45, 47, 48

Uhlenbruck, P., and R. Vogels, Zum Problem der zirkulierenden Plasmamenge (Blutmenge) bei Kreislaufstörungen, *Ztschr. f. klin. Med.* **118,** 172 (1931). [52

ULRICH, H. L., Coarctation of the aorta (adult type). A report of three cases, *Am. Heart J.* **7,** 641 (1931–32).

VAN BOGAERT, A., A. VAN GENABEEK, A. NYSSENS, H. VAN DER HENST, and J. VANDAEL, Morphologie du pouls "capillaire" pulmonaire, *Arch. d. mal du cœur* **45,** 673 (1952). [55, 56

VAN BUCHEM, F. S. P., J. NIEVEEN, B. HOMAN, and J. B. VERHEY, Rétrécissement isolé de l'artère pulmonaire, *Cardiologia* **19,** 248 (1951).

VAN BUCHEM, F. S. P., L. D. EERLAND, J. NIEVEEN, B. HOMAN, and W. MARRING, The surgical treatment of mitral stenosis, *Cardiologia* **20,** 272 (1952). [56, 58

VAN BUCHEM, F. S. P., J. NIEVEEN, B. HOMAN, and J. B. VERHEY, De zuivere Pulmonaalstenose, *Acta clin. belg.* **7,** 124 (1952).
[12, 13, 14, 15, 16, 17, 42

VANDAM, L. D., R. J. BING, and F. D. GRAY, JR., Physiological studies in congenital heart disease. IV. Measurements of the circulation in five selected cases, *Bull. Johns Hopkins Hosp.* **81,** 192 (1947).
[1, 7, 8, 9, 12, 13, 15, 17, 26, 34

VAN LINGEN, B., M. MCGREGOR, J. KAYE, M. J. MEYER, H. D. JACOBS, J. L. BRAUDO, T. H. BOTHWELL, and G. A. ELLIOTT, Clinical and cardiac catheterization findings compatible with Ebstein's anomaly of the tricuspid valve: A report of two cases, *Am. Heart J.* **43,** 77 (1952).
[42

VAN LINGEN, B., and J. WHIDBORNE, Oximetry in congenital heart disease with special reference to the effects of voluntary hyperventilation, *Circulation* **6,** 740 (1952). [16, 25, 42, 43

VARNAUSKAS, A. E., H. ELIASCH, and L. WERKÖ, Effekt av arbete vid Kammarseptum Defekt med och utan overridande aorta, *Nord. med.* **47,** 457 (1952). [27, 29, 30, 32, 38, 40

VOCI, G., F. JOLY, and J. CARLOTTI, Étude physiopathologique de la circulation pulmonaire dans un cas de complexe d'Eisenmenger, *Bull. et mém. Soc. méd. d. hôp. de Paris* **68,** 636 (1952). [38, 39, 40, 41

VOCI, G., M. TOUCHE, and F. JOLY, Étude hémodynamic de 10 observations de persistance isolée du canal artériel, *Arch. d. mal. du cœur* **44,** 1103 (1951). [1, 2, 9, 10

WADE, G., L. WERKÖ, H. ELIASCH, A. GIDLUND, and H. LAGERLÖF, The haemodynamic basis of the symptoms and signs in mitral valvular disease, *Quart. J. Med.* **21,** 361 (1952). [53, 55, 56, 59, 60

WAKIM, K. G., O. SLAUGHTER, and O. T. CLAGETT, Studies on the blood flow in the extremities in cases of coarctation of the aorta: determinations before and after excision of the coarctation, *Proc. Staff Meet., Mayo Clin.* **23,** 347 (1948).

WEBER, F. P., and G. DORNER, A case of congenital pulmonary stenosis, with special consideration of the nature of the secondary blood changes, *Lancet* 1, 150 (1911). [48, 49

WEISS, E., and W. DIETER, Die Strömung in den Kapillaren und ihre Beziehung zur Gefässfunktion, *Zentralbl. f. Herz- u. Gefässkr.* 12, 295 (1920).

WEISS, S., and L. B. ELLIS, Circulatory measurements in patients with rheumatic heart disease before and after the administration of digitalis, *J. Clin. Investigation* 8, 435 (1929–30). [52

WEISSEL, W., F. SALZMANN, and H. VETTER, Pulmonary capillary arterial pressure pulse in man, *Brit. Heart J.* 14, 47 (1952).

WELCH, K. J., J. JOHNSON, and H. ZINSSER, The significance of pulmonary vascular lesions in the selection of patients for mitral valve surgery, *Ann. Surg.* 132, 1027 (1950). [56, 60

WERKÖ, L., G. BIÖRCK, C. CRAFOORD, H. WULFF, H. KROOK, and H. ELIASCH, Pulmonary circulatory dynamics in mitral stenosis before and after commissurotomy, *Am. Heart J.* 45, 477 (1953).
[53, 55, 56, 59

WERKÖ, L., J. EK, H. BUCHT, and H. ELIASCH, Correlation between renal dynamics, cardiac output and right heart pressures in mitral valvular disease, *Scandinav. J. Clin. & Lab. Investigation* 4, 15 (1952).
[53, 55, 56, 59

WERKÖ, L., H. ELIASCH, F. BERGLUND, and C. CRAFOORD, Circulatory studies in mitral stenosis before and after commissurotomy, *Ann. Surg.* 135, 290 (1952). [53, 55, 56, 59, 60

WERKÖ, L., H. LAGERLÖF, H. BUCHT, B. WEHLE, and A. HOLMGREN, Comparison of the Fick and Hamilton methods for the determination of cardiac output in man, *Scandinav. J. Clin. & Lab. Investigation* 1, 109 (1949). [53

WEST, J. R., H. A. BLISS, J. A. WOOD, and D. W. RICHARDS, JR., Pulmonary function in rheumatic heart disease and its relation to exertional dyspnea in ambulatory patients, *Circulation* 7, 178 (1953). [53, 60

WIER, J. A., A. J. PICCOLI, D. G. GREENE, and C. W. GREENE, Mitral stenosis with exertional cyanosis and pulmonary hemosiderosis, *Circulation* 6, 868 (1952). [53, 56, 58, 60

WIGGERS, C. J., The magnitude of regurgitation with aortic leaks of different sizes. A review of experimental work, *J. A. M. A.* 97, 1359 (1931).

WILKINS, R. W., and S. E. BRADLEY, Changes in arterial and venous blood pressure and flow distal to a cuff inflated on the human arm, *Am. J. Physiol.* 147, 260 (1946).

WILSON, G. M., The blood flow to the lower limbs in peripheral arterial disease and coarctation of the aorta, *Edinburgh M. J.* 58, 125 (1951).
[51

WOOD, E. H., G. E. BROWN, JR., H. B. BURCHELL, and O. T. CLAGETT, Simultaneous studies of intraradial and intrafemoral arterial pressure before and after corrective surgery for coarctation of the aorta, *J. Clin. Investigation* 27, 562 (1948). [51

WOODBURY, R. A., E. E. MURPHY, and W. F. HAMILTON, Blood pressures in aortic coarctation. Study of pulse contours by the direct method, *Arch. Int. Med.* 65, 753 (1940). [51

WULFF, H. B., G. BIÖRCK, N. P. BERGH, H. KROOK, O. AXÉN, and O. LUNDSKOG, Studies in mitral stenosis. I. Results of one year's series of surgically treated cases, *Acta med. Scandinav.* 144, 275 (1953). [55, 56, 57, 58

WYNN, A., M. B. MATTHEWS, I. K. R. McMILLAN, and R. DALEY, The left auricular pressure pulse in normals and in mitral valve disease, *Lancet* 2, 216 (1952).

YOUNG, M. D., and H. E. GRISWOLD, Situs inversus of the abdominal viscera with levocardia. Report of eight cases submitted to the Blalock-Taussig operation, *Circulation* 3, 202 (1951). [42, 48

YU, P. N. G., R. A. BRUCE, F. W. LOVEJOY, JR., and R. PEARSON, Observations on the change of ventricular systole (QT interval) during exercise, *J. Clin. Investigation* 29, 279 (1950).

ZIEGLER, R. F., Circulation time determinations from the right ventricle, *Circulation* 4, 905 (1951). [50

ZIEGLER, R. F., The importance of patent ductus arteriosus in infants, *Am. Heart J.* 43, 553 (1952). [2, 3, 4, 5, 6, 7, 8, 9, 10

ZIMDAHL, W. T., and D. W. CHAPMAN, Intracardiac catheterization, *Ann. Int. Med.* 32, 489 (1950). [6, 7, 8, 9, 23, 24, 31

ZIMMERMAN, H. A., Left ventricular pressures in patients with aortic insufficiency studied by intracardiac catheterization, *J. Clin. Investigation* 29, 1601 (1950).

ZINSSER, H. F., and R. L. KENDRICK, Angiocardiography and cardiac catheterization as aids in the diagnosis of congenital heart disease, *Pennsylvania M. J.* 52, 1665 (1949). [6, 7, 8, 9, 23, 24, 31, 37, 40, 42

VII

PULMONARY FIBROSIS

Fibrotic pulmonary changes, severe enough in themselves to give rise to symptoms, may occur in the various types of pneumoconiosis and in extensive unresolved pneumonia, fibroid phthisis, bronchiectasis, healed war-gas poisoning and, in relatively rare cases, in patients with advanced mitral stenosis or scleroderma. The altered physiologic findings in such patients are related to the density and extent of the fibrotic process rather than to the etiologic factors involved. The cardiorespiratory dynamics may be modified, however, by the presence of fever associated with an infectious process or by myocardial insufficiency occurring late in the disease.

Subdivisions of the lung volume. — The subdivisions of the lung volume have been studied by many authors (**1**; Hurtado *et al.*, 1935*a*). The functional residual air is normal, while the residual air is normal, decreased, or increased. The reserve (supplemental) air is diminished somewhat, indicating loss of elasticity of the lungs. The considerable decrease in complemental air demonstrates impaired expansibility. The vital capacity is, of course, greatly diminished and the total capacity is also low.

Respiratory dynamics. — The tidal air is often diminished (Altschule *et al.*, 1941; Houssay and Berconsky, 1932; Richards and Barach, 1932; Donald *et al.*, 1951). However, the respiratory minute volume at rest is normal or somewhat increased (Altschule *et al.*, 1941; Böhme, 1939; Houssay and Berconsky, 1932; Kaltreider and McCann, 1937; Austrian *et al.*, 1951; Donald *et al.*, 1951; Fishman *et al.*, 1952; Roemheld *et al.*, 1940; Baldwin *et al.*, 1949; Motley *et al.*, 1950*a,b,c*; Ornstein, 1949; Robertson *et al.*, 1950; Taquini *et al.*, 1948); its value is maintained by an elevated rate (Altschule *et al.*, 1941; Houssay and Berconsky, 1932; Kaltreider and McCann, 1937). Inhalation of oxygen lowers the respiratory minute volume in pulmonary fibrosis (Richards and Barach, 1934; Taquini *et al.*, 1948). The alveolar air carbon dioxide content at rest is elevated and the oxygen content is low (Ornstein *et al.*, 1946; Donald *et al.*, 1952; Houssay and Berconsky, 1932). However, in some instances normal values may occur (Austrian *et al.*, 1951; Donald *et al.*, 1952). Mixing in the lungs is retarded (Baldwin *et al.*, 1949; Robertson *et al.*, 1950; Taquini *et al.*, 1948; Donald *et al.*, 1952; Roelsen and Bay, 1940). During exercise patients with pulmonary fibrosis are unable to increase the tidal air volume normally (Kaltreider and McCann, 1937); however, the respiratory rate rises markedly, so that the respiratory minute volume is increased to a considerable degree above normal (Böhme, 1939; Kaltreider and McCann, 1937; Austrian *et al.*, 1951; Donald *et al.*, 1952; Roemheld *et al.*, 1940; Rothkopf and Linxweiler, 1940; Zorn, 1940; Baldwin *et al.*, 1952; Motley *et al.*, 1950*a*, *b*). The latter returns to its resting level slowly after the cessation of exercise. The maximal possible ventilation per minute is reduced (Kaltreider and McCann, 1937; Baldwin *et al.*, 1949; Gilson and Hugh-Jones, 1949; Motley *et al.*, 1950*a*,*b*; Ornstein, 1949; Austrian *et al.*, 1951; Donald *et al.*, 1952; Roemheld *et al.*, 1940). While in normal subjects the response to exercise is a considerable lowering of the ventilation equivalent, that is, the volume of air breathed per hundred cubic centimeters of oxygen consumed, patients with pulmonary fibrosis show only a slight decrease in this respect. The oxygen debt after exercise is large and prolonged (Nylin, 1937, 1938); the variable findings in this respect reported by Schlomovitz *et al.* (1938) reflect the fact that the period of study used by these authors was too short. Inhalation of oxygen during exercise may prevent excessive rises in respiratory minute volume (Roemheld *et al.*, 1940; Rothkopf and Linxweiler, 1940; Zorn, 1940). Many patients with pulmonary fibrosis may absorb oxygen poorly during exercise (Baldwin *et al.*, 1949; Bruce *et al.*, 1952; Zorn, 1940; Roemheld *et al.*, 1940). Baldwin *et al.* (1949) divided their patients into two main groups according to whether the oxygen intake in exercise was normal or low; in the former group the oxygen debt was normal and in the latter increased after exercise.

The induction of additional anoxia increases the respiratory minute volume (Motley *et al.*, 1950*c*; Fishman *et al.*, 1952). The importance of anoxia in causing the respiratory symptoms in pulmonary fibrosis is evident.

Blood gases. — The arterial blood oxygen saturation is often low (**2**; Baldwin *et al.*, 1949; Hurtado *et al.*, 1935*b*); when low it may be restored to or toward normal by the inhalation of oxygen (Richards and Barach, 1932, 1934). Exercise results in variable changes in arterial blood oxygen saturation, which may fall markedly at times (Kaltreider and McCann, 1937; Baldwin *et al.*, 1949; Harvey *et al.*, 1951; Riley *et al.*, 1948; Austrian *et al.*, 1951; Donald *et al.*, 1952). Baldwin *et al.* (1949) have divided their patients into two main groups depending on whether or not oxygen saturation falls in exertion. The blood oxygen dissociation curve is normal (Taquini *et al.*, 1948). The arterial blood carbon dioxide content may be in the normal range, or above or below it at rest (Houssay and Berconsky, 1932; Hurtado *et al.*, 1935*b*; Richards and Barach, 1932; Motley *et al.*, 1950*b,c*; Austrian *et al.*, 1951; Donald *et al.*, 1952; Fishman *et al.*, 1952; Hickam *et al.*, 1952; Yeomans and Stueck, 1952; Baldwin *et al.*, 1949; Taquini *et al.*, 1948); it may fall somewhat during exercise (Baldwin *et al.*, 1949; Harvey *et al.*, 1951; Kaltreider and McCann, 1937). The increase in anoxia that occurs during exercise accounts probably for the fall in blood carbon dioxide, since induced anoxia at rest causes the same change (Fishman *et al.*, 1952). Baldwin *et al.* (1949) have divided patients into two groups, one of which shows a slight fall in exercise and the other of which shows no change; the alkali reserve falls in exercise in both groups. The fact that patients who are polycythemic consequent to severe chronic anoxia may exhibit confusing changes in blood carbon dioxide has been shown by Taquini *et al.* (1948). Although the whole blood carbon dioxide may be in the normal range, the plasma bicarbonate is elevated; the apparent discrepancy is owing to the fact that erythrocytes hold less carbon dioxide than the same volume of plasma. When the plasma bicarbonate concentration is elevated the chloride concentration is low (Taquini *et al.*, 1948; Yeomans and Stueck, 1952). The blood and plasma pH are not markedly different from the normal (Baldwin *et al.*, 1949; Taquini *et al.*, 1948; Yeomans and Stueck, 1952); Baldwin *et al.* (1949) found no change or a slight rise in exercise.

Cardiac output. — The cardiac output is normal or elevated, depending largely upon the degree of anoxia present (Brooks, 1936; Fishman *et al.*, 1951, 1952; Harvey *et al.*, 1951; Riley *et al.*, 1948; Dexter *et al.*, 1952; Ringer and Altschule, 1930; Taquini *et al.*, 1948; Doyle *et al.*, 1952; Westcott *et al.*, 1951). Low values have also been reported (Dexter *et al.*, 1952; Fowler *et al.*, 1952a). Oxygen lowers elevated values slightly (Fishman *et al.*, 1952). If anoxia is induced in patients with pulmonary fibrosis the cardiac output increases (Fishman *et al.*, 1951, 1952; Doyle *et al.*, 1952); Westcott *et al.* (1951) found no change.

Circulation time. — Normal values for arm-to-tongue and arm-to-lung time have been recorded (Miller, 1936; Piccione and Boyd, 1941; Kopelman, 1951). The prolongation of arm-to-tongue time described by Charr and Riddle (1937) is probably an artefact, since they considered the normal time to be 10 to 12 seconds, instead of the range of 12 to 18 or 20 seconds accepted by most authors. The report by Charr and Savacool (1938) of very long ether times in their patients is difficult to accept in the light of other data. Possibly their patients were suffering from the complicating factors of cor pulmonale or marked polycythemia. When the latter is present the arm-to-tongue and arm-to-lung times are normal or slow (Taquini *et al.*, 1948).

Venous blood pressure. — Normal values are recorded by most authors (Hurtado *et al.*, 1935a; Heise and Steidl, 1938; Charr and Savacool, 1938; Taquini *et al.*, 1948); however, Charr and Savacool (1938) found some patients with pulmonary fibrosis to have elevated levels.

Right ventricular and pulmonary vascular pressures. — Right ventricular and pulmonary arterial pressures are normal or elevated (Baldwin *et al.*, 1949; Bloomfield *et al.*, 1946; Cournand *et al.*, 1944; Harvey *et al.*, 1951; Johnson *et al.*, 1950; Riley *et al.*, 1948; Westcott *et al.*, 1951; Fishman *et al.*, 1952; Fowler *et al.*, 1952a; Austrian *et al.*, 1951; Doyle *et al.*, 1952). The pulmonary arterial pressure rises excessively during exercise (Johnson *et al.*, 1950; Riley *et al.*, 1948). The rise in pulmonary arterial pressure in exercise is owing largely to vasoconstriction. Elevation of pulmonary arterial pressure, while sometimes anoxic in origin (page 64), may occur in the absence of anoxia (Harvey *et al.*, 1951). However, induced anoxia in pulmonary fibrosis elevates the pulmonary arterial pressure further (Doyle *et al.*, 1952; Fishman *et al.*, 1952; Westcott *et al.*, 1951). The pulmonary capillary pressure is normal (Doyle *et al.*, 1952; Westcott *et al.*, 1951).

Arterial pressure. — Arterial pressure is not influenced by the disease.

Blood volume. — Some degree of polycythemia is fairly common in patients with severe pulmonary fibrosis, and the hematocrit and therefore the viscosity may be more or less increased (Brooks, 1936); the plasma volume is normal, however (Brooks, 1936; Doyle *et al.*, 1952; Berlin *et al.*, 1950; Taquini *et al.*, 1948). Accordingly, the blood volume may be in the normal range or show an increase (Brooks, 1936; Kaltreider *et al.*, 1934; Berlin *et al.*, 1950; Taquini *et al.*, 1948). The bone marrow is often anoxic (Berk *et al.*, 1948; Schwartz and Stats, 1949). The reticulocyte counts reported by Riska (1950) in patients with pulmonary fibrosis are incredibly high. Polycythemia may be absent in malnourished patients.

Symptoms. — The normal functional residual air volume of pulmonary fibrosis shows that there is no lack of space available for respiration in most patients with pulmonary fibrosis. Nevertheless anoxia and hypercarbia occur. One factor is poor mixing in the lungs — the "alveolar hypoventilation" of Houssay and Berconsky (1932). Such poor mixing as occurs in fibrosis is the consequence of a decrease in tidal air volume relative to the normal that may be present at rest, and that becomes manifest or more marked in exercise; marked loss of expansibility consequent to extensive scarring in the lung is largely responsible for this change. A contributory factor is loss of pulmonary elasticity, which may be fairly severe in some instances. Another contributory factor may be dyspnea due to anoxia, which may occasionally make the patient increase his respiratory rate to extreme degrees in an attempt at compensation, with a resultant further decrease in tidal air volume. Normally a quarter or a fifth of the tidal air merely washes out the dead space and does not directly participate in respiration; the diminution in tidal air in fibrosis is not accompanied by a corresponding decrease in dead space, so that all of the decrease in the former occurs in that portion used for respiratory exchange.

All factors that lower minute volume while leaving unchanged the functional residual air volume, that is, the air left in the lungs after normal respiration, upset the ratio between the two and impair mixing with and diffusion from the latter. The air remaining in the lungs after each breath consequently may contain abnormally high concentrations of carbon dioxide and low concentrations of oxygen. The abnormally large respiratory minute volumes that occur in exercise, and often even at rest, represent in part an attempt to restore these gas tensions to normal; this increased respiratory activity is inefficient as it is effected by an increase in rate, since the tidal air is increased only with difficulty. The increase in rate in itself contributes to dyspnea. Even if compensation at rest is attained it is clear that the amount of increase in respiration that can occur in exercise is limited and accordingly exertional dyspnea occurs. Failure to achieve complete compensation in this manner at rest or during exertion leads to varying degrees of arterial anoxia and carbon dioxide retention, which may also contribute to dyspnea. In addition, it must be borne in mind that fibrous thickening of alveolar walls may impair gaseous diffusion, and that flow of blood through large areas of unaerated, scarred lung may also give rise to anoxia and hypercarbia. That blood passes through unaerated lung in fibrosis was shown by Riley *et al.* (1949) and Donald *et al.* (1952). The data of Taquini *et al.* (1948), Baldwin *et al.* (1949), and Donald *et al.* (1952) show that the gaseous gradient between blood and alveolar air is increased in some patients. Since carbon dioxide diffuses very much more rapidly than oxygen, this increase in gradient shows earlier and more markedly for oxygen than for carbon dioxide. Moreover, failure to increase oxygen intake normally during exercise (page 458) causes a relative decrease in carbon dioxide formation; this phenomenon minimizes hypercarbia. Indeed, this factor and the excessive increase in respiratory activity caused by exercise may result in a fall in blood carbon dioxide. Harvey *et al.* (1949) divided their patients into groups in one of which impaired diffusion and disturbed ventilating function play important parts.

The inability to increase tidal air volume normally in exercise leads to a considerable reduction in maximal possible ventilation, so that exercise is particularly likely to cause or increase respiratory decompensation, thereby leading to an increased and prolonged oxygen debt after work. However, the role of depressed diffusion in this phenomenon must also be taken into account, since it becomes more important when increased need for oxygen occurs.

It is of interest that the application of chest binders in normal individuals may so restrict the tidal air and respiratory minute volumes as to lead to inability to absorb adequate amounts of oxygen in exercise and a consequent increased debt in the recovery period (page 126). The occurrence of this abnormal debt in patients with extensive pulmonary fibrosis probably leads to lactic acidosis, although data bearing on this point are not available. It is important, however, that anoxia even in normal subjects causes abnormally increased respiratory minute volume, oxygen debt and blood lactate (page 122) after exercise. That such lactic acidosis may occur is suggested by the marked hyperventilation and the finding that the arterial blood carbon dioxide content not infrequently show very large decreases during exercise, evidences of central respiratory stimulation. This is not conclusive, since severe anoxia and reflexes from the lungs may also result in central respiratory stimulation. However, Crisafulli and Colacresi state (1937), without recording data, that lactate tolerance is impaired in chronic pulmonary disease. If lactic acid does accumulate in the blood in excessive amounts, it must be regarded as one cause of the exertional dyspnea of pulmonary fibrosis.

It must not be concluded that dyspnea is necessarily due only to anoxia and hypercarbia in patients with pulmonary fibrosis. The impaired pulmonary expansibility that results from pulmonary fibrosis in itself favors dyspnea, since it increases the effort required to attain a given tidal air volume. Similarly, the loss of elasticity that may occur may require that expiration become an active process rather than the passive process it is normally.

Motley's comment (1952) that no one measurement describes pulmonary function adequately should always be borne in mind.

Cor pulmonale. — Pulmonary fibrosis, with its frequent increase in cardiac and even more frequent rise in right ventricular pressure, may ultimately give rise to congestive failure. Irrespective of the cause or type of pulmonary disease present, cor pulmonale with decompensation is characterized by cardiac outputs that are increased, often markedly (Ahmed *et al.*, 1950; Cournand, 1952; Ferrer *et al.*, 1950; Davies and Kilpatrick, 1951; Fowler, 1953; Kopelman, 1951; Fishman *et al.*, 1951; Gelfand, 1951; Harvey *et al.*, 1949, 1951;

Howarth *et al.*, 1947; Mounsey *et al.*, 1952; Scébat *et al.*, 1953, van Lingen *et al.*, 1951; Richards, 1945; Sharpey-Schafer, 1946; Zimmerman *et al.*, 1951). However, the cases described by these authors include some with normal cardiac outputs. In addition, some authors regularly found no patients with high cardiac outputs, the values in these patients always lying in or significantly below the normal range (Lewis *et al.*, 1925*a,b;* Fowler *et al.*, 1952*b*; Grossman *et al.*, 1953; Lenègre *et al.*, 1953; Cash and Zimmerman, 1952; Dexter *et al.*, 1952; Eichna *et al.*, 1953; Howarth *et al.*, 1947; Taquini *et al.*, 1948; Werkö, 1947). In such instances the circulation time is slow (Callaway *et al.*, 1951; Gillander, 1949; Braun and Fryd, 1951; Stone *et al.*, 1953; Rubin *et al.*, 1952; Taquini *et al.*, 1948). Irrespective of the absolute level, the values for cardiac output are low relative to the degree of anoxia present, and the administration of digitalis results in an increase, as in ordinary congestive failure (page 267). The right ventricular and pulmonary arterial pressures are normal or high (Harvey *et al.*, 1949, 1951; Ferrer *et al.*, 1950; 3). The pulmonary arterial pressure rises excessively during exercise (Lewis *et al.*, 1952*b*), and may fall with oxygen (Westcott *et al.*, 1951). The capillary pressure in the lungs is normal (Dexter *et al.*, 1952*a,b*; Fowler, 1953; Fowler *et al.*, 1952*b*; Gray *et al.*, 1952; Lenègre *et al.*, 1953; Zimmerman, 1951; Westcott *et al.*, 1951). The right auricular pressure is usually elevated (Ahmed *et al.*, 1950; Howarth *et al.*, 1947; Fowler, 1953; Fowler *et al.*, 1952*b*; Gray *et al.*, 1952; Van Lingen *et al.*, 1951) but may be normal in some instances. Similarly, the venous pressure is usually elevated (Taquini *et al.*, 1948; Callaway *et al.*, 1951; Gillanders, 1949; Braun and Fryd, 1951; Deitchman and Canter, 1952; Stone *et al.*, 1953); it may be normal (Rubin *et al.*, 1952). The renal vascular dynamics are similar to those seen in ordinary congestive failure (page 159), according to Fishman *et al.* (1951), Davies (1951), and Davies and Kilpatrick (1951). However, Eichna *et al.* (1953) and Lewis *et al.* (1952*b*) found the glomerular filtration rate normal, although renal blood flow was significantly decreased. Sodium excretion is retarded (Davies and Kilpatrick, 1951). Values for plasma volume were reported as high by Ferrer *et al.* (1950), Harvey *et al.* (1949), and Lewis *et al.* (1952*b*), while Fishman *et al.* (1951) and Gelfand (1951) found it to be normal. The impairment of pulmonary function that occurs with failure may lead to a lowering of respiratory minute volume from its high level found in pulmonary fibrosis (Taquini *et al.*, 1948); anoxia is usually severe and hypercarbia occurs (Taquini *et al.*, 1948; Mounsey *et al.*, 1952; Feltman *et al.*, 1952; Platts, 1953). An unexplained finding is an increase in heparin tolerance (Beaumont and Lenègre, 1951). With recovery, after treatment for both the congestive failure and the pulmonary disease, the cardiac output, if high, falls to normal and the abnormal pressures become normal likewise (Ferrer *et al.*, 1951; Eichna *et al.*, 1953). Basic to an understanding of these somewhat paradoxical changes are the facts that (1) anoxia causes an increase in cardiac output (page 101) and (2) anoxia causes pulmonary vasoconstriction (page 64). The sequence of events in cor pulmonale seems to be (1) chronic anoxia with variable but at most moderate increases in cardiac output and work; (2) exacerbation of anoxia leading to a marked increase in cardiac output and work, which, in the presence of severe anoxia, make the heart fail; the cardiac output quickly falls below the peak attained previously; (3) prolonged failure owing to progressive weakening of the heart leading to gradual decrease of the cardiac output to very low values. If amelioration of the primary pulmonary disorder occurs, the cardiac output decreases or increases according to whether it was high or low while the patient was in failure. An additional factor responsible for high initial outputs is the development of a left-to-right shunt via the bronchial circulation (Cockett, 1953; Liebow, 1953).

Other symptoms. — Reference was made (page 203) to the fact that anoxia causes pylorospasm, slows gastric emptying, diminishes hunger contractions, depresses gastro-intestinal tone and motility, and may impair absorption. All of the references cited describe studies made in severe anoxia of short duration, mostly in dogs under anesthesia. The validity of the use of these data to explain the anorexia, belching, indigestion, flatulence and constipation that may occur in patients with severe pulmonary fibrosis is not established. Nevertheless, these symptoms may be related to anoxia. In addition, it has been shown that inducing in normal subjects elevated blood bicarbonate levels, such as obtain in patients with severe pulmonary disease, gives rise to gastric hyperacidity (Bakaltschuk, 1928; Szilárd, 1930; Browne and Vineberg, 1932); possibly marked carbon dioxide retention caused by severe pulmonary fibrosis may also be an indirect cause of gastric symptoms.

Patients with pulmonary fibrosis often appear more plethoric than measurements show them to be. It is not unlikely that the excessively high color is a consequence in some instances of carbon dioxide retention, for carbon dioxide is a cutaneous vasodilator.

That patients with severe chronic respiratory insufficiency exhibit a notable tolerance to anoxia and hypercarbia is well known. The mechanisms that give rise to this tolerance have not been studied in pulmonary fibrosis, but judging by what occurs in pulmonary emphysema (page 484) the changes that occur include lowering of blood chloride levels and increased blood hemoglobin and carbonic anhydrase concentrations.

The blood glutathione concentration is normal in patients with pulmonary fibrosis (Platt, 1931).

Bibliography

Chapter VII

AHMED, S., R. I. S. BAYLIS, W. A. BRISCOE, and J. MCMICHAEL, The action of G-strophanthin on the circulation in man, and a comparison with digoxin, *Clin. Sc.* **9,** 1 (1950).

ALTSCHULE, M. D., H. LINENTHAL, and N. ZAMCHECK, Lung volume and pulmonary dynamics in Raynaud's disease, *Proc. Soc. Exper. Biol. & Med.* **48,** 503 (1941). [1

AUSTRIAN, R., J. H. MCCLEMENT, A. D. RENZETTI, JR., K. W. DONALD, R. L. RILEY, and A. COURNAND, Clinical and physiologic features of some types of pulmonary diseases with impairment of alveolar-capillary diffusion. The syndrome of alveolar-capillary block, *Am. J. Med.* **11,** 667 (1951). [1, 2

BAKALTSCHUK, M., Der Magen als Mitregulator des Säurebasengleichgewichts, *Klin. Wchnschr.* **7,** 1551 (1928).

BALDWIN, E. DEF., A. COURNAND, and D. W. RICHARDS, JR., Pulmonary insufficiency. II. A study of thirty-nine cases of pulmonary fibrosis, *Medicine* **28,** 1 (1949). [1, 2

BEAUMONT, J.-L., and J. LENÈGRE, La coagulabilité du sang dans l'insuffisance cardiaque avant et après le traitement, *Semaine d. hôp. de Paris* **27,** 2128 (1951).

BERK, L., J. H. BURCHENAL, T. WOOD and W. B. CASTLE, Oxygen saturation of sternal marrow blood with special reference to the pathogenesis of polycythemia vera, *Proc. Soc. Exper. Biol. & Med.* **69**, 316 (1948).

BERLIN, N. I., J. H. LAWRENCE, and J. GARLAND, Blood volume in polycythemia as determined by P^{32} labeled red blood cells, *Am. J. Med.* **9**, 747 (1950).

BLOOMFIELD, R. A., H. D. LAUSON, A. COURNAND, E. S. BREED and D. W. RICHARDS, JR., Recording of right heart pressures in normal subjects and in patients with chronic pulmonary disease and in various types of cardiocirculatory disease, *J. Clin. Investigation* **25**, 639 (1946).

BÖHME, A., Der Einfluss körperlicher Arbeit auf das Minutenvolumen der Atmung bei Gesunden und Silicosekranken, *Arch. f. Gewerbepath. u. Gewerbehyg.* **9**, 22 (1939).

BORDEN, C. W., R. H. WILSON, R. V. EBERT, and H. S. WELLS, Pulmonary hypertension in chronic pulmonary emphysema, *Am. J. Med.* **8**, 701 (1950). [3

BRAUN, K., and C. H. FRYD, The effect of priscol on the peripheral venous pressure, *Brit. Heart J.* **13**, 294 (1951).

BROOKS, W. D. W., Circulatory adjustments in polycythemia rubra vera, *Proc. Roy. Soc. Med.* **29**, 1379 (1936). [1, 2

BROWNE, J. S. L., and A. M. VINEBERG, The interdependence of gastric secretion and the CO_2 content of the blood, *J. Physiol.* **75**, 345 (1932).

BRUCE, R. A., F. W. LOVEJOY, JR., P. N. G. YU, and M. E. McDOWELL, Observations of cardiorespiratory performance in normal subjects under unusual stress during exercise, *Arch. Indust. Hyg. & Occupat. Med.* **6**, 105 (1952).

CALLAWAY, J. J., and V. A. McKUSICK, Carbon dioxide intoxication in emphysema: Emergency treatment by artificial pneumoperitoneum, *New England J. Med.* **245**, 9 (1951). [3

CARLOTTI, J., J.-R. SICOT, and F. JOLY, Cardiopathies congénitales. III. Étude de la dynamique des grosses artères pulmonaires, *Arch. d. mal. du cœur* **43**, 705 (1950). [3

CASH, H. R., and H. A. ZIMMERMAN, An evaluation of the effect of Khellin on the pulmonary circulation in man, *Dis. of Chest* **21**, 137 (1952). [3

CHARR, R., and R. RIDDLE, Pulmonary circulation in artificial pneumothorax and anthracosilicosis, *Am. J. M. Sc.* **194**, 502 (1937).

CHARR, R., and J. W. SAVACOOL, Dyspnea in anthracosilicosis. A clinicopathologic study, *Pennsylvania M. J.* **42**, 35 (1938). [1

COCKETT, F. B., Collateral circulation to the lungs, *Visceral circulation. A Ciba Foundation symposium* (Boston: Little, Brown, 1953).

COURNAND, A., A discussion of the concept of cardiac failure in the light of recent physiologic studies in man, *Ann. Int. Med.* **37**, 649 (1952). [3

COURNAND, A., H. D. LAUSON, R. A. BLOOMFIELD, E. S. BREED, and E. DE F. BALDWIN, Recording of right heart pressures in man, *Proc. Soc. Exper. Biol. & Med.* **55**, 34 (1944).

CRISAFULLI, A., and A. COLACRESI, La "prova di carico" con lattato di sodio per le diagnosi di insufficienza cardiaca, *Cuore e circolaz.* **21**, 551 (1937).

DAVIES, C. E., The effect of treatment on the renal circulation in heart-failure, *Lancet* **2**, 1052 (1951).

DAVIES, C. E., and J. A. KILPATRICK, Renal circulation in low output and high output heart failure, *Clin. Sc.* **10**, 53 (1951).

DEITCHMAN, M., and A. H. CANTER, Direct venous pressure in chronic right heart disease, *Mil. Surgeon* **110**, 402 (1952).

DEXTER, L., B. M. LEWIS, F. W. HAYNES, R. GORLIN, and H. E. J. HOUSSAY, Chronic cor pulmonale without hypoxia, *Bull. New England M. Center* **14**, 69 (1952). [3

DEXTER, L., J. L. WHITTENBERG, R. GORLIN, B. M. LEWIS, F. W. HAYNES, and R. J. SPIEGL, The effect of chronic pulmonary disease (cor pulmonale and hypoxia) on the dynamics of the circulation in man, *Tr. A. Am. Physicians* **64**, 226 (1951). [3

DONALD, K. W., Reaction to carbon dioxide in pneumokoniosis of coalminers, *Clin. Sc.* **8**, 45 (1949). [1

DONALD, K. W., A. RENZETTI, R. L. RILEY, and A. COURNAND, Analysis of factors affecting concentrations of oxygen and carbon dioxide in gas and blood of lungs: Results, *J. Appl. Physiol.* **4**, 497 (1952). [1, 2

DOYLE, J. T., J. S. WILSON, and J. V. WARREN, The pulmonary vascular responses to short-term hypoxia in human subjects, *Circulation* **5**, 263 (1952). [2

EICHNA, L., S. J. FARBER, A. R. BERGER, D. P. EARLE, B. RADER, E. PELLEGRINO, R. E. ALBERT, J. D. ALEXANDER, H. TAUBE, and S. YOUNGWIRTH, Cardiovascular dynamics, blood volumes, renal functions and electrolyte excretions in the same patients during congestive heart failure and after recovery of cardiac decompensation, *Circulation* **7**, 674 (1953).

FELTMAN, J. A., W. NEWMAN, A. SCHWARTZ, D. J. STONE, and F. J. LOVELOCK, Cardiac failure secondary to ineffective bellows action of the chest cage, *J. Clin. Investigation* **31**, 762 (1952).

FERRER, M. I., R. M. HARVEY, R. T. CATHCART, C. A. WEBSTER, D. W. RICHARDS, JR., and A. COURNAND, Some effects of digoxin upon the heart and circulation in man. Digoxin in chronic cor pulmonale, *Circulation* **1**, 161 (1950). [3

FISHMAN, A. P., M. H. MAXWELL, C. H. CROWDER, and P. MORALES, Kidney function in cor pulmonale. Particular consideration of changes in renal hemodynamics and sodium excretion during variation in level of oxygenation, *Circulation* **3**, 703 (1951).

FISHMAN, A. P., J. McCLEMENT, A. HIMMELSTEIN, and A. COURNAND, Effects of acute anoxia on the circulation and respiration in patients with chronic pulmonary disease studied during the "steady state," *J. Clin. Investigation* **31**, 770 (1952).

FOWLER, N. O., Cardiac catheterization in the diagnosis of adult heart disease, *Ann. Int. Med.* **38**, 478 (1953). [3

FOWLER, N. O., JR., R. N. WESTCOTT, and R. C. SCOTT, Pulmonary artery diastolic pressure: its relationship to pulmonary arteriolar resistance and pulmonary "capillary pressure, *J. Clin. Investigation* **31**, 72 (1952). [2

FOWLER, N. O., R. N. WESTCOTT, R. C. SCOTT, and E. HESS, The cardiac output in chronic cor pulmonale, *Circulation* **6**, 888 (1952). [3

GELFAND, M. L., Chronic cor pulmonale in long-standing bronchial asthma, *Am. J. Med.* **10**, 27 (1951). [3

GILLANDERS, A. D., Circulatory dynamics in emphysema, *Quart. J. Med.* **18**, 263 (1949).

GILROY, J. C., and V. H. WILSON, On the relationship of pulmonary hypertension to anoxaemia in cases of respiratory disease with cor pulmonale, *South African J. M. Sc.* **16**, 1 (1951). [3

GILSON, J. C., and P. HUGH-JONES, The measurement of the total lung volume and breathing capacity, *Clin. Sc.* **7**, 185 (1949). [1

GRAY, F. D., M. H. WILLIAMS, JR., and F. C. GRAY, The circulatory and ventilatory changes in chronic pulmonary disease as affected by Lanatoside C, *Am. Heart J.* **44**, 517 (1952). [3

GROSSMAN, J., R. E. WESTON, and L. LEITER, A method for determining cardiac output by the direct Fick principle without gas analysis, *J. Clin. Investigation* **32**, 161 (1953).

HARVEY, R. M., M. I. FERRER, R. T. CATHCART, D. W. RICHARDS, JR., and A. COURNAND, Some effects of digoxin upon the heart and circulation in man. Digoxin in left ventricular failure, *Am. J. Med.* **7**, 439 (1949). [3

HARVEY, R. M., M. I. FERRER, D. W. RICHARDS, JR., and A. COURNAND, Influence of chronic pulmonary disease on the heart and circulation, *Am. J. Med.* **10**, 719 (1951). [2, 3

HEISE, F. H., and J. H. STEIDL, Venous pressure in pulmonary tuberculosis. The effect of collapse therapy and other complications, *J. Thoracic Surg.* **8**, 539 (1938–39).

HICKAM, J. B., H. O. SIEKER, W. W. PRYOR, and J. M. RYAN, Carbon dioxide retention during oxygen therapy, *North Carolina M. J.* **13**, 35 (1952). [2

Houssay, B. A., and I. Berconsky, Cyanose par l'hypoventilation alvéolaire, *Presse méd.* **40**, 1759 (1932). [1, 2

Howarth, S., J. McMichael, and E. P. Sharpey-Schafer, The effects of oxygen, venesection and digitalis in chronic heart failure from disease of the lungs, *Clin. Sc.* **6**, 187 (1947).

Hurtado, A., W. W. Fray, and W. S. McCann, Studies of total pulmonary capacity and its subdivisions. IV. Preliminary observations on cases of pulmonary emphysema and of pneumoconiosis, *J. Clin. Investigation* **12**, 833 (1933). [1

Hurtado, A., N. L. Kaltreider, W. W. Fray, W. D. W. Brooks, and W. S. McCann, Studies of total pulmonary capacity and its subdivisions. VIII. Observations on cases of pulmonary fibrosis, *J. Clin. Investigation* **14**, 81 (1935a). [1

Hurtado, A., N. L. Kaltreider, and W. S. McCann, Studies of total pulmonary capacity and its subdivisions. IX. Relationship to oxygen saturation and carbon dioxide content of the arterial blood, *J. Clin. Investigation* **14**, 94 (1935b). [1, 2

Johnson, J. B., I. Ferrer, J. R. West, and A. Cournand, The relation between electrocardiographic evidence of right ventricular hypertrophy and pulmonary arterial pressure in patients with chronic pulmonary disease, *Circulation* **1**, 536 (1950). [2

Kaltreider, N. L., A. Hurtado, and W. D. W. Brooks, Study of the blood in chronic respiratory diseases with special reference to the volume of the blood, *J. Clin. Investigation* **13**, 999 (1934). [1, 2

Kaltreider, N. L., and W. S. McCann, Respiratory response during exercise in pulmonary fibrosis and emphysema, *J. Clin. Investigation* **16**, 23 (1937). [1, 2

Kopelman, H., The circulation time as a clinical test, *Brit. Heart J.* **13**, 301 (1951). [1

Kroetz, C., Gasanalytische Untersuchungen über die Endothelfunktion der Lungen, *Verhandl. d. deutsch. Gesellsch. f. inn. Med.* **41**, 449 (1929). [2

Lenègre, J., and P. Maurice, Recherches sur la pression sanguine dans la petite circulation chez l'homme, *Acta cardiol.* **2**, 1 (1947). [3

Lenègre, J., L. Scébat, H. Besson, F. Benchemoul, and J. Damien, Étude de la pression capillaire pulmonaire dans différents types de cardiopathies, *Arch. d. mal. du cœur* **46**, 1 (1953). [3

Lewis, C. S., M. C. Daines, A. J. Samuels, and H. H. Hecht, Cor pulmonale (pulmono-cardiac syndrome). A case report, *Dis. of Chest* **22**, 261 (1952). [3

Lewis, C. S., A. J. Samuels, M. C. Daines, and H. H. Hecht, Chronic lung disease, polycythemia and congestive heart failure. Cardiorespiratory, vascular and renal adjustments in cor pulmonale, *Circula-tion* **6**, 874 (1952).   [3

LIEBOW, A. A., The bronchopulmonary venous collateral circulation with special reference to emphysema, *Am. J. Path.* **29**, 251 (1953).

McCANN, W. S., A. HURTADO, N. KALTREIDER, and W. W. FRAY, The estimation of functional disability in the pulmonary fibroses, *J. A. M. A.* **103**, 810 (1934).   [1, 2

McGUIRE, J., R. N. WESTCOTT, and N. O. FOWLER, Anoxia and human pulmonary vascular resistance, *Tr. A. Am. Physicians* **64**, 404 (1951).
                                                                        [3

MILLER, H. R., Clinical observations on pulmonary blood flow in silicosis and other fibrotic conditions of the lungs, *Am. J. M. Sc.* **191**, 334 (1936).

MOTLEY, H. L., Clinical pulmonary physiology. I. Evaluation of function impairment and new developments in therapy of chronic pulmonary disease, *Arch. Indust. Hyg. & Occupat. Med.* **5**, 554 (1952).

MOTLEY, H. L., L. P. LANG, and B. GORDON, Studies on the respiratory gas exchange in one hundred anthracite miners with pulmonary complaints, *Am. Rev. Tuberc.* **61**, 201 (1950).   [1, 2

MOTLEY, H. L., B. GORDON, L. P. LANG, and P. A. THEODOS, Impairment of pulmonary function in anthrasilicosis, *Arch. Indust. Hyg. & Occupat. Med.* **1**, 133 (1950).   [1

MOTLEY, H. L., and J. F. TOMASHEFSKI, Effect of high and low oxygen levels and intermittent positive pressure breathing on oxygen transport in the lungs in pulmonary fibrosis and emphysema, *J. Appl. Physiol.* **3**, 189 (1950).   [1, 2

MOTLEY, H. L., A. COURNAND, L. WERKO, A. HIMMELSTEIN, and D. DRESDALE, The influence of short periods of induced acute anoxia upon pulmonary artery pressures in man, *Am. J. Physiol.* **150**, 315 (1947).

MOUNSEY, J. P. D., L. W. RITZMAN, N. J. SELVERSTONE, W. A. BRISCOE, and G. A. McLEMORE, Circulatory changes in severe pulmonary emphysema, *Brit. Heart J.* **14**, 153 (1952).   [3

NYLIN, G., More recent developments of heart function tests, *J. A. M. A.* **109**, 133 (1937).

NYLIN, G., The practical applicability of the cardiopulmonary function test, *Acta med. Scandinav., Supp. No. 93*, 1 (1938).

ORNSTEIN, G. G., The measurement of the function of the lungs, *Dis. of Chest* **15**, 280 (1949).   [1

ORNSTEIN, G. G., M. HERMAN, M. W. FRIEDMAN, and E. FRIEDLANDER, Pulmonary function tests. A discussion of ventilatory tests. A description of a method for measuring the diffusion of oxygen and carbon dioxide in the lungs, *Am. Rev. Tuberc.* **53**, 306 (1946).   [1

PICCIONE, F. V., and L. J. BOYD, The determination of blood velocity by lobeline, *J. Lab. & Clin. Med.* **26**, 766 (1941).

PLATT, R., The blood glutathione in disease, *Brit. J. Exper. Path.* **12**, 139 (1931).

PLATTS, M. M., The arterial blood gases in pulmonary heart failure, *Clin. Sc.* **12**, 63 (1953).

RICHARDS, D. W., JR., Cardiac output by the catheterization technique in various clinical conditions, *Federation Proc.* **4**, 215 (1945).

RICHARDS, D. W., JR., and A. L. BARACH, Effects of oxygen treatment over long periods of time in patients with pulmonary fibrosis, *Am. Rev. Tuberc.* **26**, 253 (1932). [1, 2

RICHARDS, D. W., JR., and A. L. BARACH, Prolonged residence in high oxygen atmospheres. Effects on normal individuals and on patients with chronic cardiac and pulmonary insufficiency, *Quart. J. Med.* **3**, 437 (1934). [2

RILEY, R. L., R. AUSTRIAN, K. W. DONALD, and A. COURNAND, The relation of effective pulmonary blood flow to total pulmonary blood flow in normal man and in patients with various types of chronic pulmonary disease, *J. Clin. Investigation* **28**, 805 (1949).

RILEY, R. L., A. HIMMELSTEIN, H. L. MOTLEY, H. M. WEINER, and A. COURNAND, Studies of the pulmonary circulation at rest and during exercise in normal individuals and in patients with chronic pulmonary disease, *Am. J. Physiol.* **152**, 372 (1948). [2

RILEY, R. L., A. HIMMELSTEIN, H. L. MOTLEY, H. M. WEINER, and A. COURNAND, Pulmonary circulation during exercise in normal individuals and in patients with chronic pulmonary disease, *Federation Proc.* **7**, 102 (1948).

RINGER, M., and M. D. ALTSCHULE, Studies on the circulation. II. Cardiac output in diseases of the heart, and under the influence of digitalis therapy, *Am. Heart J.* **5**, 305 (1930).

RISKA, N., The reticulocyte reaction as an indicator of respiratory insufficiency, *Acta med. Scandinav. Supp. No. 237* (1950).

ROELSEN, E., and N. BAY, Investigations of the lung function in silicotics. I. The capacity of the lungs and the conditions of the alveolar ventilation, *Acta med. Scandinav.* **103**, 55 (1940). [1

ROEMHELD, L., H. KEMPF, and H. W. WEDLER, Untersuchungen über die Lungenfunktion bei Asbestose, *Deutsches Arch. f. klin. Med.* **186**, 53 (1940). [1

ROBERTSON, J. S., W. E. SIRI, and H. B. JONES, Lung ventilation patterns determined by analysis of nitrogen elimination rates; use of the mass spectrometer as a continuous gas analyzer, *J. Clin. Investigation* **29**, 577 (1950). [1

ROTHKOPF, H., and K. LINXWEILER, Ueber Zusatzgutachten zur Beurteilung von Lunge, Herz und Kreislauf mit Hilfe von Spirographie und Ergometrie, *Beitr. z. Klin. d. Tuberk.* **94,** 309 (1940).

RUBIN, E. H., B. S. KAHN, and D. PECKER, Diffuse interstitial fibrosis of the lungs, *Ann. Int. Med.* **36,** 864 (1952).

SCÉBAT, L., J. LENÈGRE, B. RANSON-BITKER, F. BENCHEMOUL, and J. DAMIEN, Étude des gaz du sang et du débit cardiaque dans les différents types de cardiopathies, *Arch. d. mal. du cœur* **46,** 18 (1953).

SCHLOMOVITZ, B. H., A. B. THOMPSON, and L. G. GLICKMAN, A functional test in chronic pulmonary disease, *Am. Rev. Tuberc.* **37,** 369 (1938).

SCHWARTZ, B. A., and D. STATS, Oxygen saturation of sternal marrow blood in polycythemia vera, *J. Clin. Investigation* **28,** 736 (1949).   [2

SHARPEY-SCHAFER, E. P., 2-Thiouracil in the treatment of congestive heart failure, *Brit. M. J.* **2,** 888 (1946).

STONE, D. J., A. SCHWARTZ, W. NEWMAN, J. A. FELTMAN, and F. J. LOVELOCK, Precipitation by pulmonary infection of acute anoxia, cardiac failure and respiratory acidosis in chronic pulmonary disease, *Am. J. Med.* **14,** 14 (1953).

SZILÁRD, Z., Die Wirkung des Natriumhydrokarbonat auf den Magen, *Deutsches Arch. f. klin. Med.* **168,** 368 (1930).

TAQUINI, A. C., and B. B. LOZADA, Corazón pulmonar cronico con y sin insuficiencia cardiaca. Funciones respiratoria y circulatoria, *Medicina* **8,** 325 (1948).

TAQUINI, A. C., J. C. FASCIOLO, J. R. E. SUAREZ, and H. CHIODI, Respiration and circulation in pulmonary anoxemia, *Arch. Int. Med.* **82,** 534 (1948).   [1, 2

VAN LINGEN, B., J. H. GEAR, and J. WHIDBOURNE, Ballistocardiographic patterns in congestive cardiac failure before and after the intravenous administration of digitalis, *South African J. Clin. Sc.* **2,** 239 (1951).

WERKÖ, L., The influence of positive pressure breathing on the circulation in man, *Acta med. Scandinav., Supp. No. 193* (1947).

WESTCOTT, R. N., N. O. FOWLER, R. C. SCOTT, V. D. HAUENSTEIN, and J. McGUIRE, Anoxia and human pulmonary vascular resistance, *J. Clin. Investigation* **30,** 957 (1951).   [3

YEOMANS, A., and G. H. STUECK, JR., Clinical-chemical studies of acid-base abnormalities. Changes in acid-base balance observed in renal and respiratory disease, *Am. J. Med.* **13,** 183 (1952).   [2

ZIMMERMAN, H., A study of the pulmonary circulation in man, *Dis. of Chest* **20,** 46 (1951).

ZORN, O., Die quantitative Lungen- und Kreislauffunktionsprüfung bei Bergarbeitern (und besonderem Einschluss der Silikose), *Beitr. z. Klin. d. Tuberk.* **94,** 544 (1940).

VIII

CHRONIC PULMONARY EMPHYSEMA

A large amount of information bearing on respiratory and circulatory functions in chronic pulmonary emphysema has accumulated and, since the findings of almost all authors are in agreement, a satisfactory body of knowledge exists. A few authors have attempted to differentiate between senile and obstructive emphysema, but most have felt that this distinction is not a useful one. In almost all instances the patients with obstructive emphysema who have been studied developed emphysema secondary to asthma; the effects of asthma itself are described in Chapter IX. There is no agreement as to the etiology of senile or nonobstructive emphysema, some authorities believing that changes in the lungs are primary, while others consider that these changes are secondary to a disease of the spine. The former seems the more reasonable, though far from established; it appears that senile emphysema is consequent to loss of elasticity of the lungs with advancing age, much as the vessels lose their elasticity after middle life, the changes in the spine being secondary.

Lung volume and its subdivisions. — Although the validity of some of the earlier methods used for measuring residual air has been questioned, there is a remarkable degree of qualitative agreement among various authors as to the findings in patients with pulmonary emphysema. The residual air is greatly increased in volume according to most authors (**1**; Darling *et al.*, 1944); the only discordant findings are those of Bohr (1907) who described it as normal, and of Hurtado *et al.* (1934), who found it normal in senile but not in obstructive emphysema. The functional residual air is also increased, but less so than the residual (Bittorf and Forschbach, 1910; Bates and Christie, 1950; Birath, 1944; Carter *et al.*, 1950; Robertson *et al.*, 1950; Whitfield *et al.*, 1951; Wilson *et al.*, 1950; Briscoe *et al.*, 1951; Fowler *et al.*, 1952; Whitfield, 1952; Whitfield *et al.*, 1951; Christie, 1934), since much of the increase in the latter occurs at the expense of the reserve air; the reserve air is low and may fall to zero (**2**; Christie, 1934); Herxheimer's (1949) results are discordant. The complemental air is also smaller than normal (**3**; Hurtado *et al.*, 1934) according to all authors but Siebeck (1910). Accordingly, vital capacity is likewise reduced (**4**; Christie, 1934); Kountz and Alexander (1929, 1933, 1934) found the vital capacity decreased more in obstructive than in senile emphysema. The total capacity is low or normal, depending upon the relation between increase in residual air and decrease in vital capacity (**5**; Christie, 1934; Hurtado *et al.*, 1933, 1934). All authors agree, however, that the residual and functional residual air volumes are increased, often markedly, relative to the total capacity.

Pulmonary elasticity. — Most authors who measured pulmonary elasticity found low values (Christie, 1934; Paine, 1940; von Neergard and Wirz, 1927*a*, *b*); this is to be expected from the marked decrease in reserve air that occurs in pulmonary emphysema. However, Stead *et al.* (1952) found the elasticity to be normal. McIlroy and Christie (1952) concluded that elasticity was not decreased but that viscosity was increased. The pathologic finding of decrease in elastic tissue in the lungs in emphysema should not be neglected in this controversy. The change, whatever it is, causes expiratory velocity to be slowed (Gaensler, 1950, 1951; Proctor *et al.*, 1950, 1952). The tension within the lung is abnormally low (Dayman, 1951).

Intrapleural pressure. — The above-mentioned decrease in reserve air should be associated with an increased static intrapleural pressure, and indeed several good studies have demonstrated this increase (**6**; Christie, 1934); Ameuille's observations (1920) are not in accord with these more thorough studies. During respiration the inspiratory intrapleural pressure is more negative and the expiratory more positive than normal (Dean and Visscher, 1941; Paine, 1940).

Mixing in the lungs. — Mixing of gases in the lungs is impaired (**7**; Cournand *et al.*, 1937, 1941); Darling, Cournand and Richards (1944) demonstrated two different types of mixing defect, one due to a very large residual air volume and another consequent to poor mixing of tidal air associated with decreased pulmonary elasticity.

Diffusion across the alveolar walls is normal according to Christie (1934). However, Stone et al. (1952) and Lukas et al. (1951) found the oxygen gradient increased. The alveolar air carbon dioxide content usually is high (Christie, 1934; Cobet, 1924; Dautrebande, 1925; Goggio, 1944; Houssay and Berconsky, 1932; Hoover, 1913; Hoover and Taylor, 1915; Boutourline-Young and Whittenberger, 1951; Dubois et al., 1952; Marshall et al., 1952); the alveolar oxygen content is often lower than normal (Goggio, 1944; Houssay and Berconsky, 1932; Motley et al., 1950b; Donald et al., 1952).

Respiratory dynamics. — The respiratory minute volume in patients at rest is often increased, although it may be normal in milder cases (8; Kaltreider and McCann, 1937; Campbell and Poulton, 1926). In exercise it rises abnormally and returns to the resting value slowly (Campbell and Poulton, 1926; Herbst, 1928; Fishman et al., 1952; Silber et al., 1951; Kaltreider and McCann, 1937). Motley et al. (1950b) found the respiratory minute volume low in some instances and in others, in which it was normal, it failed to increase much in exercise (Motley et al., 1950a). Lewis et al. (1952) also found inadequate increases in minute volume during exercise. The tidal air volume at rest may also at times be normal or occasionally even high (Knipping et al., 1932; Reinhardt, 1912; Fowler, 1950; Wilson et al., 1950; Staehelin and Schütze, 1912); often it is found to be somewhat reduced (Campbell and Poulton, 1926; Houssay and Berconsky, 1932; Comroe et al., 1950; Gaensler and Carter, 1950; Holman and Shires, 1949; Motley el al., 1950b; Knipping et al., 1932; Paine, 1940). The respiratory dead space is increased (Birath, 1947; Fowler, 1950; Hoover, 1913), and accordingly the portion of each tidal breath that reaches the alveoli is abnormally small even when the absolute value for tidal air volume is normal. The respiratory rate is usually somewhat elevated at rest (Staehelin and Schütze, 1912; Kaltreider and McCann, 1937; Houssay and Berconsky, 1932; Campbell and Poulton, 1926; Bittorf and Forschbach, 1910). The increase in tidal air that occurs during exercise is smaller than normal (Campbell and Poulton, 1926; Kaltreider and McCann, 1937) and in some cases there may be a fall (Mathieu et al., 1951); the maximal possible ventilation is accordingly low (Herrmansen, 1938; Jansen et al., 1932; Kaltreider and McCann, 1937; Zaeper and Wolf, 1939; 9). The ventilation equivalent, that is, the volume of air breathed for each hundred cubic centimeters of oxygen absorbed, is often somewhat increased at rest (Herbst, 1928; Knipping *et al.*, 1932; Lewis *et al.*, 1952; Gaensler and Carter, 1950); it falls only slightly in exercise (Kaltreider and McCann, 1937) or even rises (Herbst, 1928), whereas in the normal subject it may fall considerably. Exercise is associated with an abnormally small increase in oxygen intake for the work performed (Lewis *et al.*, 1952), so that the debt after exercise is large and prolonged (Herbst, 1928; Herms and Rüttgers, 1931); the finding of Schlomovitz *et al.* (1938) that the debt is smaller than normal is an error based upon too short a period of study after cessation of exercise. Of great interest is the observation that breathing air enriched with oxygen during exercise increases the intake of oxygen at that time (Herrmansen, 1938; Zaeper and Wolf, 1939); a similar statement was reported for patients with pulmonary disease in general (Marzahn *et al.*, 1936). The total cost of work in oxygen consumption for a given task may be normal or occasionally high (Herms and Rüttgers, 1931); that is, efficiency may be low in some patients.

In contradistinction to the relative respiratory unresponsiveness to carbon dioxide shown in this disease (page 480), the response to induced anoxia is about normal (Donald and Christie, 1949; Motley and Tomashefski, 1950). On the other hand, giving oxygen to patients with emphysema has only inconstant effects on respiration (Fishman *et al.*, 1952), unless appreciable anoxia is present (page 481).

Cardiac output. — The values obtained by older methods are normal (Dautrebande, 1925; Scott, 1920). The observation that patients with pulmonary disease usually show normal values is based on a study that includes cases of emphysema (Ringer and Altschule, 1930). Starr and Jonas (1943), using the ballistocardiograph, found high, low or normal values for cardiac output in pulmonary disease, not an unexpected result in view of the variability of the method. More recently, studies made by cardiac catheterization have shown values that are normal or high depending in general upon whether anoxia is present (Borden *et al.*, 1950; Ferrer *et al.*, 1950; Harvey *et al.*, 1951; Hickam and Cargill, 1948; Richards, 1945; Sharpey-Schafer, 1946; Fishman *et al.*, 1952; Lewis *et al.*, 1952; Mounsey *et al.*, 1952; Silber *et al.*, 1951; Yu *et al.*, 1951). Fowler *et al.* (1952) reported some low values. The cardiac output increases normally in exercise (Hickam and Cargill, 1948; Silber *et al.*, 1951). However, the rise may be small in some cases (Lewis *et al.*, 1952).

Peripheral blood flow. — No systematic studies of peripheral blood flow are available, but a single observation suggests that when anoxia is severe the blood flow in the hands may be diminished; at least it increases when oxygen is breathed, a response that does not occur in noncyanotic individuals (Stewart, 1911). On the other hand, the cerebral flow is increased (Comroe *et al.*, 1950; Patterson *et al.*, 1952).

Circulation time. — Normal or reduced values for arm-to-tongue or -face time are reported by a majority of authors (**10**; Oppenheimer and Hitzig, 1936) in emphysema and also in pulmonary disease in general (**11**; Baer, 1940); the ether time is likewise normal in pulmonary disease (Baer, 1940; Baer *et al.*, 1938, 1940; Gillanders, 1949), as is the amyl nitrite time also (Gross, 1945). Increased circulation time is recorded by Koch (1922) and also by Kountz *et al.* (1932) in some patients with emphysema, the degree of increase varying with the increase in intrapleural pressure, according to the latter authors. The presence of polycythemia may be associated with slight slowing in some instances.

Venous pressure. — The venous pressure is usually within normal limits (**12**; Weiss and Blumgart, 1927); however, it may be elevated in some instances (**13**; Kountz and Alexander, 1934); when elevated, the change is said to be consequent to marked increases in intrapleural pressure. Kountz *et al.* (1929) found it elevated in the obstructive, but not in the senile type. Patients with emphysema may exhibit an abnormal rise in venous pressure after exercise (Schott, 1912).

Right ventricular and pulmonary arterial pressures. — The right ventricular pressure may be high at times, although often no deviation from normal occurs (Bloomfield *et al.*, 1946; Cournand, *et al.*, 1944; Battro *et al.*, 1949; Mounsey *et al.*, 1952; Ferrer *et al.*, 1950; Harvey *et al.*, 1951; Silber *et al.*, 1951). It may rise excessively during effort (Silber *et al.*, 1951). The pulmonary arterial pressure may be elevated in some instances (Borden *et al.*, 1949; Ferrer *et al.*, 1950; Fowler *et al.*, 1950; Harvey *et al.*, 1951; Hickam and Cargill, 1948; Fishman *et al.*, 1952; Fowler *et al.*, 1952; Lewis *et al.*, 1952; Gray *et al.*, 1951; Silber *et al.*, 1951; Yu *et al.*, 1951; Johnson *et al.*, 1950; Riley *et al.*, 1948*a,b*). A neurogenic mechanism for this phenomenon is suggested by the observation of Fowler *et al.* (1950) that tetraethyl ammonium lowers the elevated pressure without changing the pulmonary capillary pressure, which is normal to start with. In exercise the pulmonary arterial pressure, if normal, often rises, or if elevated, rises higher (Hickam and Cargill, 1948; Johnson *et al.*, 1950; Riley *et al.*, 1948*a,b*; Lewis *et al.*, 1952; Yu *et al.*, 1951). The observed pulmonary hypertension seems to be related to both anoxia and hypercarbia (Yu *et al.*, 1951). The pulmonary capillary (Fowler *et al.*; Yu *et al.*, 1951) and right auricular pressure (Yu *et al.*, 1951) are both normal.

Sitting up causes a fall in pulmonary arterial pressure in emphysema but not in normal subjects (Donald *et al.*, 1953).

Arterial pressure. — The systemic arterial pressure is not influenced by pulmonary emphysema.

Blood gases; tissue gas tensions. — The arterial blood oxygen saturation, though often normal, is commonly somewhat low (**14**; Hurtado *et al.*, 1935); it may fall further during exercise (Himwich and Loebel, 1927; Goggio, 1944; Gaensler and Carter, 1950; Harvey *et al.*, 1951; Motley *et al.*, 1950*c*; Riley *et al.*, 1948*b*; Donald *et al.*, 1952; Lewis *et al.*, 1952; Silber *et al.*, 1951; Whitfield, 1952); the response apparently depends on the severity of the disease and the violence of the exercise. When low, it rises when high concentrations of oxygen are breathed (page 481). The arterial blood carbon dioxide content is often high (**15**; Scott, 1919, 1920); the venous blood carbon dioxide content is also increased (Scott, 1919, 1920; Essen *et al.*, 1923). The general statement has been made also that patients with pulmonary disease often have an elevated arterial carbon dioxide content (Campbell *et al.*, 1923; Fraser, 1927; Fraser *et al.*, 1928; Porges *et al.*, 1913); some of these patients probably had emphysema. The arterial blood carbon dioxide may fall with mild exertion (Goggio, 1944; Whitfield, 1952). Patients with emphysema may have low tissue oxygen and high tissue carbon dioxide tensions (Seevers *et al.*, 1936) and the bone marrow may be anoxic (Berk *et al.*, 1948).

Blood carbonic anhydrase. — The blood carbonic anhydrase level is reported as normal by Lambie (1938). However, more recent work, employing a more accurate method, has shown that severe emphysema with polycythemia causes a rise in carbonic anhydrase activity in the blood (Altschule and Lewis, 1947).

Blood electrolytes and pH. — The alkali reserve is high in severe emphysema (Scott, 1920; Dautrebande, 1925; Donald and Christie, 1949; Boutourline-Young and Whittenberger, 1951; Yeomans and Stueck, 1952); it has also been reported high in severe pulmonary disease in general (Fraser, 1927). Holman and Shires (1949) found it to be normal in most of their cases. Accordingly, although carbon dioxide retention occurs, the blood pH is normal or only slightly lowered (Scott, 1920; Dautrebande, 1925; Fraser, 1927; Campbell *et al.*, 1923; Cobet, 1924; Comroe *et al.*, 1950; Wilson *et al.*, 1950; Boutourline-Young and Whittenberger, 1951; Stone *et al.*, 1952; Patterson *et al.*, 1952; Yeomans and Stueck, 1952). However, it falls with only mild exertion (Goggio, 1944). The increased alkali reserve of emphysema is associated with increased tolerance to breathing high concentrations of carbon dioxide (Reinhardt, 1912; Scott, 1919, 1920; Christie, 1934; Donald, 1949; Donald and Christie, 1949; Holman and Shires, 1949); that is, carbon dioxide causes less hyperpnea in patients with emphysema than in normal subjects or cardiac patients. However, dyspnea may be more severe than in normal subjects (Holman and Shires, 1949). Elevated blood bicarbonate levels are commonly associated with low blood chloride concentrations in pulmonary emphysema (Essen *et al.*, 1923; Yeomans and Stueck, 1952); the presence of emphysema or other chronic pulmonary disease may distort or abolish the usual pattern found in congestive failure, namely, low bicarbonate and high chloride levels (page 113).

The alterations in blood gases are due to poor mixing in the lungs, impaired diffusion in some cases (page 475), and the admixture of venous blood from poorly ventilated areas (Marshall *et al.*, 1952; Gray *et al.*, 1951).

The toxic effect of high concentrations of oxygen in emphysema and also in other pulmonary disorders has been noted by many: carbon dioxide is retained and the blood pH falls (Barach, 1941; Beale *et al.*, 1951; Boutourline-Young and Whittenberger, 1951; Callaway and McKusick, 1951; Comroe *et al.*, 1950; Richards and Barach, 1932; Feltman *et al.*, 1952; Hickam *et al.*, 1952; Stone *et al.*, 1952; Bickerman and Beck, 1952; Maurath and Hauer, 1952;

Patterson *et al.*, 1952; Wilson *et al.*, 1951). Plasma chloride levels fall (Callaway and McKusick, 1951; Bickerman and Beck, 1952). This change occurs owing to the fact that the relief of anoxia results in a decrease in respiratory minute volume (Boutourline-Young and Whittenberger, 1951; Comroe *et al.*, 1950; Fowler, 1950; Lander and Dortman, 1950; Bickerman and Beck, 1952; Maurath and Hauer, 1952; Patterson *et al.*, 1952; Wilson *et al.*, 1951); in some instances only the tidal volume falls (Beale *et al.*, 1951; Mithoefer, 1952), in which case the effective but not actual minute volume decreases. Patients with emphysema are insensitive to carbon dioxide excess (page 480) but normally sensitive to anoxia (page 477). Giving oxygen raises the arterial oxygen saturation markedly (Barach, 1941; Beale, 1951; Comroe *et al.*, 1950; Boutourline-Young and Whittenberger, 1951; Feltman *et al.*, 1952; Hickam *et al.*, 1952; Stone *et al.*, 1952; Gray *et al.*, 1951; Maurath and Hauer, 1952; Patterson *et al.*, 1952; Wilson *et al.*, 1951). Relief of the anoxia depresses respiration even though carbonic acidosis develops as a consequence. In addition, oversaturation of blood with oxygen prevents a removal of carbon dioxide from the tissues since the normal change from the acid oxyhemoglobin to the basic reduced hemoglobin may not occur.

The rise in spinal fluid pressure that occurs in patients with emphysema given oxygen therapy (Mithoefer, 1952) is consistent with the known effects of carbon dioxide (Cobb and Fremont-Smith, 1931; Ferris, 1941).

Lactate and pyruvate metabolism. — The resting values of blood lactate (Goggio, 1944) and pyruvate (Amatuzio and Nesbitt, 1950) are normal but the former has been shown to rise excessively with exercise (Goggio, 1944). Crisafulli and Colacresi (1937) have shown that severe pulmonary disease in general retards removal of injected lactate. These changes all are probably anoxic in origin (page 122).

Blood. — Normal or only slightly increased values for plasma or blood volume have been described in pulmonary emphysema (Hitzenberger and Tuchfeld, 1929; Rowntree and Brown, 1929; Lerman, 1929; Kaltreider *et al.*, 1934; Lewis *et al.*, 1952); the total blood volume is more likely to be increased than the plasma volume. The hematocrit is found to be elevated much less often in emphysema than in pulmonary fibrosis; some of the increase may be consequent to increased cell size (Price-Jones, 1921; Kaltreider *et al.*, 1934;

Wilson *et al.*, 1951). When the hematocrit is elevated, an associated increase in oxygen capacity is of course found. The reticulocyte count is normal but plasma iron values may be low (Wilson *et al.*, 1951).

Renal Function. — Renal vascular dynamics are normal (Lewis *et al.*, 1952).

Miscellaneous. — Plasma tocopherol values (Klatskin and Krehl, 1950) and blood glutathione (Platt, 1931) are normal.

Symptoms. — Clinicians, wont to diagnose the presence and severity of pulmonary emphysema by the shape of the thorax, are often surprised by the lack of correlation between the occurrence of dyspnea and the development of a barrel chest. This fact suggests that the fault in emphysema is not in the bony thorax. There is much evidence which indicates that the chief defect in emphysema is a loss in pulmonary elasticity consequent to disease of the lungs, or to senility. Loss of elasticity affects pulmonary function in many ways. The lungs do not collapse normally in expiration and become abnormally voluminous, thereby increasing the residual and functional residual air and lowering reserve and complemental air volumes. Failure of the lungs to collapse normally in expiration requires that expiration be associated with active effort, instead of being purely passive as it is normally.

Increased functional residual air volume changes the ratio between the tidal air and the volume of air remaining in the lungs at the end of expiration and so impairs mixing of the tidal air with the air left in the lungs; this may be accentuated by structural changes in the lungs themselves, that is, by impaired expansibility. The decrease in complemental air is an indication of the reduced expansibility of the lungs, which in some cases is sufficient to lower the total volume even at rest. Anoxia tends to occur as a consequence, as does hypercarbia also. In addition, the greatly increased volume of the lungs in respiratory diastole leads to flattening of the diaphragm; the loss of the normal arched diaphragmatic contour lowers respiratory efficiency greatly. Loss of much or all of the normal negativity of intrapleural pressure also impairs respiratory efficiency.

It is clear that a variety of factors gives rise to poor mixing in the lungs; carbon dioxide retention and lowering of arterial blood oxygen saturation may occur in spite of a compensatory increase in respiratory rate and minute volume at rest. The respiratory inefficiency and the limitation of tidal air volume become more pronounced in exercise, and although the rate and minute volume are often greatly increased, oxygen intake does not increase adequately and arterial blood oxygen saturation may fall; breathing oxygen during work prevents these changes. The oxygen debt is of course abnormally high in emphysema.

A few data indicate that abnormal lactic acidosis occurs during work in patients with emphysema (page 481); this is probably related to anoxia, for it has been shown that work done even by normal subjects under anoxic conditions elevates blood lactate levels abnormally (page 122). It is significant in this regard that lactate tolerance may be impaired in chronic pulmonary disease (page 481).

Dyspnea on exertion in patients with emphysema is the consequence of lowered arterial blood oxygen, increased arterial blood carbon dioxide, lactic acidosis and the general inefficiency of breathing, which greatly increases the effort necessary to obtain a given tidal volume. The tendency toward carbon dioxide acidosis at rest, however, is minimized by the high alkali reserve. The question whether reflexes from the overdistended lungs, that is, the Hering-Breuer reflex, or from distended pulmonary arteries also contribute to dyspnea cannot be settled; these reflexes may well be of some importance. The cyanosis of emphysema is due solely to lowered arterial blood oxygen saturation and, in accord with the small changes in the latter usually found, is commonly mild.

Some relief of the respiratory symptoms of emphysema is afforded in occasional instances by the use of a procedure suggested by the observed changes in function in that disorder. The loss of elasticity of the lungs leads to flattening of the diaphragm, so that the function of the latter is greatly impaired as its excursion is limited. Elevation of the diaphragm by means of a snug but not tight abdominal binder restores the normal diaphragmatic arch, so that that organ can function in a manner more nearly normal (Alexander and Kountz, 1934; Kountz and Alexander, 1934; Meakins and Christie, 1934). Too tight a binder, however, aggravates respiratory symptoms. Some patients are able to restore the normal arch by lying flat, and using their own abdominal viscera to press the diaphragm upward. Such patients may have dyspnea only when sitting up. The similar effects of pneumoperitoneum have been studied by Carter *et al.* (1950);

Gaensler and Carter (1950), and Callaway and McKusick (1951). The fact that forced hyperventilation by means of a respirator may restore the blood gas and electrolyte concentrations to normal and thereby cause improvement in some of the symptoms was shown by Boutourline-Young and Whittenberger (1951).

The remarkably small amount of dyspnea often seen in severe emphysema has been a matter of comment by many clinical writers. The polycythemia that may develop compensates in part for the effects of anoxia. In addition, however, polycythemia is accompanied by an increase in blood carbonic anhydrase activity, which also is useful when carbon dioxide excretion in the lungs is slowed. The increase in blood base available for formation of bicarbonate also acts to compensate for carbon dioxide retention. It is possible that other mechanisms not yet understood may also be effective in causing tolerance to carbon dioxide (Barbour and Seevers, 1943). It has been shown that the prevailing level of blood carbon dioxide is important in determining the respiratory response to added carbon dioxide: depletion of carbon dioxide by means of hyperventilation increases sensitivity to inhaled carbon dioxide in normal man (Brown *et al.*, 1948), and also in patients with emphysema (Boutourline-Young and Whittenberger, 1951). Possibly retention has the opposite effect acting through the same mechanism. Even short periods of exposure to increased inspired carbon dioxide concentrations decrease sensitivity to that gas, especially in exercise (Häbisch, 1949) but even at rest (Schäfer, 1949a). Changes in the function of the brain apparently occur (Schäfer, 1949b,c). Whether this is entirely a narcotic effect of carbon dioxide retention is doubtful, for there may be relatively little drowsiness in some cases and indeed mania may occur instead.

The circulation at rest is not affected by lesser degrees of pulmonary emphysema. As the latter increases in severity, slight elevation of venous pressure, secondary to increased intrathoracic pressure, develops. This impairment of venous return does not result in reduced cardiac output at rest, but may prevent normal increases during exertion. Increased intrapulmonary vascular pressure and accelerated circulation due to anoxia may combine to cause myocardial failure ultimately. The superimposition of changes due to myocardial insufficiency upon the high venous pressure and polycythemia that may exist as a consequence of emphysema gives rise to very marked degrees of venous engorgement and cyanosis; this condition is called "right-sided failure" by clinicians, although it is apparent that its causative mechanisms are complex. For example, Liebow (1953), has shown how left ventricular output may increase greatly in emphysema.

The possible role of anoxia in the causation of disturbances in gastro-intestinal motor function, and of hypercarbia in changes in gastric secretion have been pointed out (page 465).

Bibliography

Chapter VIII

ALEXANDER, H. L., and W. B. KOUNTZ, Symptomatic relief of emphysema by an abdominal belt, *Am. J. M. Sc.* **187**, 687 (1934).   [4, 6

ALTSCHULE, M. D., and H. D. LEWIS, Carbonic anhydrase activity of the blood in conditions of dyspnea (*To be published*).

AMATUZIO, D. S., and S. NESBITT, A study of pyruvic acid in the blood and spinal fluid of patients with liver disease with and without hepatic coma, *J. Clin. Investigation* **29**, 1486 (1950).

AMEUILLE, P., La tension intrapleurale à l'état normal et pathologique, *Compt. rend. Soc. de biol.* **83**, 485 (1920).

ANTHONY, A. J., Untersuchungen über Lungenvolumina und Lungenventilation, *Deutsches Arch. f. klin. Med.* **167**, 129 (1930).   [1, 2, 3, 4, 5

BAER, S., The clinical application of the determination of the circulation time, *Ann. Int. Med.* **13**, 2246 (1940).   [11

BAER, S., and H. J. ISARD, The value of the ether circulation time in the diagnosis of right heart failure, *Am. J. M. Sc.* **200**, 209 (1940).

BAER, S., and B. G. SLIPAKOFF, Measurement of circulation times and the agents used in their determination, *Am. Heart J.* **16**, 29 (1938).   [11

BAIN, C. W. C., Observations on the speed of the circulation, *Quart. J. Med.* **27**, 237 (1934).   [11

BARACH, A. L., The effect of low and high oxygen tensions on mental functioning, *J. Aviation Med.* **12**, 30 (1941).   [4, 14, 15

BARBOUR, J. H., and M. H. SEEVERS, A comparison of the acute and chronic toxicity of carbon dioxide with especial reference to its narcotic action, *J. Pharmacol. & Exper. Therap.* **78**, 11 (1943).

BATES, D. V., The uptake of carbon monoxide in health and in emphysema, *Clin. Sc.* **11**, 21 (1952).   [7

BATES, D. V., and R. V. CHRISTIE, Intrapulmonary mixing of helium in health and in emphysema, *Clin. Sc.* **9**, 17 (1950).   [7

BATTRO, A., H. BIDOGGIA, E. R. PIETRAFESA, and F. E. LABOURT, Intracardiac blood pressure in human subjects and its relation to the respiratory phases, *Am. Heart J.* **37**, 11 (1949).

BEALE, H. D., I. W. SCHILLER, M. H. HALPERIN, W. FRANKLIN, and F. C. LOWELL, Delirium and coma precipitated by oxygen in bronchial asthma complicated by respiratory alkalosis, *New England J. Med.* **244**, 710 (1951).

BECK, G. J., A. C. EASTLAKE, and A. L. BARACH, Venous pressure as a guide to pneumoperitoneum therapy in pulmonary emphysema, *Dis. of Chest* **22**, 130 (1952).   [12, 13

BERK, L., J. H. BURCHENAL, T. WOOD, and W. B. CASTLE, Oxygen saturation of sternal marrow blood with special reference to the pathogenesis of polycythemia vera, *Proc. Soc. Exper. Biol. & Med.* **69**, 316 (1948).

BERNSTEIN, L., J. L. D'SILVA, and D. MENDEL, The effect of the rate of breathing on the maximum breathing capacity determined with a new spirometer, *Thorax* **7**, 255 (1952).   [4, 9

BICKERMAN, H. A., and G. J. BECK, Physiologic factors in the treatment of chronic hypertrophic pulmonary emphysema, *Ann. Int. Med.* **36**, 607 (1952).   [4, 8, 9

BIRATH, G., Lung volume and ventilation efficiency; change in collapse-treated and non-collapse-treated pulmonary tuberculosis and in pulmonectomy and lobectomy, *Acta med. Scandinav., Supp. No. 154* (1944).   [1

BITTORF, A., and J. FORSCHBACH, Untersuchungen über die Lungenfullung bei Krankheiten, *Ztschr. f. klin. Med.* **70**, 474 (1910).   [1, 2, 3, 4

BLOOMFIELD, R. A., H. D. LAUSON, A. COURNAND, E. S. BREED, and D .W. RICHARDS, JR., Recording of right heart pressures in normal subjects and in patients with chronic pulmonary disease and various types of cardiocirculatory disease, *J. Clin. Investigation* **25**, 639 (1946).

BOHR, C., Die funktionellen Änderungen in der Mittelage und Vitalkapazität der Lungen. Normales und pathologisches Emphysem, *Deutsches Arch. f. klin. Med.* **88**, 305 (1906–07).   [2, 3, 4, 5

BORDEN, C. W., R. H. WILSON, R. V. EBERT, and H. S. WELLS, Pulmonary hypertension in chronic pulmonary emphysema, *Am. J. Med.* **8**, 701 (1950).   [1, 4, 14

BOUTOURLINE-YOUNG, H. J., and J. L. WHITTENBERGER, The use of artificial respiration in pulmonary emphysema accompanied by high carbon dioxide levels, *J. Clin. Investigation* **30**, 838 (1951).   [1, 4, 8, 9, 14

BRANDT, F., Die Abhängigkeit des Venendruckes von der Grösse der zirkulierenden Blutmenge, zugleich ein Beitrag zur Frage seiner klinischen Bedeutung, *Ztschr. f. klin. Med.* **116**, 398 (1931).   [12

BRISCOE, W. A., Further studies on the intrapulmonary mixing of helium in normal and emphysematous subjects, *Clin. Sc.* **11**, 45 (1952).   [7

BRISCOE, W. A., M. R. BECKLAKE, and T. F. ROSE, Intrapulmonary mixing of helium in normal and emphysematous subjects, *Clin. Sc.* **10**, 37 (1951).   [1, 7

BROWN, E. B., JR., G. S. CAMPBELL, M. N. JOHNSON, A. HEMINGWAY, and M. B. VISSCHER, Changes in response to inhalation of CO_2 before and after 24 hours of hyperventilation in man, *J. Appl. Physiol.* **1**, 333 (1948).

BRUNS, O., Die Bedeutung der spirometrischen Untersuchung von Emphysematiken und Herzkranken, *Med. Klin.* **6**, 1524 (1910).   [1, 5, 7

CALLAWAY, J. J., and V. A. McKUSICK, Carbon dioxide intoxication in emphysema: Emergency treatment by artificial pneumoperitoneum, *New England J. Med.* **245**, 9 (1951).   [4, 10, 12

CAMPBELL, J. M. H., G. H. HUNT, and E. P. POULTON, An examination of the blood gases and respiration in disease, with reference to the cause of breathlessness and cyanosis, *J. Path. & Bact.* **26**, 234 (1923).

CAMPBELL, J. M. H., and E. P. POULTON, The effect of exercise on the pulmonary ventilation and rate and depth of breathing in chronic bronchitis, *Quart. J. Med.* **20**, 27 (1926–27).   [8

CARTER, M. G., E. A. GAENSLER, and A. KYLLONEN, Pneumoperitoneum in the treatment of pulmonary emphysema, *New England J. Med.* **243**, 549 (1950).   [1, 3, 4, 9

CHRISTIE, R. V., The elastic properties of the emphysematous lung and their clinical significance, *J. Clin. Investigation* **13**, 295 (1934).   [1, 2, 4, 5, 6, 7, 8, 14, 15

CHRISTIE, R. V., and C. A. McINTOSH, The measurement of the intrapleural pressure in man and its significance, *J. Clin. Investigation* **13**, 279 (1934).   [6, 13

COBB, S., and F. FREMONT-SMITH, The cerebral circulation. XVI. Changes in the human retinal circulation and in the pressure of the cerebrospinal fluid during inhalation of a mixture of carbon dioxide and oxygen, *Arch. Neurol. & Psychiat.* **26**, 730 (1931).

COBET, R., Ueber die Wasserstoffzahl des Blutes bei Herzkranken, *Deutsches Arch. f. klin. Med.* **144**, 126 (1924).

COMROE, J. H., JR., E. R. BAHNSON, and E. O. COATES, JR., Mental changes occurring in chronically anoxemic patients during oxygen therapy, *J. A. M. A.* **143**, 1044 (1950).   [9, 14, 15

COMROE, J. H., and W. S. FOWLER, Lung function studies. VI. Detection of uneven alveolar ventilation during a single breath of oxygen, *Am. J. Med.* **10**, 408 (1951).   [7

COURNAND, A., E. D. BALDWIN, R. C. DARLING, and D. W. RICHARDS, JR., Studies on intrapulmonary mixture of gases. IV. The significance of the pulmonary emptying rate and a simplified open circuit measurement of residual air, *J. Clin. Investigation* **20**, 681 (1941). [1

COURNAND, A., H. C. A. LASSEN, and D. W. RICHARDS, JR., Distribution of respiratory gases in a closed breathing circuit. II. Pulmonary fibrosis and emphysema, *J. Clin. Investigation* **16**, 9 (1937). [7

COURNAND, A., H. D. LAUSON, R. A. BLOOMFIELD, E. S. BREED, and E. DE F. BALDWIN, Recording of right heart pressures in man, *Proc. Soc. Exper. Biol. & Med.* **55**, 34 (1944).

CRISAFULLI, A., and A. COLACRESI, La "prova di carico" con lattato di sodio per la diagnosi di insufficienza cardiaca, *Cuore e circolaz.* **21**, 557 (1937).

DARLING, R. C., A. COURNAND, J. S. MANSFIELD, and D. W. RICHARDS, JR., Studies on the intrapulmonary mixture of gases. I. Nitrogen elimination from blood and body tissues during high oxygen breathing, *J. Clin. Investigation* **19**, 591 (1940). [7

DARLING, R. C., A. COURNAND, and D. W. RICHARDS, JR., Studies in intrapulmonary mixture of gases. V. Forms of inadequate ventilation in normal and emphysematous lungs analyzed by means of breathing pure oxygen, *J. Clin. Investigation* **23**, 55 (1944). [1, 7

DAUTREBANDE, L., L'équilibre acide-base chez les emphysémateux. Ses variations au cours de la décompensation cardiaque, *Compt. rend. Soc. de biol.* **93**, 1025 (1925). [4, 8, 14, 15

DAVIES, C. E., and J. MACKINNON, Neurological effects of oxygen in chronic cor pulmonale, *Lancet* **2**, 883 (1949). [5, 13, 14, 15

DAYMAN, H., Mechanics of airflow in health and in emphysema, *J. Clin. Investigation* **30**, 1175 (1951).

DEAN, R. B., and M. B. VISSCHER, The kinetics of lung ventilation. An evaluation of the viscous and elastic resistance to lung ventilation with particular reference to the effects of turbulence and the therapeutic use of helium, *Am. J. Physiol.* **134**, 450 (1941). [6

DONALD, K. W., Reaction to carbon dioxide in pneumokoniosis of coalminers, *Clin. Sc.* **8**, 45 (1949).

DONALD, K. W., J. M. BISHOP, G. CUMMING, and O. L. WADE, The effect of nursing positions on the cardiac output in man. With a note on the repeatability of measurements on cardiac output by the direct Fick method, and with data on subjects with a normal cardiovascular system, *Clin. Sc.* **12**, 199 (1953).

DONALD, K. W., and R. V. CHRISTIE, The respiratory response to carbon dioxide and anoxia in emphysema, *Clin. Sc.* **8**, 33 (1949).

DONALD, K. W., A. RENZETTI, R. L. RILEY, and A. COURNAND, Analysis of factors affecting concentrations of oxygen and carbon dioxide in gas and blood of lungs: Results, *J. Appl. Physiol.* **4**, 497 (1952). [1, 4, 5, 9, 14, 15

DuBois, A. B., R. C. Fowler, A. Soffer, and W. O. Fenn, Alveolar CO_2 measured by expiration into the rapid infrared gas analyzer, *J. Appl. Physiol.* 4, 526 (1952).

Duras, F. P., Measurement of the circulation time with saccharin, *Lancet* 1, 303 (1944). [11

Essen, H., F. Kauders, and O. Porges, Die Beziehung der O_2-Spannung der Alveolarluft zu den Chloriden des Blutserums, *Wien. Arch. f. inn. Med.* 5, 499 (1923).

Eyster, J. A. E., Venous pressure and its clinical applications, *Physiol. Rev.* 6, 281 (1926). [13

Feltman, J. A., W. Newman, A. Schwartz, D. J. Stone, and F. J. Lovelock, Cardiac failure secondary to ineffective bellows action of the chest cage, *J. Clin. Investigation* 31, 762 (1952).

Ferrer, M. I., R. M. Harvey, R. T. Cathcart, C. A. Webster, D. W. Richards, Jr., and A. Cournand, Some effects of digoxin upon the heart and circulation in man. Digoxin in chronic cor pulmonale, *Circulation* 1, 161 (1950). [1, 4, 7, 9, 14, 15

Ferris, E. B., Jr., Objective measurement of relative intracranial blood flow in man. With observations concerning the hydrodynamics of the craniovertebral system, *Arch. Neurol. & Psychiat.* 46, 377 (1941).

Fishman, A. P., J. McClement, A. Himmelstein, and A. Cournand, Effects of acute anoxia on the circulation and respiration in patients with chronic pulmonary disease studied during the "steady state," *J. Clin. Investigation* 31, 770 (1952). [8, 15

Fowler, N. O., R. N. Westcott, V. D. Hauenstein, R. C. Scott, and J. McGuire, Observations on autonomic participation in pulmonary arteriolar resistance in man, *J. Clin. Investigation* 29, 1387 (1950).

Fowler, N. O., Jr., R. N. Westcott, and R. C. Scott, Pulmonary artery diastolic pressure: its relationship to pulmonary arteriolar resistance and pulmonary "capillary" pressure, *J. Clin. Investigation* 31, 72 (1952). [14

Fowler, W. S., Lung function studies. V. Respiratory dead space in old age and in pulmonary emphysema, *J. Clin. Investigation* 29, 1439 (1950).

Fowler, W. S., and J. H. Comroe, Lung function studies. I. The rate of increase of arterial oxygen saturation during inhalation of 100 per cent O_2, *J. Clin. Investigation* 27, 327 (1948). [7

Fowler, W. S., E. R. Cornish, Jr., and S. Kety, Lung function studies. VIII. Analysis of alveolar ventilation by pulmonary N_2 clearance curves, *J. Clin. Investigation* 31, 40 (1952). [7

Fraser, F. R., Goulstonian lectures on cardiac dyspnoea, *Lancet* 1, 529, 589, 643 (1927).

FRASER, F. R., C. F. HARRIS, R. HILTON, and G. C. LINDER, Arterial carbon dioxide pressure in cardiac dyspnoea, *Quart. J. Med.* **22**, 1 (1928).

GAENSLER, E. A., Air velocity index. A numerical expression of the functionally effective portion of ventilation, *Am. Rev. Tuberc.* **62**, 17 (1950). [4, 9

GAENSLER, E. A., Analysis of the ventilatory defect by timed capacity measurements, *Am. Rev. Tuberc.* **64**, 256 (1951). [1, 4

GAENSLER, E. A., and M. G. CARTER, Ventilation measurements in pulmonary emphysema treated with pneumoperitoneum, *J. Lab. & Clin. Med.* **35**, 945 (1950). [1, 2, 3, 4, 9, 14

GAERTNER, G., Die Messung des Drucks im rechten Vorhof, *München. med. Wchnschr.* **50**, 2038 (1903). [12

GARGILL, S. L., The use of sodium dehydrocholate as a clinical test of the velocity of blood flow, *New England J. Med.* **209**, 1089 (1933). [10

GEORG, J., Pulmonary function tests, *Scandinav. J. Clin. & Lab. Investigation* **4**, 327, (1952). [7, 9

GILLANDERS, A. D., Circulatory dynamics in emphysema, *Quart. J. Med.* **18**, 263 (1949). [10, 13

GOGGIO, A. F., The abnormal physiology of chronic pulmonary emphysema. Three contrasting illustrative cases, *New England J. Med.* **231**, 672 (1944). [4, 14, 15

GORDON, B. L., H. L. MOTLEY, P. A. THEODOS, and L. P. LANG, Studies of disability in anthrasilicosis, *Tr. A. Am. Physicians* **62**, 270 (1949). [1, 4, 9, 14

GRAY, F. D., P. R. LURIE, and R. WHITTEMORE, Circulatory changes in chronic pulmonary disease. A study of pulmonary collateral circulation, *Yale J. Biol. & Med.* **23**, 380 (1951). [14

GROSS, D., The measurement of the lung-to-face time by amyl nitrite, *Am. Heart J.* **30**, 19 (1945).

HÄBISCH, H., Ueber den Gaswechsel bei Ruhe und Arbeit unter Kurz- und Langfristiger Kohlensaureeinwirkung, *Arch. f.d.ges. Physiol.* **251**, 594 (1949).

HARVEY, R. M., M. I. FERRER, D. W. RICHARDS, Jr., and A. COURNAND, Influence of chronic pulmonary disease on the heart and circulation, *Am. J. Med.* **10**, 719 (1951). [14, 15

HERBST, R., Der Gasstoffwechsel als Mass der körperlichen Leistungsfähigkeit. II. Untersuchungen bei Emphysem, chronischer Bronchitis und Asthma bronchiale, *Deutsches Arch. f. klin. Med.* **162**, 129 (1928). [4, 8

HERMS, J., Röntgenbild und Luftgehalt der Lungen beim Emphysem, *Beitr. z. Klin. d. Tuberk.* **77**, 251 (1931). [1, 4, 5

HERMS, J., and I. RÜTTGERS, Lungenvolumina, Ventilation und Arbeitstoffwechsel beim Lungenemphysem, *Beitr. z. Klin. d. Tuberk.* **78,** 724 (1931). [1, 4, 8

HERRMANSEN, J., Die ergometrische Methode als Funktionsprüfung für Herz und Lunge, *Beitr. z. Klin. d. Tuberk.* **92,** 395 (1938).

HERXHEIMER, Reserve air as aid in diagnosis of emphysema, *Thorax* **4,** 73 (1949). [4

HICKAM, J. B., and W. H. CARGILL, Effect of exercise on cardiac output and pulmonary arterial pressure in normal persons and in patients with cardiovascular disease and pulmonary emphysema, *J. Clin. Investigation* **27,** 10 (1948).

HICKAM, J. B., H. O. SIEKER, W. W. PRYOR, and J. M. RYAN, Carbon dioxide retention during oxygen therapy, *North Carolina M. J.* **13,** 35 (1952).

HIMWICH, H. E., and R. O. LOEBEL, The oxygen saturation of hemoglobin in the arterial blood of exercising patients, *J. Clin. Investigation* **5,** 113 (1927–28).

HITZENBERGER, K., and F. TUCHFELD, Die zirkulierende Blutmenge bei Kreislaufserkrankungen im kompensierten und dekompensierten Zustand. *Wien. Arch. f. inn. Med.* **18,** 171 (1929).

HOLMAN, J., and G. T. SHIRES, Quantitative studies of ventilation during inhalation of carbon dioxide in normal and emphysematous patients, *Am. Heart J.* **37,** 1101 (1949). [4, 8, 14, 15

HOOVER, C. F., The minute volume and alveolar air in pulmonary emphysema, *Arch. Int. Med.* **11,** 52 (1913).

HOOVER, C. F., and L. TAYLOR, The ventilatory function of the lung in emphysema and asthma, *Arch. Int. Med.* **15,** 1 (1915).

HOUSSAY, B. A., and I. BERCONSKY, Cyanose par l'hypoventilation alvéolaire, *Presse méd.* **40,** 1759 (1932). [4, 8, 14, 15

HURTADO, A., W. W. FRAY, and W. S. McCANN, Studies of total pulmonary capacity and its subdivisions. IV. Preliminary observations on cases of pulmonary emphysema and of pneumoconiosis, *J. Clin. Investigation* **12,** 833 (1933). [2, 4, 5

HURTADO, A., N. L. KALTREIDER, W. W. FRAY, W. D. W. BROOKS, and W. S. McCANN, Studies of total pulmonary capacity and its subdivisions. VI. Observations on cases of obstructive pulmonary emphysema, *J. Clin. Investigation* **13,** 1027 (1934). [2, 3, 4, 5, 12

HURTADO, A., N. L. KALTREIDER, and W. S. McCANN, Studies of total pulmonary capacity and its subdivisions. IX. Relationship to oxygen saturation and carbon dioxide content of the arterial blood, *J. Clin. Investigation* **14,** 94 (1935). [4, 14, 15

JABLONS, B., J. COHEN, and M. Y. SWIRSKY, Clinical studies of circulation time with objective (photoelectric cell-dye) method, *New York State J. Med.* **44,** 398 (1944). [11

JANSEN, K., H. W. KNIPPING, and K. STROMBERGER, Klinische Untersuchungen uber Atmung und Blutgase, *Beitr. z. Klin. d. Tuberk.* **80**, 304 (1932).   ⌊14, 15

JOHNSON, J. B., I. FERRER, J. R. WEST and A. COURNAND, The relation between electrocardiographic evidence of right ventricular hypertrophy pulmonary arterial pressure in patients with chronic pulmonary disease, *Circulation* **1**, 536 (1950).   [14

KALTREIDER, N. L., A. HURTADO, and W. D. W. BROOKS, Study of the blood in chronic respiratory diseases with special reference to the volume of the blood, *J. Clin. Investigation* **13**, 999 (1934).

KALTREIDER, N. L., and W. S. McCANN, Respiratory response during exercise in pulmonary fibrosis and emphysema, *J. Clin. Investigation* **16**, 23 (1937).   [1, 4, 8, 14

KLATSKIN, G., and W. A. KREHL, The significance of the plasma tocopherol concentration and of tocopherol tolerance tests in liver disease, *J. Clin. Investigation* **29**, 1528 (1950).

KNIPPING, H. W., W. LEWIS, and A. MONCRIEFF, Über die Dyspnoe, *Beitr. z. Klin. d. Tuberk.* **79**, 1 (1932).   [1, 4

KOCH, E., Die Stromgeschwindigkeit des Blutes. Ein Beitrag zur Arbeitsprüfung des Kreislaufes, *Deutsches Arch. f. klin. Med.* **140**, 39 (1922).

KOPELMAN, H., The circulation time as a clinical test, *Brit. Heart J.* **13**, 301 (1951).   [4, 10

KOUNTZ, W. B., and H. L. ALEXANDER, Nonobstructive emphysema, *J. A. M. A.* **100**, 551 (1933).   [4, 13, 14

KOUNTZ, W. B., and H. L. ALEXANDER, Emphysema, *Medicine* **13**, 251 (1934).   [4, 13, 14

KOUNTZ, W. B., H. L. ALEXANDER, and D. DOWELL, Emphysema simulating cardiac decompensation, *J. A. M. A.* **93**, 1369 (1929).   [4, 13, 14

KOUNTZ, W. B., E. F. PEARSON, and K. F. KOENIG, Observations on intrapleural pressure and its influence on the relative circulation rate in emphysema, *J. Clin. Investigation* **11**, 1281 (1932).   [6, 10, 12, 13

KROETZ, C., Die Koeffizienten des klinisch messbaren Venendruckes, *Deutsches Arch. f. klin. Med.* **139**, 325 (1922).

KROETZ, C., Gasanalytische Untersuchungen über die Endothelfunktion der Lungen, *Verhandl. d. deutsch. Gesellsch. f. inn. Med.* **41**, 449 (1929).

LAMBIE, C. G., Observations on the carbonic anhydrase of the blood in anaemia and in other pathological conditions, *Edinburgh M. J.* **45**, 373 (1938).

LANDEN, H. C., and A. DORTMANN, Bemerkungen zum Problem der Bestimmung von Storungen in der Lungenfunktion, *Ztschr. f. klin. Med.* **147**, 292 (1950).   [4, 8, 14

LANPHIER, E. H., Determination of residual volume and residual volume/ total capacity ratio by single breath technique, *J. Appl. Physiol.* **5,** 361 (1953).   [1

LERMAN, W. S., A study of the effect of chronic pulmonary diseases on the volume and composition of the blood, *Ann. Int. Med.* **3,** 430 (1929).
                                                                              [14

LEWIS, C. S., A. J. SAMUELS, M. C. DAINES, and H. H. HECHT, Chronic lung disease, polycythemia and congestive heart failure. Cardio-respiratory, vascular and renal adjustments in cor pulmonale, *Circulation* **6,** 874 (1952).   [8, 14

LIAN, C., and J. FACQUET, La mesure de la vitesse circulatoire en dehors de l'insuffisance cardiaque, *Bull. et mém. Soc. méd. d. hôp. de Paris* **51,** 397 (1935).   [11

LIEBOW, A. A., The bronchopulmonary venous collateral circulation with special reference to emphysema, *Am. J. Path.* **29,** 251 (1953).

LUKAS, D. S., Some effects of adrenocorticotropic hormone and cortisone on pulmonary function of patients with obstructive emphysema, *Am. Rev. Tuberc.* **64,** 279 (1951).   [1, 4, 7, 9, 14

LUNDSGAARD, C., and K. SCHIERBECK, Studies on lung volume. IX. Patients with emphysema pulmonum, *Proc. Soc. Exper. Biol. & Med.* **20,** 165 (1922).   [1, 4, 5

LUNDSGAARD, C., and K. SCHIERBECK, Untersuchungen über die Volumina der Lungen. IV. Die Verhältnisse bei Patienten mit Lungenemphysem, *Acta med. Scandinav.* **58,** 541 (1923).   [1, 4, 5

MARSHALL, R., D. V. BATES, and R. V. CHRISTIE, Fractional analysis of the alveolar air in emphysema, *Clin. Sc.* **11,** 297 (1952).

MARZAHN, H., W. GILBEAU, and G. ZAEPER, Klinische Untersuchungen über die Funktion von Atmung und Kreislauf bei Gesunden und Kranken. II Mitt. Ergebnisse bei der Prüfung gesunder und kranker Lungen, *Ztschr. f. klin. Med.* **129,** 434 (1936).

MATHIEU, L., GRILLIAT, and PILLOT, Considérations diagnostiques sur la fonction ventilatoire des cardiaques, *Arch. d. mal. du cœur*, **45,** 21 (1952).   [4, 9

MAURATH, J., and P. HAUER, Säure-Basengleichgewcht und Atemregulation bei chronischer Hypoxämie, *Klin. Wchschr.* **30,** 315 (1952).

MCILROY, M. B., and R. V. CHRISTIE, A post-mortem study of the visco-elastic properties of the lungs in emphysema, *Thorax* **7,** 291 (1952).

MEAKINS, J., and R. V. CHRISTIE, Treatment of emphysema, *J. A. M. A.* **103,** 384 (1934).   [6

MILLER, F., A. HEMINWAY, R. L. VARCO, and A. O. C. NIER, Alveolar ventilation studies using the mass spectrometer, *Proc. Soc. Exper. Biol. & Med.* **74,** 13 (1950).   [7

MILLER, H. R., Velocity of blood flow in part of the pulmonary circulation, *Proc. Soc. Exper. Biol. & Med.* **31,** 942 (1934). [11

MITHOEFER, J. C., Increased intracranial pressure in emphysema caused by oxygen inhalation, *J. A. M. A.* **149,** 1116 (1952). [15

MOTLEY, H. L., B. GORDON, L. P. LANG, and P. A. THEODOS, Impairment of pulmonary function in anthrasilicosis, *Arch. Indust. Hyg. & Occupat. Med.* **1,** 133 (1950). [1, 4, 9, 14

MOTLEY, H. L., L. P. LANG, and B. GORDON, Total lung volume and maximal breathing capacity (MBC) in pulmonary emphysema after repeated periods of intermittent positive pressure breathing (IPPB), *J. Aviation Med.* **19,** 346 (1948). [1, 4, 5, 9

MOTLEY, H. L., L. P. LANG, and B. GORDON, Effect of intermittent positive pressure breathing on respiratory gas exchange, *J. Aviation Med.* **21,** 14 (1950). [1, 14, 15

MOTLEY, H. L., L. P. LANG, and B. GORDON, Studies on the respiratory gas exchange in one hundred anthracite miners with pulmonary complaints, *Am. Rev. Tuberc.* **61,** 201 (1950). [1, 8, 14

MOTLEY, H. L., and J. F. TOMASHEFSKI, Effect of high and low oxygen levels and intermittent positive pressure breathing on oxygen transport in the lungs in pulmonary fibrosis and emphysema, *J. Appl. Physiol.* **3,** 189 (1950).

MOUNSEY, J. P. D., A. W. RITZMAN, N. J. SELVERSTONE, W. A. BRISCOE, and G. A. McLEMORE, Circulatory changes in severe pulmonary emphysema, *Brit. Heart J.* **14,** 153 (1952). [1, 4, 7, 9, 14

OPPENHEIMER, B. S., and W. M. HITZIG, The use of circulatory measurements in evaluating pulmonary and cardiac factors in chronic lung disorders, *Am. Heart J.* **12,** 257 (1936). [10, 12

ORNSTEIN, G. G., The measurement of the function of the lungs, *Dis. of Chest* **15,** 280 (1949). [4, 8, 9

PAINE, J. R., The clinical measurement of pulmonary elasticity. A comparison of the methods of Christie and McIntosh and of Neergaard and Wirz, *J. Thoracic Surg.* **9,** 550 (1940). [4

PATTERSON, J. L., JR., A. HEYMAN, and T. W. DUKE, Cerebral circulation and metabolism in chronic pulmonary emphysema. With observations on the effects of inhalation of oxygen, *Am. J. Med.* **12,** 382 (1952). [14, 15

PICCIONE, F. V., and L. J. BOYD, The determination of blood velocity by lobeline, *J. Lab. & Clin. Med.* **26,** 766 (1941). [11

PLATT, R., The blood glutathione in disease, *Brit. J. Exper. Path.* **12,** 139 (1931).

PLATTS, M. M., The arterial blood gases in pulmonary heart failure, *Clin. Sc.* **12,** 63 (1953). [14, 15

PLESCH, J., Die pathologische Physiologie des Lungenvolumens und seine Beziehung zum Kreislauf, *Ztschr. f. exper. Path. u. Pharmakol.* **13,** 165 (1913). [1, 2, 3, 4, 5

PORGES, O., A. LEIMDÖRFER, and E. MARKOVICI, Ueber die Kohlensäurespannung des Blutes in pathologischen Zuständen. II. Ueber die Kohlensäurespannung des Blutes in der kardialen und pulmonalen Dyspnoe, *Ztschr. f. klin. Med.* **77,** 446 (1913).

PRICE-JONES, C., The sizes of red blood cells in emphysema, *J. Path. & Bact.* **24,** 326 (1921).

PROCTOR, D. F., Studies of respiratory air flow in measurement of ventilatory function, *Dis. of Chest* **22,** 432 (1952).

PROCTOR, D. F., J. B. HARDY, and R. MCLEAN, Studies of respiratory air flow. II. Observations on patients with pulmonary disease, *Bull. Johns Hopkins Hosp.* **87,** 255 (1950). [9

RASMUSSEN, H., and O. STORSTEIN, Studies in oxygen therapy. Part I. On the frequency of anoxemia, its occurrence in medical diseases and its relation to cyanosis, *Acta med. Scandinav.* **141,** 43 (1951). [14

REINHARDT, R., Ueber das Verhältnis von CO_2-Ausscheidung zur Atengrösse beim Lungenemphysem, *Deutsches Arch. f. klin. Med.* **109,** 192 (1912). [4, 8

RICHARDS, D. W., JR., Cardiac output by the catheterization technique in various clinical conditions, *Federation Proc.* **4,** 215 (1945).

RICHARDS, D. W., JR., and A. L. BARACH, Effects of oxygen treatment over long periods of time in patients with pulmonary fibrosis, *Am. Rev. Tuberc.* **26,** 253 (1932).

RILEY, R. L., R. AUSTRIAN, K. W. DONALD, and A. COURNAND, The relation of effective pulmonary blood flow to total pulmonary blood flow in normal man and in patients with various types of chronic pulmonary disease, *J. Clin. Investigation* **28,** 805 (1949). [14

RILEY, R. L., A. HIMMELSTEIN, H. L. MOTLEY, H. M. WEINER, and A. COURNAND, Pulmonary circulation during exercise in normal individuals and in patients with chronic pulmonary disease, *Federation Proc.* **7,** 102 (1948).

RILEY, R. L., A. HIMMELSTEIN, H. L. MOTLEY, H. M. WEINER, and A. COURNAND, Studies of the pulmonary circulation at rest and during exercise in normal individuals and in patients with chronic pulmonary disease, *Am. J. Physiol.* **152,** 372 (1948). [14

RINGER, M., and M. D. ALTSCHULE, Studies on the circulation. II. Cardiac output in diseases of the heart, and under the influence of digitalis therapy, *Am. Heart J.* **5,** 305 (1930).

ROBERTSON, J. S., W. E. SIRI, and H. B. JONES, Lung ventilation patterns determined by analysis of nitrogen elimination rates; use of the mass spectrometer as a continuous gas analyzer, *J. Clin. Investigation* **29**, 577 (1950). [4, 7, 8

ROELSEN, E., Fractional analysis of alveolar air after inspiration of hydrogen as a method for the determination of the distribution of inspired air in the lungs. Examinations of normal persons and of patients suffering from bronchial asthma and pulmonary emphysema, *Acta med. Scandinav.* **95**, 452 (1938). [1, 4, 7

ROELSEN, E., and N. BAY, Investigations of the lung function in silicotics. I. The capacity of the lungs and the conditions of the alveolar ventilation, *Acta med. Scandinav.* **103**, 55 (1940). [7

ROWNTREE, L. G., and G. E. BROWN, *The volume of the blood and plasma in health and disease* (W. B. Saunders Co., Philadelphia and London, 1929).

SCHÄFER, K.-E., Atmung und Säure-Basengleichgewicht bei langdauernden Aufenthalt in 3% CO_2, *Arch. f.d.ges. Physiol.* **251**, 689 (1949).

SCHÄFER, K.-E., Die Beeinflussung der Psyche und der Erregungsabläufe im peripheren Nervensystem unter langdauernden Einwirkung von 3% CO_2, *Arch f.d.ges. Physiol.* **251**, 716 (1949).

SCHÄFER, K.-E., Der Einfluss eines langdauernden Aufenthaltes in 3% CO_2 auf die Hirnaktionsströme, *Arch. f.d.ges. Physiol.* **251**, 726 (1949).

SCHLOMOVITZ, B. H., A. B. THOMPSON, and L. G. GLICKMAN, A functional test in chronic pulmonary disease, *Am. Rev. Tuberc.* **37**, 369 (1938).

SCHOEN, R., and E. DERRA, Untersuchungen über die Bedeutung der Zyanose als klinisches Symptom. (I), *Deutsches Arch. f. klin. Med.* **168**, 52 (1930). [14

SCHOTT, E., Die Ehröhung des Druckes im venösen System bei Anstrengung als Mass für die Funktionstüchtigkeit des menschlichen Herzens, *Deutsches Arch. f. klin. Med.* **108**, 537 (1912).

SCOTT, R. W., The total carbonate content of the arterial and venous plasma in patients with chronic pulmonary emphysema, *Proc. Soc. Exper. Biol. & Med.* **17**, 21 (1919). [15

SCOTT, R. W., Observations on the pathologic physiology of chronic pulmonary emphysema, *Arch. Int. Med.* **26**, 545 (1920). [15

SEEVERS, M. H., H. R. HATHAWAY, and R. T. STORMONT, Tissue gas studies in respiratory and circulatory disease, *Am. J. Physiol.* **116**, 140 (1936).

SESSA, T., La velocità della corrente del sangue. III. Tempo di circolazione nelle varie affezione morbose, *Cuore e circolaz.* **22**, 181 (1938). [10

SHARPEY-SCHAFER, E. P., 2-Thiouracil in the treatment of congestive heart failure, *Brit. Med. J.* **2**, 888 (1946).

SIEBECK, R., Über die Beeinflussung der Atemmechanik durch krankhafte Zustände des Respirations- und Kreislaufapparates, *Deutsches Arch. f. klin. Med.* **100**, 204 (1910). [1, 2, 4

SIEBECK, R., Über den Gasaustausch zwischen der Aussenluft und den Alveolen. III Mitt. Die Lungenventilation beim Emphysem, *Deutsches Arch. f. klin. Med.* **102**, 390 (1911). [7

SILBER, E. N., G. L. SNIDER, K. GOLDBERG, L. N. KATZ, and D. B. RODNER, The effect of khellin on cardio-pulmonary function in chronic pulmonary disease, *J. Clin. Investigation* **30**, 1046 (1951). [2, 3, 4, 8, 9, 14

SONNE, C., Des respiratorische Luftaustausch in der Lungen, *Ztschr. f. d. ges. exper. Med.* **94**, 13 (1934). [7

STAEHELIN, R., and A. SCHÜTZE, Spirographische Untersuchungen an Gesunden, Emphysematikern und Asthmatikern, *Ztschr. f. klin. Med.* **75**, 15 (1912). [8

STARR, I., and L. JONAS, Supernormal circulation in resting subjects (hyperkinemia). With a study of the relation of kinemic abnormalities to the basal metabolic rate, *Arch. Int. Med.* **71**, 1 (1943).

STEAD, W. W., D. L. FRY, and R. V. EBERT, The elastic properties of the lung in normal men and in patients with chronic pulmonary emphysema, *J. Lab & Clin. Med.* **40**, 674 (1952). [1, 4, 5, 6

STEWART, G. N., Studies on the circulation in man. IV. The influence of oxygen inhalation in a case of cyanosis, *J. Pharmacol. & Exper. Therap.* **2**, 477 (1911).

STONE, D. J., A. SCHWARTZ, W. NEWMAN, J. A. FELTMAN, and F. J. LOVELOCK, Precipitation by pulmonary infection of acute anoxia, cardiac failure and respiratory acidosis in chronic pulmonary disease, *Am. J. Med.* **14**, 14 (1953). [1, 4, 7, 9, 14, 15

TAQUINI, A. C., and B. B. LOZADA, Corazón pulmonar cronico con y sin insufficiencia cardiaca. Functiones respiratoria y circulatoria, *Medicina* **8**, 325 (1948). [1, 4, 5, 8, 10

TARR, L., B. S. OPPENHEIMER, and R. V. SAGER, The circulation time in various clinical conditions determined by the use of sodium dehydrocholate, *Am. Heart J.* **8**, 766 (1932–33). [10

TORNQUIST, H., Physiologische und klinische Studien über den Armvenendruck, *Ztschr. f. d. ges. exper. Med.* **81**, 227 (1932). [12

UHLENBRUCK, P., and R. VOGELS, Zum Problem der zirkulierende Plasmamenge (Blutmenge) bei Kreislaufstörungen, *Ztschr. f. klin. Med.* **118**, 172 (1931).

VILLARET, M. F. ST. GIRONS, and F. GRELLETY-BOSVIEL, La tension veineuse périphérique (P.V.) et ses modifications pathologiques, *Presse méd.* **31**, 318 (1923). [12

VON NEERGARD, K., and K. WIRZ, Ueber eine Methode zur Messung der Lungenelastizität am lebenden Menschen, insbesondere beim Emphysem, *Ztschr. f. klin. Med.* 105, 35 (1927a).

VON NEERGARD, K., and K. WIRZ, Die Messung der Strömungswiderstände in den Atemwegen des Menschen, insbesondere bei Asthma und Emphysem, *Ztschr. f. klin. Med.* 105, 51 (1927b).

WAHLUND, H., Determination of the physical working capacity. A physiological and clinical study with special reference to standardization of cardio-pulmonary function tests, *Acta med. Scandinav., Supp. No. 215* (1948).   [8

WEISS, S., and H. L. BLUMGART, Studies on the velocity of blood flow. VIII. The velocity of blood flow and its relation to other aspects of the circulation in patients with pulmonary emphysema, *J. Clin. Investigation* 4, 555 (1927).   [4, 10, 12

WEISS, S., G. P. ROBB, and H. L. BLUMGART, The velocity of blood flow in health and disease as measured by the effect of histamine on the minute vessels, *Am. Heart J.* 4, 664 (1928–29).   [10

WHITFIELD, A. G. W., Emphysema, *Brit. M. J.* 2, 1227 (1952).
                                                     [1, 2, 3, 4, 5, 14, 15

WHITFIELD, A. G. W., W. M. ARNOTT, and J. A. H. WATERHOUSE, The effect of ephedrine in asthma and emphysema, *Quart. J. Med.* 19, 319 (1950).   [1, 2, 3, 4, 5

WHITFIELD, A. G. W., W. M. ARNOTT, and J. A. H. WATERHOUSE, Effect of aminophylline in emphysema, *Lancet* 1, 490 (1951).   [1, 2, 3, 4, 5

WHITFIELD, A. G. W., O. E. SMITH, D. G. B. RICHARDS, J. A. H. WATERHOUSE, and W. M. ARNOTT, The correlation between the radiological appearances and the clinical and spirometric state in emphysema, *Quart. J. Med.* 20, 247 (1951).   [1, 2, 3, 4, 5

WILSON, R. H., C. W. BORDEN, and R. V. EBERT, Adaptation to anoxia in chronic pulmonary emphysema, *Arch. Int. Med.* 88, 581 (1951).   [14

WILSON, R. H., C. W. BORDEN, R. V. EBERT, and H. S. WELLS, A comparison of the effect of voluntary hyperventilation in normal persons, patients with pulmonary emphysema, and patients with cardiac disease, *J. Lab. & Clin. Med.* 36, 119 (1950).   [1, 2, 3, 4, 5, 9, 14, 15

WOLFE, W. A., and L. D. CARLSON, Studies of pulmonary capacity and mixing with the nitrogen meter, *J. Clin. Investigation* 29, 1568 (1950).
                                                            [1 4, 5, 7

WOOD, P., Right and left ventricular failure. A study of circulation time and venous blood pressure, *Lancet* 2, 15 (1936).   [10, 12

YEOMANS, A., and G. H. STUECK, JR., Clinical-chemical studies of acid-base abnormalities. Changes in acid-base balance observed in renal and respiratory disease, *Am. J. Med.* 13, 183 (1952).   [14, 15

Yu, P. N. G., F. W. Lovejoy, Jr., H. A. Joos, R. E. Nye, Jr., and W. S. McCann, Studies of pulmonary hypertension. I. Pulmonary circulatory dynamics in patients with pulmonary emphysema at rest, *J. Clin. Investigation* **32,** 130 (1953).   **[1, 4, 14, 15**

Zaeper, G., and W. Wolf, Ueber die Erkennung und quantitative Beurteilung pulmonaler Funktionsstörungen, *Beitr. z. Klin. d. Tuberk.* **92,** 487 (1939).

IX

BRONCHIAL ASTHMA

The respiratory dynamics during asthmatic attacks are very much like those of chronic emphysema, with an additional superimposed element of bronchial obstruction.

Lung volume and its subdivisions. — The residual air is usually described as increased (Anthony, 1930; Hurtado *et al.*, 1935*a, b*; Roelsen, 1938; Beale *et al.*, 1951, 1952; Taquini and Lozada, 1948; Whitfield *et al.*, 1950; Herschfus *et al.*, 1953; Briscoe and McLemore, 1952); only Bohr (1907) and Lanphier (1953) found it normal. The reserve and complemental airs (Bohr, 1907; Anthony, 1930; Knipping *et al.*, 1932; Taquini and Lozada, 1948; Whitfield *et al.*, 1950; Briscoe and McLemore, 1952; Herschfus *et al.*, 1953) are much reduced; the vital capacity is considerably decreased in volume (**1**; Myers, 1922). The total capacity may be normal or low (Bohr, 1907; Anthony, 1930; Hurtado *et al.*, 1935*a*; Taquini and Lozada, 1948; Whitfield *et al.*, 1950; Briscoe and McLemore, 1952; Herschfus *et al.*, 1953). One of the two important measurements relating to mixing is the functional residual air; this is usually increased (Fowler *et al.*, 1952; Bates, 1952; Beale *et al.*, 1952; Briscoe and McLemore, 1952) and accordingly mixing should be retarded.

Intrapleural pressure. — Kountz *et al.* (1932) found the static intrapleural pressure, that is, the intrapleural pressure during respiratory diastole, high in asthma, but Christie and McIntosh (1934) reported it as normal. It is apparent that either condition could occur under different circumstances. Changes in the dynamic intrapleural pressure do, however, occur, for von Neergard and Wirz (1927), Christie and McIntosh (1934), Paine (1940) and Kountz *et al.* (1932) found it more negative than normal in inspiration and more positive in expiration. Prinzmetal (1934), however, reported it to be more negative than normal at all times, an observation which is difficult to accept.

Respiratory dynamics. — Mixing in the lungs is impaired (Roelsen, 1938, 1939; Beale *et al.*, 1951, 1952; Robertson *et al.*, 1950; Comroe and Fowler, 1951; Fowler *et al.*, 1952; Bates, 1952; Briscoe and McLemore, 1952; Colldahl and Lundin, 1952; Herschfus *et al.*, 1953; Proctor *et al.*, 1952). The inspiratory velocity of air flow in the larger airways is slightly diminished, while the expiratory velocity is greatly reduced (von Neergard and Wirz, 1927; Gross, 1943; Gaensler, 1950b, 1951; Proctor *et al.*, 1950; Gottsegen, 1951; Herschfus *et al.*, 1953; Kennedy and Stock, 1952; Lowell *et al.*, 1953); the expiratory pressure is, however, normal (Gross, 1943). Alveolar pressure relative to expiratory velocity is high (Sheldon and Otis, 1951), an indication of the presence of obstruction. Wyss *et al.* (1951) observed that most of the slowing in expiratory velocity developed suddenly late in expiration; these authors concluded that the bronchi constricted at this point. Pulmonary elasticity is described as impaired (von Neergard and Wirz, 1927; Paine, 1940); however, this finding may be an artifact caused by marked bronchoconstriction, that is, the lung as a whole acts like a less elastic body than normal in attacks, but the parenchyma itself is not less elastic. The maximal possible ventilation may be markedly decreased (Knipping, 1935; Zaeper and Wolf, 1939; Curry *et al.*, 1950; Gaensler, 1950a,b; Ornstein, 1949; Proctor *et al.*, 1950; Lukas, 1951; Barach, 1951; Beale *et al.*, 1952; Briscoe and McLemore, 1952; Herschfus *et al.*, 1953; Kennedy and Stock, 1952). The tidal air at rest is smaller than normal according to most authors (von Neergard and Wirz, 1927; Houssay and Berconsky, 1932; Campbell and Poulton, 1926; Beale *et al.*, 1951; Paine, 1940); only Staehelin and Schütze (1912) and Bates (1952) found it large in some cases. The rate is increased, so that the minute volume of respiration is normal or even high (2; Campbell and Poulton, 1926). The ventilation equivalent — the volume of air breathed per hundred cubic centimeters of oxygen absorbed — is within normal limits at rest (Herbst, 1928; Jansen *et al.*, 1932; Knipping *et al.*, 1932). In exercise the tidal air increases less than normal (Campbell and Poulton, 1926); however, the rate rises excessively, so that the increase in respiratory minute volume is approximately normal or above it (Herbst, 1928; Campbell and Poulton, 1926). This type of change in respiratory dynamics makes for inefficient breathing. The oxygen intake during work is not adequately increased for the task (Herbst, 1928) unless air enriched with oxygen is breathed (Zaeper and Wolf, 1939); the oxygen debt after work without oxygen is consequently large and prolonged (Herbst, 1928; Nylin, 1938). Even at rest, severe attacks may prevent normal intake of oxygen owing to failure of respiratory minute volume to rise and may so lead to an oxygen debt (Colldahl, 1947).

The breath-holding time is shortened (Friedman, 1947).

Blood gases; tissue gas tensions. — The arterial blood oxygen saturation falls in attacks (Houssay and Berconsky, 1932; Knipping, 1935; Meakins, 1921; 5); it rises to, or toward normal when air enriched with oxygen is breathed (Meakins, 1921). Carbon dioxide retention occurs in asthmatics, elevating the level in the arterial blood (Houssay and Berconsky, 1932; Knipping, 1935; Beale *et al.*, 1951); a similar change occurs in the tissues (Seevers *et al.*, 1936; Sibree, 1941). The tissue oxygen tension is described by Seevers *et al.* (1936) as low, and by Sibree (1941) as within normal limits. As has been pointed out elsewhere (page 85), measurements of tissue tensions of carbon dioxide are more likely to be accurate than are those of oxygen. Carbon dioxide retention may lead to a fall in blood pH (Beale *et al.*, 1951). However, since the carbon dioxide retention usually is not chronic, the reduced respiratory response to carbon dioxide that occurs in emphysema (page 480) is not seen in uncomplicated asthma (Donald and Christie, 1949).

Circulation time. — No studies of cardiac output during asthmatic attacks are available, but many studies of circulation time have been made. The arm-to-tongue or -face time (3; Cottrell and Cuddie, 1942), the carbon dioxide time (Grubner *et al.*, 1939), the ether time (Miller, 1934; Hitzig, 1935; Oppenheimer and Hitzig, 1936; Taquini and Lozada, 1948), and the amyl nitrite time (Gross, 1945) are normal or somewhat reduced in asthmatics. In addition, the normal or short arm-to-tongue or -face, or ether times reported for patients with unspecified types of pulmonary disease (page 478) probably include data on some asthmatic persons.

Venous pressure. — Most authors report a rise in venous pressure during attacks (4; Meyer and Middleton, 1929); however, the values need not be outside the normal range (von Gönczy, 1930; Wartman, 1935; Oppenheimer and Hitzig, 1936; Kroetz, 1922). The rise that occurs is probably secondary to increases in intrathoracic pressure.

Arterial pressure. — No change in arterial pressure occurs in moderate attacks but transitory hypertension may develop during severe ones (Colldahl, 1947).

Blood carbonic anhydrase. — The blood carbonic anhydrase level is reported to be normal (Lambie, 1938).

Symptoms. — The cardiorespiratory dynamics of asthma during attacks resemble closely those of chronic pulmonary emphysema (page 474), since the bronchospasm of the attack gives rise to a type of acute emphysema. The bronchospasm in itself also exaggerates the difficulties in intrapulmonary mixing and thereby favors the more rapid and severe development of anoxia and hypercarbia. The symptomatology during attacks is usually dominated, however, by the sensation of strangulation and emotional reactions to it. Nevertheless, during protracted attacks, it is possible to discern effects of anoxia in the form of clouding of the mental faculties and progressive cyanosis.

Metabolic changes owing to asthma have not been studied extensively. The blood glutathion level is normal (Platt, 1931), as is the tocopherol concentration (Klatskin and Krehl, 1950).

Bibliography

Chapter IX

ANTHONY, A. J., Untersuchungen über Lungenvolumina und Lungenventilation, *Deutsches Arch. f. klin. Med.* **167**, 129 (1930). [1

BARACH, A. L., Remissions in bronchial asthma and hypertrophic pulmonary emphysema, *J. A. M. A.* **147**, 730 (1951). [1

BATES, D. V., Impairment of respiratory function in bronchial asthma, *Clin. Sc.* **11**, 203 (1952). [1, 2

BEALE, H. D., W. S. FOWLER, and J. H. COMROE, Pulmonary function studies in 20 asthmatic patients in the symptom-free interval, *J. Allergy* **23**, 1 (1952). [1, 2

BEALE, H. D., I. W. SCHILLER, M. H. HALPERIN, W. FRANKLIN, and F. C. LOWELL, Delirium and coma precipitated by oxygen in bronchial asthma complicated by respiratory alkalosis, *New England J. Med.* **244**, 710 (1951). [1, 2, 5

BERNSTEIN, M., and S. SIMKINS, The use of magnesium sulfate in the measurement of circulation time, *Am. Heart J.* **17,** 218 (1939).   [3

BOHR, C., Die funktionellen Änderungen in der Mittelage und Vitalkapazität der Lungen. Normales und pathologisches Emphysem, *Deutsches Arch. f. klin. Med.* **88,** 305 (1906–07).   [1

BRISCOE, W. A., and G. A. MCLEMORE, JR., Ventilatory function in bronchial asthma, *Thorax* **7,** 66 (1952).   [1

CAMPBELL, J. M. H., and E. P. POULTON, The effect of exercise on the pulmonary ventilation and rate and depth of breathing in chronic bronchitis, *Quart. J. Med.* **20,** 27 (1926–27).   [2

CHRISTIE, R. V., and C. A. MCINTOSH, The measurement of the intrapleural pressure in man and its significance, *J. Clin. Investigation* **13,** 279 (1934).

COLLDAHL, H., On the pathophysiological and clinical aspects of the crisis of asthma bronchiale. I. The pulmonary ventilation, oxygen uptake and blood pressure, *Acta med. Scandinav.* **128,** 551 (1947).   [2

COLLDAHL, H., and G. LUNDIN, Ventilatory studies of the lungs in asthma, *Acta allergica* **5,** 37 (1952).

COMROE, J. H., and W. S. FOWLER, Lung function studies. VI. Detection of uneven alveolar ventilation during a single breath of oxygen, *Am. J. Med.* **10,** 408 (1951).

COTTRELL, J. D., and D. C. CUDDIE, The arm-to-tongue circulation time in chronic asthma, *Brit. Med. J.* **1,** 70 (1942).   [3

CURRY, J. J., J. E. FUCHS, and S. E. LEARD, The effect of dihydro-ergocornine on the pulmonary response to methacholine and histamine in subjects with bronchial asthma, *J. Clin. Investigation* **29,** 439 (1950).   [1

DONALD, K. W., and R. V. CHRISTIE, The respiratory response to carbon dioxide and anoxia in emphysema, *Clin. Sc.* **8,** 33 (1949).

FOWLER, W. S., E. R. CORNISH, JR., and S. KETY, Lung function studies. VIII. Analysis of alveolar ventilation by pulmonary N_2 clearance curves, *J. Clin. Investigation* **31,** 40 (1952).

FRIEDMAN, M., Studies concerning the etiology and pathogenesis of neurocirculatory asthenia. V. The introduction of a new test for the diagnosis and assessment of the syndrone, *Psychosomat. med.* **9,** 242 (1947).

GAENSLER, E. A., Ventilatory tests in bronchial asthma. Evaluation of vital capacity and maximum breathing capacity, *J. Allergy* **21,** 232 (1950).   [1

GAENSLER, E. A., Air velocity index. A numerical expression of the functionally effective portion of ventilation, *Am. Rev. Tuberc.* **62,** 17 (1950).   [1

GAENSLER, E. A., Analysis of the ventilatory defect by timed capacity measurements, *Am. Rev. Tuberc.* **64**, 256 (1951). [1

GOLDBERG, S. J., The use of calcium gluconate as a circulation time test, *Am. J. M. Sc.* **192**, 36 (1936). [3

GOTTSEGEN, G., Vitalkapazität und Herzinsuffizienz. II Mitt. Ueber Adrenalin und Stophanthineffekte, *Cardiologia* **19**, 174 (1951). [1

GRAY, F. D., P. R. LURIE, and R. WHITTEMORE, Circulatory changes in chronic pulmonary disease. A study of pulmonary collateral circulation, *Yale J. Biol. & Med.* **23**, 380 (1951). [5

GREENE, J. A., W. D. PAUL, and A. E. FELLER, The action of theophylline with ethylenediamine on intrathecal and venous pressures in cardiac failure and on bronchial obstruction in cardiac failure and bronchial asthma, *J. A. M. A.* **109**, 1712 (1937). [1

GROSS, D., Investigations concerning vital capacity, *Am. Heart J.* **25**, 335 (1943).

GROSS, D., The measurement of the lung-to-face time by amyl nitrite, *Am. Heart J.* **30**, 19 (1945).

GRUBNER, R., S. SCHNUR, and J. H. CRAWFORD, The use of CO_2 inhalation as a test of circulation time, *J. Clin. Investigation* **18**, 395 (1939).

HERBST, R., Der Gasstoffwechsel als Mass der körperlichen Leistungsfähigkeit. II. Untersuchungen bei Emphysem, chronischer Bronchitis und Asthma bronchiale, *Deutsches Arch. f. klin. Med.* **162**, 129 (1928). [1

HERSCHFUS, J. A., E. BRESNICK, and M. S. SEGAL, Pulmonary function studies in bronchial asthma. I. In the control state, *Am. J. Med.* **14**, 23 (1953). [1, 2, 5

HERSCHFUS, J. A., E. BRESNICK, and M. S. SEGAL, Pulmonary function studies in bronchial asthma. II. After treatment, *Am. J. Med.* **14**, 34 (1953). [1, 2, 5

HERXHEIMER, H., Induced asthma in man, *Lancet* **1**, 1337 (1951). [5

HITZIG, W. M., The use of ether in measuring the circulation time from the antecubital veins to the pulmonary capillaries, *Am. Heart J.* **10**, 1080 (1934–35).

HOUSSAY, B. A., and I. BERCONSKY, Cyanose par l'hypoventilation alvéolaire, *Presse méd.* **40**, 1759 (1932). [1, 2

HURTADO, A., N. L. KALTREIDER, W. W. FRAY, W. D. W. BROOKS, and W. S. MCCANN, Studies of total pulmonary capacity and its subdivisions. VIII. Observations on cases of pulmonary fibrosis, *J. Clin. Investigation* **14**, 81 (1935a). [1

HURTADO, A., N. L. KALTREIDER, and W. S. MCCANN, Studies of total pulmonary capacity and its subdivisions. IX. Relationship to oxygen saturation and carbon dioxide content of the arterial blood, *J. Clin. Investigation* **14**, 94 (1935b).

HUSSEY, H. H., and S. KATZ, The comparative value of ether and paraldehyde as agents for measurement of the arm-to-lung circulation time in fifty patients with, and fifty patients without heart failure, *Am. J. M. Sc.* **201,** 669 (1941). [3

JABLONS, B., J. COHEN, and M. Y. SWIRSKY, Clinical studies of circulation time with objective (photoelectric cell-dye) method, *New York State J. Med.* **44,** 398 (1944). [3

JANSEN, K., H. W. KNIPPING, and K. STROMBERGER, Klinische Untersuchungen über Atmung und Blutgase, *Beitr. z. Klin. d. Tuberk.* **80,** 304 (1932). [1

KAHLER, H., Ueber Veränderungen der Blutumlaufzeit, *Wien. Arch. f. inn. Med.* **19,** 1 (1930). [3

KENNEDY, M. C. S., and J. P. P. STOCK, The bronchodilator action of Khellin, *Thorax* **7,** 43 (1952). [1

KLATSKIN, G., and W. A. KREHL, The significance of the plasma tocopherol concentration and of tocopherol tolerance tests in liver disease, *J. Clin. Investigation* **29,** 1528 (1950).

KNIPPING, H. W., Ueber die respiratorische Insuffizienz, *Klin. Wchnschr.* **14,** 406 (1935). [5

KNIPPING, H. W., W. LEWIS, and A. MONCRIEFF, Über die Dyspnoe, *Beitr. z. Klin. d. Tuberk.* **79,** 1 (1932). [1, 2

KOUNTZ, W. B., E. F. PEARSON, and K. F. KOENIG, Observations on intrapleural pressure and its influence on the relative circulation rate in emphysema, *J. Clin. Investigation* **11,** 1281 (1932). [4

KROETZ, C., Die Koeffizienten des klinisch messbaren Venendruckes, *Deutsches Arch. f. klin. Med.* **139,** 325 (1922).

KROETZ, C., Gasanalytische Untersuchungen über die Endothelfunktion der Lungen, *Verhandl. d. deutsch. Gesellsch. f. inn. Med.* **41,** 449 (1929). [5

LAMBIE, C. G., Observations on the carbonic anhydrase of the blood in anaemia and in other pathological conditions, *Edinburgh M. J.* **45,** 373 (1938).

LANGE, K., and L. J. BOYD, Objective methods to determine the speed of blood flow and their results (fluorescein and acetylene), *Am. J. M. Sc.* **206,** 438 (1943). [3

LANPHIER, E. H., Determination of residual volume and residual volume/total capacity ratio by single breath technique, *J. Appl. Physiol.* **5,** 361 (1953).

LESCHKE, E., Kreislaufzeit und Blutgeschwindigkeit, *München. med. Wchnschr.* **78,** 2117 (1931). [3

LOWELL, F. C., I. W. SCHILLER, S. E. LEARD, and W. FRANKLIN, Prolonged treatment of bronchial asthma with cortisone, *J. Allergy* **24,** 112 (1953). [1

LUKAS, D. S., Some effects of adrenocorticotropic hormone and cortisone on pulmonary function of patients with obstructive emphysema, *Am. Rev. Tuberc.* **64,** 279 (1951).

MEAKINS, J., Observations on the gases in human arterial blood in certain pathological pulmonary conditions and their treatment with oxygen, *J. Path. & Bact.* **24,** 79 (1921). [5

MEYER, O. O., and W. S. MIDDLETON, The influence of respiration on venous pressure, *J. Clin. Investigation* **8,** 1 (1929–30). [4

MILLER, H. R., Velocity of blood flow in part of the pulmonary circulation, *Proc. Soc. Exper. Biol. & Med.* **31,** 942 (1934).

MOORE, R. D., JR., The diagnostic value of venous pressure determinations in certain diseases, *South. M. J.* **30,** 1007 (1937). [4

MYERS, J. A., Studies on the respiratory organs in health and disease. VI. The significance of the vital-capacity test in pulmonary tuberculosis, bronchial asthma, pneumonia and an acute infection outside the respiratory tract, *Arch. Int. Med.* **30,** 648 (1922). [1

NYLIN, G., The practical applicability of the cardiopulmonary function test, *Acta med. Scandinav., Supp. No. 93,* 1 (1938).

OPPENHEIMER, B. S., and W. M. HITZIG, The use of circulatory measurements in evaluating pulmonary and cardiac factors in chronic lung disorders, *Am. Heart J.* **12,** 257 (1936). [3

ORNSTEIN, G. G., The measurement of the function of the lungs, *Dis. of Chest* **15,** 280 (1949). [1, 2

PAINE, J. R., The clinical measurement of pulmonary elasticity. A comparison of the methods of Christie and McIntosh and of Neergaard and Wirz, *J. Thoracic Surg.* **9,** 550 (1940). [1

PEABODY, F. W., and J. A. WENTWORTH, Clinical studies of the respiration. IV. The vital capacity of the lungs and its relation to dyspnea, *Arch. Int. Med.* **20,** 443 (1917). [1

PLATT, R., The blood glutathione in disease, *Brit. J. Exper. Path.* **12,** 139 (1931).

PLOTZ, M., Asthmatoid heart failure: a form of left ventricular failure and its differentiation from bronchial asthma by circulation time and other criteria, *Ann. Int. Med.* **13,** 151 (1939). [3

PRINZMETAL, M., The relation of inspiratory distension of the lungs to emphysema, *J. Allergy* **5,** 493 (1934).

PROCTOR, D. F., Studies of respiratory air flow in measurement of ventilatory function, *Dis. of Chest* **22,** 432 (1952).

PROCTOR, D. F., J. B. HARDY, and R. McLEAN, Studies of respiratory air flow. II. Observations on patients with pulmonary disease, *Bull. Johns Hopkins Hosp.* **87,** 255 (1950).

508 BRONCHIAL ASTHMA

RASMUSSEN, H., and O. STORSTEIN, Studies in oxygen therapy. Part I. On the frequency of anoxemia, its occurrence in medical diseases and its relation to cyanosis, *Acta med. Scandinav.* **141**, 43 (1951). [5

ROBERTSON, J. S., W. E. SIRI, and H. B. JONES, Lung ventilation patterns determined by analysis of nitrogen elimination rates; use of the mass spectrometer as a continuous gas analyzer, *J. Clin. Investigation* **29**, 577 (1950). [1, 2

ROELSEN, E., Fractional analysis of alveolar air after inspiration of hydrogen as a method for the determination of the distribution of inspired air in the lungs. Examinations of normal persons and of patients suffering from bronchial asthma and pulmonary emphysema, *Acta med. Scandinav.* **95**, 452 (1938). [1

ROELSEN, E., The composition of the alveolar air investigated by fractional sampling. Comparative investigations on normal persons and patients with bronchial asthma and pulmonary emphysema, *Acta med. Scandinav.* **98**, 141 (1939). [2

SEEVERS, M. H., H. R. HATHAWAY, and R. T. STORMONT, Tissue gas studies in respiratory and circulatory disease, *Am. J. Physiol.* **116**, 140 (1936).

SESSA, T., La velocità della corrente del sangue. III. Tempo di circolazione nelle varie affezioni morbose, *Cuore e circolaz.* **22**, 181 (1938). [3

SHELDON, M. B., JR., and A. B. OTIS, Effect of adrenaline on resistance to gas flow in the respiratory tract and on the vital capacity of normal and asthmatic subjects, *J. Appl. Physiol.* **3**, 513 (1951). [1

SIBREE, E. W., Gas tensions in the tissues in pathological conditions, *M. J. Australia* **1**, 201 (1941).

STAEHELIN, R., and SCHÜTZE, A., Spirographische Untersuchungen an Gesunden, Emphysematikern und Asthmatikern, *Ztschr. f. klin. Med.* **75**, 15 (1912). [2

TAQUINI, A. C., and B. B. LOZADA, Corazón pulmonar cronico con y sin insufficiencia cardiaca. Funciones respiratoria y circulatoria, *Medicina* **8**, 325 (1948). [1, 2

TORNQUIST, H., Physiologische und klinische Studien über den Armvenendruck, *Ztschr. f. d. ges. exper. Med.* **81**, 227 (1932). [4

VILLARET, M., and M. MARTINY, Pression veineuse et tuberculose pulmonaire. Intérêt diagnostique, pronostique et thérapeutique de la pression veineuse périphérique dans les différents formes anatomo-cliniques de la tuberculose pulmonaire, *Presse méd.* **33**, 569 (1925). [4

VON GÖNCZY, V. I., J. KISS, and Z. ENYEDY, Ueber den Venendruck und dessen Tagesschwankungen, *Ztschr. f. d. ges. exper. Med.* **70**, 236 (1930).

von Neergard, K., and K. Wirz, Die Messung der Strömungswiderstände in den Atemwegen des Menschen, insbesondere bei Asthma und Emphysem, *Ztschr. f. klin. Med.* **105,** 51 (1927). [1

Wartman, W. B., A Study of the venous blood pressure in some common diseases, *Am. J. M. Sc.* **190,** 464 (1935).

Whitfield, A. G. W., W. M. Arnott, and J. A. H. Waterhouse, The effect of ephedrine in asthma and emphysema, *Quart. J. Med.* **19,** 319 (1950). [1

Winternitz, M., J. Deutsch, and Z. Brüll, Eine klinisch brauchbare Bestimmungsmethode der Blutumlaufzeit mittels Decholininjektion, *Med. Klin.* **27,** 986 (1931). [3

Wyss, F., E. Lopez-Botet, and F. Schmid, Untersuchungen über die Ursache der Asmatischen Dyspnoe, *Helvet. med. acta* **18,** 537 (1951).

Wyss, F., and F. Schmid, Beruht die bronchialasthmatische Dyspnoe auf einer Bronchialstenose? *Schweiz. med. Wchnschr.* **81,** 916 (1951).

Zaeper, G., and W. Wolf, Ueber die Erkennung und quantitative Beurteilung pulmonaler Funktionsstörungen, *Beitr. z. Klin. d. Tuberk.* **92,** 487 (1939).

X

PLEURAL EFFUSION

Pleural effusion commonly complicates many diseases and its manifestations may alter or overshadow those of the underlying disorder. The severity of the respiratory symptoms associated with pleural effusion varies markedly from patient to patient and depends not only on the volume of fluid in the pleural space, but also on the nature of the disease causing the effusion. Appreciation of the functional changes caused by pleural effusions makes these variations intelligible.

Lung volume and its subdivisions. — Early reports of measurements on the subdivisions of the lung volume, exclusive of vital capacity, are fragmentary and based on methods no longer considered reliable (Siebeck, 1910; Bittorf and Forschbach, 1910; Plesch, 1913; Peters and Barr, 1920); in addition, the fact that the lungs themselves are often the site of disease in patients with effusions makes the interpretation of absolute values difficult. Recent studies show that the functional residual, reserve and complemental airs and the vital and total capacities are considerably diminished by pleural effusion, while the residual air shows little or no decrease (Altschule and Zamcheck, 1944); other authors have also found a decreased vital capacity in patients with pleural fluid (1; Myers, 1925).

Immediate effects of thoracentesis. — The vital capacity shows little or no immediate increases after a chest tap, in spite of the fact that dyspnea may be relieved (Peabody and Wentworth, 1917; Graham, 1920; Bendove, 1925; Altschule and Zamcheck, 1944). Similarly, the complemental air shows no significant change and the total capacity is but slightly increased (Altschule and Zamcheck, 1944).

The reserve air, however, increases markedly, often to more than double its original value (Altschule and Zamcheck, 1944); it is often diminished almost to zero when fluid is present, so that even though it may be doubled after a tap, it contributes little toward increasing the vital and total capacities. The functional residual air is also increased somewhat after thoracentesis (Altschule and Zamcheck, 1944).

Late effects of thoracentesis. — Further large increases in reserve and functional residual air volumes occur during the month following thoracentesis, with smaller increases in residual air. The complemental air, and consequently the vital capacity, likewise show slow though marked increases; the total capacity also becomes considerably larger (Altschule and Zamcheck, 1944).

Respiratory dynamics. — The tidal air volume is often lowered by pleural effusion and since the rate is usually increased, the respiratory minute volume is normal or slightly above normal (Knipping *et al.*, 1932; Altschule and Zamcheck, 1944). The maximal possible ventilation per minute is diminished (Knipping, 1932; Gaensler, 1950). The intrapleural pressure is high and may actually rise above atmospheric (Clark, 1915; Shattuck and Welles, 1919; James, 1949; Bernstein and White, 1952); it falls after thoracentesis.

Blood gases. — The arterial blood oxygen saturation is usually not lowered by pleural fluid, although in some instances decreases have been found (LeBlanc, 1922; Ihaya, 1934; Altschule and Zamcheck, 1944); thoracentesis increases low values to or toward normal. The arterial blood carbon dioxide is usually not outside the range of normal (LeBlanc, 1922; Altschule and Zamcheck, 1944); in the presence of dyspnea and hyperventilation, it may be lowered somewhat (Porges *et al.*, 1913).

Cardiac output. — Studies of cardiac output and arteriovenous oxygen difference by various methods have usually yielded normal values (LeBlanc, 1922; Ringer and Altschule, 1930; Ihaya, 1934; Altschule and Zamcheck, 1944); very large effusion may lower the cardiac output somewhat (Ihaya, 1934). Busacchi (1938) reported that he found the cardiac minute volume output to be quite low in most of his patients, with return to normal after clearing of the effusion. His observations, however, are not entirely applicable to the present discussion, since at least some of his patients had adhesive mediastinopericarditis. Moreover, his data on normal subjects are so variable as to suggest some error in procedure.

Circulation time. — The arm-to-tongue time is normal (2; Altschule and Zamcheck, 1944); the ether time is likewise normal (Hitzig, 1935; Vecchi, 1937).

Venous pressure. — The venous pressure may be either normal or somewhat elevated in patients with pleural effusion (3; Clark, 1915). No matter what its level, following thoracentesis some decrease is the rule (Clark, 1915; Taylor *et al.*, 1930; Grellety-Bosviel, 1930; Altschule and Zamcheck, 1944; Schirosa, 1947). This fall in venous pressure has been correlated with corresponding changes in intrapleural pressure caused by removal of pleural fluid (Clark, 1915; Shattuck and Welles, 1919).

Symptoms. — The decrease in functional residual air, that is, the space available for breathing, caused by pleural effusion is ordinarily not large enough to influence respiration in itself. However, the functional residual air rises somewhat immediately after thoracentesis and therefore it is apparent that pleural effusion causes atelectasis, the collapsed lung reëxpanding to some extent with removal of the thoracic fluid. Complete reëxpansion, as measured by the functional residual air, does not, however, occur for three or four weeks. Accordingly, overcoming of the atelectasis must be regarded as only of contributory importance in the immediate relief of dyspnea that may occur with thoracentesis.

Since the removal of large amounts of fluid from the chest is followed by an immediate increase in functional residual air of only a few hundred cubic centimeters, it is clear that elevation of the diaphragm must occur during thoracentesis. The diaphragm, pushed down and flattened by pleural effusion, resumes its normal arched contour as fluid is withdrawn. In its depressed, flattened state, the diaphragm is in a position that permits only limited excursion and makes for inefficient respiration; after resumption of its normal arch, diaphragmatic respiratory excursion is greatly increased and respiration becomes more efficient. This is in harmony with the clinical observation that patients with dyspnea associated with pleural effusion show active use of the accessory muscles of respiration, which is abated by thoracentesis.

The marked decrease in reserve air indicates a corresponding loss of negativity of the intrapleural pressure. Indeed, measurements of the intrapleural pressure in such patients demonstrate the loss of all or most of the normal negative pressure. Following thoracentesis, the reserve air increases markedly and the intrapleural pressure becomes more negative. Decreased negativity of the intrapleural pressure, consequent to any cause, impairs the efficiency of respiration and also influences cardiovascular dynamics, in a manner that will be discussed below.

The complemental air, a measure of the expansibility of the lungs, is markedly diminished by pleural fluid. This fluid acts to decrease pulmonary expansibility in two ways: (i) by occupying space within the thorax and (ii) by causing atelectasis, the atelectatic lung being less expansible than the normal. Although the complemental air in patients with effusions does not decrease to the volume of the resting tidal air, it is in some instances sufficiently small to prevent the normal increase in tidal air during exercise. It has been shown that there is a decrease in maximal respiration during exertion in patients with pleural effusion. The decrease in complemental air that occurs in patients with pleural effusion therefore makes for anoxia during exertion, and consequently contributes to dyspnea. Decreased arterial oxygen saturation is found only occasionally in patients studied at rest, but would probably occur in many more during severe exertion. Impaired expansibility of the lungs also favors dyspnea by requiring that the patient expend more effort in attaining a given tidal air volume; the tidal air volume is often decreased before removal of fluid. The complemental air is affected little by thoracentesis, attaining its normal volume only with complete reëxpansion of the atelectatic lung in the weeks following removal of the fluid.

Early observers of the vital capacity noted that although it is low in patients with pleural effusion, it is only slightly increased immediately after thoracentesis. The vital capacity is the sum of the reserve and complemental airs; the latter is much larger than the former, so that its lack of change overshadows the marked changes in reserve air after pleural fluid is removed. The vital capacity returns to normal with the complemental air some weeks after chest tap. It is apparent that study of the vital capacity in patients with pleural effusion affords no accurate information on the state of pulmonary function.

It is clear from all of the foregoing discussion that pleural effusion acts in many ways to impair respiratory function. Nevertheless, many patients with large effusions exhibit little or no discomfort, at least while at rest. In this connection it is important to bear in mind that although the tidal air volume is usually decreased, the functional residual air volume is lowered also. Thus the ratio between the air taken with each breath and the air remaining in the lungs after the end of expiration is not changed greatly; mixing is therefore unimpaired. The changes in pulmonary function caused by hydrothorax are, however, similar in some ways to those consequent to emphysema, diffuse pulmonary fibrosis and chronic congestive failure. Accordingly, patients with diffuse pulmonary disease — emphysema, fibrosis or congestion — are more likely to exhibit dyspnea and orthopnea when pleural fluid develops than are other patients. The severity of these respiratory symptoms varies not only with the volume of fluid in the pleural spaces, but also with the severity of the underlying pulmonary disease. Conversely, if a patient obtains marked relief from respiratory discomfort following a relatively small thoracentesis, it is likely that he also has some diffuse pulmonary lesion.

The effects of thoracentesis may be summarized as follows:

Immediate:
(1) Increased negativity of intrapleural pressure;
    (*a*) Improved respiratory efficiency,
    (*b*) Improved venous return;
(2) Removal of bulk of fluid;
    (*a*) Removal of restraint on respiration,
    (*b*) Restoration of diaphragmatic arch;
(3) Some reëxpansion of collapsed lung,

Late:
(1) Reëxpansion of atelectasis;
    (*a*) Increased respiratory space,
    (*b*) Restoration of expansibility of lung.

The above-discussed changes in intrapleural pressure in patients with pleural effusion impair venous return, for although the venous pressure is often not elevated above normal in the patients without congestive failure, it falls following throacentesis. The findings of various authors that the venous pressure is within normal limits in patients with pleural effusion are not to be considered contradictory, since they did not study their patients before and after tapping. The fall in venous pressure that occurs after thoracentesis is of particular interest because it may explain the occurrence of diuresis in some cardiac patients following this procedure.

Impairment of venous return tends to cause decreased cardiac output. However, the cardiac output at rest in patients with uncomplicated pleural effusion is found to be normal except in occasional instances, when it may be slightly decreased; this is in harmony with the recorded observations on circulation time. Although some obstruction to the return of blood from the periphery exists because of decreased negativity of intrapleural pressure, it appears that enough pressure is built up in the veins that flow is not decreased and that cardiac output therefore remains unchanged in these patients at rest. It is probable, however, that the increase in cardiac output in exercise in patients with hydrothorax would be less than normal. The possibility that impaired cardiac function may result from extreme degrees of pressure on the heart or from mediastinal displacement cannot be evaluated on the basis of the data available.

The discussion of various mechanisms that cause pleural effusions to develop is beyond the scope of this work. It should be noted, however, that negativity of intrapleural pressure has little effect (Heaton, 1950) and that respiratory activity has much (Courtice and Simmonds, 1949). Diseases of the heart or lungs that impair diaphragmatic movement in one way or another may be associated with pleural effusion.

Bibliography

Chapter X

ALTSCHULE, M. D., and N. ZAMCHECK, The effects of pleural effusion on respiration and circulation in man, *J. Clin. Investigation* **23**, 325 (1944).   [2, 3

BENDOVE, R. A., The vital capacity in artificial pneumothorax. The mechanism and the factors modifying the vital capacity, with especial reference to its clinical and prognostic value in collapse therapy, *Arch. Int. Med.* **36**, 94 (1925).   [1

BERNSTEIN, A., and F. Z. WHITE, Unusual physical findings in pleural effusion: intrathoracic manometric studies. *Ann. Int. Med.* **37**, 733 (1952).

BITTORF, A., and J. FORSCHBACH, Untersuchungen über die Lungenfüllung bei Krankheiten, *Ztschr. f. klin. Med.* **70**, 474 (1910).

BUSACCHI, V., La portata circolatoria e la gittata sistolica in condizioni normali e patologiche. Nota terza. Pleuritici, *Arch. di pat. e clin. med.* **18**, 140 (1938). [1

CLARK, A. H., A study of the diagnostic and prognostic significance of venous pressure observations in cardiac disease, *Arch. Int. Med.* **16**, 587 (1915). [3

COURTICE, F. C., and W. J. SIMMONDS, Absorption of fluids from the pleural cavities of rabbits and cats, *J. Physiol.* **109**, 117 (1949).

EYSTER, J. A. E., Venous pressure and its clinical applications, *Physiol. Rev.* **6**, 281 (1926). [3

GAENSLER, A. E., Air velocity index. A numerical expression of the functionally effective portion of ventilation, *Am. Rev. Tuberc.* **62**, 17 (1950). [1

GAERTNER, G., Die Messung des Drucks im rechten Vorhof, *München. med. Wchnschr.* **50**, 2038 (1903). [3

GRAHAM, E. A., Importance of the vital capacity in thoracic surgery, *J. A. M. A.* **75**, 992 (1920). [1

GRELLETY-BOSVIEL, P., De l'utilité de la mesure de la pression veineuse au cours du pneumothorax artificiel, *Presse méd.* **38**, 1105 (1930). [3

GRIFFITH, G. C., C. T. CHAMBERLAIN, and J. R. KITCHELL, Observation on the practical significance of venous pressure in health and disease, with a review of the literature, *Am. J. M. Sc.* **187**, 642 (1934). [3

HEATON, T. G., Pleural effusions and intrapleural pressures of the re-expansion period in pneumothorax, *Dis. of Chest* **18**, 324 (1950).

HEISE, F. H., and J. H. STEIDL, Venous pressure in pulmonary tuberculosis. The effect of collapse therapy and other complications, *J. Thoracic Surg.* **8**, 539 (1938–39). [3

HITZIG, W. M., The use of ether in measuring the circulation time from the antecubital veins to the pulmonary capillaries, *Am. Heart J.* **10**, 1080 (1934–35). [2, 3

HOOKER, D. R., Observations on the venous blood pressure in man, *Am. J. Physiol.* **35**, 73 (1914). [3

HURST, A., and M. A. BRAND, A study of venous pressure and circulation time in pulmonary tuberculosis, *J. Thoracic Surg.* **6**, 638 (1936–37). [2, 3

HUSSEY, H. H., Clinical application of venous pressure measurement, *M. Ann. District of Columbia* **5**, 232 (1936). [3

IHAYA, H., Studien über die Alveolarluft, Blutgase, Vitalkapazität und Minuten- und Schlagvolumen des Herzens bei Beriberi, Herzklappen-fehler und Pleuritis, *Mitt. d. med. Gesellsch. zu Tokyo* **48**, 2167 (1934). [1

JAMES, A. H., The mechanism of pleural and ascitic effusions with a sug-gested method for the indirect estimation of portal venous pressure, *Clin. Sc.* **8**, 291 (1949).

KAHLER, H., Ueber Veränderungen der Blutumlaufzeit, *Wien. Arch. f. inn. Med.* **19**, 1 (1930). [2

KNIPPING, H. W., Über die respiratorische insufficienz, *Klin. Wchnschr.* **14**, 406 (1935).

KNIPPING, H. W., W. LEWIS, and A. MONCRIEFF, Ueber die Dyspnoe, *Beitr. z. Klin. d. Tuberk.* **79**, 1 (1932). [1

KROETZ, C., Die Koeffizienten des klinisch messbaren Venendruckes, *Deutsches Arch. f. klin. Med.* **139**, 325 (1922). [3

LE BLANC, E., Respiratorischer Gasaustausch und Lungendurchblutung unter normalen und krankhaften Zuständen der Atemsorgane. Unter-suchungen am arteriellen und venösen Blut von Mensch und Tier, *Beitr. z. Klin. d. Tuberk.* **50**, 21 (1922).

McCLURE, C. W., and F. W. PEABODY, Relation of vital capacity of lungs to clinical condition of patients with heart disease, *J. A. M. A.* **69**, 1954 (1917). [1

MYERS, J. A., Studies on the respiratory organs in health and disease. XIX. The significance of serial vital capacity readings in the guidance of diagnosis and treatment of certain diseases of the chest, *Am. Rev. Tuberc.* **11**, 64 (1925). [1

PEABODY, F. W., and J. A. WENTWORTH, Clinical studies of the respiration. IV. The vital capacity of the lungs and its relation to dyspnea, *Arch. Int. Med.* **20**, 443 (1917). [1

PETERS, J. P., JR., and D. P. BARR, Studies of the respiratory mechanism in cardiac dyspnea. II. A note on the effective lung volume in cardiac dyspnea, *Am. J. Physiol.* **54**, 335 (1920).

PLESCH, J., Die pathologische Physiologie des Lungenvolumens und seine Beziehung zum Kreislauf, *Ztschr. f. exper. Path. u. Pharmakol.* **13**, 165 (1913).

PORGES, O., A. LEIMDÖRFER, and E. MARKOVICI, Ueber die Kohlensäure-spannung des Blutes in pathologischen Zuständen. II. Ueber die Kohlensäurespannung des Blutes in der kardialen und pulmonalen Dyspnoe, *Ztschr. f. klin. Med.* **77**, 446 (1913).

RICHARDS, D. G. B., A. G. W. WHITFIELD, W. M. ARNOTT, and J. A. H. WATERHOUSE, The lung volume in low output cardiac syndromes, *Brit. Heart J.* **13**, 381 (1951). [1

RINGER, M., and M. D. ALTSCHULE, Studies on the circulation. II. Cardiac output in diseases of the heart, and under the influence of digitalis therapy, *Am. Heart J.* **5,** 305 (1930).

SCHIROSA, G., Influenza dei versamenti pleurici sul fattore vis a frontè della circolazione venosa, *Folia Cardiol.* **6,** 263 (1947). [3

SESSA, T., La velocità della corrente del sangue. II. Tempo di circolazione nei condizione patologiche (cardiopatie), *Cuore e circolaz.* **22,** 2 (1938).

SHATTUCK, G. C., and E. S. WELLES, Intrathoracic pressure in haemothorax, pneumothorax and pleural effusion, and effects of aspiration and of oxygen replacement, *Quart. J. Med.* **12,** 151 (1919).

SIEBECK, R., Über die Beeinflussung der Atemmechanik durch krankhafte Zustände des Respirations- und Kreislaufapparates, *Deutsches Arch. f. klin. Med.* **100,** 204 (1910).

TAYLOR, F. A., A. B. THOMAS, and H. G. SCHLEITER, A direct method for the estimation of venous blood pressure, *Proc. Soc. Exper. Biol. & Med.* **27,** 867 (1930). [3

VECCHI, E., Applicazione di un nuovo metodo per la determinazione della velocità di circolazione del grande e del piccolo circolo, *Cuore e circolaz.* **21,** 61 (1937). [2

VILLARET, M., and M. MARTINY, Étude de la pression veineuse périphérique dans les syndromes médiastinaux. Son intérêt de contrôle pour le diagnostic et le pronostic, *Presse méd* **37,** 249 (1929). [3

XI

PNEUMOTHORAX

Lung volume and its subdivisions. — All published data are in agreement that the functional residual air volume decreases moderately when pneumothorax occurs (**1**; Christie, 1936). Moderate decreases in residual air, due to collapse of the lung, have also been found (**2**; Richards *et al.*, 1932). The contrary conclusions of Wolf (1928) are based upon an inaccurate method for measuring residual air and are not acceptable. Very marked diminution in reserve air, to the point of its disappearance in some cases, has been described (**3**; Leiner, 1944). In a given case the volume of the reserve air varies with the negativity of the intrapleural pressure, so that decreases in the former are to be expected when the latter approaches or exceeds atmospheric pressure.

The complemental air is also diminished, since the air in the pleural space prevents the normal expansion of the lungs during forced inspiration (**4**; Leiner, 1944). At times the complemental air may decrease so much as to approach the tidal air volume (Anthony and Heine, 1930). Tobiesen (1911) found the complemental air to be normal in his studies.

The sum of the reserve and complemental air volumes is the vital capacity, which of course is diminished (**5**; Myers and Bailey, 1925; Bendove, 1925). The decrease in vital capacity that occurs in a patient with induced pneumothorax is less than the volume of air injected, often strikingly so. One reason for this phenomenon is the decrease in residual air, but there must be, in addition, some flattening of the diaphragm to account for the marked discrepancy that often exists. The total capacity, since it is the sum of the residual air and the vital capacity, must be diminished and has been found so by all authors (6; Cournand *et al.*, 1941).

Respiratory dynamics. — The volume of air moved by each breath may be normal or decreased, depending on the size of the pneumothorax and the presence of pain (7; Leiner, 1944; von Neergard and Wirz, 1927). However, the rate usually increases (Richards *et al.*, 1932; Hirschsohn and Maendl, 1922); accordingly, the respiratory minute volume is normal or increased somewhat (Means and Balboni, 1916; Hirschsohn and Maendl, 1922; Knipping and Moncrieff, 1932; Richards *et al.*, 1932; Leiner, 1944). During exercise the respiratory minute volume increases abnormally, but not if oxygen is given (Jequier-Doge, 1943). The oxygen consumption does not deviate from the normal (Bluhm, 1935; Leiner, 1944); accordingly the ventilation equivalent, that is, the volume of air breathed per hundred cubic centimeters of oxygen absorbed, is normal or elevated (Knipping and Moncrieff, 1932; Leiner, 1944). The alveolar carbon dioxide content may be lowered if hyperventilation is present (Richards *et al.*, 1932). The degree to which ventilation per minute can increase in response to increased needs is considerably lowered in some patients with pneumothorax (Cournand and Richards, 1941; Leiner, 1944; Gaensler, 1950; Gaensler and Strieder, 1950; Jequier-Doge, 1943). The oxygen debt is described as normal or increased, and prolonged (Bluhm, 1935; Nylin, 1933, 1937), depending apparently on the size of the pneumothorax, the degree of antecedent pulmonary disease and the amount of work done in the test. Interesting measurements of the exact amount of depression of respiratory function of the collapsed lung and of the compensatory changes in function of the other have been made in patients with pneumothorax (Leiner, 1944; Pinner *et al.*, 1945; Birath, 1944; Gaensler and Strieder, 1950).

Blood gases. — Changes in arterial oxygen saturation at rest usually do not occur, although occasional slight decreases have been noted (8; Richards *et al.*, 1932). A slight decrease may occur during exercise (Callebaut *et al.*, 1949). The arterial carbon dioxide content is normal as a rule (Christie, 1936; LeBlanc, 1922; Pomplun, 1928); however, if significant hyperpnea and lowering of alveolar air carbon dioxide occur, it is decreased (Richards *et al.*, 1932). The blood pH remains in the normal range, however (Richards *et al.*,

1932). Pulmonary function, usually quite adequate at rest, may become insufficient during exertion, so that carbon dioxide retention may occur (Cournand and Richards, 1941).

Cardiac output. — The minute volume output of the heart is slightly or moderately reduced relative to metabolic needs, so that the arteriovenous oxygen difference is often somewhat increased (Richards et al., 1932; Bluhm, 1935; Cournand et al., 1935; Stewart and Bailey, 1940); in general, however, the changes are small, and Nylin (1933) found no change in his patients.

Circulation time. — The arm-to-tongue time is normal or slightly reduced (**9**; Hurst and Brand, 1937). Reduction may be due to shortening of the average pathway through the lungs as a consequence of collapse of some of the parenchyma. The arm-to-lung (ether) time is normal or slightly reduced (Hitzig, 1935; Feinsilver, 1943).

Venous pressure. — Depending apparently on the degree of change in intrapleural pressure, the venous pressure has been found to be within normal limits or somewhat elevated (**10**; Hussey, 1936). Abdominal compression causes a less than normal rise in peripheral venous pressure (Zeus, 1941).

Right heart pressures. — The right auricular and right ventricular pressures are not influenced significantly by pneumothorax in man (Bloomfield et al., 1946).

Arterial pressure. — No striking changes in arterial blood pressure occur except in some patients with massive spontaneous pneumothorax; here the systolic and pulse pressures may fall markedly, with lesser declines in diastolic, and the patient may exhibit signs of collapse.

Blood. — Hematologic changes are negligible. Riska (1950) reported incredibly high reticulocyte counts in some patients with pneumothorax.

Symptoms. — Patients who receive pneumothorax therapeutically ordinarily show little or no respiratory embarrassment following the intrapleural administration of air; although a considerable degree of pulmonary collapse may be induced in some instances, intrapleural pressures are not permitted to become excessively high and, moreover, the patients are not likely to engage in strenuous exertion thereafter. In some instances, however, and in many with spontaneous pneumothorax, severe respiratory or circulatory symptoms occur. The size of the pneumothorax and the level to which the intrapleural pressure rises evidently largely determine the occurrence of untoward manifestations. Equally important, however, is the presence or absence of extensive pulmonary disease in the uncollapsed lung. These considerations probably account for the variations in the observations reported.

The decreases in residual, and more particularly in functional residual air, that is, the amount of air in the lungs after normal expiration, diminish the volume of air that must be exchanged by mixing and diffusion. Accordingly, a decrease may make for increased efficiency of respiration, possibly accounting for the surprising lack of dyspnea in some instances. On the other hand, a decrease in this volume implies a smaller area of respiratory epithelium exposed to aeration; this decrease is not significant unless the patient already has extensive disease resulting in decreased area available for respiratory exchange, or some other derangement of pulmonary function.

The marked diminution in reserve air that occurs in pneumothorax is significant only in that it parallels the change in intrapleural pressure; decreased negativity of the intrapleural pressure decreases the efficiency of respiration somewhat and in addition gives rise to the changes in cardiovascular function discussed below. Decreased complemental air volume indicates impaired expansibility of the lung; the latter may be very much diminished in pneumothorax, thus accounting for the tendency of the tidal air volume to fall at rest, with a compensatory increase in rate and, since shallow respiration is relatively inefficient, in minute volume also. This restriction of expansibility may be of great importance during exertion, for it prevents the normal considerable increase in tidal air that should occur. The maximal possible ventilation actually has been shown to be decreased, so that the finding of carbon dioxide retention and increased and prolonged oxygen debt after exercise in some patients is not unexpected. The vital capacity merely reflects the changes in reserve and complemental air volumes and in itself, therefore, has no precise significance.

It is apparent that the changes in the subdivisions of the lung volume, while they usually cause no great impairment of pulmonary function at rest, may give rise to respiratory insufficiency during exercise. That anoxic changes which occur are not greater is consequent to the fact that, while the oxygen-absorbing function of the collapsed lung is greatly diminished and the ventilatory function somewhat decreased, compensatory increases in these functions on the other side occur, as shown by bronchospirographic studies (page 520).

A pneumothorax that is large enough in a given case to raise the intrapleural pressure significantly will result in some rise in venous pressure; in some cases the latter need not necessarily rise above the upper limit of normal. The loss of the normal negative intrapleural pressure impedes venous return; although the cardiac output may fall, it need not diminish significantly, since enough pressure may be built up in the peripheral veins to force this slight barrier. However, it is to be doubted that the cardiac output under such circumstances can increase in a normal fashion in response to exercise. This fact in itself may lead to an abnormally large oxygen debt after work. Although marked changes in circulation do not occur at rest, mild circulatory insufficiency may occur during exercise.

Collapse of the lung such as occurs in pneumothorax so shortens the average length of the pathway traversed by the substance used in measuring the circulation time as to reduce the latter somewhat. This acceleration of the circulation may be masked by a tendency toward slowing parallel with a reduction in cardiac output. In the case of a large spontaneous pneumothorax, circulatory function may be so markedly impaired by the change in intrapleural pressure as to give rise to a sudden fall in cardiac output severe enough to produce the picture of shock. This is particularly likely to occur if positive pressures develop in the pleural space; release of these high pressures or withdrawal of the air usually gives rise to rapid improvement.

The common development of effusions in a pneumothorax is explained by the results of experiments in dogs performed by Dolley and Wiese (1929). These authors found that pneumothorax reduces lymph flow and retards the taking up of material from the pleural space.

Bibliography

Chapter XI

ANTHONY, A. J., and R. HEINE, Spirographische Untersuchungen bei Lungenkollaps. I. Mitt., *Beitr. z. Klin. d. Tuberk.* **71**, 362 (1929). [2, 5, 6

ANTHONY, A. J., and R. HEINE, Spirographische Untersuchungen bei Lungenkollaps. II. und III. Mitt., *Beitr. z. Klin. d. Tuberk.* **73**, 51 (1930). [1, 2, 3, 4, 5, 6, 7

ANTHONY, A. J., and C. MUMME, Die Bewertung der Lungenvolumina beim Doppelseitigen Pneumothorax, *Beitr. z. Klin. d. Tuberk.* **83**, 753 (1933). [1, 2, 3, 4, 5, 6

ARNETT, J. H., Vital capacity of the lungs: changes occurring in health and disease, *J. Clin. Investigation* **14**, 543 (1935). [5

BENCE, A. E., A. LANARI, and E. J. RODRIQUEZ, Relacion entre el volumen del aire insuflado en la camara pleural y la disminucion del volumen pulmonar. Estudio bronchoespirometrico, *Medicina* **8**, 16 (1948). [2

BENDOVE, R. A., The vital capacity in artificial pneumothorax. The mechanism and the factors modifying the vital capacity, with especial reference to its clinical and prognostic value in collapse therapy, *Arch. Int. Med.* **36**, 94 (1925). [5

BIRATH, G., Lung volume and ventilation efficiency; change in collapse-treated and non-collapse-treated pulmonary tuberculosis and in pulmonectomy and lobectomy, *Acta med. Scandinav., Supp. No. 154* (1944). [1, 2, 3, 5, 6

BLOOMFIELD, R. A., H. D. LAUSON, A. COURNAND, E. S. BREED, and D. W. RICHARDS, JR., Recording of right heart pressures in normal subjects and in patients with chronic pulmonary disease and various types of cardiocirculatory disease, *J. Clin. Investigation* **25**, 639 (1946).

BLUHM, L., Working test as a clinical method for determining the function of the lungs. An investigation in cases of tuberculous changes especially in collapse therapy, *Acta med. Scandinav., Supp. No. 65* (1935). [5

CALLEBAUT, C., H. DENOLIN, and J. LEQUIME, Recherches oxymètriques dans les cardiopathies congénitales, *Acta cardiol.* **4**, 324 (1949).

CAMPBELL, A. H., The effect of pneumothorax on pulmonary vital capacity, *M. J. Australia* **1**, 432 (1952). [5

CHARR, R., and R. RIDDLE, Pulmonary circulation in artificial pneumothorax and anthracosilicosis, *Am. J. M. Sc.* **194**, 502 (1937). [9

CHARR, R., and J. W. SAVACOOL, Dyspnea in anthracosilicosis. A clinico-pathologic study, *Pennsylvania M. J.* **42**, 35 (1938). [9, 10

CHRISTIE, R. V., Pulmonary congestion following artificial pneumothorax. Its clinical significance, *Quart. J. Med.* **29**, 327 (1936). [1, 2, 3, 4, 5, 6

COURNAND, A., N. A. BRYAN, and D. W. RICHARDS, JR., Cardiac output in relation to unilateral pneumothorax in man, *J. Clin. Investigation* **14**, 181 (1935). [5, 8, 10

COURNAND, A., and D. W. RICHARDS, JR., Pulmonary insufficiency. II. The effects of various types of collapse therapy upon cardiopulmonary function, *Am. Rev. Tuberc.* **44**, 123 (1941). [2, 6, 9, 10

DOLLEY, F. S., and E. R. WIESE, Effects of a large closed bilateral pneumothorax on thoracic lymph flow, *Arch. Surg.* **18**, 542 (1929).

DURAS, F. P., Measurement of the circulation time with saccharin, *Lancet* **1**, 303 (1944). [9

FEINSILVER, O., Change in the rate of circulation and venous pressure following collapse therapy in pulmonary tuberculosis, *Dis. of Chest* **9**, 514 (1943), [5, 9, 10

FUCHS, L., Ueber die Messung des Venendruckes und ihre klinische Bedeutung, *Deutsches Arch. f. klin. Med.* **135**, 68 (1921). [10

GAENSLER, A. E., Air velocity index. A numerical expression of the functionally effective portion of ventilation, *Am. Rev. Tuberc.* **62**, 17 (1950). [5

GAENSLER, E. A., and J. W. STRIEDER, Pulmonary function before and after extrapleural pneumothorax. A comparison with other forms of collapse and resection, *J. Thoracic Surg.* **20**, 774 (1950). [5

GELERA, M., Il pneumogramma e la capacità vitale durante il pneumotorace arteficiale e dopo frenicoexeresi, *Minerva med.* **21**, 485 (1930). [5

GRELLETY-BOSVIEL, P., De l'utilité de la mesure de la pression veineuse au cours du pneumothorax artificiel, *Presse méd.* **38**, 1105 (1930). [10

HEISE, F. H., and J. H. STEIDL, Venous pressure in pulmonary tuberculosis. The effect of collapse therapy and other complications, *J. Thoracic Surg.* **8**, 539 (1938–39). [10

HILTON, R., La teneur en oxygène du sang artériel dans la tuberculose pulmonaire et au cours du pneumothorax artificiel, *Ann. de méd.* **17**, 322 (1925). [8

HIRSCHSOHN, J., and H. MAENDL, Notiz zur Kenntnis der Hämodynamik beim Pneumothorax, *Beitr. z. Klin. d. Tuberk.* **49**, 64 (1922). [5, 7, 9

HITZIG, W. M. The use of ether in measuring the circulation time from the antecubital veins to the pulmonary capillaries, *Am. Heart J.* **10**, 1080 (1934–35). [9, 10

HURST, A., and M. A. BRAND, A study of venous pressure and circulation time in pulmonary tuberculosis, *J. Thoracic Surg.* **6**, 638 (1936–37). [9, 10

HUSSEY, H. H., Clinical application of venous pressure measurement, *M. Ann. District of Columbia* **5**, 232 (1936). [10

JEQUIER-DOGE, E., La fonction cardio-pulmonaire dans le double pneumo-thorax, *Helvet. med. acta* **10**, 71 (1943). [5, 8

KALTREIDER, N. L., H. van Z. HYDE, and W. W. FRAY, Pulmonary capacity in lobar pneumonia, with special reference to collapse therapy, *Arch. Int. Med.* **59**, 408 (1937). [1, 2, 3, 4, 5, 6

KNIPPING, H. W., and A. MONCRIEFF, The ventilation equivalent for oxygen, *Quart. J. Med.* **1**, 17 (1932).

KOCHS, K., Studien über die Vitalkapazität bei kunstlichen Pneumothorax, bei Phrenicusexerese und einseitigen Brustheftpflasterverband, *Beitr. z. Klin. d. Tuberk.* **73**, 734 (1930). [5

KROETZ, C., Die Koeffizienten des klinisch messbaren Venendruckes, *Deutsches Arch. f. klin. Med.* **139**, 325 (1922). [10

KROETZ, C., Gasanalytische Untersuchungen über die Endothelfunktion der Lungen, *Verhandl. d. deutsch. Gesellsch. f. inn. Med.* **41**, 449 (1929). [8

LE BLANC, E., Respiratorischer Gasaustausch und Lungendurchblutung unter normalen und krankhaften Zuständen der Atmungsorgane. Untersuchungen am arteriellen und venösen Blut von Mensch und Tier, *Beitr. z. Klin. d. Tuberk.* **50**, 21 (1922). [7, 8

LEINER, G. C., Spirometric and bronchospirometric studies in pneumo-thorax, *Am. Rev. Tuberc.* **50**, 267 (1944). [3, 4, 5, 7

LEITNER, J., Zur Bewertung der Spirometrie bei der doppelseitigen Pneu-mothoraxbehandlung der Lungentuberkulose, *Ztschr. f. Tuberk.* **63**, 184 (1932). [5

LEVINSON, J. P., D. M. CALDWELL, L. H. HETHERINGTON, and C. H. MARCY, Studies of venous pressure, vital capacity, circulation times and electrocardiograms during the course of pulmonary collapse therapy, *Dis. of Chest* **14**, 19 (1948). [5, 9, 10

LINDSKOG, G. E., P. HARPER, and I. FRIEDMAN, Changes in lung volume during treatment with artificial pneumothorax for lobar pneumonia, *Am. J. Dis. Child.* **57**, 523 (1936). [1, 2, 3, 4, 5, 6

MEANS, J. H., and G. M. BALBONI, The various factors of respiration in persons with pneumothorax, *J. Exper. Med.* **24**, 671 (1916). [5, 7

MYERS, J. A., Studies on the respiratory organs in health and disease. VI. The significance of the vital-capacity test in pulmonary tuber-culosis, bronchial asthma, pneumonia and an acute infection outside the respiratory tract, *Arch. Int. Med.* **30**, 648 (1922). [5

MYERS, J. A., and W. BAILEY, Studies on the respiratory organs in health and disease. XX. The value of the vital-capacity test in artificial pneumothorax treatment, *Am. Rev. Tuberc.* **10**, 597 (1925). [5

NYLIN, G., Untersuchungen über das Minutenvolumen des Herzens in 2 Fällen mit einseitigen künstlichen Pneumothorax, *Beitr. z. klin. Tuberk.* **83**, 470 (1933).

PNEUMOTHORAX 527

NYLIN, G., More recent developments of heart function tests, *J. A. M. A.* **109**, 1333 (1937).

OVERHOLT, R. H., and L. S. PILCHER, 2nd, Changes in venous pressure after thoracoplasty. Its significance in relation to the extent of rib removal, *J. Thoracic Surg.* **4**, 269 (1934). [10

PEABODY, F. W., and J. A. WENTWORTH, Clinical studies of the respiration. IV. The vital capacity of the lungs and its relation to dyspnea, *Arch. Int. Med.* **20**, 443 (1917). [5

PINNER, M., G. C. LEINER, and W. A. ZAVOD, Bronchospirometry, *Ann. Int. Med.* **22**, 704 (1945). [3, 4, 6

POMPLUN, F., Untersuchungen zur Physiologie und Pathologie der Blutgase beim Tuberkülosen. I. Mitt. Allgemeine Darstellung, *Ztschr. f. Tuberk.* **50**, 387 (1928). [8

RICHARDS, D. W., JR., C. B. RILEY, and M. HISCOCK, Cardiac output following artificial pneumothorax in man, *Arch. Int. Med.* **49**, 994 (1932). [2, 5, 6, 8

RISKA, N., The reticulocyte reaction as an indicator of respiratory insufficiency, *Acta med. Scandinav.*, *Supp. No. 237* (1950).

SCHILL, E., Pneumothoraxstudien. II. Teil. Ueber den Zusammenhang von Vitalkapazität, Pneumothoraxdruck, und Lungenkollaps bei mit Pneumothoraxbehandelten Lungenkranken, *Beitr. z. Klin. d. Tuberk.* **65**, 492 (1927). [5

SIEPER, H., Die Vitalkapazität bei der Lungenphthise, besonders bei der Lungenkollapstherapie, *Beitr. z. Klin. d. Tuberk.* **65**, 725 (1927). [5

STEWART, H. J., and R. L. BAILEY, The effect of unilateral spontaneous pneumothorax on the circulation in man, *J. Clin. Investigation* **19**, 321 (1940). [5, 8, 10

TOBIESEN, F., Spirometrische Untersuchungen an Schwindsüchtigen, *Skandinav. Arch. f. Physiol.* **25**, 209 (1911). [1, 2, 3, 5, 6

VILLARET, M., and M. MARTINY, Pression veineuse et tuberculose pulmonaire. Intérêt diagnostique, pronostique et thérapeutique de la pression veineuse périphérique dans les différents formes anatomocliniques de la tuberculose pulmonaire, *Presse méd.* **33**, 569 (1925). [10

VILLARET, M., and M. MARTINY, Étude de la pression veineuse périphérique dans les syndromes médiastinaux. Son intérêt de contrôle pour le diagnostic et le pronostic, *Presse méd.* **37**, 249 (1929). [10

VON NEERGARD, K., and K. WIRZ, Ueber eine Methode zur Messung der Lungenelastizität am lebenden Menschen, insbesondere beim Emphysem, *Ztschr. f. klin. Med.* **105**, 35 (1927). [7

WARTMAN, W. B., A study of the venous blood pressure in some common diseases, *Am. J. M. Sc.* **190,** 464 (1935). [10

WOLF, H. J., Die nervöse Atmungsregulation bei der Lungentuberkulose. III. Mitt. Der Einfluss des künstlichen Pneumothorax auf den Ausfall der Funktionsprüfungen der Atmung und auf das Verhalten der Lungenvolumina, *Ztschr. f. d. ges. exper. Med.* **63,** 616 (1928).

[3, 4, 5, 6

ZEUS, L., Beeinflussbarkeit des Venendruckes durch intra-abdominelle Drucksteigerung, *Arch. f. Kreislaufforsch.* **8,** 330 (1941). [10 fever, the changes in the subdivisions of the lung volume may persist for two months or more (Kaltreider *et al.*, 1937).

Respiratory dynamics. — The respiratory minute volume is increased in pneumonia (Beddard and Pembrey, 1908; Meakins, 1920; Binger and Davis, 1928; Knipping and Moncrieff, 1932); this occurs as a consequence of a marked rise in respiratory rate (Meakins, 1920; Binger and Davis, 1928). The tidal air volume falls as a rule, often markedly (Meakins, 1920; Binger and Davis, 1928; Lindskog *et al.*, 1936). The increased respiratory activity may result in a fall in alveolar carbon dioxide content (Beddard and Pembrey, 1908); the amount of air breathed per hundred cubic centimeters of oxygen absorbed rises (Knipping and Moncrieff, 1932), so that respiration becomes less efficient. The maximal possible respiration per minute is considerably diminished (Jansen *et al.*, 1932). It should be noted that much of this change, or in some cases all, might be due to fever alone (Altschule and Freedberg, 1945).

Blood gases; tissue gas tensions. — A decrease in arterial oxygen saturation has long been recognized to be of common occurrence in pneumonia (**1**; Barach and Woodwell, 1921; Stadie, 1919); the beneficial effects of the administration of oxygen have been established (Barach and Woodwell, 1921; Binger, 1928; Meakins, 1921; Stadie, 1922). Changes in arterial carbon dioxide concentration are more variable, high, normal, or low values being reported (**2**; Barach and Woodwell, 1921; Binger *et al.*, 1927, 1928). These differences are due to the opposite effects of carbon dioxide retention on one hand, and, on the other hand, of the consequences of blowing off of carbon dioxide owing to stimulation of the respiratory center by fever, anoxia, or reflexes from the lungs (Porter and Newburgh, 1916, 1917). The arterial pH may be normal or slightly elevated (Binger *et al.*, 1927). If carbon dioxide retention occurs or if metabolic changes owing to fever are marked, the pH may fall (Johnstone and Bruck, 1950). A single report records normal or low oxygen tensions in the tissues in patients with pneumonia (Del Baere, 1939).

Cardiac output. — Lauter (1930) recorded a large increase in cardiac output, greatly in excess of the rise in oxygen consumption, in one patient, a change probably consequent to fever, although anoxia may also have played a part. Buhr (1953) found a small increase in cardiac output or none at all during effort.

XII

PNEUMONIA

The cardiorespiratory manifestations of pneumonia are largely determined by the changes due to fever; the latter have been reviewed elsewhere (Altschule and Freedberg, 1945). The function of the circulation and respiration in pneumonia may be further modified by the occurrence of certain complications such as marked anoxia, abdominal distention, pleural effusion or pericarditis, most of which have already been discussed. Accordingly, the present discussion will involve consideration of the immediate changes caused by the modifications of pulmonary structure consequent to a pneumonic process; these are of minor importance unless a good deal of the parenchyma of the lung is affected.

Lung volume and its subdivisions. — The accuracy of measurement of the subdivisions of the lung volume is often impaired to a large extent by the occurrence of pleuritic pain, which may result in false low readings for reserve air, complemental air, and vital capacity; in addition, by causing extremely shallow breathing, pleuritic pain may sometimes cause inaccurate results when the residual air is measured. The functional residual air is reported decreased by all authors (Siebeck, 1910; Binger and Brow, 1924; Lindskog *et al.*, 1936; Kaltreider *et al.*, 1937); a certain degree of parallelism between the amount of this reduction and the extent of the pneumonic lesion appears to exist. The residual air is normal or somewhat reduced in volume (Siebeck, 1910; Lindskog *et al.*, 1936; Kaltreider *et al.*, 1937). The reserve air, vital capacity and total capacity usually show marked decreases (Siebeck, 1910; Myers, 1922; Lindskog *et al.*, 1936; Kaltreider *et al.*, 1937). Following subsidence of the

Circulation time. — The arm-to-tongue or -face time is normal or reduced (Koch, 1922; Tarr *et al.*, 1932; Hitzig, 1935; Bernstein and Simkins, 1939); the ether time is reported as normal (Hitzig, 1935). Here again it is impossible to evaluate the role of fever and other influences in addition to changes in the lungs themselves.

Pulmonary arterial pressure. — A rise in pulmonary arterial pressure was found in one patient with pneumonia by Fowler *et al.* (1950); the administration of tetraethylammonium lowered the pressure, showing that vasoconstriction was its cause.

Venous pressure. — Normal values for venous pressure have been found by most observers (3; Kastlin and MacLachlan, 1931); Moore (1937), however, described it as elevated. A late rise in venous pressure may occur in patients who are doing poorly (Fuchs, 1921; Kastlin and MacLachlan, 1931). The rise in venous pressure during exertion is normal in patients with pneumonia (Schott, 1912). A few studies by Buhr (1953) showed excessive rises.

Symptoms. — Symptoms due solely to the pneumonic lesion in the lungs may be greatly overshadowed by those of fever, anoxia, pericarditis, pleural fluid, and so on.

The above-described decrease in functional residual air diminishes to a variable extent the space available for breathing; this is hardly of significance, except in patients in whom most of the lung tissue is involved. The elasticity of the lung is somewhat impaired, as is shown by the decreased reserve air. The latter finding, although it is evidence of some lessening of the negativity of the intrapleural pressure, indicates no great change in that direction. Decreased expansibility of the lung, shown by the considerable decrease in complemental air and in maximal possible minute ventilation, is probably consequent both to pleuritic pain and to increased rigidity of the lungs caused by congestion, interstitial edema and exudate.

Except in extreme cases, the decreased pulmonary expansibility is not likely to be of primary importance in the genesis of dyspnea or hyperventilation in patients with pneumonia, in spite of the increased oxygen consumption caused by fever. The shallow tidal air volume that occurs is largely due to pleuritic pain, increased pulmonary rigidity playing only a minor role. A considerable increase in respiratory rate and minute volume may partly or wholly compensate for shallow respiratory exchange. This increased respiratory activity, however, is

only partly consequent to anoxia, for it is often not markedly influenced by oxygen; two additional causative factors are fever and,
as first shown by Porter and Newburgh (1916, 1917), reflex stimulation of the respiratory center by irritation of pulmonary parenchyma.

The lowered arterial blood oxygen saturation that is common in
patients with extensive pneumonia appears to be largely consequent
to impaired diffusion of oxygen in the damaged lungs and to the flow
of blood through unaerated pulmonary tissue. Markedly shallow
respiration may further lower arterial oxygen saturation (page 101).
Carbon dioxide is more freely diffusible than oxygen and consequently carbon dioxide retention is of less common occurrence. Indeed, the hyperventilation consequent to fever and to reflexes arising
in the lungs may far overshadow the tendency toward carbon dioxide
retention, so that normal or even low values for arterial blood carbon
dioxide content are common. Consequently, the arterial blood pH is
usually normal or slightly alkalotic; dyspnea due to carbon dioxide
acidosis is not usual.

Cardiovascular dynamics are not demonstrably influenced by the
presence of a pneumonic process *per se;* whatever changes have been
observed in the fragmentary studies available appear to be those of
any febrile illness and, in extreme cases, of anoxia. Additional data
would be helpful, however. The increased cardiac output that occurs
in febrile illnesses is not sufficiently large to affect deleteriously the
normal heart, but it may cause a previously damaged myocardium to
fail. The occurrence of venous engorgement in elderly or cardiac patients with pneumonia who are doing poorly is difficult to interpret,
since it may be the result of marked changes in intrapleural pressure
consequent to massive pulmonary involvement combined with extreme degrees of abdominal distention, to congestive failure, to the
development of pleural fluid, to pericarditis, or to a combination of
these various factors. Whatever its mechanism, it should not be considered an indication for venesection.

Bibliography

Chapter XII

ALTSCHULE, M. D., and A. S. FREEDBERG, Circulation and respiration in fever, *Medicine* **24,** 403 (1945).

BARACH, A. L., and M. N. WOODWELL, Studies in oxygen therapy. II. In pneumonia and its complications, *Arch. Int. Med.* **28,** 394 (1921).
[1, 2

BEDDARD, A. P., and M. S. PEMBREY, Observations on pulmonary ventilation in disease, *Brit. M. J.* **2,** 580 (1908).

BERNSTEIN, M., and S. SIMKINS, The use of magnesium sulfate in the measurement of circulation time, *Am. Heart J.* **17,** 218 (1939).

BINGER, C. A. L., Anoxemia in pneumonia and its relief by oxygen inhalation, *J. Clin. Investigation* **6,** 203 (1928–29). [1

BINGER, C. A. L., and G. R. BROW, Studies on the respiratory mechanism in lobar pneumonia. A study of lung volume in relation to the clinical course of the disease, *J. Exper. Med.* **39,** 677 (1924). [1

BINGER, C. A. L., and J. S. DAVIS, The relation of anoxemia to the type of breathing in pneumonia. A study of respiration by means of a body plethysmograph, *J. Clin. Investigation* **6,** 171 (1928–29). [1, 2

BINGER, C. A. L., A. B. HASTINGS, and J. SENDROY, A further study of blood reaction and blood gases in pneumonia, *J. Exper. Med.* **45,** 1081 (1927). [1, 2

BUHR, G., Pneumonie und Kreislauf. Ueber die Auswirkung körperlicher Belastung auf die Kreislaufdynamik bei acuten Pneumonien, *Deutsche med. Wchnschr.* **78,** 216 (1953).

DEL BAERE, L. J., Die Sauerstoffversorgung des Körpers, *Ztschr. f. klin. Med.* **136,** 43 (1939).

EYSTER, J. A. E., Venous pressure and its clinical applications, *Physiol, Rev.* **6,** 281 (1926). [3

EYSTER, J. A. E., and W. S. MIDDLETON, Clinical studies on venous pressure, *Arch. Int. Med.* **34,** 228 (1924). [3

FOWLER, N. O., R. N. WESTCOTT, V. D. HAUENSTEIN, R. C. SCOTT, and J. McGUIRE, Observations on autonomic participation in pulmonary arteriolar resistance in man, *J. Clin. Investigation* **29,** 1387 (1950).

FUCHS, L., Ueber die Messung des Venendruckes und ihre klinische Bedeutung, *Deutsches Arch. f. klin. Med.* **135,** 68 (1921). [3

HASTINGS, A. B., J. M. NEILL, H. J. MORGAN, and C. A. L. BINGER, Blood reaction and blood gases in pneumonia, *J. Clin. Investigation* **1,** 25 (1924–25). [1, 2

HITZIG, W. M., The use of ether in measuring the circulation time from the antecubital veins to the pulmonary capillaries, *Am. Heart J.* **10**, 1080 (1934–35). [3

HÜRTER, Untersuchungen am arteriellen menschlichen Blute, *Deutsches Arch. f. klin. Med.* **108**, 1 (1912). [1

JANSEN, K., H. W. KNIPPING, and K. STROMBERGER, Klinische Untersuchungen über Atmung und Blutgase, *Beitr. z. Klin. d. Tuberk.* **80**, 304 (1932). [2

JOHNSTONE, D. E., and E. BRUCK, Respiratory acidosis in children with cerebral, pulmonary and cardiovascular disorders, *Am. J. Dis. Child.* **80**, 578 (1950). [1

KALTREIDER, N. L., H. VAN Z. HYDE, and W. W. FRAY, Pulmonary capacity in lobar pneumonia, with special reference to collapse therapy, *Arch. Int. Med.* **59**, 408 (1937). [1, 2

KASTLIN, G. J., and W. W. G. MACLACHLAN, Venous pressure in pneumonia, *Ann. Int. Med.* **4**, 959 (1931). [3

KNIPPING, H. W., and A. MONCRIEFF, The ventilation equivalent for oxygen, *Quart. J. Med.* **1**, 17 (1932).

KOCH, E., Die Stromgeschwindigkeit des Blutes. Ein Beitrag zur Arbeitsprüfung des Kreislaufes, *Deutsches Arch. f. klin. Med.* **140**, 39 (1922).

LAUTER, S., Kreislaufprobleme, *München. med. Wchnschr.* **77**, 593 (1930). [1

LE BLANC, E., Respiratorischer Gasaustausch und Lungendurchblutung unter normalen und krankhaften Zuständen der Atmungsorgane. Untersuchungen am arteriellen und venösen Blut von Mensch und Tier, *Beitr. z. Klin. d. Tuberk.* **50**, 21 (1922). [1

LINDSKOG, G. E., P. HARPER, and I. FRIEDMAN, Changes in lung volume during treatment with artificial pneumothorax for lobar pneumonia. Report of three cases, *Am. J. Dis. Child.* **15**, 523 (1936).

MEAKINS, J., Harmful effects of shallow breathing with special reference to pneumonia, *Arch. Int. Med.* **25**, 1 (1920).

MEAKINS, J., Observations on the gases in human arterial blood in certain pathological pulmonary conditions and their treatment with oxygen, *J. Path. & Bact.* **24**, 79 (1921). [1

MOORE, R. D., JR., The diagnostic value of venous pressure determinations in certain diseases, *South. M. J.* **30**, 1007 (1937).

MYERS, J. S., Studies on the respiratory organs in health and disease. VI. The significance of the vital-capacity test in pulmonary tuberculosis, bronchial asthma, pneumonia and an acute infection outside the respiratory tract, *Arch. Int. Med.* **30**, 648 (1922).

PORTER, W. T., and L. H. NEWBURGH, The vagus nerves in pneumonia, *Am. J. Physiol.* **42**, 175 (1916).

PORTER, W. T., and L. H. NEWBURGH, Further evidence regarding the role of the vagus nerves in pneumonia, *Am. J. Physiol.* **43**, 455 (1917).

RASMUSSEN, H., and O. STORSTEIN, Studies in oxygen therapy. Part I. On the frequency of anoxemia, its occurrence in medical diseases and its relation to cyanosis, *Acta med. Scandinav.* **141**, 43 (1951). [5

RASMUSSEN, H., and O. STORSTEIN, Studies in oxygen therapy. Part II. On the effect of oxygen therapy on the oxygen unsaturation of the arterial blood, *Acta med. Scandinav.* **141**, 52 (1951). [5

SCHOEN, R., and E. DERRA, Untersuchungen über die Bedeutung der Zyanose als klinisches Symptom. (I.), *Deutsches Arch. f. klin. Med.* **168**, 52 (1930). [1

SCHOTT, E., Die Erhöhung des Druckes im venösen System bei Anstrengung als Mass für die Funktionstüchtigkeit des menschlichen Herzens, *Deutsches Arch. f. klin. Med.* **108**, 537 (1912). [3

SIEBECK, R., Über die Beeinflussung der Atemmechanik durch krankhafte Zustände des Respirations- und Kreislaufapparates, *Deutsches Arch. f. klin. Med.* **100**, 204 (1910).

STADIE, W. C., The oxygen of the arterial and venous blood in pneumonia and its relation to cyanosis, *J. Exper. Med.* **30**, 215 (1919). [1

STADIE, W. C., The treatment of anoxemia in pneumonia in an oxygen chamber, *J. Exper. Med.* **35**, 337 (1922). [1, 2

TARR, L., B. S. OPPENHEIMER, and R. V. SAGER, The circulation time in various clinical conditions determined by the use of sodium dehydrocholate, *Am. Heart J.* **8**, 766 (1932–33).

WARTMAN, W. B., A study of the venous blood pressure in some common diseases, *Am. J. M. Sc.* **190**, 464 (1935). [3

INDEX

INDEX

Aberrant pulmonary veins, 396
Abdominal distention
  and circulation, 210
  and lung volumes, 209
  and respiratory function, 209
Acetylcholine
  in anoxia, 223
  and blood pyruvate, 223
Acidosis, cerebral blood flow in, 274
Adrenal hormones, 176
Albuminuria
  in congestive failure, 132, 164
  in exercise, 164
  and plasma proteins, 133
Alveolar air gases
  with ammonium chloride, 272
  in auricular fibrillation, 357
  in congestive failure, 109
  with digitalis, 268
  and dyspnea, 109
  in heart block, 365
  in pneumonia, 530
  in pneumothorax, 520
  in pulmonary emphysema, 475
  in pulmonary fibrosis, 457, 459
  and respiratory dynamics, 109
  in ventricular tachycardia, 363
Aminophylline
  blood flow, peripheral, after, 319
  cardiac output after, 319
  cardiac pain after, 319
  cerebrospinal fluid pressure after, 319
  circulation time after, 319
  collapse after, 320
  dyspnea after, 319
  and gastric acid, 284
  peripheral resistance after, 319
  venous pressure after, 319
  vital capacity after, 319
Ammonium chloride
  alveolar air carbon dioxide after, 272
  blood electrolytes after, 272
  blood gases after, 272
  blood pH after, 272
  cardiac output after, 273

  in hypochloremia, 274
  in mercurial diuresis, 274
  metabolism after, 273
  oxygen debt after, 272
  respiratory function after, 272
  tissue fluid electrolytes after, 272
  urinary electrolytes after, 272
Angina pectoris
  arterial pressure in, 342, 343
  cardiac output in, 341, 342
  circulation time in, 342
  reflexes in, 344
  venous pressure in, 342
  vital capacity in, 342
Anoxia
  acetylcholine synthesis in, 224
  blood flow in, 100
  blood lactic acid in, 121, 243, 244
  blood volume in, 149
  capillary function in, 71, 228
  cardiac pain in, 344
  in congestive failure, 242
  edema in, 230
  efficiency for work in, 127
  erthrocytes in, 151
  gastro-intestinal function in, 203
  hepatic function in, 194
  oxygen debt in, 127
  respiratory dynamics in, 91
  vasoconstriction, general, in, 44
  vasoconstriction, pulmonary, in, 62
  venous pressure in, 48
  thiamine metabolism in, 224
Aortic insufficiency
  blood flow, peripheral, in, 415
  capillary pulsation in, 416
  cardiac output in, 414
  cardiac pain in, 416
  pulse in, 415
Aortic septal defect, 396
Aortic stenosis
  arterial pressure in, 414
  pulse in, 414
  syncope in, 414
Arterial pressure
  in angina pectoris, 342, 343